1495
T

Modern Foundations of
SYSTEMS ENGINEERING

Modern Foundations of
SYSTEMS ENGINEERING

William A. Porter

THE UNIVERSITY OF MICHIGAN

The Macmillan Company, New York
Collier-Macmillan Limited, London

First Printing

Library of Congress catalog card number: 66-22533.

THE MACMILLAN COMPANY, NEW YORK
COLLIER-MACMILLAN CANADA, LTD., TORONTO, ONTARIO

Printed in the United States of America

To Donna

Whose faith and understanding
are reasons enough

PREFACE

As with most science-based disciplines, systems engineering is experiencing an explosive technological growth with the inevitable problems for the practicing engineer, the student, the researcher, and the teacher alike. Since systems engineering relies heavily on the study of mathematical models which approximate physical phenomena, it is not surprising that many of these problems stem from the increasing use of sophisticated mathematical and scientific concepts within the field. Now, more than ever before, it is imperative that systems engineers be trained to accept the responsibility for the rapid translation of mathematical and scientific theories into engineering accomplishments.

Toward this end systems engineering programs have strengthened science and mathematics requirements and revised (on a yearly basis) curricula content. To develop an efficient and balanced program is by no means a simple task, particularly in a period of rapid technological growth.

This book is based on a course offered in the Department of Electrical Engineering of The University of Michigan during the years 1963 and 1964. The objectives of this course were many: to promote a uniformity in student background, to serve as a foundation for subsequent courses, to establish a link between systems engineering and its mathematical prerequisites, to equip the student with specific tools, and to orient student thinking in the "direction of evolution" of systems engineering. This book itself reflects these objectives.

In some respects this book is a semifinished product; certainly it would benefit both from additional aging under classsroom conditions and from thorough review by other workers within the field. Its publication now is a recognition of the tempo of the period. It is felt that teachers, students, practicing engineers, authors of future texts, and the community as a whole will benefit more from the early appearance of the text than from its appearance in a polished but belated form.

A glance at the table of contents will give a fairly good idea of the scope of the text. The philosophy of the treatment is dealt with in the introduction, and so we shall limit ourselves here to a few specific remarks on the structure of the book.

For purposes of precision and clarity the main results and conclusions have been stated in the form of theorems, lemmas, corollaries, remarks, or discussions. In spite of its mathematical flavor, the orientation of the exposition is dictated by engineering considerations and conciseness rather than mathematical elegance. Although the text is for the most part self-contained, it is not intended as an end item but rather as a point of departure for many directions of engineering inquiry.

The level of the treatment is geared to the background of a first-year graduate student. To be more specific, it is assumed that the reader has the usual background in calculus, differential equations, complex variables, Laplace transforms, linear circuits, and matrices. Additional background, such as linear algebra, advanced calculus, set-theoretic topology, and state-space system concepts, would be helpful but is not at all necessary.

The chapters are both greater in length and fewer in number than is usual in a book of this kind. Each major chapter is in reality a phase of the development and is composed of related subchapters, each dealing with a specific concept or line of thought. With one or two exceptions, each subsection is designed to be conveniently covered in two readings. Although theory and applications are both present to some degree in all chapters, the emphasis shifts from theoretical considerations in the early sections to applications in the later ones; whereas Chapter 1 is intended to establish a uniform level of mathematical proficiency, Chapter 4 is devoted to solving a specific class of problems in optimal control.

For the reader's convenience the reference literature is compiled in two master lists at the end of the text. Those references that are pertinent to the individual sections are pointed out in the discussion at the end of each chapter and each appendix as well. A limited number of direct references to the literature are also included in the body of the book.

W. A. P.

ACKNOWLEDGMENTS

I wish to acknowledge the generous encouragement and support given to this undertaking by the staff of the Institute of Science and Technology and the Department of Electrical Engineering at The University of Michigan. In particular James P. Williams has been a constant and trusted source of criticism and suggestion throughout the writing of the text and particularly in Chapter 4. The development of the book was expedited by the work of Mrs. Patricia Wessling and Miss Caroline Rehberg who unflinchingly typed draft after draft of the manuscript. Finally, the National Science Foundation and the Department of Defense, through the Army Signal Corps, the Army Research Office Durham, and the Air Force Systems Command, have my thanks for their financial support of the research which underlies several of the book's sections.

CONTENTS

Modern Foundations of
SYSTEMS ENGINEERING

INTRODUCTION

In this introductory section none of the concrete results that abound in later sections will be developed. Our intention is rather to provide a conceptual framework that will help the reader to keep perspective on the discussions that follow. Let us avoid the pitfall of an explicit statement of the meaning of the word *system*. Instead, we shall rely on the popular or intuitive concept of a system that is lodged in the experience of the individual reader. That we are able to do so illustrates one of the facets of system theory which make it so important; namely, we can find the ideas and techniques of systems theory in such seemingly unrelated areas as computer design, investigation of the human nervous system, missile guidance, and various sociological and biological problems.

For purposes of the present discussion it suffices to consider a system as a "black box" equipped with a set of accessible terminals and obeying some physical law. It is often convenient to separate the quantities that characterize the system into the following categories: (a) excitation variables—the external stimuli that influence the system behavior, (b) response variables—which represent those aspects of system behavior that are of interest to the investigator, and (c) intermediate variables—which are neither excitation nor response variables. In Figure 0.1 the terminals at which excitation is applied (i.e., the input terminals) are identified by arrows pointing toward the system. The output terminals represent the response variables and are identified by arrows pointing away from the system. The intermediate variables, if they exist, are embedded inside the box.

The scientific and engineering aspects of a system problem usually span

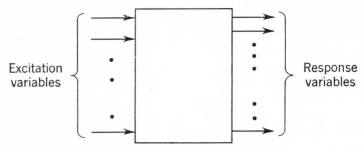

Figure 0.1   A hypothetical system.

a broad spectrum of activities: the observation of physical phenomena to determine the laws governing its behavior, the study of mathematical models that approximate physical phenomena, the mathematical design of a system for a prescribed behavior, and the physical realization of a mathematical design. Of these four activities this book emphasizes problems of analysis and design based on known mathematical models. In terms of the black box, the mathematical model must express the system response and/or intermediate variables related to its inputs. Because different methods of characterization (i.e., different types of mathematical model) are better suited to different objectives, it is not surprising that many approaches to system theory exist. Let us inquire into possible objectives for choosing a particular formulation.

0.1 MATHEMATICAL MODELING OBJECTIVES

One possible objective is the desire to obtain a qualitative understanding of the properties and behavior of systems in general, in which case a characterization that yields a conceptual model compatible with a large class of systems might be required. It is apparent that to a varying degree any judiciously chosen method of characterization contributes to our knowledge and insight concerning system problems. A second objective might be the quantitative study of certain restricted classes of systems. It might then be desirable to tailor the representation to suit the chosen class of systems, even at the loss of completeness of generality of the characterization. Another objective that is frequently a factor is to develop a characterization suited to a particular type of analysis. Naturally, a particular formulation may or may not be suited for accomplishing all three objectives for a particular system.

The popularity of most mathematical techniques currently used in the analysis of system problems can be attributed to their strength in one of the three objective categories. To illustrate this assertion let us consider the two approaches that are most frequently used for analyzing "lumped" parameter systems (i.e., systems characterized by ordinary differential and integral equations). For a linear stationary system a classical approach uses the Laplace or Fourier transform to characterize the system in terms of its transfer function. This formulation is ideally suited to the study of linear time-invariant systems of differential equations because the transform technique converts these equations to an algebraic form for which many analysis and synthesis objectives can be easily formulated. Hence, for this formulation a great wealth of design and analysis technology has been developed over the last twenty years. In spite of the many attempts to extend the transform technique to a larger class of systems, its prime weakness remains the relative difficulty with which it is applied to the analysis of nonlinear or nonstationary systems. Thus the transform technique is typical of an approach that analyzes a very restricted class of systems extremely well.

The state variable approach currently in vogue in the engineering community utilizes a time-domain description of the system behavior. Thus the state formulation is more closely identified with the physical system and provides more insight into system behavior than is possible with the transfer function formulation. In this formulation time-invariant, time-varying, and nonlinear systems can be approached from the same viewpoint, although solution of a nonlinear problem may still be difficult. The state variable formulation also provides a natural setting for some types of optimization problems.

A weakness inherent in both the transform and the state variable formulations is that the system description is tied closely to the concrete nature of the system operation; thus the general or abstract properties of the system tend to become obscured. By this statement we mean that the system response to a particular input rather than to a class of inputs is emphasized. In addition, many physical systems are meaningfully formulated only with considerable difficulty within the transform or the state variable approach. Systems that fall into this category include distributive control and thermodynamics systems as well as many others.

Let us now consider two concrete system problems that provide motivation for the remainder of this introduction.

Example 1.   As a simple example, frequently observed in mechanical and electrical systems, let us consider a problem treated by H. D. Block.[1] Figure 0.2 displays a unit mass supported by a rod and acted on by a force $P(t)$. The function $x(t)$ represents the displacement of the mass from the initial equilibrium position at time t and $\mathscr{F}$ denotes the restoring force exerted by the rod on the mass. If we ignore friction effects, the governing motion is given by

$$\frac{d^2x(t)}{dt^2} + \mathscr{F}(t) = P(t). \tag{1}$$

[1]H. D. Block, "Periodic Solutions of Forced Systems Having Hysteresis," *IRE PGCT*, 423–31 (Dec. 1960). Figures 0.2 and 0.3 are used with permission of the publisher, Institute of Electrical and Electronics Engineers, New York.

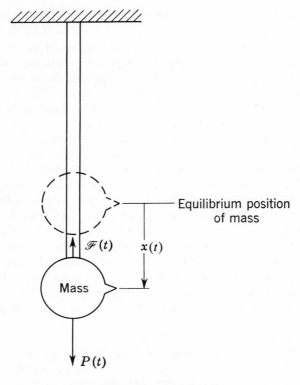

Figure 0.2 A mechanical system.

We use the elaborate letter $\mathscr{F}$ intentionally for a number of reasons. Suppose that we undertake to determine $\mathscr{F}$ experimentally. If we assume that the rod has a hysteresis effect in its restoring action, the stress-strain diagram shown in Figure 0.3 is the typical result when we vary x and observe $\mathscr{F}$. If, as an experiment, we increase x from x_0 to x_1, reduce it to x_2, increase it to x_3, and decrease it to x_4, the corresponding point in the $(x, \mathscr{F})$-plane runs along the paths shown from P_0 to P_1, P_1 to P_2, ..., P_6 to P_7. We note that the value of the force $\mathscr{F}$, although affected by x, is not a function of the value of x alone. Indeed, when x is at the value ξ, for example, there are four possible values for $\mathscr{F}$ shown, and there would also be many other possible values for $\mathscr{F}$ if x arrived at ξ by a different sequence of events. Nor would specifying the value of x, dx/dt, etc., help to determine $\mathscr{F}$. Finally, it is clear that $\mathscr{F}$ is not determined as a function of t, valid for arbitrary loading histories. Thus we conclude that $\mathscr{F}$ is not a function of one or more real variables at all and that Eq. 1 is not the usual differential equation. On the other hand, if the function $x(t)$ is specified for $0 \leq t \leq T$, $\mathscr{F}$ is determined as a function of t for $0 \leq t \leq T$. In particular, if $x(t)$ is given for all $t \geq 0$, $\mathscr{F}$

is determined for all $t \geq 0$. Thus $\mathscr{F}$ is a mapping of the function $x(t)$ into another function $[\mathscr{F}(x)](t)$.

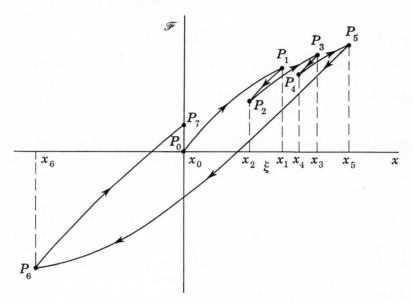

Figure 0.3   A hysteresis profile.

Example 2.   In this example we refer to the system of Figure 0.1 in which $x_1, \ldots, x_m$ and $y_1, \ldots, y_n$ denote the input and output variables, respectively. Rather than thinking of the inputs as time functions or time sequences, for instance, we shall require that m classes of admissible inputs $X_1, \ldots, X_m$ be defined such that each input x_i will be a member of the input class X_i for $i = 1, 2, \ldots, m$.

The definition of admissible input classes is usually based on physical or design considerations. For example, X_1 may consist of time functions defined on an interval $a \leq t \leq b$, all of which have some similar features: (a) all elements in X_1 may be continuous functions; (b) all elements in X_1 are square integrable, that is, $\int_a^b x^2(t)\, dt < \infty$; (c) all elements in X_1 have maximum values less than a fixed constant; and (d) all elements in X_1 have the form $x(t) = \sin(n\pi t)$ for some rational n. Similarly, it can usually be determined that the outputs of the system are also elements of function classes. Hence the system itself can be visualized as a mapping or correspondence between input and output classes.

The systems investigator is interested in a broad spectrum of problems that may be concisely formulated in this characterization of the system of Figure 0.1. For instance, problems of optimization typically take this form:

given some system task to perform and a specific index of performance, find the particular set of inputs $x_1, \ldots, x_m$ from the admissible input classes $X_1, \ldots, X_m$ which not only perform the task but maximize performance.

0.2 THE FUNCTION SPACE APPROACH

The two examples of Section 0.1 are typical system analysis problems. From a study of these and other examples that we shall meet later it soon becomes evident that the natural representation for most systems is a correspondence between input and output elements. This approach, of necessity, utilizes as its tools the concepts of function spaces (roughly sets whose elements are functions) and operations on function spaces. Functional analysis is the mathematical trade name for the study and application of these tools. Although in this text the function-space approach to system analysis receives primary emphasis, neither state variable nor transformation techniques are excluded.

Although functional analysis has been an area of active mathematical inquiry for more than a decade, the adoption of function-space techniques in a system context has for practical purposes taken place since 1960. The rapid growth of this approach to system problems may be attributed not only to an ability to formulate less restrictive (hence less approximate) problems but to the fact that the classical formulations are viewed with increased clarity in the functional analysis setting. Although it is not yet apparent why this is so, we shall be satisfied with the remark that this approach to system problems is free of the concrete nature of the system; that is, many of the formulations hold for systems that are distributive, digital, nonlinear, or biological. Of course, results obtained on the basis of an abstract formulation must then be given concrete identification in its various physical forms.

To fulfill the objectives of this book efficiently there is no alternative but to develop the rudimentary concepts from the disciplines of functional analysis. Its early sections therefore present a methodical introduction of the topics essential to a fluent discussion of system theory. Since systems are devices that associate elements in input and output function classes, the first objective is a study of these classes. The reader will find that Chapter 1 in its entirety is set aside for this purpose. Since space is at a premium, no attempt has been made to sugarcoat this material with lengthy examples of artificial systems.

In the first two sections of Chapter 2 the rudimentary properties of mappings between function spaces are developed. Attention then turns from the abstract to the concrete as the remainder of the chapter considers the properties of linear dynamic systems. By the end of Chapter 2 the reader should feel at ease with the function-space formulation of system problems. The remainder of the book is a blend of theory and application. Attention is called to the fact that appendices are used to supplement the material in the regular sections.

In closing this introduction, acknowledgment should be made that this book injects many ideas and definitions that are new to the system context. To facilitate their absorption either a geometric or an intuitive point of view is stressed. For instance, it will be necessary to define such concepts as the distance between the length of, and the angle between, two or more members of a function space. In these definitions equivalent concepts for vectors in the conventional three dimensional space are used as models to help the "mind's eye" to picture the related meaning in the abstract setting. The reader may often find it useful to sketch a rudimentary diagram in a simplified setting as each definition is given.

This closes our introduction to the philosophy, objectives, and structure of this book. To the succeeding chapters remains the task of supplying substances to this framework which has been so hastily sketched.

1 FUNCTION SPACES

This chapter consists of a collection of mathematical topics which serves as a basis for the text. By reserving this initial chapter for mathematical foundations we shall be able to collect together most of the notation, terminology, and concepts necessary to the remainder of the text. Since the prerequisites are rather imprecise (see the Preface), it will also provide the reader with an opportunity to "make repairs" when necessary by consulting the peripheral literature. (Some suggestions are made for each topic at the end of the chapter.)

Wherever sections of mathematical development are concerned it is important to establish a firm connection between the mathematics and the physical factors that motivate their study. To this end the reader must keep in mind the multiple input–multiple output system of Figure 0.1. We are told in the introduction that it is desirable to think of this system as an association between input and output function spaces. This chapter focuses attention on the function spaces themselves in preparation for the study of the associations that represent physical systems.

1.1 SETS

The theory of sets and set operations is a potentially useful tool in most mathematically based engineering disciplines. In view of the importance of set operations, a brief résumé of the most frequently used set-theoretic notations is supplied. The treatment is informal, for we assume that the concept of a set is already intuitive to the reader. In the present context we shall think of a set as an assemblage, aggregation, or collection of objects, or elements, grouped according to some rule. As examples, we have the set of all positive integers, the set of all rational points on the real line, and the set of all points in the complex plane.

If the elements of a set consist of other sets, "class" is used rather than "set"; that is, "set of sets" is replaced by "class of sets." The words element, set, and class, however, are not intended to be rigidly fixed in their usage. For instance, we can identify a straight line not as a set of points but as a single entity in itself, in which case we might refer to the set of all straight lines in a plane.

The second intuitive concept of set theory is that of "belonging." If x belongs to a set A (i.e., x is an element of set A or x is contained in set A) we write $x \in A$. It is also convenient to write $x \notin A$ for the situation in which the element x is not contained in the set A. The concept of equality of sets is based on the concept of belonging. The relation between belonging and equality of sets is the following.

AXIOM OF EXTENSION. *Two sets A and B are equal, $A = B$, if and only if they contain exactly the same elements; that is, $x \in A$ if and only if $x \in B$.*

For example, if A is the set of roots to the equation $x^2 - 6x + 8$ and $B = \{2,4\}$, then $A = B$. If A and B are not equal, we use $A \neq B$. Another important concept is that of a subset.

DEFINITION A. *For any sets A and B, A is a subset of B (written $A \subseteq B$) if and only if $x \in A$ implies $x \in B$.*

Let B denote the set of all Big Ten football teams and A, those teams in the first division. We say $A \subseteq B$. One consequence of this definition is that the possibility that $A = B$ is also included in the statement $A \subseteq B$. As a refinement of the subset concept, the set A is called a proper subset of B (written $A \subset B$) if and only if $A \subseteq B$ and $A \neq B$. If $A \subseteq B$ (or $A \subset B$), we may write $B \supseteq A$) (or $B \supset A$), in which case we say B includes (or properly includes) A.

It will often be convenient to use a symbol for logical implication; $\Rightarrow$ is that symbol. If p and q are statements, $p \Rightarrow q$ means that p implies q (or if p is true then q is also true). Similarly, $\Leftrightarrow$ is our symbol for two-way implication or logical equivalence. It means that the statement on each side implies the statement on the other and is usually read "if and only if" or "is equivalent to."

The following properties of set inclusion are obvious consequences of the above axiom and definition:

(1) $A \subseteq A$ for every A,
(2) $A \subseteq B$ and $B \subseteq A \Rightarrow A = B$,
(3) $A \subseteq B$ and $B \subseteq C \Rightarrow A \subseteq C$.

It is interesting to observe that (1) and (2) can be combined into the single statement that $A = B \Leftrightarrow A \subseteq B$ and $B \subseteq A$. This remark contains a useful principle of proof; namely, that one way to determine whether two sets are equal, apart from merely inspecting them, is to show that each is a subset of the other.

To designate a set two natural techniques are employed in the sequel. First, we display the elements of the set between braces. Thus $A = \{1,4,7\}$ means that A is the set whose elements are the numbers 1, 4, and 7. More frequently a set is defined by specifying a property common to all its elements. When this is done, the so-called set builder notation is used. We write

$$A = \{x : P(x)\},$$

in which $P(x)$ is a sentence or equation which describes the properties of the elements of A. This notation reads A is the set of all elements x such that x has the property $P(x)$.

For example, consider the sets $\{1,2,3,4,5\} = \{x : x$ is an integer such that $1 \le x \le 5\}$. The axiom of extension guarantees the uniqueness of a set specified in this manner. As a further example of the set-builder notation we have

$$\{\pm 1, \pm 3, \pm 5, \dots \} = \{n : n \text{ is an odd integer}\}.$$

We often shorten our notation. For instance, the last set, mentioned might well be written $\{n : n$ is odd$\}$. Our purpose is to employ minimum notation consistent with clarity and lucidity.

Because of their frequent occurrence we use a special system of notation to designate various intervals on the real line. If a and b are real numbers, $a < b$, the following symbolism is adopted as standard:

$$[a,b] = \{x : a \le x \le b\},$$

$$(a,b] = \{x : a < x \le b\},$$

$$[a,b) = \{x : a \le x < b\},$$

$$(a,b) = \{x : a < x < b\}.$$

We speak of these symbols as closed, open-closed, closed-open, and, open intervals from a to b.

Another set that occurs frequently is the empty or null set, which is denoted by $\varnothing$ and defined by $\varnothing = \{x : x \ne x\}$. Because there is no x such that $x \ne x$, it is clear that $\varnothing$ has no elements. It is an immediate consequence of the axiom of extension that there is only one empty set. It also follows from Definition A that, for any set A, $\varnothing \subseteq A$.

Algebraic Operations with Sets

It is natural and desirable to construct new sets from those already at hand. To avoid certain logical difficulties we shall assume throughout that all statements are made in the context of a universal set designated by Ω. The universal set Ω varies to suit the discussion. For instance, in studying sets of real numbers we take Ω to be the set R of all real numbers. In studying sets of complex numbers we take Ω to be the set C of all complex numbers. Generally speaking, the universal set Ω is at our disposal and we are free to select it to fit the needs of the moment.

A geometric picture frequently helps one to visualize sets and operations on sets. To this end the universe Ω may be represented by a rectangular area in a plane and the elements of Ω, by the points within the rectangle. Sets can then be represented by areas within this rectangle and diagrams can be drawn to illustrate operations on sets and the relations between them. For instance, if A and B are sets in Ω, Figure 1.1 describes the circumstance

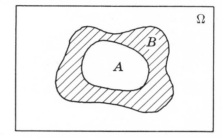

Figure 1.1 B contains A.

that A is a subset of B (we think of each set as consisting of all points within the corresponding closed curve). Such graphic displays are frequently called Venn diagrams.

Four simple operations on sets will be useful later. The first operation is the union depicted by Figure 1.1.

DEFINITION B.   *For any sets A and B the union of A and B is the set*

$$A \cup B = \{x : x \in A \text{ or } x \in B\}.$$

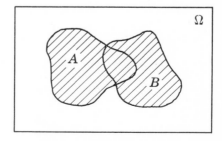

Figure 1.2 A union B.

Thus in the "union" operation we lump the elements of A and B together as a single set $A \cup B$. To visualize the union of two sets, consider Figure 1.2, in which the shaded area contains the points of $A \cup B$.

THEOREM A.   *For any sets A and B, $A \subseteq B$ if and only if $A \cup B = B$.*

PROOF.   This theorem is obvious from Figure 1.2. It is instructive, however, to give a formal proof. Assume that $A \cup B = B$. If $x \in A$, then $x \in A \cup B = B$ or $x \in B$. Hence $A \subseteq B$. Assume now that $A \subseteq B$. If $x \in A \cup B$, then $x \in A$ or $x \in B$, but if $x \in A$ then $x \in B$, since $A = B$. Thus $A \cup B \subseteq B$. That $B \subseteq A \cup B$ follows immediately from Definition B. Hence $B = A \cup B$. An obvious corollary to Theorem A is: *for any set A, $A \cup A = A$, $\varnothing \cup A = A$.*

The second basic set operation is that of intersection, written $A \cap B$. The intersection of two sets is the collection of the common elements.

DEFINITION C.   *For any sets A and B, the intersection of A and B is the set*

$$A \cap B = \{x : x \in A \text{ and } x \in B\}.$$

Figure 1.3, in which the shaded area contains the points of the set $A \cap B$, is an illustration of set intersection.

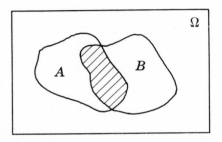

Figure 1.3   *A* intersection *B*.

THEOREM B.   *For any sets A and B, $A \subseteq B$ if and only if $A \cap B = A$.*

Again this theorem is an obvious conclusion from Figure 1.3. The formal proof follows closely the proof of Theorem A and we leave the details to the reader. As a consequence of Theorem B it is immediate that for any set A, $A \cap A = A$ and $\varnothing \cap A = \varnothing$.

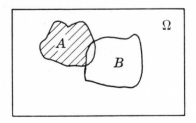

Figure 1.4   *A* minus *B*.

DEFINITION D.   *For any sets A and B, the difference of A and B is the set*

$$A \sim B = \{x : x \in A \text{ and } x \notin B\}.$$

Figure 1.4 illustrates set subtraction. The shaded area contains the points of the set $A \sim B$. In set subtraction operation only the points in $A \cap B$ are removed from A.

THEOREM C.   *For any sets A and B, $A \subseteq B$ if and only if $A \sim B = \varnothing$.*

P R O O F.   If $A \subseteq B$, then, for all $x \in A$, $x \in B$. Hence $A \sim B = \varnothing$. If $A \sim B = \varnothing$, there exists no element x such that $x \in A$ and $x \notin B$. Hence $x \in A$ implies $x \in B$ and $A \subseteq B$. It is clear that, for any set A, $A \sim A = \varnothing$ and $\varnothing \sim A = \varnothing$.

The last of the simple set operations is complementation. The complement of a set A, denoted by A', is the set of all elements that are not in A. Because the only elements we consider are those that make up Ω, A' is formally represented by the following definition:

DEFINITION E.   *The complement A' of any set A is the set*

$$A' = \{x: x \notin A\}.$$

Figure 1.5 (in which A' is shaded) illustrates this operation.

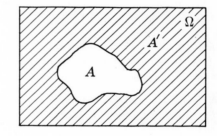

Figure 1.5   *A* complement.

The four simple operations of union, intersection, subtraction, and complementation are by no means independent of one another. For instance, a comparison of Definitions D and E immediately yields the relationship

$$A' = \Omega \sim A$$

between complementation and subtraction. As a consequence of this relationship, the set equalities $\varnothing' = \Omega$ and $\Omega' = \varnothing$ are immediate. The equality

$$(A')' = A$$

may also be deduced from the expansion $(A')' = \Omega \sim (\Omega \sim A)$.

The simple set operations may be combined in several natural ways to form more complex operations. The following theorem lists seven useful set identities that occur with sufficient frequency to merit specific mention.

THEOREM D.   *For any sets A, B, and C, all of which are subsets of a universe Ω,*

(1) $A \cup (B \cup C) = (A \cup B) \cup C$,
(2) $A \cap (B \cap C) = (A \cap B) \cap C$,
(3) $A \cup (B \cap C) = (A \cup B) \cap (A \cup C)$,
(4) $A \cap (B \cup C) = (A \cap B) \cup (A \cap C)$,
(5) $(A \cup B)' = A' \cap B'$,
(6) $(A \cap B)' = A' \cup B'$,
(7) $A \subseteq B \Leftrightarrow B' \subseteq A'$.

The proofs of these basic properties are left as exercises. The reader should note that some of the statements may be proved without resort to the concept of "belonging." For example, (6) may be shown to follow from (5) by replacing A and B in (5) with A' and B' and taking the complement of both sides.

Properties (1) and (2) may easily be extended to n sets. Indeed, by repeated use of these properties it is readily verified that the sets

$$\bigcup_{i=1}^{n} A_i = A_1 \cup A_2 \cup, \ldots, \cup A_n$$

$$\bigcap_{i=1}^{n} A_i = A_1 \cap A_2 \cap, \ldots, \cap A_n$$

may be formed with the unions and intersections taken in any order without ambiguity. In some instances it is necessary to utilize an index set consisting of the values that the set subscripts can take on.

DEFINITION F. *Let I be an index set and let A_i represent a set for each $i \in I$. Then the union of the sets A_i is the set*

$$\bigcup_{i \in I} A_i = \{x : \text{there exists } i \in I \text{ such that } x \in A_i\}$$

and the intersection of the sets A_i is the set

$$\bigcap_{i \in I} A_i = \{x : \text{for all } i \in I, \, x \in A_i\}.$$

When the index set I is obvious, these notations may be safely abbreviated to $\bigcup_i A_i$ and $\bigcap_i A_i$. If the class $\{A_i : i \in I\}$ consists of a sequence of sets, that is, $A_1, A_2, A_3, \ldots$, their union and intersection may be written in the form $\bigcup_{i=1}^{\infty} A_i$ and $\bigcap_{i=1}^{\infty} A_i$. For completeness let us note the following generalization of the preceding theorem. [Parts (3) and (4) are called DeMorgan's laws.]

THEOREM E

(1) $A \cup \left(\bigcap_{i \in I} B_i \right) = \bigcap_{i \in I} (A \cup B_i)$,

(2) $A \cap \left(\bigcup_{i \in I} B_i \right) = \bigcup_{i \in I} (A \cap B_i)$,

(3) $\left(\displaystyle\bigcup_{i \in I} A_i\right)' = \bigcap_{i \in I} A'_i,$

(4) $\left(\displaystyle\bigcap_{i \in I} A_i\right)' = \bigcup_{i \in I} A'_i.$

In the study of the various relationships between set operations it is not uncommon to discover that a variety of proofs may be found for a specific relationship. Frequently, the ingenuity and experience of the individual play a more important part than any formal procedure. To illustrate, let us consider the set equality $(A \cup B) \sim C = (A \sim C) \cup (B \sim C)$. From the implication $x \in (A \cup B) \sim C \Rightarrow x \in A \cup B$ and $x \notin C$ it follows that either $x \in A$ or $x \in B$ and $x \notin C$. If $x \in A$ and $x \notin C$ is the case, then $x \in (A \sim C)$ and $x \in (A \sim C) \cup (B \sim C)$. Similarly, if $x \in B$ and $x \notin C$, then obviously $x \in (A \sim C) \cup (B \sim C)$; thus $(A \cup B) \sim C \subseteq (A \sim C) \cup (B \sim C)$. Now, to prove the converse relation, let $x \in (A \sim C) \cup (B \sim C) \Rightarrow$ either $x \in (A \sim C)$ or $x \in (B \sim C)$. If $x \in (A \sim C)$ is the case, then $x \in A$, $x \notin C$. Therefore $x \in A \cup B$, and since $x \notin C$ we have $x \in (A \cup B) \sim C$ and $(A \sim C) \cup (B \sim C) \subseteq (A \cup B) \sim C$, which completes the proof.

A second and more direct route uses Theorem D; namely, $A \cup B \sim C = (A \cup B) \cap C' = (A \cap C') \cup (B \cup C') = (A \sim C) \cup (B \sim C)$.

Cartesian Products

In dealing with multivariate systems, we shall find that the concept of the Cartesian product of sets is a useful tool. This concept has its ancestry in the Cartesian coordinate system of analytical geometry. The reader will recall that two-dimensional Cartesian coordinates are formed by laying two real lines at right angles on the plane with their zero values coincident. Any point z on the plane is located by its orthogonal projection along the two axes; that is, $z = (x,y)$, in which x is the coordinate along the first axis and y is the coordinate along the second.

One important geometric property is that if $z_1 = (x_1, y_1)$ and $z_2 = (x_2, y_2)$ are points on the plane then

$$z_1 = z_2 \Leftrightarrow x_1 = x_2 \qquad \text{and} \qquad y_1 = y_2.$$

In more formal terms, a set $\{a,b\}$ is called an ordered pair and is written (a,b) if it is a member of a class of sets for which the following axiom holds.

AXIOM OF ORDERED PAIRS.   *For any two ordered pairs (a,b) and (c,d), $(a,b) = (c,d)$ if and only if $a = c$ and $b = d$.*

Suppose now that Y_1 and Y_2 are any two nonempty sets. By analogy with the Cartesian representation of the complex plane we make the following definition:

DEFINITION G.   *For any two sets Y_1 and Y_2 the Cartesian product $Y_1 \times Y_2$ of Y_1 and Y_2 is defined by $Y_1 \times Y_2 = \{(y_1, y_2): y_1 \in Y_1 \text{ and } y_2 \in Y_2\}$.*

In other words, the set $Y_1 \times Y_2$ is a collection of all ordered pairs $\{(y_1, y_2)\}$ such that $y_1 \in Y_1$ and $y_2 \in Y_2$. In spite of the arbitrary nature of Y_1 and Y_2, it is sometimes helpful to visualize $Y_1 \times Y_2$ in a manner similar to the usual description of the coordinate plane.

The definition of the product of two sets extends naturally to n sets. For instance, if $Y_1, Y_2, \ldots, Y_n$ are nonempty sets, their Cartesian products, denoted by $Y_1 \times Y_2 \times \cdots \times Y_n$, are the set of all ordered n-tuples $(y_1, y_2, \ldots, y_n)$, where $y_i \in Y_i$ for each subscript i. If the Y_i are all copies of a single set Y, their product is indicated by the symbol Y^n. For example, R^1 is just R, the real line, and R^2 is a coordinate plane, whereas R^3 denotes the set of all ordered real triplets which underlies the classical development of solid analytical geometry.

As a second example, recall the multivariate system of Figure 0.1. By introducing the sets $X = X_1 \times \cdots \times X_m$ and $Y = Y_1 \times \cdots \times Y_n$ we make it clear that this system can be thought of as an association between elements of X and Y rather than the more awkward representation as an association between the classes $\{x_i\}$ and $\{y_i\}$. Thus there is no real reason for considering multivariate and single variate systems as distinct.

In dealing with ordered tuplets, we frequently call y_i the ith coordinate and Y_i the ith coordinate set. If $z = (y_1, \ldots, y_i, \ldots, y_n) \in Y_1 \times \cdots \times Y_n = Z$, then y_i is frequently called the projection of z into the set Y_i. Similarly, Y_i is the projection of the set Z into its ith coordinate set.

The elementary set operations can be extended readily to Cartesian products sets. It will be implicitly understood that a new universe is defined by taking products of the coordinate universes. The following theorem contains three examples of useful set equalities in product spaces.

THEOREM F.   *For any sets A, B, and C,*
  (1) $A \times (B \cup C) = (A \times B) \cup (A \times C)$,
  (2) $A \times (B \cap C) = (A \times B) \cap (A \times C)$,
  (3) $A \times (B \sim C) = (A \times B) \sim (A \times C)$.

   P R O O F.   (1) If $(x,y) \in A \times (B \cup C)$, then $x \in A$ and $y \in B \cup C$. Hence $y \in B$ or $y \in C$, so that $(x,y) \in A \times B$ or $(x,y) \in A \times C$. Therefore $(x,y) \in (A \times B) \cup (A \times B)$ and $A \times (B \cup C) \subseteq (A \times B) \cup (A \times C)$.   If $(x,y) \in (A \times B) \cup (A \times C)$, then $(x,y) \in A \times B$ or $(x,y) \in A \times C$. Hence $x \in A$, and $y \in B$ or $y \in C$. Therefore $y \in B \cup C$ and $(x,y) \in A \times (B \cup C)$, so that $(A \times B) \cup (A \times C) \subseteq A \times (B \cup C)$. Hence $A \times (B \cup C) = (A \times B) \cup (A \times C)$.

Exercises

  1. Let Ω be the set $\{1, 2\}$. There are four subsets. List them. If Ω is the set $\{1, 2, \ldots, n\}$, how many subsets are there?

  2. Complete the proofs of Theorem B and D.

3. Verify the following set equalities:
  (a) $A \cup (A \cap B) = A = A \cap (A \cup B)$,
  (b) $(A \cup B) \sim C = (A \sim C) \cup (B \sim C)$,
  (c) $A \sim (B \cup C) = (A \sim B) \sim C$.

4. The set $A \approx B = (A \sim B) \cup (B \sim A)$ is called the *symmetric difference* of the sets A and B. Prove the following formulas:
  (a) $A \approx (B \approx C) = (A \approx B) \approx C$ (associativity),
  (b) $A \cap (B \approx C) = A \cap B \approx A \cap C$ (distributivity),
  (c) $A \cup B = A \approx B \approx A \cup B$,
  (d) $A \sim B = A \approx A \cap B$.

5. Prove parts (2) and (3) of Theorem F.

6. Describe a cylinder of radius r and height h as a product of sets.

1.2 METRIC SPACES

In Section 1.1 we introduced the basic concepts and terminology prerequisite to an efficient discussion of abstract set operations. Although there are many interesting applications of these concepts, it is not until the "set" is given some mathematical structure that it becomes useful for our purposes. A set and a certain structure, that is, the relations between or operations on its elements, is called a "space." The structure can usually be identified as being geometric or algrebraic.

In this section the concept of distance, which is basically geometric in nature, is developed. The distance between two points x and y on the real line is defined by the expression $|x - y|$, and in two dimensions the distance between the ordered pairs $z_1 = (x_1, y_1)$ and $z_2 = (x_2, y_2)$ is usually given as $\{(x_1 - x_2)^2 + (y_1 - y_2)^2\}^{1/2}$. The extension of the distance concept to three and higher dimensions is apparent.

As students of system engineering, we shall find it mandatory to have a notion of distance that is applicable to abstract sets. The points and sets in which we are most interested, for instance, are, time functions or time sequences. For sets of this kind the distance concept is not so obvious as it is in these geometric examples. Such expressions as

$$\max_{t \in [a,b]} |u_1(t) - u_2(t)|,$$

$$\int_a^b |u_1(t) - u_2(t)| dt,$$

or

$$\left[\sum_{t_k \in \sigma} [u_1(t_k) - u_2(t_k)]^2 \right]^{1/2}$$

are the natural candidates for the distance between the two functions u_1 and u_2. In the multivariate system such complicated expressions as

$$\left[\left(\sum_{j=1}^{k}\int_{a}^{b}|u_j(t)-v_j(t)|^p dt\right)^{2/p}\left(\sum_{j=k+1}^{n}\sum_{t_i \in \sigma}[u_j(t_i)-v_j(t_i)]^p\right)^{2/p}\right]^{1/2}$$

are not uncommon as distance measures for the separation between the ordered pairs $u = (u_1, \ldots, u_n)$ and $v = (v_1, \ldots, v_n)$.

The complexity of these examples suggests that we would do well to consider the elementary properties of the distance concept before becoming entangled in concrete expressions. A metric space (to be defined later) is nothing more than a nonempty set on which a measure of distance has been successfully defined. If the geometric distance concept is examined with the intention of listing its important properties as axioms, the natural result would seem to be the following:

DEFINITION A. *Let X be a nonempty set. A distance measure or metric on X is a real function ρ of pairs of elements of X such that if x, y, $z \in X$ the following three conditions will hold*:

(1) $\rho(x,y) \geq 0$, all $x,y \in X$ and $\rho(x,y) = 0 \Leftrightarrow x = y$ (identity);
(2) $\rho(x,y) = \rho(y,x)$ (symmetry);
(3) $\rho(x,y) \leq \rho(x,z) + \rho(z,y)$ (triangle inequality).

The number $\rho(x,y)$ is the distance between the elements x and y, which we need, and the three conditions are the metric axioms. A moment's reflection will show that these axioms summarize the fundamental properties that one might intuitively expect in any distance concept.

DEFINITION B. *A metric space consists of two objects: a nonempty set X and a metric ρ on X.*

The elements of X are called the points of the metric space (X,ρ). Whenever it can be done without causing confusion, we denote the metric space (X,ρ) by the symbol X, which is used for the underlying set of points. It is important to keep in mind, however, that a metric space is not merely a nonempty set: it is a nonempty set with a metric function.

The definition of a metric ρ on a set X is not unique. In fact, it often happens that several different metrics can be defined on a single nonempty set. Use of distinct metrics makes the set into distinct metric spaces. It is important that we feel completely at ease with the metric axioms of Definition A. To this end, let us now consider the following examples of metric spaces, taking care to observe the natural form that the metric axioms assume in each case.

Example 1.   For any points x, y on the real line R we now define a metric by

$$\rho(x,y) = |x - y|.$$

It is easy to verify the three conditions required by our definition.

(1) $\rho(x,y) = |x - y| = 0 \Leftrightarrow x = y$,

(2) $\rho(x,y) = |x - y| = |-(y - x)| = |y - x| = \rho(y,x)$,

(3) $\rho(x,y) = |x - y| = |(x - z) + (z - y)| \leq |x - z| + |z - y|$
$\qquad = \rho(x,z) + \rho(z,y)$.

The metric $|x - y|$ is called the *usual metric* on R. Unless otherwise stated the set R as a metric space is implicitly assumed to have this metric.

Example 2. If C is the set of all complex numbers $z = a + jb$, one suitable metric is given by

$$\rho(z_1,z_2) = \{(z_1 - z_2)(\overline{z_1 - z_2})\}^{1/2} = |z_1 - z_2|.$$

This metric is called the *usual metric* for C and the reader may verify the metric axioms as Exercise 3.

Example 3. We recall that R^n (or C^n) is the set of real (or complex) ordered n-tuplets $x = (x_1, x_2, \ldots, x_n)$, $y = (y_1, y_2, \ldots, y_n)$. R^n (or C^n) can be converted to a metric space by the distance measure

$$\rho(x,y) = \left\{ \sum_{i=1}^{n} |x_i - y_i|^2 \right\}^{1/2}.$$

Metric Axioms 1 and 2 obviously hold. The proof of Axiom 3, although not at all difficult, is deferred to a later section in which it is proved in a more general setting. This metric for R^n (or C^n) is called the Euclidean metric; the space R^n (C^n) with this metric is called the Euclidean space and given the special symbol E^n.

To emphasize an earlier point, let us illustrate also that the definition of the metric function is by no means unique. The reader may wish to verify that the following expressions are also metric functions on the set R^n:

$$\rho_2(x,y) = \sum_{i=1}^{n} |x_i - y_i|,$$

$$\rho_3(x,y) = \sum_{i=1}^{n} a_i |x_i - y_i|, \qquad a_i > 0, \qquad i = 1, \ldots, n.$$

In the analysis of physical systems we shall often have flexibility in the choice of the metric. This flexibility can be used to advantage by adopting a metric that fits closely the physical situation at hand or alternatively permits some simplification in the details of the analysis.

Example 4. The Hilbert space l_2 is the set of all sequences of real numbers $x = (x_1, x_2, \ldots, x_i, \ldots)$ such that the series $\sum_{i=1}^{\infty} |x_i|^2$ is convergent. Here the distance used in defining the space is understood to be

$$\rho(x,y) = \left\{ \sum_{i=1}^{\infty} |x_i - y_i|^2 \right\}^{1/2}.$$

The proof that ρ is a metric on l_2 is given in Example 4, Section 1.4.

Before proceeding with Example 5, let us consider the set $A \subset R$, in which A is a nonempty bounded set. The adjective *bounded* means that an $x_0 \in R$ exists such that for every $x \in A$, $|x| \leq x_0$. Now, if A has an upper bound $x_0 < \infty$, A must have a "least" upper bound (or supremum) that is a number $\hat{x} \in R$ such that $x \in A \Rightarrow x \leq \hat{x}$ and $\hat{x}$ is the smallest number for which this is true. This is the "axiom of completeness." For a brief exposition of the basic properties of the real line see Chapter 2 of Taylor [A82]. Similarly, y is called a lower bound for A if $y \leq x$ for each $x \in A$ and is called a greatest lower bound (or infimum) of A if y is greater than or equal to every lower bound of A. To formalize these definitions we introduce the following notation:

DEFINITION C. *Let A be a bounded subset of R; inf (A) denotes the $x \in R$, which is the greatest lower bound of A and sup (A) denotes the $x \in R$, which is the least upper bound of A.*

The set A may also have a maximum element, denoted max (A), which is an element of the set equal or larger than all others. The distinction between max (A) and sup (A) is illustrated by the set $[0,1)$ for which sup $(A) = 1$ and max (A) does not exist because the element 1 is not in the set. Indeed, if sup $(A) \in A$, then max $(A) = $ sup (A). The distinction between min (A), a minimum element, and inf (A) is analogous. The concepts of supremum and infimum are convenient also because they always exist, whereas the maximum and minimum may not.

Example 5.   Let $C(a,b)$ denote the set of continuous real functions over the interval $[a,b]$. The *usual metric* for this set is given by[1]

$$\rho(x,y) = \sup |x(t) - y(t)|$$

and is called the *uniform metric*. From the definition it is clear that $\rho(x,y) = \rho(y,x) \geq 0$ and $\rho(x,y) = 0 \Leftrightarrow x(t) = y(t)$ all $t \in [a,b]$. Furthermore,

$$|x(t) - z(t)| = |[x(t) - y(t)] + [y(t) - z(t)]| \leq |x(t) - y(t)| + |y(t) - z(t)|$$

$$\leq \sup |x(t) - y(t)| + \sup |y(t) - z(t)| = \rho(x,y) + \rho(y,z),$$

and taking the supremum of the left-hand side of this expression we have

$$\rho(x,z) \leq \rho(x,y) + \rho(y,z);$$

hence the metric axioms are satisfied.

---

[1]Here the function $\varepsilon(t) = |x(t) - y(t)|$ might take on its maximum value at a or b, in which case use of the supremum rather than the maximum ensures that

$$\sup_{[a,b]} \varepsilon(t) = \sup_{[a,b)} \varepsilon(t) = \sup_{(a,b]} \varepsilon(t) = \sup_{(a,b)} \varepsilon(t)$$

and all of these intervals can be treated without distinction.

This last example is indicative of the metric spaces that occur in the later chapters. Although the points of the space $C(a,b)$ seem much more complicated than the points of the space E^n, it is significant that the metric definition and the verification of the metric axioms are carried out as easily in $C(a,b)$ as they are in E^n.

Since the metric space is in many ways an abstraction of the properties of E^2, it seems reasonable to expect that most of the distance-related concepts in E^2 can be carried over to the more general setting. The concept of a spherical neighborhood, set diameter, and distance between a point and a set are the first such concepts that we shall express in the metric-space terminology.

DEFINITION D. *Let X be a metric space with $x_0 \in X$ and r a positive real number. The subset $S_r(x_0) = \{x : x \in X$ and $\rho(x,x_0) < r\}$ is called an open spherical neighborhood of x_0 with radius r.*

Similarly, a closed spherical neighborhood is a set that differs from $S_r(x_0)$ only in that the set of points for which $\rho(x,x_0) = r$ is included. This definition is consistent with the more elementary notions of neighborhoods. To illustrate, Figure 1.6 shows the neighborhood for E^1 and E^2 spaces.

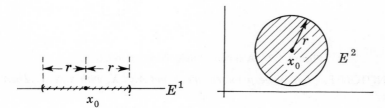

Figure 1.6   Spherical neighborhoods in E^1 and E^2 spaces.

As a more sophisticated example, we consider spherical neighborhoods in the space $C(0,1)$ (with the usual metric). Let f_0 be a continuous function on $(0,1)$. Figure 1.7 illustrates $S_r(f_0)$, an open spherical neighborhood about the function f_0; $S_r(f_0)$ consists of all functions $f \in C(0,1)$ whose graphs lie within the shaded band of vertical width $2r$ centered about f_0.

Associated with the concept of neighborhood is the concept of the diameter of a set.

DEFINITION E. *Let A be a set of a metric space X. The least upper bound of the distances $\rho(x,y)$ between all possible pairs of points x, $y \in A$ is called the diameter of the set A and is denoted by diam (A):*

$$\text{diam } (A) = \sup \{\rho(x_1,x_2) : x_1,x_2 \in A\}.$$

For sets $A \subset R$ the relation diam $(A) = \sup (A) - \inf (A)$ evidently holds; that is, diam (A) is the length of the smallest interval containing A. In R^2, diam (A) is the diameter of the circle of smallest radius containing A. In R^3, diam (A) is twice the radius of the smallest sphere containing A; in fact, for all spherical neighborhoods $A = S_r(x_0)$ in any metrix space diam $(A) \leq 2r$.

Subsets of metric spaces with finite diameters are said to be bounded. For example, the closed interval $0 \leq x \leq 1$ is bounded. The same is true of a square and the n-dimensional cube. On the other hand, the half-line $x \leq 0$, the real line, and the space E^n are examples of unbounded sets.

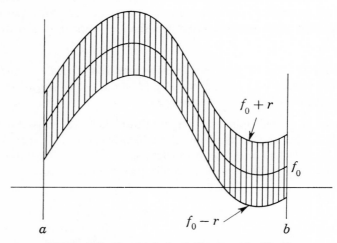

Figure 1.7   A spherical neighborhood in $C(a,b)$.

DEFINITION F.   *Let X be a metric space and $A \subset X$, with $x_0 \in X$. Then the number*

$$\rho(x_0; A) = \inf \{\rho(x_0,a): a \in A\}$$

is defined as the distance from the point x_0 to the set A.

The distance $\rho(x_0; A)$ may also be formulated as the radius of the largest spherical neighborhood of x_0 which does not intersect A. The interpretations of $\rho(x_0; A)$ in the spaces E^1, E^2, and E^3 are self-evident.

Exercises

1. Let X be a set. For x, $y \in X$ define the function ρ by $\rho(x,x) = 0$ and $\rho(x,y) = 1$ for all $x \neq y$. Prove that X with this metric is a metric space.

2. Let X be a metric space with metric ρ. Define a new function $\rho'(x,y)$ by

$$\rho'(x,y) = \frac{\rho(x,y)}{1 + \rho(x,y)}.$$

Prove that ρ' is a metric for X and that $0 \leq \rho' < 1$.

3. Complete the proof of Example 2. Verify that the functions ρ_2 and ρ_3 of Example 3 satisfy the metric axioms.

4. If A is a subset of a metric space X, verify that diam $(A) \geq 0$, and, if $x \in X$, then $\rho(x;A) < +\infty$.

5. Let $X_1, \ldots, X_n$ be a class of metric spaces with metrics $\rho_1, \ldots, \rho_n$. Show that $\bar{\rho} = \max\{\rho_i(x_i,y_i)\}$ and $\hat{\rho} = \sum_{i=1}^{n}\rho_i(x_i,y_i)$ are suitable metrics for the product space $X = X_1 \times X_2 \times \cdots \times X_n$.

6. (a) Show that if the sets A and B are not void and $A \subseteq B$, then diam $(A) \leq$ diam (B).

(b) Prove the inequality diam $(A \cup B) \leq$ diam $(A) +$ diam (B) under the assumption that $A \cap B = \varnothing$.

Convergence in Metric Spaces

Since series and series convergence play an important part in many areas of analysis and engineering applications, it is useful to consider the abstract form of these concepts. First a sequence of real numbers,

$$\{x_n\} = \{x_1, x_2, \ldots, x_n, \ldots\},$$

is said to be convergent if a real number x exists (called the limit of the sequence) and that, given any $\varepsilon > 0$, a positive integer n_0 can be found such that $n \geq n_0 \Rightarrow |x_n - x| < \varepsilon$. This condition means that x_n must be "close" to x for all sufficiently large n. Frequently used symbolism includes $x_n \to x$ or $\lim_{n\to\infty} x_n = x$ and is expressed by saying that x_n approaches x or x_n converges to x.

When dealing with an arbitrary metric space we generalize these statements to the following definition:

DEFINITION G. *Let $\{x_n\}$ denote a sequence of points in the metric space X. If for every $\varepsilon > 0$ an n_0 can be found such that $n \geq n_0 \Rightarrow \rho(x_n,x) < \varepsilon$, then $\{x_n\}$ is said to converge to x.*

Most of the basic properties of convergence in the real line carry over to the metric space setting. For reference purposes the following theorem summarizes the more familiar examples:

THEOREM A. *Let $\{x_n\}$ denote a sequence of points in the metric space X.*
(1) *If $\{x_n\}$ converges, then every subsequence $\{x_{n_k}\}$ will converge to the same point.*
(2) *The sequence $\{x_n\}$ can have at most one limit.*
(3) *If $\{x_n\}$ converges, the set of numbers $\{\rho(x_n,\theta)\}$ will be bounded for every $\theta \in X$.*
(4) *Convergence of $\{x_n\}$ is not dependent on any finite number of terms.*

P R O O F.   Part (1) is evident from the fact that if $\rho(x_n,x) < \varepsilon$ for $n \geq n_0(\varepsilon)$ then also $\rho(x_{n_k},x) < \varepsilon$ for $n_k \geq n_0(\varepsilon)$. To prove part (2) assume $x_n \to x$ and $x_n \to y$. Using the metric axiom, we have $\rho(x,y) \leq \rho(x,x_n) + \rho(x_n,y) < \varepsilon$ for sufficiently large n. Since x and y are fixed and ε is an arbitrary positive number, this inequality can hold only if $\rho(x,y) = 0$, that is, $x = y$. Part (4) is self-evident and the proof of part (3) is left for the exercises.

To familiarize ourselves further with convergence, we consider two examples:

Example 6.   Let $x^k = (x_1^k, \ldots, x_n^k)\, k = 1, 2, \ldots$ be the members of a convergence sequence in E^n with the usual Euclidean metric. If

$$\lim_{k \to \infty} \rho(x,x^k) = 0,$$

where $x = (x_1, \ldots, x_n)$ is a fixed element of E^n, then

$$\left[\sum_{j=1}^{n} (x_j^k - x_j)^2 \right]^{1/2} \to 0,$$

as $k \to \infty$; hence we establish that $(x_j^k - x_j)^2 \to 0$, $j = 1, \ldots, n$ as $k \to \infty$, and thus convergence in this space is coordinatewise.

Example 7.   Now consider convergence in the space $C(a,b)$. Let a sequence $\{x_n\}$ of elements of $C(a,b)$ be given so that this sequence will converge to x. This means

$$\sup_t |x(t) - x_n(t)| \to 0 \qquad \text{for } n \to \infty:$$

that is, a natural number $n_0 = n_0(\varepsilon)$ exists for every $\varepsilon > 0$ and

$$\sup_t |x(t) - x_n(t)| < \varepsilon \qquad \text{for all } n \geq n_0(\varepsilon).$$

Hence $|x(t) - x_n(t)| < \varepsilon$ for all $n \geq n_0(\varepsilon)$ and for every $t \in (a,b)$. But this would imply that the sequence $\{x_n(t)\}$ converges uniformly to the function $x(t)$. The converse also holds: if a sequence $x_n(t)$ converges uniformly to $x(t)$, then $\rho(x_n,x) \to 0$. Thus convergence in the space $C(a,b)$ is uniform convergence in the interval (a,b). This result is the reason that the supremum metric on $C(a,b)$ is called the uniform metric.

DEFINITION H.   *A point x_0 is said to be an accumulation point (limit point) of the set A if it can be expressed as the limit of an infinite sequence of points which are members of the set A and distinct from x_0.*

The meaning of this definition is clear, the main idea being that the points of A pile up at x_0. The reader is cautioned, however, against passing too quickly over statements of this kind. What this definition does *not* say is that point x_0 must be a member of the set A. Thus the sequence $\{1, \tfrac{1}{2}, \tfrac{1}{3}, \ldots\}$

of the real line has 0 as a limit point; in fact, 0 is its only limit point. The interval $[0,1)$ has 0 as a limit point which is in the set and 1 as a limit point which is not in the set; further, every real number x such that $0 < x < 1$ is also a limit point contained in this set.

DEFINITION I.   *Every point of the set A that is not an accumulation point is called an isolated point of A.*

In the set $\{1, \frac{1}{2}, \frac{1}{3}, \ldots\}$, for example, point 0 is the only accumulation point of the set. All other points are isolated points.

The following two theorems are consequences of these two definitions. In fact, many authors use them as the definitions of limit and isolated points.

THEOREM B.   *A necessary and sufficient condition that point x_0 be an accumulation point of the set A is that every open spherical neighborhood of x_0 contain some point distinct from x_0 of the set A.*

In a final attempt at clarification, we let A be a set in a metric space X. If a point $x \in A$ is a limit point of A, in every spherical neighborhood of x at least one other point of A, that is, at least one point of the set $(A \sim x)$, must be found. Hence $S_r(x) \cap (A \sim x) \neq \emptyset$ for every r. By similar reasoning we have the following theorem:

THEOREM C.   *A necessary and sufficient condition that point x_0 be an isolated point of the set A is that there exist a spherical neighborhood $S_r(x_0)$ such that $S_r(x_0) \cap A = \{x_0\}$.*

The distinction between the terms limit and limit point is often a source of confusion for the novice. On the real line, for instance, the sequence $\{1, 1, \ldots, 1, \ldots\}$ is convergent with limit 1. Point 1, however, is not a limit point because the points in this sequence are not distinct from the limit (as required by our definition). Thus a sequence may have a limit but not a limit point. Conversely, we shall see later that the set of points of a sequence may have a limit point but not a limit. The following theorem relates these concepts:

THEOREM D.   *If a convergent sequence in a metric space has infinitely many distinct points, its limit is a limit point of the set of points of the sequence.*

P R O O F.   Let $\{x_n\}$ be a convergent sequence in the metric space X with limit x. Assume that x is not a limit point of the set of points of the sequence. Our assumption implies that an open sphere $S_r(x)$ centers on x which contains no point of the sequence different from x. However, since x is the limit of the sequence, all x_n's for some $n > n_0$ must lie in $S_r(x)$; hence all of these x_n's must coincide with x. This implies that there are only finitely many distinct points in the sequence, which contradicts the hypothesis of the theorem.

We have seen that the limit points of a set M need not belong to the set itself. If to the set A we add all the limit points of A, we form a new set called the closure of the set A, which is denoted by $\overline{A}$ and defined as follows:

DEFINITION J. *Let A be a subset of a given metric space. We denote by $\overline{A}$ a subset of this space, called the closure of the set A. A point x_0 is in the set $\overline{A}$ if either $x_0 \in A$ or there exists a sequence of points $x_1, x_2, \ldots, x_n, \ldots$ in the set A such that $\lim_{n \to \infty} x_n = x_0$.*

As an example, if A is the open unit disk $\{z: \rho(z,0) < 1\}$, then $\overline{A}$ is the closed disk $\{z: \rho(z,0) \leq 1\}$.

This definition can also be formulated as follows: a necessary and sufficient condition that point x_0 not belong to the set $\overline{A}$ is that there be a spherical neighborhood of x_0 which is disjoint from the set A.

Exercises

7. (a) Using the triangular inequality, prove part (3) of Theorem A.

(b) Show that if $\{x_n\}$ and $\{y_n\}$ are convergent sequences in x such that $x_n \to x$ and $y_n \to y$ then $\rho(x_n,y_n) \to \rho(x,y)$.

8. Verify the following set equalities: (a) $\overline{M \cup N} = \overline{M} \cup \overline{N}$, (b) $M \subseteq \overline{M}$, (c) $M = \overline{M}$, (d) $\overline{\varnothing} = \varnothing$, (e) $\overline{M} \sim \overline{N} \subset \overline{M \sim N}$, (f) $\overline{M \cap N} \subseteq \overline{M} \cap \overline{N}$.

Closed and Open Sets

The concepts of the closed and open set are also important in mathematical analysis. Indeed, the theories of measure, integration, and topological spaces utilize either the open or the closed set as a basic quantity. As we shall see, these sets are closely related. In fact, many developments in terms of open sets have a dual development in terms of closed sets and vice versa.

DEFINITION K (Open Set). *A subset G of the metric space X is called an open set if for every point x in G there is a positive real number r such that $S_r(x) \subseteq G$.*

That is, each point of G can be made the center of some open sphere containing only points in G. Loosely speaking, a set is open if each of its points is "inside" the set in the sense made precise by the definition. A set on the real line consisting of a single point is not open, for each open interval centered on this point contains points not in the set. Similarly, the subset $[0,1)$ of the real line is not open because the point 0 in $[0,1)$ has the property that each open interval centered on it (no matter how small it may be) contains points not in $[0,1)$, for example, points just to the left of 0. If we omit the offending point 0, the resulting bounded open interval $(0,1)$ is an open set.

THEOREM E.   *In any metric space X, the empty set $\emptyset$ and the full space X are open sets.*

P R O O F.   To show that $\emptyset$ is open, we must show that each point in $\emptyset$ is the center of an open sphere contained in $\emptyset$, but since there are no points in $\emptyset$, this requirement is automatically satisfied. X, we recall, is the universal set and is clearly open, since every open sphere centered on each of its points can contain only points in X.

DEFINITION L (Closed Set).   *A subset F of a metric space X is called a closed set if it contains all of its limit points.*

In loose terms, the set F is closed if none of its points gets arbitrarily close to points outside F. A single point set on the real line is closed, for this set has no limit points, hence contains all of them. Every finite set of points is similarly closed. The interval $[0,1)$ as a subset of the real line is not closed, since point 1 is a limit point, yet is not in the set itself. If we add the offending point to the set, the resulting interval $[0,1)$ is closed.

THEOREM F.   *In any metric space Ω, the empty set $\emptyset$ and the full space Ω are closed sets.*

P R O O F.   The empty set has no limit points; it contains them all and is therefore closed. The full space Ω contains all points; hence it automatically contains its own limit points and thus is closed.

The following theorem exposes the relationship between closed sets and open sets.

THEOREM G.   *Let X be a metric space. A subset F of X is closed $\Leftrightarrow$ its complement F' is open.*

P R O O F.   First we assume that F is closed and show that F' is open. If $F' = \emptyset$, it is open and we suppose that F' is nonempty. Let x be any point in F'. Since F is closed, x is neither in F nor is it a limit point of F. If this is so, an open sphere $S_r(x)$ exists about x which is disjoint from F; that is, $S_r(x)$ is an open sphere centered on x and contained in F', and, since x was taken to be any point of F', F' is open.

Assume now that F' is open. The only way F can fail to be closed is to have a limit point in F'. This cannot happen, for, if F' is open, each of its points is the center of an open sphere disjoint from F and no such point can be a limit point of F.

The logic used in this proof is quite typical of set theoretic arguments.

THEOREM H.   *Let X be a metric space.*
   (1) *Any union of open sets in X is an open set.*
   (2) *Any finite intersection of open sets in X is an open set.*
   (3) *Any finite union of closed sets in X is a closed set.*
   (4) *Any intersection of closed sets in X is a closed set.*

In view of Theorem G the last two assertions follow from (1) and (2). The proofs of (1) and (2) are left to the reader. The examples

$$[a,b] = \bigcap_{n=1}^{\infty} (a - \frac{1}{n}, b + \frac{1}{n}), \quad \varnothing = \bigcap_{n=1}^{\infty} (n, \infty), \quad \bigcap_{n=1}^{\infty} (a, b + \frac{1}{n}) = (a,b]$$

show that a countable intersection of open sets may be closed, open, or neither open nor closed. A similar statement for countable intersections of closed sets is obtained by taking complements.

In terms of the closure concept, we have the following relations. Let X be a metric space and A a set in X.

(1) A is closed $\Leftrightarrow A = \bar{A}$.
(2) $\bar{A}$ is the smallest closed set containing A; that is, $\bar{A}$ is contained in any closed set which contains A.
(3) $\bar{A}$ equals the intersection of all closed sets containing A.

As a model for our recent concepts, we choose the complex plane as our universe. In Figure 1.8 the set A is shown with heavy lines for points on

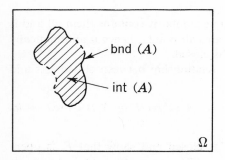

Figure 1.8 A set, its boundary, and its interior.

the boundary of A belonging to A and dashed lines for boundary points not in A. The set $\bar{A}$ differs from A by the addition of the appropriate limit points, and the interior of A consists of A minus its boundary points. In this visualization we have introduced the concepts of interior and boundary. It will take just a moment to express these ideas in mathematical form.

Let X be an arbitrary metric space containing the set A. A point in A is called an interior point of A if it is the center of some open sphere contained in A.

DEFINITION M. *The interior of A, denoted by* int (A), *is the set of all its interior points. Symbolically,*

$$\text{int } (A) = \{x \colon x \in A \text{ and } S_r(x) \subseteq A \text{ for some } r\}.$$

The basic properties of interiors are the following:

(1) int (A) is an open subset of A which contains every open subset of A (this is often expressed by saying that the interior of A is the largest open subset of A),

(2) A is open $\Leftrightarrow A = \text{int } (A)$,

(3) int (A) equals the union of all open subsets of A,

(4) int $(A) = [(\overline{A'})]'$.

DEFINITION N. *A point x of a subset A of the metric space X is called a boundary point if every open sphere containing x intersects both A and A'. The boundary of A is the set of all its boundary points; that is,* bnd $(A) = \overline{A} \cap \overline{(A')}$.

It follows easily from the definition of bnd (A) and property (4) that for any set A

$$\overline{A} = \text{int } (A) \cup \text{bnd } (A).$$

Exercises

9. Let X be a metric space and show that any two distinct points of X can be separated by open spheres in the following sense: if x and y are distinct points in X, a disjoint pair of open spheres exists, each of which is centered on one of the points.

10. Let X be a metric space. If $\{x\}$ is a subset of X consisting of a single point, show that its complement $\{x\}'$ is open. More generally, show that A' is open if A is any finite subset of X.

11. Let X be a metric space and $S_r(x)$ the open sphere in X with center x and radius r. Let A be a subset of X with a diameter less than r which intersects $S_r(x)$. Prove that $A \subseteq S_{2r}(x)$.

12. Describe the interior of each of the following subsets of the real line: the set of all integers; the set of all rationals; the set of all irrationals; $(0,1)$; $[0,1]$; $[0,1) \cup [1,2]$. Do the same for each of the following subsets of the complex plane: $\{z : |z| < 1\}$; $\{z : |z| \leq 1\}$; $\{z : \text{Im } (z) = 0\}$; $\{z : \text{Re } (z) \text{ is rational}\}$.

13. Let A and B be two subsets of a metric space X and prove the following:
(a) int $(A) \cup \text{int } (B) \subseteq \text{int } (A \cup B)$.
(b) int $(A) \cap \text{int } (B) = \text{int } (A \cap B)$.
Give an example of two subsets A and B of the real line such that int $(A) \cup \text{int } (B) \neq \text{int } (A \cup B)$.

14. Let X be a metric space and extend Exercise 9 by proving that any point and a disjoint closed set in X can be separated by open sets in the sense that if x is a point and F a closed set that does not contain x there exists a disjoint pair of open sets G_1 and G_2 such that $x \in G_1$ and $F \subseteq G_2$.

15. Let X be a metric space and A a subset of X. If x is a limit point of A, show that each open sphere centered on x contains an infinite number of distinct points of A. Use this result to show that a finite subset of X is closed.

16. Let X be a metric space and A a subset of X. Prove the following facts:

(a) $(\bar{A})' = \text{int}\,(A')$.

(b) $\bar{A} = \{x: \rho(x\,;A) = 0\}$.

Complete Spaces

In the theory of real-number sequences a sequence of reals $\{x_n\}$, with the property that an integer $N_0(\varepsilon)$ can always be found for every $\varepsilon > 0$ such that $|x_m - x_n| < \varepsilon$ for all $m,n > N$, is called a Cauchy sequence. This condition is not only necessary but sufficient for convergence in R (and C, as well). In an arbitrary metric space, however, the Cauchy test may not be sufficient to establish convergence. Definition P of this section isolates those metric spaces for which the Cauchy test is a useful tool. First, let is formalize the concept of a Cauchy sequence.

DEFINITION O. *A sequence $\{x_n\}$ of elements of an arbitrary metric space X is called a Cauchy sequence if there exists an integer $N(\varepsilon)$ for every $\varepsilon > 0$ such that $\rho(x_m,x_n) < \varepsilon$ for all $m,n > N$.*

Consider now an arbitrary convergent sequence $\{x_n\}$ with the limit x, in which x and $\{x_n\}$ are all members of the metric space X. From the definition of convergence we have the existence of an N for every $\varepsilon > 0$ such that $\rho(x_n,x) < \varepsilon/2$ for $n \geq N_0$. From the triangle inequality in metric spaces $\rho(x_m,x_n) \leq \rho(x_m,x) + \rho(x_n,x) < \varepsilon$ for $m,n \geq N$. This is summarized by Theorem I.

THEOREM I. *Let X be a metric space. If a sequence $\{x_n\} \subset X$ converges to a limit $x \in X$, it is a Cauchy sequence.*

Unfortunately, the converse of this theorem is not true; that is, a Cauchy sequence is not necessarily convergent. The problem lies in the fact that in some metric spaces there are Cauchy sequences that do not converge to a member of the space in question. As an example, consider first the space $X = (0,1]$. The sequence $\{1/n\}$ is a Cauchy sequence. The point 0 to which this sequence wants to converge is not a member of X and so the sequence is not convergent.

Second, let X be the metric space of rational numbers, with $\rho(x_1,x_2) = |x_1 - x_2|$. In this space the sequence $\{x_n\}$, in which $x_n = (1 + 1/n)^n$, is a Cauchy sequence. It approaches arbitrarily close to the irrational number e which is not in X, hence is not convergent.

The difficulty that is inherent in these examples is based on the fact that the notion of a convergent sequence is not completely intrinsic to the sequence itself but also depends on the structure of the space in which it lies. In other words, a convergent sequence is not convergent on its own; it must converge to some point in the space. If the space in question has the property that the converse of Theorem I holds, we shall use the term "complete" as a description of the space.

DEFINITION P.   *If, in a metric space X, every Cauchy sequence converges to a limit (which is an element of X), the space X is called complete.*

To conclude this section we consider an example which is fairly indicative of the kind of argument that must be used to establish the property of completeness in a metric space. The exercises that follow suggest several additional facts which are occasionally useful. Attention is also directed to Appendix 1, which supplements the present section. The reader should not infer that the topics of any of the appendices are of lesser importance than those of the chapters.

Example 8.   Consider first the space $C_R(a,b)$ of real continuous functions. Let $\{x_n\}$ be a Cauchy sequence in $C_R(a,b)$. This means that to each $\varepsilon > 0$ there corresponds an integer n_0 such that $m \geq n_0$, $n \geq n_0$ imply

$$\sup |x_n(t) - x_m(t)| < \varepsilon.$$

In particular, if we fix $t = t_0$, the numerical sequence $\{x_n(t_0)\}_{n=1}^{\infty}$ is a Cauchy sequence. Since R is complete, there is a real number, which depends on t_0 and which we write $x(t_0)$, such that

$$|x_n(t_0) - x(t_0)| \to 0 \qquad \text{as } n \to \infty.$$

By applying the same argument to each t in $[a,b]$ we obtain a real valued function $x = x(t)$. It remains to prove that x belongs to C_R and that $x_n \to x$ in C_R.

Now for $n,m \geq n_0$, we have

$$|x_n(t) - x_m(t)| < \varepsilon$$

for each t in $[a,b]$. By letting $m \to \infty$ it follows that

$$|x_n(t) - x(t)| \leq \varepsilon$$

for each t; that is,

$$\sup |x_n(t) - x(t)| \leq \varepsilon, \qquad \text{for } n \geq n_0.$$

We have therefore shown that to each $\varepsilon > 0$ there corresponds an integer n_0 such that $\|x_n - x\| \leq \varepsilon$ for all $n \geq n_0$; that is, the sequence $\{x_n\}$ converges to x in the sense of the metric in C_R. In other words, we have reduced the question "Does every Cauchy sequence in C_R converge?" to "If a Cauchy sequence in C_R converges, does the limit belong to C_R?" or to "If the sequences $\{x_n\}$ of continuous functions converge uniformly to a function $x = x(t)$, is x necessarily continuous?" It is easy to answer this last question. Thus, by using the triangle inequality, we can write for any t, t_0 in $[a,b]$, and for any n,

$$|x(t) - x(t_0)| \le |x(t) - x_n(t_0)| + |x_n(t_0) - x_n(t)| + |x_n(t) - x(t)_0|.$$

Since the convergence is *uniform*, the first and third terms on the right can be made $<\varepsilon$ simply by choosing n large enough. Thus for a suitably large but fixed n we have

$$|x(t) - x(t_0)| < 2\varepsilon + |x_n(t) - x_n(t_0)|.$$

Since the function x_n is continuous, there is a $\delta > 0$ such that if $|t - t_0| < \delta$ then $|x_n(t) - x(t_0)| < 3\varepsilon$. This means that x is continuous at t_0, and since t_0 is arbitrary we are done. The proof that the space of complex-valued functions is complete is obtained from the preceding by simply replacing "since R is complete" with "since C is complete."

Exercises

17. Prove that a closed subset of a complete space is a complete space.

18. Prove that every Cauchy sequence is bounded. HINT: Assume an $\varepsilon > 0$ and an associated N. Show that if $r \ge \max\{e, \rho(x, x_N), \dots, \rho(x_{N-1}, x_N)\}$ then $\rho(x_n X_N) \le r$ all n.

19. Let $\{S_n\}$ denote a sequence of closed spherical neighborhoods of X such that $S_{n+1} \subseteq S_n$ all n. Prove that if X is complete and the radius of S_n approaches zero as $n \to \infty$ the spheres S_n have a nonvoid intersection consisting of a single point.

20. Prove that E^n is complete. HINT: Use the fact that convergence in E^n coordinates with the completeness of R.

21. Discuss the pointwise and uniform convergence of the sequences $\{x_n\}$ and $\{y_n\}$ of $C(0,1)$ in which

$$x_n(t) = t^n, \qquad\qquad t \in [0,1],$$

$$y_n(t) = \frac{t^2 + nt}{n}, \qquad t \in [0,1].$$

Draw a few sample functions in each case. Which sequence is Cauchy?

1.3   LINEAR SPACES

We have seen in the preceding section that by slightly generalizing the notion of distance several of the important function spaces of interest to the engineer can be regarded as metric spaces. Specifically, if we require of the notion of distance only the properties of Definition A, Section 1.2, then, with a little ingenuity in defining metrics, the spaces R, C, R^n, $C(a,b)$ may be regarded as special instances of the general concept of a metric space. In particular, any theorem valid in an abstract metric space is simultaneously a valid assertion in each of these concrete spaces.

It is clear, however, that the notion of distance does not exhaust the structure of the foregoing examples. Indeed, each of these spaces has an operation of "addition" which is independent of the metric. In the present section we show that, provided we do not require too much of the notion of "vector," each of these spaces is a concrete example of an abstract linear space, which itself is an abstraction of the ordinary three-dimensional Euclidean space with which the reader is already familiar.

In the sequel we shall have occasion to use the set of real or complex numbers as multipliers for our function spaces. The Greek letters $(\alpha, \beta, \gamma, \dots)$ indicate the scalar multipliers and, as before, the elements of the set X are denoted by the letters x, y, z, ... Furthermore, we assume that (a) there is a rule that will allow us to construct, for every two elements x and y in X, a third element $z \in X$, called the sum of the elements x and y and denoted by $x + y$, and (b) there is a rule that will allow us to construct for every element $x \in X$ and every scalar α an element $u \in X$, called the product of the element x and the scalar α, denoted by αx.

DEFINITION A.   *A set X is called a linear space if addition and scalar multiplication are defined on X and the following rules hold*:

(1) $x + y = y + x$ *for any x and y in X.*

(2) $(x + y) + z = x + (y + z)$ *for any x, y, z in X.*

(3)   *There exists an element $0 \in X$ (the zero element) such that $x + 0 = x$ for any $x \in X$.*

(4)   *For any $x \in X$ there exists an element $y \in X$ (the inverse of x) such that $x + y = 0$.*

(5) $1x = x$ *for any $x \in X$.*

(6) $\alpha(\beta x) = (\alpha\beta)x$ *for any $x \in X$ and any α and β.*

(7) $(\alpha + \beta)x = \alpha x + \beta x$ *for any $x \in X$ and any α and β.*

(8) $\alpha(x + y) = \alpha x + \alpha y$ *for any x, $y \in X$ and any α.*

A linear space is called real or complex according to whether the scalars are the real or complex number system. The advantage of using the term scalar is that we can handle both the real and complex linear spaces simultaneously. The elements of a linear space are called vectors. Note that any *complex* linear space is automatically a *real* linear space.

The axioms in the definition of a linear space imply four additional properties. These properties, which are listed in Theorem A, are so directly related to the linear concept that we shall think of them as part of the basic definition.

THEOREM A.   *In any linear space X, the following apply*:

(1)   *The null element is unique.*
(2)   *The inverse of each element is unique.*
(3) $0x = 0$ *holds for every $x \in X$.*
(4)   *The element $y = (-1)x$ is the inverse for x.*

P R O O F.   Since this theorem presents the first opportunity to utilize the defining axioms, we carry out the proof in some detail. The existence of at least one zero vector is asserted in Definition A(3). Suppose that there are two zero vectors 0_1 and 0_2 in the space R. Setting $x = 0_1$, $0 = 0_2$ in Definition A(3), we obtain

$$0_1 + 0_2 = 0_1.$$

Setting $x = 0_2$, $0 = 0_1$, in the same definition we obtain

$$0_2 + 0_1 = 0_2.$$

By comparing the first of these relations with the second and using Axiom 1(a), we find that $0_1 = 0_2$, as required.

The existence of at least one inverse element is asserted in Definition A(4). Suppose that an element x has two inverses y_1 and y_2. Adding the element y_2 to both sides of the equation $x + y_1 = 0$ and using Definitions A(2) and A(3),

$$y_2 + (x + y_1) = (y_2 + x) + y_1 = 0 + y_1 = y_1,$$

$$y_2 + (x + y_1) = y_2 + 0 = y_2,$$

hence $y_1 = y_2$, as required.

Consider now the element $0x + 1x$. Using Definitions A(7) and A(5), we obtain

$$0x + 1x = (0 + 1)x = 1x = x, \qquad 0x + 1x = 0x + x,$$

whence $x = 0x + x$. Adding to both sides of this equation the element y, which is the inverse of x, we find that

$$0 = x + y = (0x + x) + y = 0x + (x + y) = 0x + 0 = 0x,$$

whence $0 = 0x$, as required. Finally, letting $y = (-1)x$ in the sum $x + y$, we find that

$$x + y = 1x + (-1)x = (1 - 1)x = 0x = 0,$$

as required.

The reader will observe that the zero symbol 0 is being used in two different meanings in this theorem. In the expression $0x = 0$ zero is a scalar on the left and the null element on the right. Fortunately, it is always possible to distinguish the usage from the context.

The inverse of a given element x will now be denoted by $-x$, since the preceding theorem makes this a natural notation. The presence of an inverse allows us to introduce the operation of subtraction; that is, the difference $x - y$ is defined as the sum of x and $-y$. This definition agrees with the definition of subtraction in arithmetic.

Let us now examine several concrete spaces to see whether we can formulate operations on those spaces that obey the linear space axioms.

Example 1 : *R.*   The set of all real numbers is a real linear space in which the operations of multiplication and addition are taken in their usual sense. The null vector in this space is the number zero. Note, however, that if the scalars are allowed to be complex, *R* is *not* a linear space. Thus not every real linear space is a *complex* linear space.

Example 2 : [0,1].   The set of real numbers $0 \le x \le 1$ is not a linear space in the usual meanings of addition and multiplication, for any $x > \frac{1}{2}$, when multiplied by a $\lambda > 2$, falls outside the interval.

Example 3 : $C(a,b)$.   In this set the elements are functions $x(t)$ which are continuous for $a \le t \le b$. Here addition and scalar multiplication are defined in the usual way. Thus, if $x,y \in C(a,b)$, then $x + y$ is the function whose value at t is $x(t) + y(t)$:

$$(x + y)(t) = x(t) + y(t).$$

Similarly, (λy) is defined by

$$(\lambda y)(t) = \lambda x(t).$$

It is clear that $x + y$ and λx are continuous functions on $a \le t \le b$, hence belong to $C(a,b)$. The zero element in this space is the function whose value is 0 at each $t \in [a,b]$. The verification of the axiom of Definition A is left to the reader.

Example 4.   Let P be the set of all polynomials, with real coefficients, defined on the closed unit interval [0,1]. If the linear operations are interpreted as the usual addition of two functions and the multiplication of a function by a real number, then P is a real linear space. The zero polynomial is the null element.

Example 5.   For a given positive integer n, let P_n be the subset of P consisting of the polynomial that is identically zero and all polynomials of degree less than n. P_n is a real linear space with respect to the linear operations defined in P.

Example 6.   The set R^n of all n-tuples of real numbers is a real linear space if we define the linear operations as follows. *Let* $x = (x_1, x_2, \ldots, x_n)$ *and* $y = (y_1, y_2, \ldots, y_n)$ *and let* $x + y$ *and* αx *be defined by*

$$x + y = (x_1 + y_1, x_2 + y_2, \ldots, x_n + y_n)$$

$$\alpha x = (\alpha x_1, \alpha x_2, \ldots, \alpha x_n).$$

Observe that when $n = 3$ the operations of vector addition and scalar multiplication in R^3, defined in Example 6, coincide [provided we identify the vector (x_1, x_2, x_3) with the directed line segment from the origin to the point (x_1, x_2, x_3)] with the usual "parallelogram" and "magnification" rules of elementary physics.

Now that we are familiar with the linear space concept and have seen several concrete examples it will be an easy task to identify some additional basic characteristics exhibited by these examples.

DEFINITION B. *Let M be a nonempty subset of the elements of the linear space X. M is called a linear subspace (manifold) of X if M itself is a linear space.*

This definition is equivalent to the condition that M contain all sums, negatives, and scalar multiples of its elements. Since $-x = (-1)x$, this condition in turn is equivalent to the condition that M be closed under addition and scalar multiplication. In line with previous notions, if the subspace M is a proper subset of X, we shall call it a proper subspace of X. The zero space $\{0\}$ and the full space X itself are always subspaces of X. It is clear that the intersection of an arbitrary collection of subspaces of X is a subspace of X.

Referring to the foregoing examples, we see that P_n is a subspace of P for each positive integer n and furthermore that P is a subspace of $C[0,1]$. In the linear space R^3 the following are recognized as proper subspaces:

$$M_1 = \{(x_1, 0, 0)\}, \qquad M_2 = \{(0, x_2, 0)\}, \qquad M_3 = \{(0, 0, x_3)\},$$

$$M_4 = \{(0, x_2, x_3)\}, \qquad M_5 = \{(x_1, 0, x_3)\}, \qquad M_6 = \{(x_1, x_2, 0)\},$$

in which the nonzero entries may take on any real values.

Consider now the elements $\{x_1, \ldots, x_m\}$ of a linear space X. The element y, defined by

$$y = \alpha_1 x_1 + \cdots + \alpha_m x_m,$$

is in X. Formally, y is called a linear combination of the vectors $x_1, \ldots, x_m$, and the $\alpha_1, \ldots, \alpha_m$ are called the coefficients of the linear combination.

DEFINITION C. *Let X be a linear space and let $\{x_1, \ldots, x_m\}$ be a finite nonempty set in X. The set $\{x_1, \ldots, x_m\}$ is called linearly dependent if there are coefficients $\alpha_1, \ldots, \alpha_n$ not all zero such that $\alpha_1 x_1 + \cdots + \alpha_m x_m = 0$.*

If the set $\{x_1, \ldots, x_m\}$ is *not* linearly dependent, we call it *linearly independent*. To rephrase Definition C, one might say that if $\alpha_1 x_1 + \cdots + \alpha_m x_m = 0$ is possible only for the case in which $\alpha_1 = \alpha_2 = \cdots = \alpha_m = 0$ the set $x_1, \ldots, x_m$ is linearly independent.

If the combination

$$\alpha_1 x_1 + \cdots + \alpha_j x_j = 0 \qquad (\text{not all } \alpha_1, \ldots, \alpha_j \text{ zero}),$$

certainly

$$\alpha_1 x_1 + \cdots + \alpha_j x_j + 0 x_{j+1} + \cdots + 0 x_m = 0 \qquad (\text{not all } \alpha_1, \ldots, \alpha_m \text{ zero});$$

and, in particular, if $\alpha_k \neq 0$, then

$$x_k = -\frac{\alpha_1}{\alpha_k} x_1 - \cdots - \frac{\alpha_{k-1}}{\alpha_k} x_{k-1} - \frac{\alpha_{k+1}}{\alpha_k} x_{k+1} - \cdots - \frac{\alpha_m}{\alpha_k} x_m.$$

These properties are summarized by the following lemma:

LEMMA A. *If some subset $\{x_1, \ldots, x_k\}$ is linearly dependent, any larger set $\{x_1, \ldots, x_n\}$ is linearly dependent. The elements $x_1, \ldots, x_k$ are linearly dependent if one of the elements can be expressed as a linear combination of the others.*

A set of vectors $x_1, x_2, \ldots, x_k$ in the linear space M is said to span or to determine M if every vector in M can be represented as a linear combination of $x_1, x_2, \ldots, x_k$; that is, for any vector y in M there are scalars $\alpha_1, \alpha_2, \ldots, \alpha_k$ depending on y, such that

$$y = \alpha_1 x_1 + \cdots + \alpha_k x_k.$$

Since it is possible in linear spaces to define new elements by forming linear combinations of fixed elements, the idea of a spanning set is one important way of forming subspaces. To be precise, we introduce the following definitions.

DEFINITION D. *Let $S = \{x_1, \ldots, x_n\}$ denote a nonempty set in the linear space X. The set $L(S)$, called the linear subspace spanned by S, is defined by*

$$L(S) = \{x; \ x = \sum_{i=1}^{n} \alpha_i x_i, \ \alpha_j \ \text{arbitrary scalars}\}.$$

It is clear that $L(S)$ is a linear subspace of X. Indeed, $L(S)$ is a subspace which must be contained in every subspace containing S. Thus $L(S)$ is the smallest linear subspace containing S. Clearly, the set S itself spans $L(S)$. If, however, the set S is not a linearly independent set, we shall see that proper subsets of S also span $L(S)$.

Consider now two subspaces $M_1, M_2 \subset X$. The set E

$$E = \{z: z = x + y, \ x \in M_1, \ y \in M_2\}$$

is called the *sum* of M_1 and M_2 (written $E = M_1 + M_2$). Since M_1 and M_2 are subspaces, it is evident that E is a subspace. Extending this idea, we say that E is the sum of the subspaces M_i $(i = 1, \ldots, n)$ (written $E = \sum_i M_i$) if every $x \in E$ has a representation of the form

$$x = \sum_{i=1}^{n} x_i, \qquad x_i \in M_i, \qquad i = 1, \ldots, n.$$

In the applications the most important sum of subspaces is the direct sum. In this case the requirement of uniqueness of representation is added.

DEFINITION E. *Let X be a linear space and M_i, $i = 1, \ldots, n$ be linear subspaces of X. If we can write every element $x \in E$ uniquely in the form*

$$x = x_1 + x_2 + \cdots + x_n, \qquad x_i \in M_i, \qquad i = 1, 2, \ldots, n,$$

we say that the space E is a direct sum of subspaces $M_1, \ldots, M_n$ and write $E = M_1 \oplus M_2 \oplus \cdots \oplus M_n$ or more simply $E = \oplus_i M_i$.

The key word in this definition is "unique," for the uniqueness of the representation, as we shall see, implies the disjointness of the subspaces.

THEOREM B. *Let a linear space X be the sum of two subspaces M_1 and M_2 so that $X = M_1 + M_2$. Then $X = M_1 \oplus M_2 \Leftrightarrow M_1 \cap M_2 = \{0\}$.*

Assume that $X = M_1 \oplus M_2$ and that M_1 and M_2 contain an element $u \neq 0$. Then for every $x \in X$ with

$$x = y + z, \qquad y \in M_1, \qquad z \in M_2$$

we also have the representation

$$x = (y - u) + (z + u), \qquad y - u \in M_1, \qquad z + u \in M_2,$$

which is different from the first representation. Therefore, if $u \neq 0$, we have no unique representation for x.

Now let every element $x \in X$ be representable in the form

$$x = y + z, \qquad y \in M_1, \qquad z \in M_2$$

and $M_1 \cap M_2 = \{0\}$.

To test the uniqueness of this representation, assume that a second representation exists; that is,

$$x = y + z = y_1 + z_1, \qquad y, y_1 \in M_1, \qquad z, z_1 \in M_2.$$

Then by subtracting we have

$$y - y_1 = z_1 - z, \qquad y - y_1 \in M_1, \qquad z_1 - z \in M_2;$$

that is, the right side is in M_1, and the left side is in M_2. Since $M_1 \cap M_2 = \{0\}$, both sides are zero and $y = y_1$, $z = z_1$. The representation is unique.

The condition that $X = M_1 \oplus M_2$ is often expressed by saying that X is decomposed into the subspaces M_1 and M_2. In spite of the fact that M_1 and M_2 have the zero element in common (all linear spaces must contain the zero element), M_1 and M_2 are said to be disjoint. The conditions for decomposition of a linear space into three or more subspaces is the subject of Exercise 7.

In dealing with linear spaces the reader must contend with three distinct operations; mainly product, union, and sum. To illustrate the distinction consider the subspaces $M_1 = \{(x,0)\}$ and $M_2 = \{(0,y)\}$. From the definitions we have that $M_1 \oplus M_2 = R^2$, whereas the set $M_1 \cup M_2$ consists *only* of those points *on* the usual coordinate axis in R^2. The set $M_1 \times M_2 = \{(x,0,0,y)\}$ of course is a subspace of R^4. The relationship $M_1 \oplus M_2 = L(M_1 \cup M_2)$ is sometimes helpful in distinguishing between the three operations.

Exercises

1. Is it true that if x, y, and z are linearly independent vectors so also are $x + y$, $y + z$, and $z + x$?

2. Each of the following conditions determines a subset of the real linear space R^3 of all triples $x = (x_1,x_2,x_3)$ of real numbers: (a) x_1 is an integer; (b) $x_1 = 0$ or $x_2 = 0$; (c) $x_1 + 2x_2 = 0$; (d) $x_1 + 2x_2 = 1$. Which of these subsets are subspaces of R^3?

3. Each of the following conditions determines a subset of the real linear space $C[-1,1]$ of all continuous real functions $y = f(x)$ defined on $[-1,1]$: (a) f is differentiable; (b) f is a polynomial of degree 3; (c) f is an even function in the sense that $f(-x) = f(x)$ for all x; (d) f is an odd function in the sense that $f(-x) = -f(x)$ for all x; (e) $f(0) = 0$; (f) $f(0) = 1$; (g) $f(x) \geq 0$ for all x. Which of these subsets are subspaces of $C[-1,1]$?

4. In the preceding exercise show that $C[-1,1]$ is the direct sum of the subspaces defined by conditions (c) and (d). (HINT: Observe that $f(x) = [f(x) + f(-x)]/2 + [f(x) - f(-x)]/2$.)

5. Suppose that x, y, u, and v are vectors in R^4; let M and N be the subspaces of R^4 spanned by $\{x,y\}$ and $\{u,v\}$, respectively. In which of the following is it true that $R^4 = M \oplus N$?
   (a) $x = (1,1,0,0)$, $y = (1,0,1,0)$,
        $u = (0,1,0,1)$, $v = (0,0,1,1)$.
   (b) $x = (-1,1,1,0)$, $y = (0,1,-1,1)$,
        $u = (1,0,0,0)$, $v = (0,0,0,1)$.
   (c) $x = (1,0,0,1)$, $y = (0,1,1,0)$,
        $u = (1,0,1,0)$, $v = (0,1,0,1)$.

6. If X is the set consisting of the six vectors $(1,1,0,0)$, $(1,0,1,0)$, $(1,0,0,1)$, $(0,1,1,0)$, $(1,1,0,1)$, $(0,0,1,1)$ in E^4, find two different maximal linearly independent subsets of X. (A maximal linearly independent subset of X is a linearly independent subset Y of X which becomes linearly dependent every time a vector of X not already in Y is adjoined to Y.)

7. Let a linear space X be the sum of certain subspaces $M_1, M_2, \ldots,$ M_n $(n > 2)$ and show that X is the direct sum of these subspaces $\Leftrightarrow$ each M_i is disjoint from the subspace spanned by all the others. The latter condition clearly implies that each M_i is disjoint from each of the others. Show that the converse of this statement is false by exhibiting three subspaces M_1, M_2, M_3 of R^3 such that $M_1 \cap M_2 = M_1 \cap M_3 = M_2 \cap M_3 = \{0\}$ and $M_1 \cap (M_2 + M_3) \neq \{0\}$.

Dimension and Basis

Among the first six examples in this section the real vector space R^3 is by far the most familiar. In addition to the properties discussed, several other notions have proved useful in an analysis of problems in R^3. In this section the notions of coordinate axis and dimension are discussed. It is comforting to know that these highly visual concepts can be extended to arbitrary linear spaces in a natural and useful manner.

In carrying out this objective, we shall exploit our present understanding of linear dependence and a spanning set. The following two lemmas begin the development by sharpening the contents of Definition D.

LEMMA B. *Let $\{x_1, \ldots, x_n, y\}$ be elements of a linear space. If the vector y belongs to the linear manifold $L(x_1, \ldots, x_n)$, then $L(x_1, \ldots, x_n)$ contains the linear manifold $L(x_1, \ldots, x_n, y)$.*

Because $y \in L(x_1, \ldots, x_n)$ implies that y has a representation as a linear combination of the set $\{x_1, \ldots, x_n\}$ it follows that if z is formed from the larger set $\{x_1, \ldots, x_n, y\}$ it also has a linear combination representation in terms of $\{x_1, \ldots, x_n\}$. Hence z belongs to the subspace $L(x_1, \ldots, x_n)$. This implies $L(x_1, \ldots, x_n) \supset L(x_1, \ldots, x_n, y)$.

LEMMA C. *Every element of the system $\{x_j\}$ that is linearly dependent on the other elements of the set may be eliminated without changing the linear manifold spanned by the set.*

P R O O F.   If the vector x_1, say, is linearly dependent on the vectors $x_2, x_3, \ldots$, it means that $x_1 \in L(x_2, x_3, \ldots)$. It follows by Lemma B that

$$L(x_1, x_2, \ldots, x_n) \subset L(x_2, \ldots, x_n).$$

On the other hand, obviously,

$$L(x_2, \ldots, x_n) \subset L(x_1, x_2, \ldots, x_n).$$

This pair of relations implies that $L(x_1, x_2, \ldots, x_n) = L(x_2, \ldots, x_n)$.

DEFINITION F. *Let the set* $\{x_1, \ldots, x_n\}$ *be elements of a linear space X.*
This set is called a basis for a subspace M if $L(x_1, \ldots, x_n) = M$ *and* $\{x_1, \ldots, x_n\}$
is a linearly independent set.

Every $x \in M$ has a representation as a linear combination of $x_1, \ldots, x_n$,
which is called an expansion of x in terms of the basis. It is easy to see that
under the assumed conditions the coefficients in the basis expansion are
uniquely determined. In fact, if we can write two expansions,

$$x = \alpha_1 x_1 + \alpha_2 x_2 + \cdots + \alpha_n x_n,$$

$$x = \beta_1 x_1 + \beta_2 x_2 + \cdots + \beta_n x_n,$$

for a vector x, by subtracting them term by term we obtain the relation

$$0 = (\alpha_1 - \beta_1)x_1 + (\alpha_2 - \beta_2)x_2 + \cdots + (\alpha_n - \beta_n)x_n,$$

from which, by the assumption that the vectors $x_1, x_2, \ldots, x_n$ are linearly
independent, we find that

$$\alpha_1 = \beta_1, \qquad \alpha_2 = \beta_2, \qquad \ldots, \qquad \alpha_n = \beta_n.$$

These uniquely defined numbers $\alpha_1, \alpha_2, \ldots, \alpha_n$ are called the components of
the vector x with respect to the basis $\{x_i\}$.

To extend these concepts to arbitrary nonempty finite or infinite sets
of vectors in X, we shall say that such a set is linearly independent if every
finite nonempty subset is linearly independent. Otherwise, it is said to be
linearly dependent. With this minor extension to the concept of linear
dependence, we say that an arbitrary (not necessarily countable) linearly
independent subset $\{x_\alpha\}$ of X is a basis for M if each vector in the subspace
M is uniquely expressible as a (*finite*) linear combination of the vectors in
$\{x_\alpha\}$.

It can be shown that every vector space has a basis. This is not a trivial
result. The real numbers may be considered a linear space with the existence
of a collection of real numbers $\{x_\alpha\}$ such that every real number x can be
expressed in the form

$$x = \sum v_\alpha x_\alpha,$$

where the v_α are rational numbers and the sum involves only finitely many
$\neq 0$ terms. Moreover, the x_α are linearly independent in the sense that a
finite sum $\sum v_\alpha x_\alpha$, in which v_α are rational, can vanish only if each $v_\alpha = 0$.
Since there is only a countable number of rational multiples of a fixed-basis
vector x_α, it follows that there is an uncountable number of x_α (for R this is
often called a Hamel basis).

Consider now the linear manifolds L_β spanned by the collection of
vectors x_α in which $\alpha = \beta$. It is clear that we obtain in this way an uncountable

number of distinct subspaces L_β of R. In particular, we have demonstrated the existence of uncountable distinct subgroups[1] of R, each of which contains an uncountable number of elements!

One important result of the concept of a basis for a linear space is that when a basis is specified the linear operations in the spaces, which were originally abstract, become ordinary linear operations with the scalars—that is, the components of the vectors with respect to the given basis. To illustrate, we select the set $\{x_1, \ldots, x_n\}$ as a basis for the space X. Then, if x and y are arbitrary elements in X, we have

$$x = \alpha_1 x_1 + \alpha_2 x_2 + \cdots + \alpha_n x_n,$$

$$y = \beta_1 x_1 + \beta_2 x_2 + \cdots + \beta_n x_n.$$

By the axioms of addition in linear spaces, we have

$$x + y = (\alpha_1 + \beta_1)x_1 + (\alpha_2 + \beta_2)x_2 + \cdots + (\alpha_n + \beta_n)x_n,$$

and, if λ is an arbitrary scalar,

$$\lambda x = (\lambda\alpha_1)x_1 + (\lambda\alpha_2)x_2 + \cdots + (\lambda\alpha_n)x_n.$$

If, in a linear space X, we can find n linearly independent vectors, when all $n + 1$ vectors of the space are linearly dependent, the number n is called the *dimension* of the space X and the space X itself is n-dimensional. A linear space in which we can find an arbitrarily large number of linearly independent vectors is called infinite-dimensional.

THEOREM C. *If X is a linear space of dimension n, then there exists a basis consisting of n vectors; moreover, any set of n linearly independent vectors in X is a basis for the space.*

P R O O F . Let $e_1, e_2, \ldots, e_n$ be a set of n linearly independent vectors of the given n-dimensional space X. If x is any vector of the space, the set of $n + 1$ vectors

$$\{x, e_1, e_2, \ldots, e_n\}$$

is linearly dependent; that is, there is a relation of the form

$$\alpha_0 x + \alpha_1 e_1 + \cdots + \alpha_n e_n = 0,$$

in which at least one of the coefficients $\alpha_0, \alpha_1, \ldots, \alpha_n$ is different from zero. We can assert that the coefficient α_0 is different from zero; in fact, if this were not the case, we would obtain linear dependence between the vectors $e_1, e_2, \ldots, e_n$, which by hypothesis cannot occur. Thus, in the usual way, that is, by dividing the equation by α_0 and transposing all the other terms to the other side, we find that x can be expressed as a linear combination of

---

[1]G is a subgroup of R if $0 \in G$ and if $x - y \in G$ whenever x and y belong to G.

the vectors $e_1, e_2, \ldots, e_n$. Since x is an arbitrary vector of the space X, we have shown that the vectors $e_1, e_2, \ldots, e_n$ form a basis for the space.

The following theorem completes the current line of reasoning for the finite dimensional space.

THEOREM D.   *Let X be a linear space. If X has a finite basis, $B_1 = \{e_i\} = \{e_1, e_2, \ldots, e_n\}$ with n elements, then any other basis, $B_2 = \{f_j\}$, is also finite and also has n elements.*

P R O O F.   The proof that B_2 is finite is easily constructed by assuming the opposite. Let us tackle the more difficult task of showing that if B_2 is finite and given by

$$B_2 = \{f_j\} = \{f_1, f_2, \ldots, f_m\},$$

for some positive integer m, m and n are equal. Since the e_i's span X, f_1 is a linear combination of the e_i's and the set $S_1 = \{f_1, e_1, e_2, \ldots, e_n\}$ is linearly dependent. Hence one of the e_i's, say e_{i_0}, is a linear combination of the elements in S_1. Deleting e_{i_0} from S_1 leaves the set $S_2 = \{f_1, e_1, \ldots, e_{i_0-1}, e_{i_0+1}, \ldots, e_n\}$ which still spans X, and, as before, the set $S_3 = \{f_1, f_2, e_1, \ldots, e_{i_0-1}, e_{i_0+1}, \ldots, e_n\}$ is linearly dependent. Since the f_j's are linearly independent, one of the e_i's must be dependent on the other elements. If we delete this element, the remaining set again spans X. If we continue in this way, it is clear that we cannot run out of e_i's before the f_j's are exhausted, for if we do the remaining f_j's will be linear combinations of those already used, which contradicts the linear independence of the f_j's. This shows that n is not less than m or, equivalently, that $m \leq n$. If we reverse the roles of the e_i's and f_j's, precisely the same reasoning yields $n \leq m$, from which we conclude that $m = n$.

From the preceding remarks it is clear that if there is a finite basis in the space X the dimension of X equals the number of basis vectors.

For infinite dimensional spaces an analogous statement can be made on the basis of the theorem:

THEOREM E.   *Let X be a linear space. If $B_1 = \{e_i\}$ and $B_2 = \{f_j\}$ are any two bases for X, then B_1 and B_2 have the same number of elements; that is, the elements of B_1 and B_2 can be put in one-to-one correspondence.*

To conclude this section, we illustrate to some extent the great variety of possible linear spaces. What should be made apparent by these examples is that our objective in this chapter has been to consider the most useful and frequently occurring classes of functions in engineering and scientific applications. The common features of these classes are abstracted and studied to emphasize the underlying similarities.

Example 7.   The simplest example of a real linear space is R^n. The definitions of addition and multiplication by scalars are given in Example 6 of this section. We define $0 = (0, \ldots, 0)$ and $-x = (-\zeta_1, \ldots, -\zeta_n)$. It is easy to verify that the eight linear space axioms are satisfied.

The dimension of R^n is n; to prove this let $e_1 = (1, 0, \ldots, 0)$, $e_2 = (0, 1, 0, \ldots, 0)$, $\ldots$, $e_n = (0, 0, \ldots, 0, 1)$. If $x = (\zeta_1, \ldots, \zeta_n)$, observe that $x = \zeta_1 e_1 + \cdots + \zeta_n e_n$. Thus the set $e_1, \ldots, e_n$ generates the whole space and moreover is linearly independent. For $\alpha_1 e_1 + \cdots + \alpha_n e_n = (\alpha_1, \ldots, \alpha_n) = 0 \Leftrightarrow$ all the α's are zero. Thus $e_1, \ldots, e_n$ constitute a basis for R^n.

In the space R^3 the linear manifolds have a particularly appealing form. Let $x_1 \in R^n$. The one-dimensional manifold $M_1 = L(x_1)$ is the straight line along x_1. Similarly, if $x_1, x_2 \in R^n$ and are linearly independent, $M_2 = L(\{x_1, x_2\})$ is the plane containing x_1 and x_2. The reader can easily verify these statements geometrically for the space R^3.

Example 8. Let C^n denote the set of all n-tuples $x = (\zeta_1, \ldots, \zeta_n)$ of complex numbers; C^n is a complex n-dimensional linear space with complex scalar multipliers. Again it is easy to see that the n vectors $e_1 = (1, 0, \ldots, 0)$, $\ldots$, $e_n = (0, \ldots, 0, 1)$ form a basis for C^n. The elements of R^n belong to C^n; however, R^n is not a subspace of C^n, for if α is complex and x is in R^n then αx is in C^n but not always in R^n [e.g., $i e_1 = (i, 0, \ldots, 0)$ is not in R^n].

It is possible to regard the set C^n as a real linear space using the real scalars as multipliers. One possible basis consists of the vectors $e_1, \ldots, e_n$ and $i e_1, \ldots, i e_n$, in which case C^n is of dimension $2n$ rather than n. Normally C^n is a complex space.

Example 9. The space $C(a,b)$ of continuous functions on $[a,b]$ is a linear space (see Example 3, Section 1.3); $C(a,b)$ is infinite-dimensional. Let $x_0(t) = 1$, $x_n(t) = t^n$, $n = 1, 2, \ldots$. Clearly, $x_0, x_1, \ldots, x_n$ all belong to $C(a,b)$. This set of elements is linearly independent no matter how large n is; for, by well-known properties of polynomials, if $\alpha_0 + \alpha_1 t + \cdots + \alpha_n t^n = 0$ for every t such that $a \le t \le b$, then $\alpha_0 = \alpha_1 = \cdots = \alpha_n = 0$. Therefore $C(a,b)$ cannot be finite-dimensional.

As a subspace of $C(a,b)$ we have P_k—the set of all polynomials in t of degree no higher than k. This linear manifold evidently is spanned by the system of functions $\{1, t, t^2, \ldots, t^k\}$. Hence this set forms a basis for P_k which shows P_k to be $(k + 1)$-dimensional.

A second basis for the manifold P_k is the set

$$p_0 = a_{00}$$

$$p_1 = a_{10} + a_{11} t$$

$$\vdots$$

$$p_k = a_{k0} + a_{k1} t + \cdots + a_{kk} t^k,$$

where the matrix (a_{ij}) is nonsingular (i.e., no $a_{jj} = 0$). To establish this we note that the nonsingularity of (a_{ij}) guarantees that t^i can be expressed as a combination of $p_0, \ldots, p_n$; hence $t^i \in L(p_0, \ldots, p_n)$, which implies that $L(t^0, \ldots, t^k) \subseteq L(p^0, \ldots, p^k)$. Obviously, $L(p_0, \ldots, p_k) \subseteq L(t^0, t, \ldots, t^k)$. Hence the manifolds are equal.

Example 10.   Let f be an analytic function of the complex variable z in the open unit circle $|z| < 1$. The class of all such functions is a complex vector space if $f + g$ and αf are defined in the usual way. This space, of course, is infinite-dimensional. As a subspace we mention the class of all those functions f in the space for which $f(0) = 0$.

Example 11.   Let $x(t)$ be a complex-valued function of the real variable t such that $x(t)$, $x'(t)$, and $x''(t)$ are all defined and continuous on the closed interval $[a,b]$. The set of all such functions is a linear space with respect to the usual addition and scalar multiplication. It is frequently denoted by $C^3(a,b)$ and is infinite-dimensional.

As a subset we consider $H_1 = \{x : x \in C^3(0,\pi) \text{ and } x''(t) + x(t) = 0\}$. H_1 is of dimension 2. One basis of H_1 is furnished by the functions $\{e^{it}, e^{-it}\}$ and another by $\{\sin t, \cos t\}$. $H_2 = \{x(t) : x(t) \in C^3(0,\pi) \text{ and } x(0) = x(\pi) = 0\}$, also a subspace of interest, is infinite-dimensional, for it contains the infinite linearly independent set consisting of $\{\sin nt, n = 1, 2, \ldots\}$.

1.4 BANACH SPACES

The topics of the preceding sections have been selected to serve two purposes. First, the concepts, definitions, and notation necessary to an efficient discussion of the important topics to follow have been introduced. Second, I am hopeful that the reader will have become adjusted to the abstract point of view that emphasizes the concept or operation itself, without restriction to its concrete form.

The topics of metric and linear spaces could certainly be developed to a much finer degree than that presented here. However, being mindful of the applications which are the objective of this text, we again take up the yoke of sustained progress.

The classes of functions of prime importance in systems theory are the Banach and Hilbert spaces. The significance of these spaces is not truly apparent until a discussion of the linear operators or linear functionals acting on them is taken up. In this section we limit ourselves to the general properties of these spaces and leave the deeper topics and the applications for the later chapters.

If the extension of geometric ideas to abstract spaces is to be successful, we shall need, among other things, to be able to measure not only the distance between elements (metric) but the size or the magnitude of the elements as well. The introduction of such a measure concept leads to the topics of normed linear spaces and, more specifically, Banach spaces. We begin by offering the following definitions,

DEFINITION A.   *A linear space is called a normed linear space if a rule exists which associates with every element, $x \in X$, a real number (called the norm of an element x and denoted by $\|x\|$). This rule must obey the following conditions (norm axioms):*

(1) $\|x\| \geq 0$ and $\|x\| = 0$ only if $x = 0$,

(2) $\|x + y\| \leq \|x\| + \|y\|$,

(3) $\|\lambda x\| = |\lambda|(\|x\|)$.

The non-negative real number $\|x\|$ can be thought of as the length of the element x. The rule by which $\|x\|$ is computed is a real function defined on the points of the space; hence we sometimes refer to $\|x\|$ as the norm on X. A vector x which has length 1 is said to be *normalized*. Every nonzero vector y can be normalized (i.e., multiplied by a number λ to produce a vector of length 1). In fact, by solving the equation $\|\lambda y\| = 1$ for λ we obtain

$$|\lambda| = \frac{1}{\|y\|}.$$

Since the same yardstick should be used to measure distances as well as lengths in a normed linear space, it is natural to define the metric of the space by

$$\rho(x,y) = \|x - y\|.$$

It can easily be shown that this definition of distances satisfies all metric axioms. We leave it for the exercises. In terms of the norm metric the concept of limit and convergence becomes

$$x = \lim_{n \to \infty} x_n \Leftrightarrow \lim_{n \to \infty} \|x_n - x\| = 0.$$

Thus convergence in a normed linear space is called norm convergence. It is to be implicitly understood that in dealing with a normed linear space the norm metric is always assumed unless otherwise specified.

An additional property which follows from the norm axioms is

$$\|x\| - \|y\| \leq \|x - y\|.$$

To prove this statement we simply note that $x = (x - y) + y$; now by Definition A(2), $\|x\| \leq \|x - y\| + \|y\|$, or by transposing we have the above inequality. A stronger inequality which follows from this expression is established by noting that

$$\|y\| - \|x\| \leq \|y - x\| = \|(-1)(x - y)\| = \|x - y\|,$$

which together with the previous results yields

(4) $\left| \|x\| - \|y\| \right| \leq \|x - y\|.$

DEFINITION B.   *A Banach space is a normed linear space which is also a complete metric space with respect to the metric $\rho(x,y) = \|x - y\|$ induced by the norm.*

A Banach space B is apparently a linear space whose elements x have a length $\|x\|$ which conforms to a few simple and geometric properties, namely the norm axioms. In terms of the metric $\rho(x,y) = \|x - y\|$, all Cauchy sequences converge successfully to a point of the space B. Because every normed linear space may be considered as a metric space the concepts of convergence, limit points, open sets, closed sets, and interior and boundary points, as defined in Section 1.2, carry over to the normed linear space setting.

Consider now a linear space X equipped with two norms $\| \ \|_1$ and $\| \ \|_2$. We shall say that the two norms are *equivalent* if any sequence in X which is convergent with respect to $\| \ \|_1$ is also convergent with respect to $\| \ \|_2$ and vice versa. Because convergence is the only concept necessary to define a limit point, it follows that any set S will be open (or closed) in the space X equipped with $\| \ \|_1$ if and only if S is open (or closed) in the space X equipped with the equivalent norm $\| \ \|_2$.

THEOREM A.   *In order that two norms $\| \ \|_1$ and $\| \ \|_2$ may be equivalent on the linear space X, it is necessary and sufficient that constants a, $b > 0$ exist such that*

$$a\|x\|_1 \le \|x\|_2 \le b\|x\|_1$$

will hold for all $x \in X$.

This theorem follows directly from the foregoing remarks and the proof is left as an exercise. The reader should note that the theorem also implies that the relationship $(1/b)\|x\|_2 \le \|x\|_1 \le (1/a)\|x\|_2$ holds for all $x \in X$; hence the equivalence concept is symmetric. Before proceeding to the examples of Banach spaces we state without proof a theorem that isolates two special properties of normed linear spaces with finite dimension. The proof may be found in any of the references at the end of the chapter.

THEOREM B.   *Every normed linear of finite dimension is complete. All norms on a finite dimensional space are equivalent.*

We now consider some of the most frequently occurring Banach spaces, in each of which the linear operations (addition, scalar multiplication) are understood to be defined as coordinate or pointwise, whichever is appropriate. The notation in these examples may be considered as definitions for the respective spaces.

Example 1.   The spaces R and C—the real numbers and the complex numbers—are the simplest of all Banach spaces. The norm of a number x is given by the rule $\|x\| = |x|$, the absolute value of x. The metric induced by this norm agrees with Examples 1 and 2, Section 1.2. Each space is complete with respect to this norm, hence is a Banach space. The subset [0,1] is normed and complete, but not linear, hence is not a Banach space.

Example 2. The linear spaces R^n and C^n of n-tuples $x = (x_1, x_2, \ldots, x_n)$ formed from real or complex numbers can be made into an infinite variety of Banach spaces, as we shall see in Example 3. The function on this space defined by

$$\|x\| = \left(\sum_{i=1}^{n} |x_i|^2 \right)^{1/2}$$

is a norm. The metric $\rho(x,y) = \|x - y\|$ induced by this norm agrees with the metric of Example 3, Section 1.2. Both the real and complex Euclidean spaces thus defined are denoted by E^n as in earlier sections. Both spaces are complete, hence are Banach spaces.

As in the present case, the following examples consist of n-tuples of scalars, scalar sequences, or scalar-valued functions. The scalars are allowed to be real or complex numbers. Throughout the sequel it should be emphasized that both possibilities are allowed unless otherwise stated. Also, we make no distinction in notation between the real case and the complex case. If it is necessary to distinguish the two cases, we shall do so by referring, for instance, to "the complex space."

Example 3. Let p be a real number such that $1 \le p < \infty$. We shall use the standard notation $l_p(n)$ for the space formed from the spaces R^n and C^n by the introduction of the norm

$$\|x\| = \left(\sum_{i=1}^{n} |x_i|^p \right)^{1/p} \qquad 1 \le p < \infty.$$

Since the Euclidean space is obviously a special case of $l_p(n)$ for which $p = 2$, we shall frequently use the alternative notation $l_2(n)$ for the real or complex space E^n. It is not hard to show that $\| \ \|$ does indeed satisfy the norm axioms. The property of triangularity $\|x_1 + x_2\| \le \|x_1\| + \|x_2\|$ is the same as Minkowski's inequality (discussed later in this section) for finite sums, namely,

$$\left[\sum_{i=1}^{n} |\zeta_i + \eta_i|^p \right]^{1/p} \le \left[\sum_{i=1}^{n} |\zeta_i|^p \right]^{1/p} + \left[\sum_{i=1}^{n} |\eta_i|^p \right]^{1/p}.$$

The verification that $l_p(n)$ is complete is suggested as an exercise.

Example 4. We consider now the infinite dimensional extension of $l_p(n)$. Let p be a real number such that $1 \le p < \infty$ and denote by l_p the space of all infinite sequences

$$x = \{x_1, x_2, \ldots, x_n, \ldots \}$$

of scalars such that $\sum_{n=1}^{\infty} |x_n|^p < \infty$, with the norm defined by

$$\|x\| = \left(\sum_{n=1}^{\infty} |x_n|^p \right)^{1/p}.$$

The spaces l_p are indeed Banach spaces. Minkowski's inequality of Example 3 is valid for infinite sums, which makes verification that $\|\ \|$ satisfies the norm axioms an easy task.

Our next two examples consider the limiting cases of l_p and $l_p(n)$ as p becomes very large.

Example 5.   As in Example 3, we begin with the linear space of all scalar n-tuples $x = (x_1, x_2, \ldots, x_n)$. Let the norm this time be defined by

$$\|x\| = \max\{|x_1|, |x_2|, \ldots, |x_n|\}.$$

The result is a Banach space, commonly denoted by $l_\infty(n)$. This practice owes its origin to the interesting fact that

$$\max\{|x_i|\} = \lim_{p \to \infty} \left(\sum_{i=1}^{n} |x_i|^p \right)^{1/p}.$$

To determine why this is so we inspect briefly the case $n = 2$. Let $x = (x_1, x_2)$ be an ordered pair of real numbers. No generality is lost by assuming that x_1 and $x_2 \geq 0$. If $x_1 = x_2$, then

$$\lim_{p \to \infty} \|x\| = \lim_{p \to \infty} (2x_2^p)^{1/p} = x_2 = \|x\|_\infty,$$

and if $x_1 < x_2$ then

$$\lim_{p \to \infty} \|x\| = \lim_{p \to \infty} (x_1^p + x_2^p)^{1/p} = \lim_{p \to \infty} \left(\left[\left(\frac{x_1}{x_2} \right)^p + 1 \right] x_2^p \right)^{1/p}$$

$$= \lim_{p \to \infty} \left[\left(\frac{x_1}{x_2} \right)^p + 1 \right]^{1/p} x_2 = x_2 = \|x\|_\infty.$$

Example 6.   Consider now, as in Example 4, the linear space of all bounded scalar sequences $x = \{x_1, x_2, \ldots, x_n, \ldots\}$. By analogy with Example 5 we define the norm by

$$\|x\| = \sup_n |x_n|$$

and we denote the Banach space that results by l_∞. As in Example 5, we may show that the l_∞ norm is the limiting case of the l_∞ norm as $p \to \infty$. In fact,

$$\sup_n |x_n| = \lim_{n \to \infty} [\lim_{p \to \infty} (|x_1|^p + \cdots + |x_n|^p)^{1/p}].$$

If we let c denote the set of all *convergent sequences*, it can easily be shown that c is a closed linear subspace of l_∞, hence is itself a Banach space. Another Banach space in this family is the subset c_0 of c, which consists of all convergent sequences with limit 0.

Our first six examples of Banach spaces have been scalar tuplet or sequence spaces with a variety of norms. In the physical applications the spaces of interest are just as likely to be function spaces as sequence spaces. No dearth of Banach function spaces exists at all, and the next three examples present three of the more important classes.

Example 7. Let T be any nonempty set, and let $B(T)$ denote the class of all real or complex bounded functions x defined on T. Then $B(T)$ becomes a normed linear space if we define

$$\|x\| = \sup_{t \in T} |x(t)|.$$

Note that l_∞ is the special case of $B(T)$ in which T is the set of positive integers. In the case in which T is an interval $[a,b]$ of the real axis, we shall denote $B(T)$ by $B[a,b]$. We leave the proof of the completeness of $B(T)$ as an exercise for the reader.

Example 8. The space $C[a,b]$ of continuous scalar-valued functions on the interval $[a,b]$ with the norm

$$\|f\| = \sup|f(t)|$$

is a closed subspace of $B[a,b]$, hence a Banach space. (The fact that C is closed is the theorem that the uniform limit of a sequence of continuous functions is continuous (see Example 7, Section 1.2).) The completeness of $C(a,b)$ has been demonstrated in Example 8, Section 1.2.

The Function Spaces L_p

Let us denote by $C_L(a,b)$ the space of continuous scalar-valued functions defined on the interval $[a,b]$ and equipped with the norm

$$\|x\| = \int_a^b |x(t)| dt.$$

It is clear that this expression defines a legitimate norm on the set; hence the space $C_L(a,b)$ qualifies as a normed linear space. Unlike the space $C(a,b)$ of Example 8, the space $C_L(a,b)$ is not complete. As a simple illustration of this deficiency, consider the sequence $\{x_n\}$ in $C_L(0,2)$, defined by

$$x_n(t) = \begin{cases} t^n, & 0 \le t \le 1, \\ 1, & 1 \le t \le 2. \end{cases}$$

It is easily shown that this sequence is Cauchy with respect to the integral norm but converges to the step function

$$x(t) = \begin{cases} 0, & 0 \le t < 1, \\ 1, & 1 \le t \le 2, \end{cases}$$

which lies outside the space $C_L(0,2)$. [Incidentally, the sequence is not Cauchy with respect to the uniform norm of $C(0,2)$.]

This example suggests that to define successfully a Banach function space with an integral norm we must begin with a set that is at least large enough to include sectionally continuous functions. Unfortunately, the problem of attaining completeness for the space cannot be solved by such a simple maneuver. One difficulty lies with the Riemann integral. The crux of the problem is that it is possible to define a sequence $\{x_n\}$ of scalar-valued functions on an interval, each x_n of which is Riemann integrable, but the limit function x of this sequence is not smooth enough to be integrated in the Riemann sense.

To alleviate this difficulty a stronger form of integration, namely, Lebesgue integration, has been devised. The Lebesgue integral and the Riemann integral coincide on a class of functions which can be integrated in the Riemann sense. Therefore for our purposes it is convenient to consider Lebesgue integration as an extension of Riemann integration. In the Lebesgue integration technique a set of measure zero is any collection of points that takes up essential zero area on the real axis. A countable number of points is an example of a set of measure zero. Any function that is zero except on a set of measure zero will have a zero Lebesgue integral. The Dirichlet function z, which, on an interval $[a,b]$, is defined by

$$z(t) = \begin{cases} 1, & t\text{—rational,} \\ 0, & t\text{—irrational,} \end{cases} \quad t \in [a,b],$$

is one such function.

It is clear that if two functions x and y differ in value on only a set of measure zero the function $|x - y|$ will be nonzero on only a set of measure zero, hence will have a zero Lebesgue integral. If, for the norm defined, we are to retain the property $\|x - y\| = 0 \Leftrightarrow x = y$, we must consider as equal (or, more rigorously, as equivalent) any two functions that differ on a set of measure zero. This assumption is not only acceptable from an engineering viewpoint but is in good taste mathematically as well.

Example 9.   The space $L_p(a,b)$, $1 \le p < \infty$, denotes the class of scalar-valued functions, defined and integrable (in the sense of Lebesgue) on the interval $[a,b]$ equipped with the norm

$$\|f\| = \left[\int_a^b |f(t)|^p dt \right]^{1/p}.$$

For $1 \le p < \infty$ the Minkowski inequality

$$\left[\int_a^b |f(t) + g(t)|^p dt \right]^{1/p} \le \left[\int_a^b |f(t)|^p dt \right]^{1/p} + \left[\int_a^b |g(t)|^p dt \right]^{1/p}$$

holds, which shows that $\|f + g\| \le \|f\| + \|g\|$. The other norm axioms are readily apparent, and we have already asserted that, given the tools of modern integration theory, $L_p(a,b)$ can be shown to be complete; hence $L_p(a,b)$ is a Banach space.

As in Examples 5 and 6, an interpretation of the limiting case $p = \infty$ can be made. It can easily be shown that for any finite interval $[a,b]$, $B(a,b) \subset L_p(a,b)$, $1 \le p < \infty$; furthermore, for $x \in B(a,b)$, $\|x\|_p \to \sup_t |x(t)|$, as $p \to \infty$. If the space $B(a,b)$ is modified to exclude functions that are not integrable and to include functions that are bounded, except on a set of measure zero, and the norm on this larger class is

$$\|x\| = \text{ess sup } \{|x(t)|: t \in [a,b]\},$$

in which the essential supremum (ess sup) is the smallest value M such that $|x(t)| \ge M$ on only a set of measure zero, we may take the notation $L_\infty(a,b)$ to mean the space $B(a,b)$.

To develop on a rigorous basis the theory of the L_p spaces it is apparent that an understanding of modern measure and integration theory is prerequisite. Fortunately, the main properties and results concerning the L_p spaces can be appreciated and used without resorting to such detail. In the sequel we shall continue to treat the integrals involved in the Riemann sense. The reader may feel safe with the knowledge that, by appropriate interpretation, the results can be justified on a completely rigorous basis.

DISCUSSION. Except for a few scattered remarks, the development of the early sections has been unmotivated as far as engineering applications are concerned. We have now progressed to the point at which a short discourse on some physical implications of our example Banach spaces seems in order. Consider the continuous system in which input u, output x, and impulse response function W satisfy at time t the relation

$$x(t) = \int_{t_0}^t W(t,s)u(s)ds, \qquad t \ge t_0. \tag{1}$$

Since Eq. 1 represents the usual two terminal circuit, as well as a variety of mechanical systems (at rest at time $t = t_0$), we shall leave to the individual reader's ingenuity the simple task of concocting a physical problem to satisfy it. Let $t_f > t_0$ denote a fixed time and $\tau = [t_0, t_f]$ the time interval of interest. Furthermore, we shall assume that the final time t_f is of prime interest; hence by evaluating Eq. 1 at this point we have the relationship

$$x(t_f) = \int_{t_0}^{t_f} W(t_f, s)u(s)ds. \tag{2}$$

Among the many physical situations that frequently occur only two are mentioned here. First, visualize the function u as representing a fuel flow rate; that is, the fuel flow rate at time t is equal to $|u(t)|$. Clearly, then, the total fuel consumed over the interval τ is exactly

$$\int_\tau |u(t)|dt = \|u\|_1.$$

In such cases it is natural to regard Eq. 2 as defining an operation on the elements of the function space $L_1(\tau)$.

A second class of problems, which occurs frequently, is that of controlling a system while satisfying amplitude constraints. For instance, in a missile boost system u might represent an angular deviation of the thrusting engine from a nominal direction. Here it is clear that the magnitude of u must be small at all times, and a measure of the size of u itself might be given by

$$\|u\|_\infty = \sup_{t\in\tau} |u(t)|.$$

In this case the space $L_\infty(\tau)$ is the natural candidate for the functions which are the admissible controls.

We have seen that the function spaces $L_p(\tau)$ arise naturally in an analysis of continuous systems. The companion sequence spaces have a corresponding importance in describing the behavior of discrete (or sampled) systems. Consider, for example, the set $\sigma = \{t_0, t_1, \ldots, t_k, \ldots, t_f\}$ and the set of inputs $X = \{u: u(t_k), t_k \in \sigma\}$ consisting of discrete time scalar functions defined on σ. If $l_p(\sigma)$ denotes the set X equipped with the norm,

$$\|u\|_p = \left(\sum_\sigma |u(t_k)|^p\right)^{1/p}$$

Then the discrete two-terminal system with output x and input u which satisfy

$$x(t_f) = \sum_{j=0}^{f} W(t_f,t_j)u(t_j) \tag{3}$$

is the analog of the system of Eq. 1.

In completing the analogy with the continuous case, we note that the discrete "fuel" of an input is evidently the number

$$\sum_\sigma |u(t_k)| = \|u\|_1,$$

whereas the amplitude measure becomes

$$\max\{|u(t_k)|\} = \|u\|_\infty.$$

Thus the Banach spaces $l_p(\sigma)$, $L_p(\tau)$, $1 \le p \le \infty$, and $C(a,b)$ appear as natural tools for analyzing dynamic system behavior. This impression is substantiated as the subsequent development unfolds.

Inequalities for the *p*-Spaces

In dealing with the Banach spaces l_p and L_p, a working knowledge of a few standard inequalities is essential. We treat real and complex spaces simultaneously.

THEOREM C. *If* $x, y \in L_p(a,b)$, *then* $x + y \in L_p(a,b)$, $1 \leq p < \infty$. *If* $p \geq 1$, *then* $L_p(a,b) \subset L_1(a,b)$.

P R O O F. Let x, y be arbitrary elements of $L_p(a,b)$. Divide the interval $[a,b]$ according to the relationships

$$A = \{t: |x(t)| \leq |y(t)|\}, \qquad B = [a,b] \sim A;$$

then for $t \in A$

$$|x(t) + y(t)|^P \leq [|x(t)| + |y(t)|]^P \leq 2^P |y(t)|$$

and consequently

$$\int_A |x(t) + y(t)|^P dt \leq 2^P \int_A |y(t)|^P dt < +\infty.$$

Similarly, we can show that the integral $\int_B |x(t) + y(t)|^P dt$ is finite and thus $x + y \in L_p(a,b)$. To show that $L_p(a,b) \subset L_1(a,b)$ choose the partition of $[a,b]$ according to the rule

$$C = \{t; |x(t)| \leq 1\}, \qquad D = [a,b] \sim C.$$

The integral $\int_C |x(t)| dt$ clearly exists and the existence of $\int_D |x(t)| dt$ follows from the fact that $|x(t)|^P \geq |x(t)|$ for $t \in D$ and that $x \in L_p(a,b)$.

Suppose now that $p > 1$. The number q which satisfies the relationship $1/p + 1/q = 1$ [i.e., $q = p/(p-1)$] is called the *conjugate index* to p. In proving the next theorem we need the lemma concerning conjugate indices.

LEMMA A. *For arbitrary* $r, s \in R$, *which satisfies* $r \geq 0$, $s \geq 0$ *and* p, q *conjugate indices,*

$$(r)^{1/P}(s)^{1/q} \leq \frac{r}{p} + \frac{s}{q}.$$

P R O O F. For $0 < \alpha < 1$ consider the function

$$\psi(x) = x^\alpha - \alpha x, \qquad 0 < x < \infty.$$

Its derivative $\psi'(x) = \alpha(x^{\alpha - 1} - 1)$ is positive for $0 < x < 1$ and negative over the range $x > 1$. Thus the maximum of ψ is attained uniquely at $x = 1$. The inequality $\psi(x) \leq \psi(1) = 1 - \alpha$ implies that $x^\alpha \leq \alpha x + (1 - \alpha)$ for all $x > 0$. Let r, s be positive, and by substituting $x = r/s$ we have

$$\left(\frac{r}{s}\right)^\alpha \leq \alpha\left(\frac{r}{s}\right) + (1 - \alpha).$$

Multiplying through by s and setting $\alpha = 1/p$, $1 - \alpha = 1/q$, we have

$$(r)^{1/p}(s)^{1/q} \leq \frac{r}{p} + \frac{s}{q}.$$

This inequality obviously holds when either r or s or both are zero, and thus the lemma is proved.

Our next theorem establishes the Hölder inequalities for sums and integrals.

THEOREM D. *Let p satisfy $1 < p < \infty$ and $q = p/(p - 1)$. Then for the arbitrary elements $x = (x_1, \ldots, x_n, \ldots) \in l_p$ and $y = (y_1, \ldots, y_n, \ldots) \in l_q$ the relation*

$$\Sigma|x_i y_i| \leq [\Sigma|x_i|^p]^{1/p} \cdot [\Sigma|y_i|^q]^{1/q} = \|x\| \cdot \|y\|$$

holds. Similarly, for arbitrary $x \in L_p(\tau)$ and $y \in L_q(\tau)$ the relationship

$$\int_\tau |x(t)y(t)|dt \leq \left[\int_\tau |x(t)|^p\right]^{1/p} \cdot \left[\int_\tau |y(t)|^q\right]^{1/q} = \|x\| \cdot \|y\|$$

is valid.

P R O O F.   Since the theorem is trivial whenever x or y is the zero element, we consider the nontrivial case only. For $x \in L_p$ and $y \in L_q$ form $\alpha = x/\|x\|$ and $\beta = y/\|y\|$. In the preceding lemma let us set $s = |\alpha(t)|^p$ and $r = |\beta(t)|^q$ to obtain

$$|\alpha(t)\beta(t)| \leq \frac{|\alpha(t)|^p}{p} + \frac{|\beta(t)|^q}{q}.$$

Thus the integrability of the product $\alpha\beta$ (hence the product xy) is established. Integrating this expression over the interval τ and noting that $\int_\tau |\alpha(t)|^p dt = 1 = \int_\tau |\beta(t)|^q dt$, we have

$$\int_\tau |\alpha(t)\beta(t)|dt \leq \frac{1}{p} + \frac{1}{q} = 1.$$

The Hölder inequality follows at once from this expression and the definition of α, β. The Hölder inequality for sums may be established in precisely the same way.

THEOREM E. *Let x,y denote arbitrary elements in l_p (or L_p). Then for $1 \le p < \infty$*

$$\|x + y\| = [\Sigma|x_i + y_i|^p]^{1/p} \le [\Sigma|x_i|^p]^{1/p} + [\Sigma|y_i|^p]^{1/p}$$

$$= \|x\| + \|y\|$$

or

$$\|x + y\| = \left[\int_\tau |x(t) + y(t)|^p dt\right]^{1/p} \le \left[\int_\tau |x(t)|^p dt\right]^{1/p}$$

$$+ \left[\int_\tau |x(t)|^p dt\right]^{1/p} = \|x\| + \|y\|.$$

P R O O F.   In the case of l_p we have

$$\|x + y\|^p = \sum_i |x_i + y_i|^p = \sum_i (|x_i + y_i| \cdot |x_i + y_i|^{p-1})$$

$$\le \sum_i |x_i| \cdot |x_i + y_i|^{p-1} + \sum_i |y_i| \cdot |x_i + y_i|^{p-1}.$$

Thus by using Theorem B, with the tuplet $(|x_1 + y_1|^{p-1}, \ldots, |x_n + y_n|^{p-1}, \ldots)$ playing the role of an element in l_q, we have

$$\|x + y\|^p \le (\|x\| + \|y\|)\|x + y\|^{p/q};$$

division by $\|x + y\|^{p/q}$ yields the desired result. The L_p counterpart is proved in the same manner. The final theorem of this section is stated for reference purposes without proof.

THEOREM F (Jensen's Inequality).   *If $0 < p < q$, then*

$$\left(\sum_i |x_i|^q\right)^{1/q} \le \left(\sum_i |x_i|^p\right)^{1/p}.$$

As a corollary of Jensen's inequality, observe that if $1 < p < q < \infty$ we have the inclusions

$$l_1 \subset l_p \subset l_q \subset c_0 \subset c \subset l_\infty.$$

It is easy to construct examples to show that each of these inclusions is proper.

Some Potential Applications

In concluding this section let us consider some of the typical system problems that use the Banach space setting to advantage. Taking Eqs. 1 and 3 as a model for a single variate system, we shall let B_1 and B_2 denote Banach spaces such that the system associates with every input $u \in B_1$ an output $x \in B_2$. The notation $x = F(u)$ will be used to denote this association.

With the tools at hand, the following simple sensitivity problem may be formulated.

Let $\bar{u}$ and $\bar{x} = F(\bar{u})$ denote a reference input-output pair and u a function close to $\bar{u}$; that is, $u = \bar{u} = \delta u$ with $\|\delta u\|$ small. If $x = \bar{x} + \delta x$ is the output corresponding to u [i.e., $x = F(u) = F(\bar{u} + \delta u)$], it follows that

$$\delta x = F(\bar{u} + \delta u) - F(\bar{u}). \tag{4}$$

If the system is additive as in Eqs. 1 and 3, then $F(\bar{u} + \delta u) = F(\bar{u}) + F(\delta u)$, and Eq. 4 becomes

$$\delta x = F(\delta u). \tag{5}$$

As a measure of system sensitivity, the ratio $\|\delta x\|/\|\delta u\|$ for $\delta u \neq 0$ seems appropriate. If "sensitivity" over an ε neighborhood of $\bar{u}$ is of interest, the number

$$S = \sup_{\|\delta u\| < \varepsilon} \left\{ \frac{\|\delta x\|}{\|\delta u\|} : \quad \delta u \neq 0 \right\}$$

might better serve as a sensitivity measure.

This discussion has unfolded without specifying B_1 or B_2. If F is the system of Eq. 1 with $B_1 = L_p(a,b)$ and $W(t_f,t) \in L_q(a,b)$, then, using Hölder's inequality, the following inequality chain holds:

$$|\delta x| = \left| \int_{t_0}^{t_f} W(t_f,s)\delta u(s)ds \right| \leq \int_{t_0}^{t_f} |W(t_f,s)| \, |\delta u(s)|ds$$

$$\leq \left(\int_{t_0}^{t_f} |W(t_f,s)|^q ds \right)^{1/q} \left(\int_{t_0}^{t_f} |\delta u(s)|^p ds \right)^{1/p}$$

$$= (\|W\|_q)(\|\delta u\|_p), \tag{6}$$

and it is immediately apparent that $S \leq \|W\|_q$. (We shall see later that this relation holds with equality.) Similarly, for the discrete system of Eq. 3 with $B_1 = l_p(\sigma)$ and $W(t_f,t_k) \in l_q(\sigma)$, the analogous result is

$$|\delta x| \leq \left(\sum_\sigma |W(t_f,t_k)|^q \right)^{1/q} \left(\sum_\sigma |\delta u(t_k)|^p \right)^{1/p} = (\|W\|_q)(\|\delta u\|_p). \tag{7}$$

In this development it is important to note that an abstract concept of distance has allowed the entire spectrum of l_p and L_p cases, $1 \leq p < \infty$, to be covered simultaneously, while avoiding the rather cumbersome integrals or summations involved in the concrete cases. By using the concepts of norm and neighborhood the essential features of the problem rather than the computational specifics are emphasized.

Our second problem also concerns the hypothetical systems of Eqs. 2 and 3. As in the sensitivity problem, we shall let $x = F(u)$ denote the association, defined by these systems, between the input signal $u \in B_1$ and the corresponding output $x(t_f) \in R$. If $\xi \in R$ is a fixed target point, the question we shall now answer is whether a signal $u_\xi \in B_1$ exists which satisfies $\xi = F(u_\xi)$ while minimizing the perform index $\|u\|$. In other words, has the class of inputs which the system associates with the output $x(t_f) = \xi$ an element with minimum norm? Judging by the variety of physical interpretations that can be identified with the norm (i.e., fuel, amplitude, energy), this is the prototype of an extremely important class of system optimization problems (which incidentally are studied in detail in Chapter 4).

To solve this problem we return first to the proof of Lemma A. Notice that in the relation $(r)^{1/p}(s)^{1/q} \le (r/p) + (s/q)$ equality is taken on if and only if $r = s$. This uniqueness is maintained throughout the proof of Theorem D and translates into the fact that for each $x \in l_p$ equality in Eq. 1 holds if and only if the components of $y \in l_q$ are given uniquely, within a constant $k > 0$, by the conditions

$$|x_i|^p = k|y_i|^q, \qquad i = 1, 2, \dots, \qquad k > 0.$$

Similarly, for each $x \in L_p$ the equality in Eq. 2 is taken on only by the functions $y \in L_q$ to satisfy

$$|x(t)|^p = k|y(t)|^q, \qquad k > 0, \qquad t \in \tau. \tag{8}$$

It is clear that as long as $1/p + 1/q = 1$ the numbers p and q play a dual role in these relationships.

Let us restrict our attention to the system of Eq. 2 and assume that the function $W(t_f, s) \in L_q$. Equation 8 tells us that the input with unit norm that maximizes the output is given by

$$u(t) = \text{sign} \left[W(t_f, t) \right] \frac{|W(t_f, t)|^{q/p}}{\|u\|} .$$

The optimal control is the unique scalar multiple of this signal which satisfies the output condition $x(t_f) = \xi$.

In dealing with multivariate systems the Cartesian product of Banach spaces is important. To illustrate this point let $\{B_1 : i = 1, \dots, n\}$ be a collection of Banach spaces and $B = B_1 \times \cdots \times B_n$ the usual Cartesian product of this collection. One is hopeful that B itself is a Banach space. With the natural definitions of addition and scalar multiplication B is a linear space. Of course, the question of defining a norm on B must be settled and the completeness of B established. This is not usually a difficult matter. Indeed, the existing flexibility in the choice of the norm provides an opportunity for the analyst to pattern the norm function to the physical situation at hand.

To illustrate, consider the tuplet $x = (x_1, \dots, x_n) \in B$. We use the notation $\| \ \|_i$ to denote the norm on B_i; the tuplet of norms $\eta(x) = (\|x_1\|_1, \dots, \|x_n\|_n)$ is then evidently a well-defined element in R^n. If $| \ |$ denotes any norm whatsoever on R^n, the function $| \ |$ defined on B by

$$|x| = |\eta(x)|, \qquad x \in B, \tag{9}$$

is a norm on B. If, for example, $|\ |$ is an $l_p(n)$ norm, $|\ |$ takes the form

$$|x| = \left(\sum_{i=1}^{n} \|x_i\|_i^p \right)^{1/p}, \qquad 1 \le p < \infty.$$

Exercises

1. If A and B are subsets of the Banach space X, let $A + B$ denote the set of all elements x of the form $x = a + b$ for some $a \in A$ and $b \in B$. Show that if either A or B is open then $A + B$ is open. Give an example of two closed subsets A, $B \subset R$ such that $A + B$ is not closed.

2. Using Example 8 of Section 1.2 as a model, prove the completeness of the space $B(\tau)$ defined in Example 7. Prove that l_p is complete.

3. Let X be an n-dimensional space with basis $\{e_1, \ldots, e_n\}$. For every $x \in X$ there are scalars, denoted by $\{\alpha_1(x), \ldots, \alpha_n(x)\}$, for which we have the unique expansion $x = \sum_{i=1}^{n} \alpha_i(x)e_i$. If $|\ |$ denotes a norm on R^n (or C^n), show that the function

$$|x| = |[\alpha_1(x), \ldots, \alpha_n(x)]|, \qquad x \in X$$

is a norm on X. Conclude that norm convergence and component convergence are equivalent in finite-dimensional spaces.

4. Verify that the function $|\ |$ defined in Eq. 9 is a norm on B. If $B_i = L_{p_i}(a,b)$, $i = 1, \ldots, k$, and $B_i = l_{p_i}(\sigma)$ for $i = k + 1, \ldots, n$, write out Eq. 9 in full detail.

5. Verify the following assertions:
   (a) c_0 is closed in c; c is closed in l_∞.
   (b) If l_1 is regarded as a subspace of l_∞, its closure is c_0. (Note that it follows from (a) that c_0 is closed in l_∞.)
   (c) l_p is dense in l_∞ (a set E in a metric space X is said to be *dense* in X if $\bar{E} = X$).
   (d) Let M be the one-dimensional subspace of c spanned by the vector $(\frac{1}{2}, \frac{2}{3}, \frac{3}{4}, \ldots)$. Then $c = c_0 \oplus M$.

6. Let a Banach space B be the direct sum of the linear subspaces M and N, so that $B = M \oplus N$. If $z = x + y$ is the unique expression of a vector z in B as the sum of vectors x and y in M and N, a new norm can be defined on the linear space B by $\|z\|' = \|x\| + \|y\|$. Prove that this actually is a norm. If B' symbolizes the linear space B equipped with this new norm, prove that B' is a Banach space if M and N are closed in B.

7. Let N be a normed linear space. Prove that N is a Banach space $\Leftrightarrow \{x : \|x\| \le 1\}$ is complete.

1.5 HILBERT SPACES

The Banach spaces of Section 1.4 can be viewed as little more than linear spaces for which an appropriate notion of vector length exists. An important geometric concept, which is still missing at this point, is that of the inner product (dot product) between two elements. In this section the notion of an abstract inner product is introduced and several of its important consequences are developed.

Consider the real three-dimensional Euclidean space E^3. A vector or element in E^3 is an ordered real triple $x = (x_1, x_2, x_3)$ in which the norm is defined by

$$\|x\| = (|x_1|^2 + |x_2|^2 + |x_3|^2)^{1/2}.$$

In elementary vector algebra the inner product (dot product) of x with another vector $y = (y_1, y_2, y_3)$ is defined by[1]

$$\langle x,y \rangle = x_1 y_1 + x_2 y_2 + x_3 y_3$$

and thus in E^3 the norm is given in terms of the inner product by

$$\|x\|^2 = \langle x,x \rangle.$$

In the space E^3 the angle θ between x and y is also defined and is related to the norm by the equation

$$\langle x,y \rangle = \|x\| \cdot \|y\| \cos \theta.$$

In particular x and y are orthogonal when $\langle x,y \rangle = 0$ and colinear when $\langle x,y \rangle = \pm \|x\| \cdot \|y\|$. In the complex space E^3 the inner product between any two vectors $x = (x_1, x_2, x_3)$ and $y = (y_1, y_2, y_3)$ can be defined (see Example 2, Section 1.4) by

$$\langle x,y \rangle = x_1 \bar{y}_1 + x_2 \bar{y}_2 + x_3 \bar{y}_3,$$

in which complex conjugates[2] are necessary in this definition to guarantee that the usual norm will satisfy the expression

$$\langle x,x \rangle = \|x\|^2.$$

Because $\langle x,y \rangle$ *is not always real in the complex case*, it is clear that it is no longer possible, in general, to consider the angle between x and y. Nevertheless, the conditions $\langle x,y \rangle = 0$ and $\langle x,y \rangle / \|x\| \cdot \|y\| = \pm 1$ define orthogon-

---

[1]No universal agreement exists in the literature regarding the notation to be used to indicate an inner product. The notation $x \cdot y$ is most frequently used in introductory texts and (x,y) often appears in advanced tests. The choice of the notation $\langle x,y \rangle$ for the present treatment is a concession to the later chapters in which complicated expressions, involving many parentheses, make a distinctive notation mandatory for clarity.

[2]The bar denotes complex conjugate.

ality and colinearity, respectively, and these concepts are just as useful as in
a real space.

Using these ideas as a background, let us now formulate the basic
definition of an inner product in an abstract linear space.

AXIOM (Inner Product). *Let X be a complex linear space. A rule which
assigns a scalar $\langle x,y \rangle$ to every pair of elements $x, y \in X$ is called an inner
product function if the following conditions are satisfied*:

(1) $\langle x, y \rangle = \overline{\langle y,x \rangle}$,   *commutative law*
(2) $\langle x, y + z \rangle = \langle x,y \rangle + \langle x,z \rangle$,   *distributive law*
(3) $\langle \lambda x,y \rangle = \lambda \langle x,y \rangle$,   *for any complex λ.*
(4) $\langle x,x \rangle \geq 0$ where $\langle x,x \rangle = 0 \Rightarrow x = 0$.

As in the defining axioms of linear spaces, several additional relationships
are a direct consequence of Axioms (1), (2), (3), and (4). We shall begin
with the proof of these supplementary conditions. Consider three elements
x, y_1, y_2 of X. Then by applying Axioms (1), (2), and (1) (in that order)
we find that the equality chain

$$\langle y_1 + y_2,x \rangle = \overline{\langle x,y_1 + y_2 \rangle} = \overline{\langle x,y_1 \rangle} + \overline{\langle x,y_2 \rangle} = \langle y_1,x \rangle + \langle y_2,x \rangle$$

holds and thus, as a supplement to Axiom 2, we have the following:

(2′) $\langle y_1 + y_2,x \rangle = \langle y_1,x \rangle + \langle y_2,x \rangle.$

Application of Axioms (1), (3), and (1), in that order, justifies the equality
chain

$$\langle x,\lambda y \rangle = \overline{\langle \lambda y,x \rangle} = \overline{\lambda}\overline{\langle y,x \rangle} = \overline{\lambda}\langle x,y \rangle;$$

hence as a complement to Axiom (3) we have the following:

(3′) $\langle x,\lambda y \rangle = \overline{\lambda}\langle x,y \rangle.$

Finally, using Axiom (2), we have

$$\langle x,0 \rangle = \langle x,0 + 0 \rangle = \langle x,0 \rangle + \langle x,0 \rangle;$$

thus

$$\langle x,0 \rangle = 0 = \langle 0,x \rangle \quad \text{for any } x \in X.$$

DEFINITION A. *A complex linear space X is called an inner product space*[1]
if a complex-valued inner product function is defined on it.

Our experience with the space E^3 makes us hopeful that in an arbitrary
inner product space the inner product function can be used to form a norm.
In particular, the function $[\langle x,x \rangle]^{1/2}$ seems to be a promising candidate for
a norm. Intuition in this case is true, for we shall now verify that the proposed

---

[1]Note that the cases in which X is real are not excluded.

function satisfies all the conditions of the norm axiom. For instance, the equality

$$\sqrt{\langle \alpha x, \alpha x \rangle} = \sqrt{|\alpha|^2 \langle x, x \rangle} = |\alpha| \sqrt{\langle x, x \rangle}$$

verifies the third norm axiom. The first axiom is a restatement of property (4) of the inner product. To prove the second axiom we shall need the following theorem:

THEOREM A (Cauchy's Inequality). *Let x, y be any elements of an inner product space X. Then*

$$|\langle x, y \rangle| \leq \|x\| \cdot \|y\|.$$

P R O O F. The geometric motivation for this relation is described in

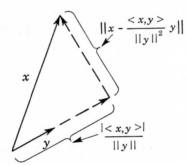

Figure 1.9   The inner product.

Figure 1.9. We begin by taking arbitrary $x, y \in X$ and an arbitrary scalar λ. Then

$$\langle x + \lambda y, x + \lambda y \rangle = \langle x, x \rangle + \bar{\lambda}\langle x, y \rangle + \lambda\langle y, x \rangle + |\lambda|^2 \langle y, y \rangle \geq 0.$$

Now, assuming that $\|y\| \neq 0$ (the equality is finally valid otherwise), we put

$$\lambda = \frac{-\langle x, y \rangle}{\langle y, y \rangle}$$

and the foregoing expression becomes

$$\langle x, x \rangle - \frac{\overline{\langle x, y \rangle}\langle x, y \rangle}{\langle y, y \rangle} = \frac{\langle x, y \rangle\langle y, x \rangle}{\langle y, y \rangle} + \frac{|\langle x, y \rangle|^2}{|\langle x, y \rangle|^2}\langle y, y \rangle \geq 0,$$

which reduces to

$$\langle x, x \rangle - \frac{|\langle x, y \rangle|^2}{\langle y, y \rangle} - \frac{|\langle x, y \rangle|^2}{\langle y, y \rangle} + \frac{|\langle x, y \rangle|^2}{\langle y, y \rangle} \geq 0,$$

or, finally, clearing fractions, we have

$$\langle x,x\rangle\langle y,y\rangle \geq |\langle x,y\rangle|^2 \Leftrightarrow \|x\|\cdot\|y\| \geq |\langle x,y\rangle|.$$

We may now complete the verification that $[\langle x,x\rangle]^{1/2}$ is a norm on X.

THEOREM B. *If X is an inner product space, then*

$$\|x\| = [\langle x,x\rangle]^{1/2}$$

is a norm on X. Moreover, for any $x, y \in X$ the parallelogram law

$$\|x + y\|^2 + \|x - y\|^2 = 2\|x\|^2 + 2\|y\|^2 \tag{1}$$

is valid.

The parallelogram law is readily proved by writing out the expression on the left in terms of inner products:

$$\begin{aligned}
\|x + y\|^2 + \|x - y\|^2 &= \langle x + y,x + y\rangle + \langle x - y,x - y\rangle \\
&= \langle x,x\rangle + \langle x,y\rangle + \langle y,x\rangle + \langle y,y\rangle + \langle x,x\rangle - \langle x,y\rangle \\
&\quad - \langle y,x\rangle + \langle y,y\rangle \\
&= 2\langle x,x\rangle + 2\langle y,y\rangle = 2\|x\|^2 + 2\|y\|^2.
\end{aligned}$$

Now that we are familiar with the inner product, the concept of a Hilbert space follows quite naturally.

DEFINITION B (Hilbert Space). *A linear space X is called a Hilbert space if X is an inner product space that is complete with respect to the norm induced by the inner product.*

Equivalently, a Hilbert space is a Banach space whose norm is induced by an inner product. Many authors include the requirement that the Hilbert space be infinite-dimensional and reserve the title Euclidean space for all finite-dimensional inner product spaces. For the purposes of the present treatment is it unnecessary to distinguish between the two.

Let us now consider some specific examples of Hilbert spaces. We will recognize most of them as old friends. To emphasize that Hilbert spaces, when viewed as Banach spaces, have a specfiic norm and, when viewed as metric spaces, have in turn a specific metric, the particular norm and metric is displayed in each case.

Example 1 : $l_2(n)$. If $x = (x_1, \ldots, x_n)$ and $y = (y_1, \ldots, y_n)$ are two vectors of the space $l_2(n)$, we make the following natural definitions for the inner product operation:

$$\langle x,y\rangle = \sum_{i=1}^{n} x_i\bar{y}_i.$$

The usual norm and metric on $l_2(n)$ are given by

$$\|x\| = \left(\sum_{i=1}^{n} |x_i|^2 \right)^{1/2}$$

$$\rho(x,y) = \|x - y\| = \left(\sum_{i=1}^{n} |x_i - y_i|^2 \right)^{1/2}.$$

Example 2: l_2. For the space l_2 the inner product of the vectors

$$x = (x_1, x_2, \ldots, x_n, \ldots) \qquad \text{and} \qquad y = (y_1, y_2, \ldots, y_n, \ldots)$$

is defined by

$$\langle x,y \rangle = \sum_{n=1}^{\infty} x_n \bar{y}_n.$$

The usual norm and metric on l_2 are

$$\|x\| = [\langle x,x \rangle]^{1/2} = \left(\sum_{i=1}^{\infty} |x_i|^2 \right)^{1/2},$$

$$\rho(x,y) = \|x - y\| = \left(\sum_{i=1}^{\infty} |x_i - y_i|^2 \right)^{1/2}.$$

Example 3: $L_2(a,b)$. Let $x(t)$ and $y(t)$ be two functions from the space $L_2(a,b)$. For the inner product we choose the function

$$\langle x,y \rangle = \int_a^b x(t)\bar{y}(t)dt.$$

The natural norm and metric on $L_2(a,b)$ are given by

$$\|x\| = [\langle x,x \rangle]^{1/2} = \left[\int_a^b |x(t)|^2 dt \right]^{1/2},$$

$$\rho(x,y) = \|x - y\| = \left[\int_a^b |x(t) - y(t)|^2 dt \right]^{1/2}.$$

The inner products which have been chosen in these examples seem to be natural for the function spaces involved. These definitions, however, are by no means unique. One example should suffice to illustrate the great generality that exists in defining inner products.

Example 4. In the space $L_2(a,b)$ it is often convenient to generalize Example 3 slightly. Let $\mu(t)$ be any function $\mu(t) > 0$ over the interval (a,b). Then a valid inner product would be

$$\langle x,y \rangle = \int_a^b \mu(t)x(t)\bar{y}(t)dt;$$

in this case

$$\|x\| = \left[\int_a^b \mu(t)|x(t)|^2 dt \right]^{1/2}$$

and

$$\rho(x,y) = \|x - y\| = \left[\int_a^b \mu(t)|x(t) - y(t)|^2 dt \right]^{1/2}.$$

The space $L_2(a,b)$ equipped with this inner product is denoted by $L_2(a,b;\mu)$. Each distinct $\mu(t)$ used in this fashion generates a distinct Hilbert space.

Since every Hilbert is also a Banach space, the definitions and discussions of convergence and the other metric properties of the preceding section carry over immediately to the present setting. Let us note also that the Hölder inequalities reduce, when $p = 2$, to the Cauchy-Schwarz inequality. The Minkowski inequality, of course, is also valid for the special Hilbert space cases.

It is really important to realize fully the significance of the proofs of properties such as the Cauchy-Schwarz inequality in the abstract setting. For emphasis, let us take note of the concrete form that the Cauchy-Schwarz inequality takes in these first four Hilbert spaces. In abstract form we have $|\langle x,y \rangle| \le \|x\| \cdot \|y\|$. The concrete forms are given by

1. The space $l_2(n)$, elements $x = (x_1, \ldots, x_n)$, $y = (y_1, \ldots, y_n)$,

$$|\langle x,y \rangle| = \left| \sum_{i=1}^n x_i \bar{y}_i \right| \le \left[\sum_{i=1}^n |x_i|^2 \right]^{1/2} \left[\sum_{i=1}^n |y_i|^2 \right]^{1/2}.$$

2. The space l_2, elements $x = (x_1, \ldots, x_n, \ldots)$, $y = (y_1, \ldots, y_n, \ldots)$,

$$|\langle x, y \rangle| = \left| \sum_{i=1}^\infty x_i \bar{y}_i \right| \le \left[\sum_{i=1}^\infty |x_i|^2 \right]^{1/2} \left[\sum_{i=1}^\infty |y_i|^2 \right]^{1/2}.$$

3. The space $L_2(a,b)$, elements $x = x(t)$, $y = y(t)$, $t \in [a, b]$,

$$|\langle x,y \rangle| = \left| \int_a^b x(t)\bar{y}(t)dt \right| \le \left[\int_a^b |x(t)|^2 dt \right]^{1/2} \left[\int_a^b |y(t)|^2 dt \right]^{1/2}.$$

4. The space $L_2(a,b;\mu)$, elements $x = x(t)$, $y = y(t)$, $t \in [a,b]$,

$$|\langle x,y \rangle| = \left| \int_a^b \mu(t)x(t)\bar{y}(t)dt \right|^2 \le \left[\int_a^b \mu(t)|x(t)|^2 dt \right]^{1/2} \left[\int_a^b \mu(t)|y(t)|^2 dt \right]^{1/2}.$$

Thus in any Hilbert space whatsoever we can be assured of the existence of equality and inequality relationships of this kind.

The parallelogram law yields another interesting relationship between Banach and Hilbert spaces. In any Hilbert space the inner product can be expressed in terms of the norm by the following identity:

$$\langle x,y \rangle = \tfrac{1}{4}\{\|x + y\|^2 - \|x - y\|^2 + i\|x + iy\|^2 - i\|x - iy\|^2\}, \tag{2}$$

which may be directly verified by expanding the expression on the right in terms of inner products.

THEOREM C. *If B is any complex Banach space whose norm obeys the parallelogram law (Eq. 2) and an inner product is defined on B by Eq. 2, then B is a Hilbert space.*

The proof of Theorem C is suggested as an exercise. This theorem helps to determine why all Banach spaces, in particular the spaces l_p and L_p with $p = 2$, *cannot* be made into Hilbert spaces.

Orthonormal Sets

In the opening remarks of this section we emphasized the similarities between Banach and Hilbert spaces. The availability of an inner product and the concept of orthogonality, however, are essential differences in many of the engineering applications. In the next several paragraphs we shall explore some of the more useful properties that tend to set Hilbert spaces apart from Banach spaces.

Let $\{x_1, \ldots, x_n\}$ denote a set of elements from the Hilbert space H. The matrix $G(x_1, \ldots, x_n)$ defined by

$$G(x_1, \ldots, x_n) = \begin{bmatrix} \langle x_1,x_1 \rangle & \cdots & \langle x_1,x_n \rangle \\ \langle x_2,x_1 \rangle & & \\ \vdots & & \\ \langle x_n,x_1 \rangle & \cdots & \langle x_n,x_n \rangle \end{bmatrix}$$

is called the *Gram matrix* of the set. Similarly, the determinant of this matrix is called the *Gram determinant* of the set and is denoted by Δ_n.

THEOREM D. *A set of functions $\{x_1, \ldots, x_n\}$ of the Hilbert space H is linearily dependent if and only if the Gram determinant of the set is zero.*

PROOF. Suppose that the set $\{x_1, \ldots, x_n\}$ is linearly dependent. Then scalars $\{\alpha_1, \ldots, \alpha_n\}$ exist (not all zero) such that

$$\alpha_1 x_1 + \cdots + \alpha_n x_n = 0.$$

The inner product of this equality with $x_1, \ldots, x_n$ in turn produces the equation set

$$\alpha_1 \langle x_1,x_1 \rangle + \cdots + \alpha_n \langle x_1,x_n \rangle = 0,$$

$$\vdots$$

$$\alpha_1 \langle x_n,x_1 \rangle + \cdots + \alpha_n \langle x_n,x_n \rangle = 0.$$

If we regard the α_k as unknowns in this linear nth-order equation set, we see immediately that for a nontrivial solution $(\alpha_1, \ldots, \alpha_n)$ to exist Δ_n must be zero.

Conversely, if $\Delta_n = 0$, a nontrivial solution $(\alpha_1, \ldots, \alpha_n)$ exists for the system. Rewriting the system as

$$\langle x_i, \sum_{j=1}^{n} \alpha_j x_j \rangle = 0, \qquad i = 1, \ldots, n,$$

we make clear that multiplying the ith equation by α_i and adding all equations will produce

$$\langle \sum_{i=1}^{n} \alpha_i x_i, \sum_{j=1}^{n} \alpha_j x_j \rangle = \| \Sigma \alpha_i x_i \|^2 = 0,$$

which implies that $\sum_{i=1}^{n} \alpha_i x_i = 0$; hence the set is linearly dependent.

COROLLARY. *The rank of the Gram matrix equals the dimension of the linear manifold $L(x_1, \ldots, x_n)$. If $\Delta_n \neq 0$, the Gram determinant of any subset $\{x_1, \ldots, x_k\}$ is also nonzero.*

P R O O F.   Since $\Delta_n = 0$ implies that $\{x_1, \ldots, x_n\}$ is linearly independent, any subset $\{x_1, \ldots, x_k\}$ is also linearly independent; hence the Gram determinant of this subset is nonzero. The proof of the first assertion is left as an exercise.

DEFINITION C. *Two elements x, y of a Hilbert space H are said to be orthogonal if $\langle x,y \rangle = 0$.*

The fact that x is orthogonal to y is frequently written $x \perp y$. Since $\langle x,y \rangle = \overline{\langle y,x \rangle}$, we have $x \perp y \Leftrightarrow y \perp x$. It is also clear that $x \perp 0$ for every x, and $\langle x,x \rangle = \|x\|^2$ shows that 0 is the only vector orthogonal to itself. Moreover, it is easy to verify that the Pythagorean theorem holds in the following form:

$$\|x + y\|^2 = \|x\|^2 + \|y\|^2 \Leftrightarrow x \perp y.$$

DEFINITION D. *Let S be a nonempty subset of a Hilbert space H. S is called an orthogonal set if $x \perp y$ for every pair $x, y \in S$ and $x \neq y$. If, in addition, $\|x\| = 1$ for every $x \in S$, then S is called an orthogonal set.*

LEMMA A. *Every orthogonal set is linearly independent. If x is orthogonal to every element of the set $\{x_1, \ldots, x_n\}$, then x is orthogonal to manifold $L(x_1, \ldots, x_n)$.*

P R O O F.   The Gram matrix of an orthogonal set is zero except for the diagonal terms $\|x_1\|^2 \cdots \|x_n\|^2$; hence $\Delta_n = \|x_1\|^2 \cdot \|x_2\|^2 \cdot \cdots \cdot \|x_n\|^2 \neq 0$ and the linear independence of this set follows from Theorem D. If $\langle x,x_i \rangle = 0$ $i = 1, \ldots, n$, then for any $y \in L(x_1, \ldots, x_n)$ we have

$$y = \sum_{i=1}^{n} \alpha_i x_i;$$

hence

$$\langle x,y \rangle = \sum_{i=1}^{n} \alpha_i \langle x,x_i \rangle = 0,$$

which completes the proof.

Lemma A reduces to an obvious truth in the space E^n. The reader should construct for himself a picture (or at least a mental picture) of these and succeeding results. We turn our attention now to the construction of orthogonal sets.

Let $X = \{x_1, \ldots, x_k\}$ be any finite set of linearly independent vectors and $L(x_1, \ldots, x_k)$, the manifold spanned by the set X. We ask if an orthonormal set $E = \{e_i, \ldots, e_k\}$ can always be found as a basis for L. The answer is yes. By a method known as the *Gram-Schmidt orthogonalization process* a set of mutually orthogonal vectors $\{e_i\}$ may be constructed from any set of linearly independent vectors $\{x_i\}$. The construction itself is of interest and goes as follows: set

$$y_1 = x_1$$

and generate y_2 by the formula

$$y_2 = x_2 - \frac{\langle x_2,y_1 \rangle}{\langle y_1,y_1 \rangle} y_1,$$

so that y_2 is x_2 minus its projection on y_1; hence $\langle y_2,y_1 \rangle = 0$. Generate similarly a third element y_3 by the formula

$$y_3 = x_3 - \frac{\langle x_3,y_1 \rangle}{\langle y_1,y_1 \rangle} y_1 - \frac{\langle x_3,y_2 \rangle}{\langle y_2,y_2 \rangle} y_2,$$

so that y_3 is x_3 minus its projection on the plane of y_1 and y_2; hence

$$\langle y_3,y_1 \rangle = \langle y_3,y_2 \rangle = 0.$$

Suppose the vectors $y_1, y_2, \ldots, y_{j-1}(j < k)$ have been defined; we put y_j equal to x_j minus its projection onto the subspace $L(y_1, y_2, \ldots, y_{j-1})$:

$$y_j = x_j - \sum_{i=1}^{j-1} \frac{\langle x_j,y_i \rangle}{\langle y_i,y_i \rangle} y_i.$$

Clearly, y_j is orthogonal to $y_1, \ldots, y_{j-1}$. Also y_j is not the zero vector, for, if it were, x_j would be linearly dependent on $y_1, y_2, \ldots, y_{j-1}$ and therefore dependent on $y_1, y_2, \ldots, y_{j-2}, x_{j-1}$ because of the definition of y_{j-1}. It follows that eventually x_j would be linearly dependent on $x_1, x_2, \ldots, x_{j-1}$, but this contradicts our original assumption that the original vectors $x_1, x_2, \ldots, x_k$ are linearly independent. Consequently, the process generates a set of k nonzero vectors which are mutually orthogonal.

The vectors $\{y_j\}$ can now be normalized to produce the set $\{e_j\}$. It is clear from the construction that each e_i may be expressed as a linear combination of the x_j's and, conversely, that each x_j is a linear combination of the e_i's. Therefore $L(x_1, x_2, \ldots, x_k) = L(e_1, e_2, \ldots, e_k)$. If this process is continued in the same way, it is clear that the following theorem will hold.

THEOREM E (Gram-Schmidt). *If $X = \{x_i\}$ is a finite or countably infinite set in the Hilbert space H, there exists an orthogonal set $Y = \{e_i\}$ such that $L(X) = L(Y)$.*

Example 5. Consider the subset $S = \{e_1, e_2, \ldots, e_n\}$ of $l_2(n)$, in which e_i is the n-tuple with 1 in the ith place and 0's elsewhere; S is evidently an orthonormal set in this space. Similarly, if e_n is the sequence with 1 in the nth place and 0's elsewhere, then $\{e_1, e_2, \ldots, e_n, \ldots\}$ is an orthonormal set in l_2.

Example 6. Let X be the real space E^3 and consider the given set of vectors $x_1 = (a_1,0,0)$, $x_2 = (a_2,b_2,0)$, $x_3 = (a_3,b_3,c_3)$. We shall generate an orthogonal set by the Gram-Schmidt procedure. First

$$y_1 = x_1 = (a_1,0,0),$$

$$y_2 = x_2 = -\frac{\langle y_1,x_2\rangle}{\langle y_1,y_1\rangle}\, y_1 = (0,b_2,0).$$

Similarly,

$$y_3 = x_3 - \frac{\langle x_3,y_1\rangle}{\langle y_1,y_1\rangle}\, y_1 - \frac{\langle x_3,y_2\rangle}{\langle y_2,y_2\rangle}\, y_2,$$

$$y_3 = (a_3,b_3,c_3) - \left[\frac{a_1 a_3}{|a_1|^2}\right](a_1,0,0) - \frac{b_2 b_3}{|b_2|^2}(0,b_2,0) = (0,0,c_3).$$

A different orthogonal set can be derived by letting $y_1 = x_3$. For ease of analysis we assign numerical values to the coefficients before beginning. Let

$$x_1 = (1,0,0),$$
$$x_2 = (1,4,0),$$
$$x_3 = (1,2,2).$$

Now take

$$y_1 = x_3 = (1,2,2),$$

$$y_2 = (1,4,0) - \frac{(1+8)}{(1+4+4)}\,(1,2,2),$$

which reduces to

$$y_2 = (0,2,-2).$$

Finally,

$$y_3 = (1,0,0) - \frac{(0)}{4+4}(0,2,-2) - \frac{1}{(1+4+4)}(1,2,2),$$

which reduces to

$$y_3 = \tfrac{1}{9}(8,-2,-2).$$

The orthogonality of these two sets can be verified directly.

Example 7.   Consider now the set $S = \{\tfrac{1}{2}, \cos t, \sin t, \cos 2t, \sin 2t, \ldots, \cos nt, \sin nt, \ldots\}$; S is easily shown to be an orthonormal set in the real space $L_2(-\pi,\pi;\mu)$, where $\mu(t) = 1/\pi$. The inner product in this space is given by

$$\langle x,y \rangle = \frac{1}{\pi} \int_{-\pi}^{\pi} x(t)y(t)dt.$$

The theory and application of orthonormal sets is one of the most fruitful areas of applied mathematics, physics, and engineering. Included within the frame of this topic are the familiar Fourier expansions. Appendix 2 develops the orthonormal set concept in this direction.

Orthogonal Decompositions

Let x be a fixed element of the Hilbert space H. Let us temporarily denote by M_x the set of all vectors orthogonal to fixed vector x. Lemma A asserts that M_x is always a vector subspace. We assert that M_x is also closed. To see this, let y be a limit point of M_x. Then a sequence $y_n \in M_x$ converges to y. Since

$$\langle x,y \rangle = \lim_{n\to\infty} \langle x,y_n \rangle = 0,$$

it follows that $y \in M_x$.

Definition E generalizes these considerations.

DEFINITION E.   *If S is any nonempty set of vectors in H, we say that y is orthogonal to S and write $y \perp S$ if $y \perp x$ for every x in S. The set of all vectors orthogonal to S is denoted by $S^\perp$ and called the orthogonal complement of S.*

We note the following consequences of the definition.

LEMMA B.   *If S and T are nonempty subsets of H, then*
  (1) $\{0\}^\perp = H, \qquad H^\perp = \{0\}$,
  (2) $S \cap S^\perp = \{0\}$,
  (3) $S \subset T \Rightarrow S^\perp \supset T^\perp$,
  (4) $S \subset S^{\perp\perp}$ [here $S^{\perp\perp}$ is defined as $(S^\perp)^\perp$],
  (5) $S^\perp$ *is a closed linear subspace of H,*
  (6) $S^{\perp\perp}$ *is the smallest closed linear subspace of H that contains S.*

P R O O F.   The proof of (1)–(4) is straightforward and is left to the reader.

To prove (5) observe that the inclusion $y \in S$ means that $y \in M$ for each $x \in S$. Thus

$$S = \bigcap_{x \in S} \{M\}$$

is an intersection of closed subspaces and is therefore a closed subspace.

Consider now the assertion in (6). We apply (5) to $S^{\perp}$, and it follows that $S^{\perp\perp} = (S^{\perp})^{\perp}$ is a closed linear subspace of H, which by (4) contains S. If M is the smallest closed subspace of H containing S, it follows that $S^{\perp\perp} \supset M$.

Next let us identify the elements of M. Because M is a subspace containing S, it is clear that it contains all finite linear combinations of elements of S. Because it is closed, M contains all limits of elements of this form. On the other hand, it is easy to verify that this latter set is a closed subspace containing S. Hence M is the set of all vectors $x = \lim_{n \to \infty} x_n$, in which each x_n is a finite linear combination of vectors of S.

It now follows that if $y \in S^{\perp}$ and $x = \lim_{n \to \infty} x_n$ is an arbitrary vector in M we have $\langle x, y \rangle = \lim_{n \to \infty} \langle x_n, y \rangle = 0$, so that $y \in M^{\perp}$. Since by (3) we have $M^{\perp} \subset S^{\perp}$, this shows that $M^{\perp} = S^{\perp}$. Thus S and the closed subspace it generates have the same orthogonal complement.

Putting the pieces together, we have reduced (6) to the following assertion.

LEMMA C.   *If M is a closed linear subspace of H, then $M^{\perp\perp} = M$.*

A direct but rather involved proof can be given. A much simpler proof can be based on the Hahn-Banach theorem, which we introduce in Section 3.2. Accordingly, we defer the proof of Lemma C until then (Exercise 12, Section 3.2).

Before proceeding to the next theorem, let us examine briefly the preceding concepts in the three-dimensional Euclidean space E^3. If we identify the vector $x = (x_1, x_2, x_3)$ in E^3 with the directed line segment from the origin to the point (x_1, x_2, x_3), it is clear that the (one-dimensional) subspace spanned by x is the line determined by the two points $(0,0,0)$ and (x_1, x_2, x_3). Similarly, the (two-dimensional) subspace of E^3 spanned by $x = (x_1, x_2, x_3)$ and $y = (y_1, y_2, y_3)$ is the plane determined by the three points $(0,0,0)$, (x_1, x_2, x_3), (y_1, y_2, y_3). Moreover, we know that each vector in E^3 can be written as the sum of its components along the x-, y-, and z-axes, respectively. More generally, we may effect the same decomposition of each vector in E^3 relative to *any* three mutually orthogonal vectors. Equivalently, we may select any plane L through the origin and then decompose each vector in E^3 into the sum of a vector in L with a vector orthogonal to L; that is, $E^3 = L \oplus L^{\perp}$. (Thus $L^{\perp}$ is, in the precise sense of direct sum, the rest of E^3 and is justifiably called the orthogonal *complement* of L.)

In view of the fact that our abstract notion of Hilbert space was designed to isolate the "essential" properties of E^3, we would naturally expect that if

H is a Hilbert space and L a linear subspace, the same decomposition of H as $L \oplus L^\perp$ is valid. Since $L \cap L^\perp = \{0\}$ for any set L, the only question is whether or not $L \oplus L^\perp$ is all of H. This is clearly the same as asking whether each x in H can be written $x = y + z$ with y in L and z in $L^\perp$. If L is not required to be closed, examples may be given to show that the assertion is false. For closed subspaces we have the following theorem.

THEOREM F (Projections). *Let L be a closed linear subspace of H. Then each x in H has a unique representation $x = y + z$ where $y \in L$ and $z \in L^\perp$* (the vector y is called the projection of x onto L).

P R O O F. The uniqueness of such a representation is trivial. Indeed, if

$$x = y + z, \qquad y \in L, \qquad z \in L^\perp,$$
$$x = y' + z', \qquad y' \in L, \qquad z' \in L^\perp,$$

are two such representations of x, the vector $y - y' = z'-z$ belongs to both L and $L^\perp$; hence by (2) of Lemma B we must have $y-y' = 0 = z'-z$.

As remarked earlier, it suffices to show that $H = L \oplus L^\perp$. Now, if $M = L \oplus L^\perp$, we have $L \subset M$ and $L^\perp \subset M$, whence $M^\perp \subset L$ and $M^\perp \subset L^\perp$, so that $M^\perp = \{0\}$. Hence $M^{\perp\perp} = H$, and it remains to be proved that M is closed (Lemma C).

Suppose that x is a limit point of M. There is a sequence $\{x_n\}$ in M such that $x_n \to x$. Now each x_n is of the form $x_n = y_n + z_n$ with $y_n \in L$, $z_n \in L^\perp$. Because

$$\|x_n - x_m\|^2 = \|(y_n - y_m) + (z_n - z_m)\|^2$$
$$= \|y_n - y_m\|^2 + \|z_n - z_m\|^2 \geq \|y_n - y_m\|^2,$$

it follows that $\{y_n\}$ is a Cauchy sequence in L; hence, since L is closed, $y_n \to y \in L$. Similarly, $z_n \to z \in L^\perp$. Then

$$\|x_n - (y + z)\|^2 = \|y_n - y\|^2 + \|z_n - z\|^2$$

implies that $x = \lim_{n \to \infty} x_n = y + z$ and so $x \in M$. This completes the proof.

R E M A R K 1. The projection theorem undoubtedly contains the basic fact about Hilbert spaces. We shall see its significance in the sequel. We point out here that for proper prospective a Hilbert space should be regarded as a Banach space whose norm is sufficiently well behaved (i.e., derivable from an inner product) to make the projection theorem meaningful and valid.

R E M A R K 2. A useful technique for proving the equality of two closed subspaces L and M is based on the projection theorem. Suppose that it is known that $L \subset M$. Then $L = M$ if and only if the conditions $x \in M$ and $x \perp L$ imply $x = 0$. In particular, if S is a collection of vectors in H and $\langle x,s \rangle = 0$ for all $s \in S$ implies $x = 0$, the closure of the linear manifold $L(S)$ spanned by S is all of H.

R E M A R K 3.   Let M be a closed subspace of H. The projection theorem guarantees the existence of a unique vector $y \in M$ (the projection of x onto M) for each $x \in H$, such that $x - y \in M$. We leave as an exercise the proof that y satisfies

$$\|x - y\| \le \|x - m\|$$

for all $m \in M$. Conversely, if $y' \in M$ satisfies this condition, then $y' = y$. (The projection of x onto M may be characterized as *the* vector in M that is closest to x.)

R E M A R K 4.   Let us call attention once again to the problems posed in the Discussion on page 52. For the continuous system of Eq. 2 or the discrete system of Eq. 3 of Section 1.4, let us assume that the functions $W(t_f,t)$ and $W(t_f,t_k)$ are elements of the Hilbert spaces $L_2(a,b)$ and $l_2(\sigma)$, respectively. If H denotes either of these spaces we may write, without distinguishing between the discrete and continuous cases, the equation

$$x = \langle w,u \rangle \tag{3}$$

as the representation for the system.

Consider now a fixed element $\xi \in R$. For the system of Eq. 3 find the element $u_\xi \in H$ such that

$$\xi = \langle w,u \rangle \tag{4}$$

holds and $\|u_\xi\|$ is minimized over the set of all such elements. This simple optimal control problem has an almost immediate solution; namely,

$$u_\xi = kw \tag{5}$$

in which the scalar k is given by

$$k = \xi/\|w\|^2. \tag{6}$$

To see that this control is indeed optimal we may set $p = 2$ in the previous solution. As an alternative derivation let H be decomposed into the direct sum

$$H = L(w) \oplus L^\perp(w).$$

Then for every $u \in H$ we may write uniquely

$$u = u_1 + u_2,$$

in which $u_1 \in L(w)$ and $u_2 \perp u_1$. By noting that

$$\langle w,u \rangle = \langle w,u_1 + u_2 \rangle = \langle w,u_1 \rangle + \langle w,u_2 \rangle = \langle w,u_1 \rangle + 0$$

and that $\|u\| = \|u_1\| + \|u_2\|$, hence

$$\|u_1\| \le \|u\|,$$

we find that if a $u \in L(w)$ can be found to satisfy Eq. 4 the control will be the solution u_ξ. Equations 5 and 6 obviously define this control. To be explicit, the solution for the continuous system is the function whose value at time $t \in (t_0, t_f)$ is given by

$$u_\xi(t) = \xi \left[\int_{t_0}^{t_f} |W(t_f, s)|^2 ds \right]^{-1} W(t_f, t).$$

The solution in the discrete case is the function whose value at $t_k \in \sigma$ is given by

$$u_\xi(t_k) = \xi \left[\sum_\sigma |W(t_f, t_k)|^2 \right]^{-1} W(t_f, t_k).$$

The problem thus posed and solved is a simple prototype of what is usually called a minimum-energy control problem. The use of the term energy in connection with Hilbert spaces stems from such physical expressions as the energy in a current i through a resistance R which is given by

$$R \int_a^b i^2(t) dt = R \langle i, i \rangle.$$

In Chapter 4 it is shown that several sophisticated examples of minimum energy problems can be analyzed with little more complexity than this example.

Products of Hilbert Spaces

It is possible to construct new Hilbert spaces by means of the Cartesian product of component Hilbert spaces. If $\{H_i\}$ denotes a finite collection of Hilbert spaces, the set $H = H_1 \times H_2 \times \cdots \times H_n$ is a linear space with addition and scalar multiplication defined on the tuplets of H in the usual manner. If $x = (x_1, x_2, \ldots, x_n)$ and $y = (y_1, y_2, \ldots, y_n)$ are two elements of H, an inner product on H may be defined on H by the expression

$$\langle x, y \rangle = \sum_{i=1}^n \langle x_i, y_i \rangle_i. \tag{7}$$

in which $\langle x_i, y_i \rangle_i$ denotes the inner product of x_i and y_i in the component space H_i. This particular formula is called the *usual* inner product on H.

It is a trivial matter to verify that the usual inner product formula satisfies the inner product axioms. The norm induced on H evidently takes the form

$$\|x\|^2 = \sum_{i=1}^n \|x_i\|_i^2$$

and the Cauchy-Schwarz inequality becomes

$$|\langle x, y \rangle| \leq \left[\sum_{i=1}^n \|x_i\|_i^2 \right]^{1/2} \left[\sum_{i=1}^n \|y_i\|_i^2 \right]^{1/2}.$$

To show that H is complete with respect to the usual inner product function we note that if $\{x^1, \ldots, x^k\}$ is a Cauchy sequence the relationship

$$\|x^m - x^p\|^2 = \sum_{i=1}^{n} \|x_i^m - x_i^p\|^2 < \varepsilon^2, \qquad n, p > N_0, \qquad (8)$$

implies that

$$\|x_i^m - x_i^p\|_i < \varepsilon, \qquad i = 1, \ldots, n, \qquad n, p > N_0;$$

thus the component sequences must be Cauchy. Since the component spaces H_i are complete the sequences $\{x_i^k\}$, $i = 1, \ldots, n$ are convergent to the limits $\bar{x}_i$, $i = 1, \ldots, n$. Taking the limit $p \to \infty$ in Eq. 8, we have

$$\|x^m - \bar{x}\|^2 = \sum_{i=1}^{n} \|x_i^m - \bar{x}_i\|^2 < \varepsilon^2, \qquad m > N_0,$$

which holds for some $N_0(\varepsilon)$ for every ε. Thus the sequence $x^k \to (\bar{x}_1, \ldots, \bar{x}_n) \in H$.

The definition of an inner product on the Cartesian product of Hilbert spaces is by no means unique. The exercises suggest some of the different ways that frequently prove useful in the applications.

Exercises

1. Let $\{x_i\}$ and $\{y_j\}$ be any two finite sets in the Hilbert spaces H. Prove that for arbitrary scalars $\{\alpha_i\}$ and $\{\beta_j\}$

$$\left\langle \sum_i \alpha_i x_i, \sum_j \beta_j y_j \right\rangle = \sum_{i,j} \alpha_i \bar{\beta}_j \langle x_i, y_j \rangle.$$

If H is finite-dimensional with basis $\{e_i\}$, conclude that the inner product of arbitrary elements $x = \sum \alpha_i e_i$, $y = \sum \beta_j e_j$ in H is determined completely by the scalar relationship

$$\langle x, y \rangle = \sum_{i,j} \alpha_i \bar{\beta}_j k_{ij},$$

in which $k_{ij} = \langle e_i, e_j \rangle$.

2. Let $\langle \, , \, \rangle$ be an inner product function on the linear space X. Show that

$$\langle x, y \rangle = \langle x + y, x + y \rangle - \langle x - y, x - y \rangle,$$

when X is real, and that

$$4\langle x, y \rangle = \langle x + y, x + y \rangle - \langle x - y, x - y \rangle$$
$$+ i[\langle x + iy, x + iy \rangle - \langle x - iy, x - iy \rangle],$$

when X is complex. Deduce that if $\langle x, x \rangle = 0$ for $x \in M$ a linear subspace of X, then $\langle x, y \rangle = 0$ all $x, y \in M$.

3. Prove Theorem C when B is a real Banach space.

4. Let x, y, z, and ω be four elements of the Hilbert space H. Show that

$$\|x - z\| \cdot \|y - \omega\| \leq \|x - y\| \cdot \|z - \omega\| + \|y - z\| \cdot \|x - \omega\|.$$

When does equality hold?

5. Let $\{x_1, ..., x_n\}$ denote a linearly independent set in H. Let ψ_n be defined by the determinant

$$\psi_n = \begin{vmatrix} \langle x_1, x_1 \rangle & \cdots & \langle x_1, x_{n-1} \rangle & x_1 \\ \vdots & & \vdots & \vdots \\ \langle x_n, x_1 \rangle & \cdots & \langle x_n, x_{n-1} \rangle & x_n \end{vmatrix}.$$

Show that $\langle \psi_n, x_k \rangle = 0$, $k < n$, and $\langle \psi_n, x_n \rangle = \Delta_n$, the Gram determinant for the set. Show also that

$$\langle \psi_n, \psi_n \rangle = \Delta_{n-1} \Delta_n.$$

Finally, verify that the functions

$$e_1 = \frac{x_1}{\|x_1\|}, \qquad e_j = \frac{\psi_j}{\sqrt{\Delta_{j-1}\psi_j}}, \qquad j = 2, ..., n,$$

form an orthonormal set which spans $L(x_1, ..., x_n)$.

6. Complete the proof of Lemma B.

7. If S is a nonempty subset of H, show that $S^{\perp} = S^{\perp\perp\perp}$.

1.6 REFERENCES FOR CHAPTER 1

The topics in Chapter 1 cut across a broad spectrum of mathematics, and our treatment has of necessity been selective in scope and depth. Attention is directed to Appendices 1 and 2, which supplement this chapter and which are referred to on occasion in the remainder of the text. In addition to these supplements, the reader will find an abundance of fine texts that relate to the various topics.

In parts of Chapters 1 and 2 the development is strongly influenced by the excellent text of Simmons [A77]. The books by Kolmogorov and Fomin [A49], Shilov [A76], and Vulikh [A93] are also closely related in level and context to our treatment. Those by Friedman [A30], Goertzel and Tralli [A32], Hildebrand [A40], and Indritz [A44] are similar in level but were developed with different applications in mind. On a somewhat higher level the reader may find Akhiezer and Glazman [A2], Dieudonné [A21], Dunford and Schwartz [A22,A23], Liusternik and Sobolev [A56], Riesz and Sz-Nagy [A72], Taylor [A83], and Hille and Phillips [A41] useful.

For outside reading related to Sections 1.1 and 1.2 the introductory texts by Anderson and Hall [A4], Arnold [A6], Bartle [A9], and Kuratowski [A54] are recommended. As supplements on linear spaces Halmos [A35], Mirsky [A62], Nering [A64], and Stoll [A81] should be read. On Banach and Hilbert spaces books by Banach [A8], Halmos [A36], Lorch [A57], and Natanson [A63] should be mentioned in addition to the general references already cited. For the reader wishing to examine the Lebesgue integral Halmos [A37], Hartman and Mikusinki [A39], Kolmogorov and Fomin [A50], Natanson [A63], Rudin [A73], and Williamson [A94] will prove helpful.

2 TRANSFORMATIONS

2.1 FUNCTIONS

The concept of a function is basic to all parts of analysis. Its most familiar form is that of a rule by which one set of real numbers is associated with another. For example, the formula $y = x^3$ is a function or a functional relationship. What we mean by this equality is a rule which states that for every real number x another real number is linked to it, namely x^3. The process or formula (take its cube) that defines this link is the function. It is possible, of course, to have simple explicit algebraic formulas for functions in only a limited number of cases. Some functions, not describable by formula, occur so frequently that they have been tabulated to great precision and given special names such as $\sin x$ and $\log x$.

In Chapter 1 the concept of a function was used without the benefit of a formal definition. In dealing with time sequences or time functions, it is possible to use an intuitive definition. To treat a system as a function, however, requires a well-defined concept. The definition that we shall use is only a slight generalization on the classical definition outlined in the first paragraph.

DEFINITION A. *Let X and Y be arbitrary nonempty sets. A correspondence f that associates with each element x, in a subset D_f of X, an element $y \in Y$ is called a function from X into Y. The subset $D_f \subset X$ on which the function is defined is called the domain of the function. The subset $R_f \subset Y$ of points associated with points $x \in D_f$ is called the range of the function.*

For example, grading performers in a gymnastics meet can be viewed as the construction of a function which associates a real number with the performance of each participant. Here X might denote the gymnasts of the nation, D_f, the gymnasts participating in the meet, Y, the real integers $0 \leq n \leq 100$, and R_f, the set of all scores given. As a second example, let X be the set of all squares in a plane and Y the set of all circles in the same plane. We can define a function $y = f(x)$ by requiring that the rule f associate with each square $x \in X$ the circle $y \in Y$ inscribed in it. Here $D_f = X$ and $R_f = Y$.

Definition A has three objects: two nonempty sets and a rule which assigns to each element x in a subset of X a single uniquely determined $y \in Y$. The notation $f: X \rightarrow Y$ denotes the function with rule f, domain $D_f \subset X$, and range $R_f \subset Y$. This notation is useful because the essential parts of the function are displayed in a manner which emphasizes that it is a composite object, the center of which is the rule f. However, if it is clear from the context what the sets X and Y are, or if there is no real need to specify them explicitly, it is common practice to abbreviate the notation $f: X \rightarrow Y$ to f and to speak of f alone (without mentioning the sets X and Y). In other cases it clarifies matters to use simply $x \rightarrow f(x)$ to indicate the function f.

The element y of Y associated by the function f with the element $x \in D_f$ is called the image of the point x. If $y \in Y$ and $y = f(x)$, then x is called a preimage of y. Each element $x \in D_f$ must have a unique image $y \in Y$. Each $y \in Y$, however, may have multiple preimages. A natural generalization of the image of an element is the image of a set of elements.

DEFINITION B. *Let $f: X \rightarrow Y$ be given. For each subset A of D_f the subset $B = \{y \in Y = f(x)$ for some x in $A\}$ is called the image of A under f. We write $B = f(A)$ to indicate that B is the image of A.*

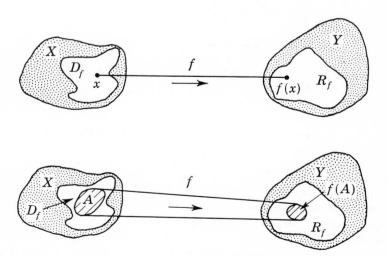

Figure 2.1   The function as a transformation.

A function is often called a mapping, transformation, or operator. These terms are appropriate in the sense that the function can be thought of as carrying a point $x \in D_f$ into a point $f(x) \in Y$. Similarly, a subset $A \subset D_f$ is carried into a subset $B \subset R_f$ by the mapping $f(A) = B$. To illustrate these ideas Figure 2.1 is frequently useful.

We have successfully defined a function without recourse to a graphical context. Since curves and graphs are part of our intuitive heritage, it is interesting to note how they fit into the present framework.

DEFINITION C.   *Let $f: X \to Y$. The subset $G_f = \{(x,y): y = f(x), x \in D_f\}$ of $X \times Y$ is called the graph of f.*

It is often useful to consider Definition C as the basic definition of a function. The statement, *a function is a set of ordered pairs in which no two distinct pairs have the same first coordinate*, is certainly simpler than Definition A and contains just as much information. From this latter viewpoint a function and its graph are indistinguishable.

Figure 2.2 illustrates these concepts. Note that if X and Y are sets, and G_f

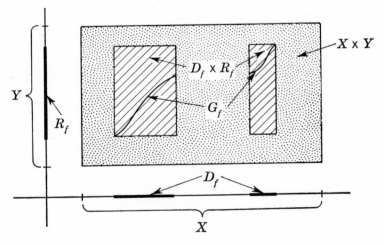

Figure 2.2   The function as a set of ordered pairs.

is a given subset of $X \times Y$, G_f is the graph of f for a function $f: X \to Y$ if for each x there is one and only one element of G_f of the form (x,y). Less precisely, G_f is the graph of a function $f: X \to Y$ if for each $x \in D_f$ the "vertical" line through x meets G_f at exactly one point.

Two functions, f and g, are said to be *equal* if their domains are identical and if for each x in this common domain $f(x) = g(x)$. In terms of their graphs, we have $f = g$ if and only if the sets G_f and G_g are identical. A function $f: X \to Y$

with $D_f = X$ is called a mapping of X into Y. We mean to suggest by this that $f(X) \subseteq Y$. If, indeed, $f(X) = Y$, then f is called a mapping of X *onto* Y. In both cases Y is called the *range set* (or range space, as the case may be) and $f(X)$ is called the *range*. Thus an onto mapping has an equal range and range space.

DEFINITION D. *A function $f: X \to Y$ is called one-to-one if $f(x) = f(x')$ implies $x = x'$ for every x, x' in D_f.*

Thus $f: X \to Y$ is one-to-one if for each $y \in R_f$ there is only one $x \in D_f$ such that $f(x) = y$. If $f: X \to Y$ is both *onto* and *one-to-one*, we can define its inverse mapping $f^{-1}: Y \to X$ as follows: for each y in Y we find that unique element x in D_f such that $f(x) = y$ (x exists and is unique since f is onto and one-to-one); we then define $f^{-1}(y)$ as x. It is clear that this procedure defines a function f^{-1} from Y into X according to Definition A. If the ordered pair is adopted as our basic definition of " function," then f^{-1} is simply the set of ordered pairs $(y,x) \in Y \times X$ and (x,y) is a member of f. Geometrically, a function $f: X \to Y$ has an inverse f^{-1} if and only if, for each y in Y, the " horizontal " line (in $X \times Y$) through y meets G_f at exactly one point. The equation $x = f^{-1}(y)$ is the result of solving $y = f(x)$ for x in just the same way as $x = \log y$ is the result of solving $y = e^x$ for x.

DEFINITION E. *Let f be a one-to-one function with domain $D_f \subset X$ and range $R_f = Y$. If $G_g = \{(y,x) \in Y \times X : (x,y) \in G_f\}$, then g is a one-to-one function with domain Y and with range $R_g = D_f \subset X$. The function g is called the inverse of f and is ordinarily denoted by f^{-1}.*

A point of confusion that plagues the novice is the distinction between a function and the values of the function. In this regard it is best to think of the function as either a transformation or a graph. The value of a function at the point $x \in D_f$ is the element $y = f(x) \in R_f$. Thus, in speaking of the space $C(a,b)$, we should refer to the function $x \in C(a,b)$ whose value at time $t \in [a,b]$ is given, for example, by $x(t) = t^2$. In many cases the only way of specifying the function is to list all its values $\{f(x)\}$ as x moves over the domain D_f. A function $f: X \to Y$ is called a *constant* function if there is a fixed point $y \in Y$ such that $f(x) = y$ for each $x \in D_f$. A function $f: X \to X$ is called the *identity* function (on X) and is denoted by I (or I_X) if $f(x) = x$ for each $x \in X$.

The Composition of Functions

Consider the two functions $t \to x$ and $x \to y$ with values defined by

$$x(t) = 2\pi t - 5, \qquad t \in [0, t_f],$$

$$y(t) = \sin x, \qquad x \in [-\infty, \infty].$$

These two functions can be composed, or placed in series, to form a third function $t \rightarrow y$ given by

$$y(t) = \sin (2\pi t - 5), \qquad t \in [0, t_f].$$

This simple example of composing functions is indicative of the general case.

DEFINITION F.   *Let $f\colon X \rightarrow Y$ and $g\colon Y \rightarrow Z$ be functions with $D_f = X$ and $D_g = Y$. The composition of f and g is the mapping that associates with each element $x \in X$ the element $z = g[f(x)] \in Z$. This new function is written as $h = gf\colon X \rightarrow Z$.*

In other words, an element $x \in X$ is taken by f into an element $f(x) \in Y$, which in turn is taken into $g(f(x))$, an element of Z. A function $h\colon X \rightarrow Z$ is therefore the composition of $f\colon X \rightarrow Y$ and $g\colon Y \rightarrow Z$ for each $x \in X$, $h(x) = g[f(x)]$, as illustrated in Figure 2.3.

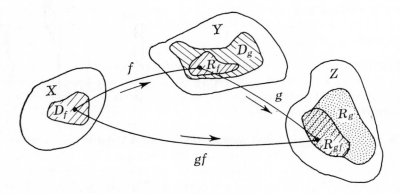

Figure 2.3   The composition *gf.*

We observe that the two mappings involved here are not entirely arbitrary, for the set Y which contains the range of the first function is the domain of the second function. More generally, the product of two mappings is meaningful only if the range of the first is contained in the domain of the second (or if the first function is understood to be restricted to a set $A \subset D_f$ such that $f(A) = R_f \cap D_g$). We shall always regard f as the first mapping and g as the second in the product gf.

The concept of the composition of functions is extended to the composition of a finite number of functions. In all cases the range of each function in the composition must be contained in the domain of the succeeding function. We have noted that an inverse function can be defined for functions that are one-to-one and onto. In terms of composite functions, we rephrase Definition E as follows:

Let $f: X \to Y$ and $g: Y \to X$ be given. The function f is called the inverse of g and the function g is called the inverse of f if $g[f(x)] = x$ and $f[g(y)] = y$ for all $x \in D_f = R_g$, $y \in D_g = R_f$. In this event we shall also say that f and g are inverse functions and that each of them is invertible. Let $i: X \to X$ and $j: Y \to Y$ be the identity functions on D_f and D_g. The statement $f: X \to Y$ and $g: Y \to X$ are inverse functions is equivalent to the statement that $i = gf$ and $j = fg$.

Let us now prove that these remarks are equivalent to the statement that f and g are both one-to-one and onto. Assume that these conditions hold and that $f(x_1) = f(x_2)$ for some x_1, $x_2 \in D_f$. Then $x_1 = g[f(x_1)] = g[f(x_2)] = x_2$ and therefore f is one-to-one. To show that f is onto, let $y \in R_f$. We have $g(y) \in D_f$ and $f[g(y)] = y$; therefore, if we set $x = g(y)$, $y = f(x)$, and f is onto. The roles of the two functions may be interchanged because the definition of inverse functions imposes conditions symmetrical with regard to the two functions. Therefore $g: R_f \to D_f$ is also one-to-one and onto.

We have shown that a necessary condition for a given function $f: X \to Y$ to be invertible is that the function be one-to-one and onto (or, alternatively, we choose to define f^{-1} only on R_f). It is not difficult to show that this condition is also sufficient. Furthermore the function $g: Y \to X$ is uniquely determined.

Example 1.   Let $X = \{x: 0; \le x \le 2\}$ and $Y = R$, the space of real numbers. Define f by the relation $f(x) = x^2$ for all $x \in X$. In this case we see that an equivalent definition would be $f = \{(x,y): y = x^2 \text{ and } x \in X\}$. (This defines the graph of f according to Definition D.)

It is clear that the range $f(X)$ of this function is the closed interval $0 \le y \le 4$. Moreover, f is one-to-one from X onto $f(X)$, hence has an inverse f^{-1}. Evidently f^{-1} is the function on $0 \le y \le 4$ which assigns to each y its positive square root.

The same correspondence $x \to x^2$ also defines a function g on $X = \{x: -1 \le x \le 1\}$ into $Y = R$. Here $g(X)$ is the interval $0 \le y \le 1$ and the range of the inverse mapping g^{-1} is a proper subset of X.

The correspondence $x \to \sqrt{x}$ clearly does not define a function on $-1 \le x \le 1$.

Example 2.   The "Dirichlet function" f is defined on R into R as follows:

$$f(x) = \begin{cases} 1, & \text{if } x \text{ is rational,} \\ 0, & \text{if } x \text{ is irrational.} \end{cases}$$

Example 3.   For each x in $[0,1]$ the equation $e_x(f) = f(x)$ defines a function e_x which maps $C(0,1)$ into the complex numbers (e_x is often referred to as the "point evaluation at x").

If E is a subset of a metric space X, the equation $\rho(x;E) = \inf\{\rho(x,y): y \in E\}$ defines a real-valued function $x \to \rho(x;E)$ on X.

Example 4. In systems utilizing digital elements the "sample" and "clamp" operations play an important role. Recall that $B(\tau)$ is the class of bounded scalar functions defined on τ (see Example 7, Section 1.4) and let $\sigma = \{t_k: k = 1, \ldots, n\}$ with $t_k < t_{k+1}$ denote an ordered subset of $[a,b]$. Then, if $X = B(a,b)$ and $Y = B(\sigma)$, the sample operation S can be written as a function on X to Y defined for every $x \in X$ by

$$(Sx)(t_k) = x(t_k), \qquad t_k \in \sigma. \tag{1}$$

Similarly, the zero-order clamp is the transformation C from Y to X defined by

$$(Cy)(t) = y(t_k), \qquad t \in [t_k, t_{k+1}], \, t_k \in \sigma \tag{2}$$

for every $y \in Y$.

Example 5. A transformation $T: C(0,1) \to C(0,1)$ is defined by specifying that the image of f in $C(0,1)$ under T is to be the function whose value at $t \in [0,1]$ is $\int_0^t f(s)ds$. In symbols, Tf is the element of $C(0,1)$, defined by

$$(Tf)(t) = \int_0^t f(s)ds, \qquad 0 \le t \le 1.$$

Similarly, $f \to (d/dt)f$ is a transformation from the space $C_n(0,1)$ of functions with n continuous derivatives into the space $C_{n-1}(0,1)$.

The theory of Lebesgue integration is concerned with the extension of the domain of the mapping ϕ, initially defined by Riemann on $C(0,1)$ by the equation

$$\phi(f) = \int_0^1 f(t)dt$$

to a larger class of functions. This larger domain $L_1(0,1)$, for example, includes the Dirichlet function already mentioned.

Example 6. Let $W(t,s)$ denote a $n \times n$ matrix, each element $W_{ij}(t,s)$ of which is a member of $B(\tau \times \tau)$ [i.e., $W_{ij}(t,s)$ is defined and bounded for every $t, s \in \tau$]. First let $\tau = [a,b]$ and take $X = L_{p_1}(a,b) \times \cdots \times L_{p_n}(a,b)$. The multivariate system with input $x = (x_1, \ldots, x_n) \in X$ and output $y = (y_1, \ldots, y_n) \in X$, defined by

$$y(t) = (Fx)(t) = \int_a^t W(t,s)x(s)ds, \qquad t \in [a,b], \tag{3}$$

is a function $F: X \to X$. At any fixed time $t' \in \tau$ the value $y(t')$ of the system output is an element of R^n and the relationship

$$y(t') = Tx = \int_a^{t'} W(t',s)x(s)ds \tag{4}$$

defines another transform $T: X \to R^n$.

The discrete analogy of Eqs. 3 and 4 is easily developed. Letting $\tau = \sigma$ and $X = l_{p_1}(\sigma) \times \cdots \times l_{p_n}(\sigma)$, we have $F: X \to X$, which denotes the function whose value at $t_k \in \sigma$ is given by

$$(\dot{F}x)(t_k) = \sum_{j=0}^{k} W(t_k,t_j)x(t_j), \qquad t_k \in \sigma, \tag{5}$$

whereas the mapping $T: X \to R^n$ is given by

$$Tx = \sum_{j=0}^{k} W(t_k',t_j)x(t_j), \tag{6}$$

in which $t_k' \in \sigma$ is a fixed point.

These two characterizations of multivariate systems are fundamental in the later chapters, and this example reoccurs frequently for further properties as the development unfolds.

Exercises

1. Let $f: A \to B$ be given and let X and Y be subsets of A. Prove the following:
   (a) $f(X \cup Y) = f(X) \cup f(Y)$.
   (b) $f(X \cap Y) \subset f(X) \cap f(Y)$.
   (c) If $f: A \to B$ is one-to-one, then $f(X \cap Y) = f(X) \cap f(Y)$.

2. Let f be defined by $f(x) = x^2 - 1$. Draw the graph and label the range and domain sets for the set $A = \{x: |x| \leq 1\}$. Is this function one-to-one?

3. Let A be the set of positive real numbers. For each $a \in A$ let $f_a: R \to A$ be the function defined by the correspondence $f_a(x) = a^x$, $x \in R$, and let $g_a: A \to R$ be the function defined by the correspondence $g_a(x) = \log_a x$, $x \in A$. Prove that for each $a \in A$, $f_a: R \to A$ and $g_a: A \to R$ are inverse functions.

4. Let $f: [-1,1] \to R$ be the function defined by the correspondence $f(x) = \text{arc sin } x$, $x \in [-1,1]$ and let $g: R \to [-1,1]$ be the function defined by the correspondence $g(x) = \sin x$, $x \in R$. Prove that these two functions are not inverse.

5. Recall that two mappings $f: X \to Y$ and $g: X \to Y$ are said to be equal (and we write this $f = g$) if $f(x) = g(x)$ for every x in X. Let

f, g, and h be any three mappings of a nonempty set X into itself and show that multiplication of mappings is associative in the sense that $f(gh) = (fg)h$.

6. Let X be a nonempty set and let f and g be one-to-one mappings of X onto itself. Show that fg is also a one-to-one mapping of X onto itself and that $(fg)^{-1} = g^{-1}f^{-1}$.

7. Assume that the two circuits in Figure 2.4 have initial conditions

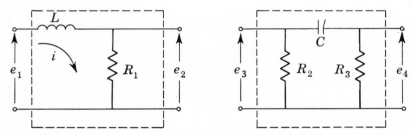

Figure 2.4

$i(0) = i_0$ and $q(0) = q_0$ where q is the charge on the capacitor. Describe the relationships $e_1 \to e_2$ and $e_3 \to e_3$ as functions. If $e_1, e_2 \in C(0, \infty)$, what can you say about the range of these functions? If the two circuits are connected, such that $e_2 = e_3$ is the resultant function $e_1 \to e_3$, what is the composition of the original two? If $i_0 = 0$, $q_0 = 0$, does your answer change? In physical terms, what implicit assumption does the concept of composition of functions make?

8. Let $\sigma = \{t_k : k = 1, 2, \dots\}$ and $l_1(\sigma)$ be the Banach space $\{x = (x(t_1), \dots, x(t_k), \dots) : \sum_\sigma |x(t_k)| < \infty\}$. In the system of this problem (Figure 2.5) the "clamp" C and "sample" S operations of Example 4 have

Figure 2.5

been connected with the first circuit of Exercise 7. Analyze the system as a mapping $x \to y$ with domain $l_1(\sigma)$. Can the system be represented as the composition of the subblocks in the diagram? What is the system range?

9. Let f be a mapping of the set X into the set Y. For each subset E of Y write $f^{-1}(E)$ for the subset of X defined by

$$f^{-1}(E) = \{x \in X : f(x) \in E\}.$$

Let A, B be subsets of Y. Prove the following assertions:
(a) $f^{-1}(A \sim B) = f^{-1}(A) \sim f^{-1}(B)$,
(b) $f^{-1}(A \cap B) = f^{-1}(A) \cap f^{-1}(B)$,
(c) $f^{-1}(A \cup B) = f^{-1}(A) \cup f^{-1}(B)$;

$f^{-1}(E)$ is called the *preimage* of E under f. Observe that the correspondence $E \to f^{-1}(E)$ is always a well-defined function from the space of subsets of Y into the space of subsets of X. This is to be contrasted with our earlier use of f^{-1} to denote the inverse (point) function which need not exist in the general case. If, however, f has an inverse point function, then, for any set $E \subset Y$, $f^{-1}(E)$ is the image of E under f^{-1} according to either meaning of f^{-1}.

10. Let X and Y be nonempty sets and f a mapping of X into Y. If A and B are subsets of X and Y, show the following:
(a) $ff^{-1}(B) \subseteq B$ and $ff^{-1}(B) = B$ is true for all $B \Leftrightarrow f$ is onto,
(b) $A \subseteq f^{-1}f(A)$ and $A = f^{-1}f(A)$ is true for all $A \Leftrightarrow f$ is one-to-one,
(c) $f(A_1 \cap A_2) = f(A_1) \cap f(A_2)$ is true for all A_1 and $A_2 \Leftrightarrow f$ is one-to-one.

11. Let S denote the sample operation of Example 4. Let S have domain $C(0,1)$ and x be in the range of S. What does the set $S^{-1}(x)$ consist of?

Continuous Functions

It is in the study of elementary calculus that the word "continuity" first appears. In discussing the condition or conditions that a function must satisfy in order to be called continuous at a point x_0, we arrive at the necessity of a precise formulation of the statement; if f is continuous, then $f(x)$ will be close to the number $f(x_0)$ whenever the number x is close to x_0. But how close must $f(x)$ be to $f(x_0)$? Instead of specifying some particular degree of closeness, it is much more satisfactory to require that no matter what choice is made for the degree of closeness of $f(x)$ to $f(x_0)$ it can be arranged by taking x close enough to x_0. To be precise, a function $f: R \to R$ is said to be continuous at the point $x_0 \in R$ if, given any $\varepsilon > 0$, there is a $\delta > 0$ such that $|f(x) - f(x_0)| < \varepsilon$ whenever $|x - x_0| < \delta$.

The functions of most interest in system theory are mappings with ranges and domains that are metric spaces. The following definition is the natural extension of continuity to functions defined on and with values in metric spaces.

DEFINITION G. *Let X and Y be metric spaces with metrics ρ_1 and ρ_2 and let f be a mapping of X into Y; f is said to be continuous at a point x_0 in X if either of the following equivalent conditions is satisfied:*

(1) *For each $\varepsilon > 0$ there exists $\delta > 0$ such that $\rho_1(x,x_0) < \delta \Rightarrow \rho_2(f(x), f(x_0)) < \varepsilon$,*

(2) *For each open sphere $\delta_\varepsilon(f(x_0))$ centered on $f(x_0)$ there exists an open sphere $S_\delta(x_0)$ centered on x_0 such that $f(S_\delta(x_0)) \subseteq S_\varepsilon(f(x_0))$.*

The first option is an obvious extension of our rudimentary concept, whereas the second option is a formulation that is sometimes more convenient for proving certain theorems. The reader should satisfy himself that conditions (1) and (2) are equivalent.

THEOREM A. *Let X and Y be metric spaces and let $f: X \to Y$. Then f is continuous at $x_0 \Leftrightarrow f(x_n) \to f(x_0)$ whenever $x_n \to x_0$.*

P R O O F. First let us assume that f is continuous at x_0. Then, if $\{x_n\}$ is a sequence in X such that $x_n \to x_0$, we must show that $f(x_n) \to f(x_0)$. Let $S_\varepsilon(f(x_0))$ be an open sphere centered on $f(x_0)$. Since f is continuous, there exists an open sphere $S_\delta(x_0)$ centered on x_0 such that $f(S_\delta(x_0)) \subseteq S_\varepsilon(f(x_0))$. Now $x_n \to x_0$; thus all x_n's for $n \geq$ some N lie in $S_\delta(x_0)$. On the other hand, $f(S_\delta(x_0)) \subseteq S_\varepsilon(f(x_0))$; hence all $f(x_n)$'s, $n >$ lie in $S_\varepsilon(f(x_0))$. This, of course, implies that $f(x_n) \to f(x_0)$.

To prove the converse, assume that f is not continuous at x_0. Then there exists an open sphere $S_\varepsilon(f(x_0))$ such that the image under f in each open sphere centered on x_0 is not contained in it. Consider the sequence of open spheres $S_1(x_0)$, $S_{1/2}(x_0)$, ..., $S_{1/n}(x_0)$, ... Form a sequence $\{x_n\}$ such that $x_n \in S_{1/n}(x_0)$ and $f(x_n) \notin S_\varepsilon(f(x_0))$. It is clear that x_n converges to x_0 and that $f(x_n)$ does not converge to $f(x_0)$. Hence, if f is not continuous, $x_n \to x_0$ does *not* imply $f(x_n) \to f(x_0)$.

A mapping of one metric space X into another is said to be *continuous on X* if it is continuous at each point in X. Similarly, if we let X and Y be metric spaces and $f: X \to Y$, then f is continuous on X if and only if $x_n \to x \Rightarrow f(x_n) \to f(x)$ for every $x \in X$. Thus, the continuous mappings of one metric space into another are precisely those that preserve convergence.

Another concept that is often useful in the applications is uniform continuity. The reader will note that in the definition of continuity of a function at a point x_0, given an $\varepsilon > 0$, a $\delta > 0$ can always be found such that $\rho_1(x,x_0) < \delta \Rightarrow \rho_2(f(x),f(x_0)) < \varepsilon$. It is clear here that δ will depend on ε. It is also true that, in general, δ depends on x_0. If $f: X \to Y$ is a continuous function on the space X and for each ε we can find a δ that works uniformly over the entire space X, in the sense that it does not depend on x_0, then f is called uniformly continuous. To be precise, we have the following definition.

DEFINITION H. *If X and Y are metric spaces with metrics ρ_1 and ρ_2, a mapping $f: X \to Y$, $D_f = X$ is said to be uniformly continuous if for each*

$\varepsilon > 0$ *there exists* $\delta > 0$ *such that* $\rho_1(x,x') < \delta \Rightarrow \rho_2(f(x),f(x')) < \varepsilon$ *for all* $x, x' \in X$.

Obviously any uniformly continuous mapping is continuous. The real function f defined on the entire real line R by $f(x) = 2x$ is uniformly continuous. The function g defined on R by $g(x) = x^2$ is continuous but not uniformly continuous. An important type of uniformly continuous mapping that occurs in practice is called an isometry.

DEFINITION I. *If X and Y are metric spaces with metrics ρ_1 and ρ_2, a mapping f of X into Y is called an isometry (or an isometric mapping) if $\rho_1(x,x') = \rho_2(f(x),f(x'))$ for all points $x, x' \in D_f$. If such a mapping exists with $D_f = X$ and $R_f = Y$, we say that X is isometric to Y.*

It is clear that an isometry is necessarily one-to-one. If X is isometric to Y, the points of these spaces can be put into one-to-one correspondence in such a way that the distances between pairs of corresponding points are the same. The spaces therefore differ only in the nature of their points and this is often unimportant. In fact, we frequently consider isometric spaces to be identical with one another.

For example,[1] let $\{e_n\}_{n=1}^{\infty}$ be an orthonormal basis in a (separable) Hilbert space H. Parseval's equation shows that the mapping which sends x in H into the sequence $\{\gamma_n\}$ of its Fourier coefficients is an isometry of H into l_2:

$$\|x\|^2 = \sum_{n=1}^{\infty} |\gamma_n|^2, \qquad \gamma_n = \langle x,x_n \rangle.$$

Since it is clear that if $\{\gamma_n\}$ is a sequence in l_2, the vector $x = \sum_{n=1}^{\infty} \gamma_n e_n$ belongs to H and any separable Hilbert space is isometric with l_2.

Example 7.   Let X be a Banach space and let $f: X \to R$ be defined by

$$f(x) = \|x\|.$$

From the inequality of Section 1.4,

$$|f(x) - f(x_n)| = |(\|x\| - \|x_n\|)| \le \|x - x_n\|,$$

we conclude that the norm is a continuous function; for example,

$$x_n \to x \Rightarrow \|x_n\| \to \|x\|.$$

In fact, the norm is a uniformly continuous function.

Example 8.   Let X be a Banach space and consider two sequences $x_n \to x$ and $y_n \to y$. From the relations

$$\|(x_n + y_n) - (x + y)\| = \|(x_n - x) + (y_n - y)\| \le \|x_n - x\| + \|y_n - y\|$$

[1] See Appendix 2.

we deduce directly that

$$x_n + y_n \rightarrow x + y,$$

hence addition is a continuous function.

Example 9.   Let y be a fixed vector in the Hilbert space H. The mapping $x \rightarrow \langle x,y \rangle$ is continuous.

Example 10.   The evaluation function $e_{t_0}(x) = x(t_0)$ (see Example 3) is a continuous function from the metric space $C(0,1)$ into the metric space C of complex numbers. Observe that if $\{x_n\}$ is a sequence in $C(0,1)$, which converges to x, then

$$\sup_{0 \leq t \leq 1} |x_n(t) - x(t)| \rightarrow 0$$

as $n \rightarrow \infty$. In particular,

$$|x_n(t_0) - x(t_0)| \rightarrow 0$$

and this is the statement that $e_{t_0}(x_n) \rightarrow e_{t_0}(x)$.

The reader may similarly verify that the function which maps $x \rightarrow C(0,1)$ into the function $y(t) = \int_0^t x(s)ds$ is a continuous mapping from $C(0,1)$ into $C(0,1)$. On the other hand, the Dirichlet function is not continuous at any point.

DEFINITION J.   *Let f be a function sending the metric space X into the metric space Y; f is said to satisfy a Lipschitz condition on the set $S \subset D_f$ if a real scalar $0 < M < \infty$ exists such that*

$$\rho_2(f(x), f(y)) \leq M\rho_1(x,y)$$

for all $x, y \in S$. If $M < 1$, then f is called a contraction.

When f satisfies a Lipschitz condition on a set S, we say that f is Lipschitz on S and the real scalar M is called a *Lipschitz constant* for f. The infimum of all possible Lipschitz constants is called the Lipschitz norm for the function and is denoted by $\llbracket f \rrbracket_S$, or when the set S is clear the subscript is dropped. Formally, we have

$$\llbracket f \rrbracket_S = \sup\{\rho_2(f(x_1), f(x_2))/\rho(x_1,x_2): x_1, x_2 \in S\}.$$

In the case in which X and Y are Banach spaces this expression becomes

$$\llbracket f \rrbracket_S = \sup\{\|f(x_1) - f(x_2)\|/\|x_1 - x_2\|: x_1, x_2 \in S\}.$$

A function between two Banach spaces X and Y is said to be *bounded* on a set S if a constant $c > 0$ exists such that

$$\|f(x)\| \leq c\|x\|$$

holds for all $x \in S$.

THEOREM B. *Let S denote a linear subspace of the Banach space X. If f
is a Lipschitz function on S with values in the Banach space Y, then*
(1) *$f(0) = 0$ implies f is bounded on S,*
(2) *f is uniformly continuous on S.*

The theorem is apparent from the expression

$$\|f(x) - f(y)\| \leq \Box f \Box_S \cdot \|x - y\|.$$

Indeed (1) follows by choosing $y = 0$ and (2) follows immediately from
definition H by choosing $\delta = \varepsilon / \Box f \Box_S$.

Apart from Theorem B, however, the concepts of continuity, boundedness,
and the Lipschitz condition are independent. To illustrate, consider the
function $f: R \to R$ defined by $f(x) = ax + b$ with $a \neq 0, b \neq 0$; f is Lipschitz
with $\|f\| = |a|$ but is not bounded in the vicinity of $x = 0$. Similarly, the
function on R defined by $x \to x^2$ is continuous but not uniformly continuous
and neither Lipschitzian nor bounded. Finally, the function with domain
$D_f = [0,1]$ defined by $x \to x^2$ is uniformly continuous but fails to satisfy a
Lipschitz condition.

Exercises

12. Let f be a mapping from the metric space X into the metric space Y.
Prove the equivalence of the following assertions:
(a) f is continuous.
(b) $f^{-1}(G)$ is an open set in X for each open set G in Y.
(c) $f^{-1}(F)$ is a closed set in X for each closed set F in Y.
(d) For each subset E of Y, $f(\overline{E}) = \overline{f(E)}$. Here the bar denotes, as
usual, the closure operations in X and Y.

13. Let X and Y be metric spaces and f a mapping of X into Y. If f is a
constant mapping, show that f is continuous. Use this to show that a
continuous mapping need not have the property that the image of
every open set is open.

14. Consider the network with output x and input u and satisfying
at time t_1 the relation $x(t_1) = \int_0^{t_1} W(t_1, \tau) u(\tau) d\tau$. Assuming that
$\int_0^{t_1} W^2(t_1, \tau) d\tau < \infty$, regard this system as a function with domain
$L_2(0, t_1)$ and a range in the real numbers. Show that this function is
continuous. If x_0 is a fixed point of any Hilbert space H, is the
function $f(x) = \langle x, x_0 \rangle$, $x \in H$, continuous? Is it uniformly continuous?

15. Determine which of the following functions are uniformly continuous
on the open unit interval $(0,1)$: $1/(1 - x)$; $\sin x$; $\sin(1/x)$; $x^{1/2}$; x^3.
Which are uniformly continuous on the open interval $(0, +\infty)$?

16. Let f, g be functions from the metric space X into itself with $D_f = D_g = X$. If f and g are continuous on X, show that the combinations $\alpha f + \beta g$ and fg are continuous functions on X (α, β arbitrary scalars). Show that a polynomial function

$$h(x) = f^n(x) + a_{n-1}f^{n-1}(x) + \cdots + a_1 f(x) + a_0 x, \qquad x \in X$$

is continuous on X.

17. Show that the function $f: l_2 \to R$ defined on $x = (x_1, x_2, \ldots) \in l_2$ by the rule

$$f(x) = \sum{}' n(|x_n| - 1),$$

where the sum $\sum{}'$ extends over values of the index for which $|x_i| \geq 1$, is continuous but not bounded on every sphere with a radius larger than one.

18. Let f, g, and h denote the clipper, half-wave, full-wave rectifier circuits in Figure 2.6. If the domain of each function is $C(0,t_1)$, what

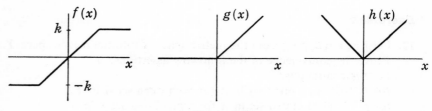

Figure 2.6

are the respective ranges. Which of these functions is continuous, uniformly continuous, bounded, Lipschitz? Over what subsets are these functions one-to-one? With z in the respective ranges describe the sets $f^{-1}(z)$, $g^{-1}(z)$, $h^{-1}(z)$.

19. Repeat Exercise 18 for the approximate hysteresis functions F and G (Figure 2.7) and the hysteresis function $\mathscr{F}$ of Section 0.1.

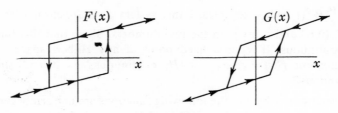

Figure 2.7

20. In many physical systems time delay in signal transmission is an intrinsic feature of system behavior. Discuss the pure time delay in Figure 2.8 (delay time τ) as a function on $L_2(0,t_1)$.

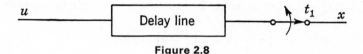

Figure 2.8

2.2 LINEAR TRANSFORMATIONS

In this section attention is focused on a special class of functions which operate on linear spaces. That the properties and descriptions of such linear transformations (as these functions are called) are important in almost all phases of analysis will become increasingly apparent as the treatment unfolds. The theory of linear transformations can be developed on a wide variety of levels, each of which has associated degrees of sophistication, generality, and prerequisite background. Our treatment is just abstract enough to take full advantage of the concepts of Chapter 1, yet concrete enough to be readily interpreted in terms of specific physical problems.

It is customary to denote linear transformations by capital letters. The value of a transformation A at the vector x is denoted by $A(x)$ or Ax.

DEFINITION A.   *Let X and Y be two linear spaces with a common set of scalars and let $A: X \rightarrow Y$ be a function defined on X with values in Y. Then A is called a linear transformation from X into Y if it has the following properties*:
(1) $A(x_1 + x_2) = Ax_1 + Ax_2$ any $x_1, x_2 \in X$.
(2) $A(\alpha x) = \alpha Ax$ any $x \in X$ and any scalar α.

Thus a linear transformation is a function which is defined on and has values in two linear spaces and which is additive (condition 1) and homogeneous (condition 2). A linear transformation from a linear space X into itself ($T = X$) is called a (*linear*) *operator* on X. If Y is the set of scalars, then A is a *linear functional* on X.

Let A be a linear transformation from X into Y. Let us investigate some of the consequences of the additive hypothesis of (1). First we have

$$A(0) = A(0 + 0) = A(0) + A(0);$$

hence A maps the zero vector in its domain into the zero vector in its range. Similarly, for any $x \in X$

$$0 = A(0) = A(x - x) = A(x) + A(-x),$$

so that $A(-x) = -A(x)$. Since

$$A(nx) = A(x + x + \cdots + x) = A(x) + A(x) + \cdots + A(x),$$

we see that $A(nx) = nA(x)$ if n is a positive integer. Because

$$A(-nx) = A(n(-x)) = nA(-x) = -nA(x),$$

this holds also if n is negative. Next $A(x) = A[n(1/n)x] = nA[(1/n)x]$ implies that $A[(1/n)x] = (1/n)Ax$ and, finally, if $r = n/m$ is a rational number, then

$$A(rx) = A\left(n\frac{1}{m}x\right) = nA\left(\frac{1}{m}x\right) = rA(x).$$

A natural question is whether any additive function on a linear space is automatically linear. A moment's reflection shows that if X is *complex* and A is only assumed to be additive, we cannot conclude that it is linear. Indeed, the function $x \to \bar{x}$, which sends a vector in the one-dimensional complex linear space C into its complex conjugate, is easily seen to be additive but not linear. The answer is again negative when X is real, but the reason is much more subtle. We shall be content for the moment with the remark that even in the simplest real linear space—R itself—there are many additive functions that are not linear. The interested reader will find a list of references and a short discussion of this phenomenon in Boas [A11], p. 108.

In the event that A is defined only on a subspace of X, the notation D_A denotes, as usual, the *domain* of A. The reader should observe that Definition A always requires D_A to be a linear subspace of X. The *range* of A is denoted by R_A and is given by $R_A = \{y : y = Ax, x \in D_A\}$. The notation N_A is used to denote the *null space* of A, which is defined by

$$N_A = \{x : x \in D_A, Ax = 0\}.$$

It is trivial that N_A is a linear subspace of X.

THEOREM A. *Let A be a linear transformation with domain $D_A \subset X$ and range $R_A \subset Y$ (where X and Y are linear spaces). Then R_A is a linear subspace of Y.*

P R O O F. Suppose that $y_1, y_2 \in R_A$ and let α be a scalar. We have to prove that $y_1 + y_2$ and αy_1 are in R_A. Since $y_1 \in R_A$, there is an $x_1 \in D_A$ for which $Ax_1 = y_1$. Similarly, an $x_2 \in D_A$ exists for which $Ax_2 = y_2$. Now, since A is linear, $A(x_1 + x_2) = Ax_1 + Ax_2 = y_1 + y_2$ and $A(\alpha x_1) = \alpha Ax_1 = \alpha y_1$; since $x_1 + x_2 \in D_A$ and $\alpha x_1 \in D_A$, the theorem is proved.

In Section 2.1 the concept of continuity was introduced, and it is apparent that this notion carries over without change to the present situation. We emphasize, however, that continuity of the transformation $A : X \to Y$ is *norm* continuity; that is, A is continuous at a point $x \in X$ if it is true that $\|Ax_n - Ax\| \to 0$ whenever $\{x_n\}$ is a sequence in X such that $\|x_n - x\| \to 0$. In contrast to the general situation in which continuity is defined first at "a point" and then on the "whole space," the next theorem shows that continuity of linear transformations need be established only at a single point.

THEOREM B. *If A is a linear (or merely additive) transformation from X into Y which is continuous at some $x_0 \in X$, then A is continuous at every point $x \in X$.*

P R O O F.   If $x_n \to x$, then $x_n - x + x_0 \to x_0$; hence $A(x_n - x + x_0) \to Ax$. Because of the additivity of A, however, $A(x_n - x + x_0) = Ax_n - Ax + Ax_0$; hence $x_n \to x$ implies $Ax_n \to Ax$.

A second observation concerning the notion of continuity is that any additive mapping A from a real Banach space X into any Banach space Y is homogeneous if it is continuous. We recall that an additive function on a linear space is always rational homogeneous. If r is a given irrational number and $\{r_n\}$ a sequence of rational numbers converging to r, then $\|r_n x - rx\| = \|x\| \cdot |r_n - r| \to 0$ and, by continuity of A, $r_n Ax = A(r_n x) \to A(rx)$. Since, however, $r_n Ax$ evidently converges to rAx, this shows that $A(rx) = rAx$ and A is therefore real homogeneous.

Let us recall the definition of a bounded transformation.

DEFINITION B. *Let A be a transformation defined on X with values in Y, where X, Y are Banach spaces. A is said to be bounded if there is a constant M such that $\|Ax\| \le M\|x\|$ for all $x \in X$.*

The reader should note that $\|Ax\|$ is the norm in the space Y, but $\|x\|$ is the norm in X. For purposes of clarity, it will sometimes be useful to subscript the norm symbol. Thus we might write $\|Ax\|_Y \le M\|x\|_X$ as an alternative for the foregoing expression.

If A is a bounded linear transformation, it is easy to see that boundedness of any set $X' \subset X$ implies boundedness of the image set $A(X') = Y' \subset Y$. We have just seen that every continuous additive function is a linear operator (i.e., the function is also homogeneous). The following theorem sheds further light on the interrelationships of linear transformation properties.

THEOREM C. *Let X, Y be Banach spaces and A a transformation from X to Y. Then A is bounded $\Leftrightarrow$ A is continuous.*

S U F F I C I E N C Y .   Let $A: X \to Y$ and assume that A is unbounded. There then exists a sequence $\{x_n\}$ such that for every n

$$\|Ax_n\| > n\|x_n\|.$$

Now we define a new sequence by $x'_n = x_n/n\|x_n\|$. Clearly, $x'_n \to 0$ for $\|x'_n\| = 1/n$. On the other hand, we have

$$\|Ax'_n\| = \left\| A\left(\frac{x_n}{n}\|x_n\|\right)\right\| = \frac{1}{n\|x_n\|} \cdot \|Ax_n\| > 1,$$

and therefore $\|Ax'_n\|$ does not tend to $\|A0\|$ as $n \to \infty$. Thus A cannot be continuous at the origin, which contradicts the assumption.

N E C E S S I T Y .   Let A be additive and bounded; thus $\|Ax\| \le M\|x\|$. If $x_n \to x$, then $\|Ax_n - Ax\| = \|A(x_n - x)\| \le M\|x_n - x\|$ implies that $Ax_n \to Ax$, which completes the proof of the theorem.

The following theorem summarizes our results so far.

THEOREM D.   *Let X, Y be Banach spaces and $A: X \to Y$. Then, if A is linear, the following conditions on A are equivalent to one another.*
   (1) *A is continuous.*
   (2) *A is continuous at the origin.*
   (3) *There exists a real number $M \ge 0$ such that $\|Ax\| \le M\|x\|$ for every $x \in X$.*
   (4) *If $S_1(0) = \{x : \|x\| \le 1\}$, its image $A(S_1(0))$ is a bounded set in Y.*

The validity of this theorem actually does not require that X, Y be complete spaces—only that they be normed and linear. In Section 2.1 the concept of the Lipschitz norm was defined in terms of an arbitrary function between metric spaces. For linear functions the Lipschitz norm definition reduces to the following:

DEFINITION C.   *Let X and Y be normed linear spaces and let A be a bounded linear transformation from X to Y. The smallest number M, for which $\|Ax\|_Y \le M\|x\|_X$ holds for all x, is called norm of A and denoted by $\|A\|$.*

According to this definition, the real number $\|A\|$ is such that

$$\|Ax\|_Y \le \|A\| \cdot \|x\|_X$$

for arbitrary x; moreover, for every $\varepsilon > 0$ there exists an x' such that

$$\|Ax'\|_Y > (\|A\| - \varepsilon) \|x'\|_X.$$

We can easily show that this definition is equivalent to

$$\|A\| = \sup \{\|A(x)\|_Y : \|x\|_X \le 1\}.$$

When X is not the null space, the homogeneity of A allows the equivalent form

$$\|A\| = \sup \{\|A(x)\|_Y : \|x\|_X = 1\}.$$

From Theorem B we find that the set of all upper bounds for A equals the set of all radii of closed spheres centered on the origin which contains $A(S_1(0))$. This yields yet another expression for the norm of A, namely,

$$\|A\| = \inf \{K : K \ge 0 \text{ and } \|A(x) \le K\|x\|_X \text{ for all } x\}.$$

From this we see at once that

$$\|A(x)\|_Y \le \|A\| \cdot \|x\|_X$$

for all x. These remarks show that the following formulas are equivalent:

$$\|A\| = \sup_{\|x\| \leq 1} \|Ax\|,$$

$$\|A\| = \sup_{\|x\| = 1} \|Ax\|,$$

$$\|A\| = \sup_{x \neq 0} \frac{\|Ax\|}{\|x\|}.$$

The subscripts on the norm notation have been used to emphasize the dependence of the definition of $\|A\|$ and the definitions $\| \|_X$ and $\| \|_Y$, respectively; that is, the linear spaces X, Y may have a variety of norms defined on them. Just as each norm makes a distinct space out of X, Y, each norm induces a different norm on the operator A. We shall see in the next section that the function $\|A\|$ satisfies the axioms for a norm; hence the present terminology is justified.

Before proceeding, let us note several linear transformations.

Example 1. It is easy to verify that function T (Example 5, Section 2.1)

$$(Tx)(t) = \int_a^t x(s)ds, \qquad a \leq t \leq b,$$

defines a continuous linear operator on $C(a,b)$. Similarly, the mapping

$$\phi(x) = \int_a^b x(t)dt,$$

which sends $L_1(a,b) \to R$, is bounded and linear. The null space of ϕ is infinite-dimensional. For example, when $b = \pi$, $a = -\pi$ the set $\{x: x(t) = \sin nt, \cos nt, n = 1, 2, \dots\}$ of linearly independent functions satisfies $\phi(x) = 0$.

Example 2. The evaluation functional $e_{t_0}(x) = x(t_0)$ (see Examples 3 and 10, Section 2.1) is a continuous complex linear functional on $C(0,1)$. The only new assertion here is the linearity that follows from

$$e_{t_0}(\alpha x + \beta y) = (\alpha x + \beta y)(t_o) = \alpha x(t_o) + \beta y(t_o).$$

Similarly, Examples 4, 6, and 9 of Section 2.1 are continuous linear functions.

Example 3. A single input-output time-invariant system has the description $Y(s) = H(s)X(s)$ in the Laplace transform domain, where $H(s)$ is the system transfer function, $X(s)$ the system input, and $Y(s)$ the system output. In proving the linearity of the operation "$H(s)$ times," we trace out the usual steps in proving the superposition principle in linear systems.

Example 4. Let X be the space of all real functions defined on the interval $0 \leq t < \infty$ such that $x(t)$ is integrable and $\lim_{t \to \infty} |x(t)| < Ae^{\alpha t}$ for some

$\alpha < \infty$. The function L defined by

$$(Lf)(s) = \int_0^\infty e^{-st} f(t) dt$$

is a linear transformation mapping X into the space of complex functions of a complex variable.

The next three examples have an intimate connection with several types of system problems; hence we shall examine these prototype problems in some detail.

Example 5.   The engineering literature gives ample testimony to the importance of linear transformations on finite dimensional spaces. In mechanics multidimensional stress-strain relationships may be described (at least on an incremental basis) as linear transformations on E^n. In the design of navigation and guidance systems various sensor signals which describe motion in sensor-coordinates must be reduced to a common coordinate system. Such changes of coordinates are usually linear transformations. Indeed, the list of applications is so extensive that the rudiments of matrix analysis play a part comparable in importance to calculus in most engineering disciplines.

In this example $X = Y = R^n$, and we consider the transformation A, associated with the real $n \times n$ matrix $[a_{ij}]$, which sends $x = (\xi_1, \ldots, \xi_n)$ into $y = (\eta_1, \ldots, \eta_n)$ according to the rule

$$\eta_i = \sum_{j=1}^n a_{ij} \xi_j, \qquad i = 1, \ldots, n. \tag{1}$$

Since $\lambda x = (\lambda \xi_1, \ldots, \lambda \xi_n)$, it follows from Eq. 1 and the equalities

$$\sum_{j=1}^n a_{ij} \lambda \xi_j = \lambda \left(\sum_{j=1}^n a_{ij} \xi_j \right), \qquad i = 1, \ldots, n$$

that $A \lambda x = \lambda A x$. It is just as easy to verify that A is additive; hence A is linear. Since R^n is finite dimensional, we find immediately that A is continuous.

In Section 1.4 we saw that many distinct norms can be defined on the space R^n. In particular, for $x = (\xi_1, \ldots, \xi_n)$ the function

$$\|x\|_p = \left[\sum_{i=1}^n |\xi_i|^p \right]^{1/p}$$

is a norm for any $1 \le p < \infty$. To illustrate the fact that the norm of A is dependent on the norms of the domain and the range spaces we shall consider three cases specifically.

For convenience the range and domain spaces have identical norms in each case.

C A S E 1: $l_1(n) \to l_1(n)$, $\|x\|_1 = \sum_{i=1}^{n} |\xi_i|$.   The number $\|A\|_1$ is explicitly given by $\|A\|_1 = \max_j \sum_{i=1}^{n} |\alpha_{ij}|$; that is, the norm of A, considered as an operator on $l_1(n)$, is the maximum of the $l_1(n)$ norms of the column vectors of $[\alpha_{ij}]$.

C A S E 2: $l_2(n) \to l_2(n)$, $\|x\|_2 = [\sum_{i=1}^{n} |\xi_i|^2]^{1/2}$.   The norm $\|A\|_2$ of A induced by the $l_2(n)$ norm is given by $\|A\|_2 = \lambda_{max}^{1/2}$, where λ_{max} is the largest eigenvalue of the matrix $B = A^*A$. We discuss eigenvalues in some detail in the next chapter.

C A S E 3: $l_\infty(n) \to l_\infty(n)$.   Here the norm on R^n is given by $\|x\|_\infty = \max \{|\xi_i|\}$. The norm induced on A, which we denote by $\|A\|_\infty$, is given by $\|A\|_\infty = \max_i \sum_{j=1}^{n} |\alpha_{ij}|$. Thus, considered as an operator on $l_\infty(n)$, norm of A is the maximum of the $l_1(n)$ norms of the row vectors of $[\alpha_{ij}]$.

Case 3 can be proved without too much trouble. The proof illustrates a constructive process which is frequently useful in determining the norm of a bounded operator. We begin by recalling that

$$\|A\|_\infty = \sup_{\|x\|_\infty = 1} \|Ax\|_\infty.$$

If A has matrix $[\alpha_{ij}]$ and $y = Ax$, where x is the vector $x = (\xi_1, \dots, \xi_n)$ and $y = (\eta_1, \dots, \eta_n)$ with η_i for $i = 1, \dots, n$ computed by Eq. 1, then

$$|\eta_i| \le \sum_{j=1}^{n} |\alpha_{ij}| \, |\xi_j|.$$

Since $\|y\|_\infty = \max_i \{|\eta_i|\}$, we find immediately that

$$\|Ax\|_\infty = \|y\|_\infty = \max_i |\eta_i| \le \max_i \sum_{j=1}^{n} |\alpha_{ij}| \cdot |\xi_j|.$$

Now   if $\|x\|_\infty = 1$, clearly $|\xi_j| \le 1$ for all j. Combining this with the preceding inequality, we have

$$\|A\|_\infty = \sup_{\|x\|_\infty = 1} \|Ax\|_\infty \le \max_i \sum_{j=1}^{n} |\alpha_{ij}|.$$

Next suppose that $\sum_{j=1}^{n} |\alpha_{ij}|$ attains its greatest value when $i = k$. We construct the vector x^0 with components

$$\xi_j^0 = \begin{cases} 0, & \text{if } \alpha_{kj} = 0, \\ \dfrac{|\alpha_{kj}|}{\alpha_{kj}}, & \text{if } \alpha_{kj} = 0, \qquad j = 1, 2, \dots, n. \end{cases}$$

Clearly $\|x^0\|_\infty = 1$ and, furthermore,

$$\sum_{j=1}^{n} \alpha_{kj} \xi_j = \sum_{j=1}^{n} |\alpha_{kj}|.$$

Hence the vector x^0 satisfies

$$\|Ax^0\|_\infty = \sum_{j=1}^n |\alpha_{kj}| = \max_i \sum_{j=1}^n |\alpha_{ij}|$$

and the proof is completed.

  Example 6. In Section 1.4 attention has been called to the circuit, mechanism, etc., which carries the input signal x into the output y, according to the rule

$$y(s) = \int_0^1 k(s,t)x(t)dt, \qquad 0 \le s \le 1.$$

Here the system is at rest at $t = 0$ [$y(0) = 0$], and $k(s,t)$ denotes the impulse response (or Green's function) of the system. If $x \in C(0,1)$ and $k(s,t)$ is a continuous function on the square $0 \le s, t \le 1$, it is easy to see that the function y defined for $0 \le s \le 1$ by this expression is continuous. If we write $y = Tx$, it follows that T maps $C(0,1)$ into itself. We can easily see that T is a linear operator on $C(0,1)$ for

$$[T(x_1 + x_2)](s) = \int_0^1 k(s,t)[x_1(t) + x_2(t)]dt$$

$$= \int_0^1 k(s,t)x_1(t)dt + \int_0^1 k(s,t)x_2(t)dt$$

$$= (Tx_1)(s) + (Tx_2)(s) = (Tx_1 + Tx_2)(s)$$

implies

$$T(x_1 + x_2) = Tx_1 + Tx_2,$$

and similarly, for any scalar α,

$$T(\alpha x_1) = \alpha Tx.$$

In computing the norm of T we shall assume that the usual norm $\|x\| = \sup_{0 \le t \le 1} |x(t)|$ is to be used. From the inequality

$$\left| \int_0^1 k(s,t)x(t)dt \right| \le \int_0^1 |k(s,t)| \cdot |x(t)|dt \le \sup_t |x(t)| \int_0^1 |k(s,t)|dt$$

we find immediately that

$$\|Tx\| = \sup_{0 \le s \le 1} \left| \int_0^1 k(s,t)x(t)dt \right| \le \|x\| \sup_{0 \le s \le 1} \int_0^1 |k(s,t)|dt.$$

Hence

$$\|T\| \le \sup_{0 \le s \le 1} \int_0^1 |k(s,t)|dt.$$

It can in fact be shown [A56, p. 83] that equality holds:

$$\|T\| = \sup_{0 \le s \le 1} \int_0^1 |k(s,t)|\,dt.$$

There is an analogy between Example 6 and Case 3, Example 5, that may be brought out by rephrasing Case 3 in slightly different terminology. Thus the vectors $x = (\xi_1, \ldots, \xi_n)$ of $l_\infty(n)$ may be regarded as functions from the set $\{1, 2, \ldots, n\}$ into R. The norm of the vector (function) x is the sup norm. The matrix $[\alpha_{ij}]$ is a real-valued function on the "rectangle" $1 \le i, j \le n$. Finally, the value of the operator determined by $[\alpha_{ij}]$ at a vector $x = (\xi_1, \ldots, \xi_n)$ is obtained by integrating the product $[\alpha_{ij}]x$, and we showed that the norm of this operator is the maximum of the L_1-norms of the columns of $[\alpha_{ij}]$.

Alternatively, $k(s,t)$ may be viewed as a matrix with a continuum of rows and columns and the vectors of $C(0,1)$ as a tuplet (x_t) with continuously many coordinates. The tth coordinate x_t is the value of the function x at t. Example 6, in this sense, is an extension of Case 3, Example 5.

These heuristic remarks are not intended to be rigorous. It is sufficient to say, however, that these two examples, and indeed many others that we will encounter, may in fact be treated as special examples of the same abstract operator with the techniques of modern integration theory. The reader is advised to think through for himself other analogies between discrete and continuous phenomena that we have or will meet.

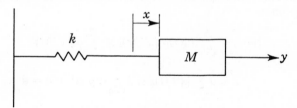

Figure 2.9   A mechanical system.

Example 7.   Consider the simple spring mass damper system of Figure 2.9.

$$Mx^{(2)}(t) + fx^{(1)}(t) + kx(t) = y(t), \qquad t_0 \le t,$$

$$x^{(1)}(t_0) = x_0^1, \qquad x^{(2)}(t_0) = x_0^2.$$

In this example we shall investigate the function $x \to y$ defined by the system equations.[1] To be somewhat more general, we shall consider the transformation $y = \mathbf{L}x$ defined by the equations

$$y(t) = a_n(t)x^{(n)}(t) + \cdots + a_1(t)x^{(1)}(t) + a_0(t)x(t)$$

$$x^{(n-1)}(t_0) = x_0^{n-1}, \ldots, x(t_0) = x_0.$$

[1] Here the kth time derivative of x at time t is denoted by $x^{(k)}(t)$; of course, $x^{(0)}(t) = x(t)$.

In considering the transformation L, we shall use the function space $C_n(a,b)$, which consists of the set of all functions x on the interval $[a,b]$ that are continuous and have continuous derivatives up to and including the nth order and equipped with the norm

$$\|x\| = \sum_{i=0}^{n} \sup_t |x^{(i)}(t)|.$$

It is easy to verify that the norm axioms are fulfilled. For example, for $x, y \in C_n[a,b]$, and for any $j = 0, 1, \ldots, n$,

$$|x^{(j)}(t) + y^{(j)}(t)| \le |x^{(j)}(t)| + |y^{(j)}(t)| \le \sup |x^{(j)}(t)| + \sup |y^{(j)}(t)|;$$

hence

$$\sup |x^{(j)}(t) + y^{(j)}(t)| \le \sup |x^{(j)}(t)| + \sup |y^{(j)}(t)|.$$

Summing on the index j on both sides of this inequality produces the triangle inequality. It can be shown that $C_n(a,b)$ is a Banach space.

In fact, that L is well defined and linear on the domain $C_n(a,b)$ is self-evident. The null space of L consists of all solutions to the nth order differential equation $Lx = 0$. A standard existence theorem (see Theorem A, Appendix 4) states that this equation has exactly n linearly independent solutions, $x_1, \ldots, x_n$ (sometimes called the complimentary solutions), from which we conclude that the null space of L is the linear manifold $L(x_1, \ldots, x_n)$. To prove that L is bounded, define $\bar{a}_k = \sup |a_k(t)|, k = 0, 1, \ldots, n$, and $\bar{a} = \max\{\bar{a}_1, \ldots, \bar{a}_n\}$. Then, if $y = Lx$, we have

$$|y(t)| \le \sum_{k=0}^{n} |a_k(t)| \cdot |x^{(k)}(t)| \le \sum_{k=0}^{n} \bar{a}_k |x^{(k)}(t)|$$

$$\le \bar{a} \sum_{k=0}^{n} |x^{(k)}(t)| \le \bar{a} \sum_{k=0}^{n} \sup |x^{(k)}(t)| = \bar{a}\|x\|;$$

hence $\|y\| = \sup |y(t)| \le \bar{a}\|x\|$.

Since $N_L \ne \phi$, the mapping L is many-to-one and is not invertible. It is possible to restrict the domain of L further, to the extent that L is one-to-one on the new domain. If X is the Banach space,

$$X = \{x : x \in C_n(a,b), x(a) = x^{(1)}(a) = \cdots = x^{(n-1)}(a) = 0\},$$

by a second existence theorem on differential equations (see Theorem D, Appendix 4) there is exactly one $x \in X$ for every $y \in C(a,b)$, such that $y = Lx$; that is, $R_L \subset C(a,b)$, and the preimage of $y \in C(a,b)$ in X is unique. From the inclusion $C_k(a,b) \subset C(a,b)$ and the definition of L it follows that $R_L = C(a,b)$; hence L is invertible on the domain X.

The inverse of L provides a connection with Example 1. Consider the special case

$$y(t) = (Lx)(t) = x^{(2)}(t).$$

Integrating twice and interchanging the order of integration we obtain

$$x(t) = \int_a^t du \int_a^u y(s)ds = \int_a^t (s - t)y(s)ds.$$

Letting

$$k(t,s) \begin{cases} (s - t), & a \leq s \leq t, \\ 0, & t < s \leq b, \end{cases}$$

we have

$$x(t) = \int_a^b k(t,s)y(s)ds,$$

which is in the form of Example 6.

*The Space of Linear Transformations

Let X and Y denote linear spaces and use the notation $L(X,Y)$ to denote the set of all linear transformations which map X into Y. We saw in Example 1 that every matrix $[a_{ij}]$ may be associated with a linear transformation $A: R^n \rightarrow R^n$. Similarly, in Example 2 every kernel $k(s,t)$, which is continuous in both variables on the square $a \leq s$, $t \leq b$, may be identified with a linear operator $T: C(0,1) \rightarrow C(0,1)$. Thus the set $L(X,Y)$ contains all of these operators.

It is possible to introduce the linear operations in $L(X,Y)$. Let X and Y be two linear spaces with identical scalars. Let A and B be two transformations in the set $L(X,Y)$. We define the sum $T = A + B$ by

$$Tx = (A + B)x = Ax + Bx, \qquad x \in X$$

and by multiplication with a scalar, $T = \lambda A$, by

$$Tx = (\lambda A)x = \lambda Ax.$$

It is easily proved that these definitions convert the set $L(X,Y)$ into a linear space. The zero transformation 0 (i.e., the zero element of this linear space) and the negative $-T$ of a transformation T are defined by $0(x) = 0$ and $(-T)(x) = -T(x)$, respectively. In summary, we have

THEOREM E. *Let X and Y be two linear spaces with the same system of scalars. Then the set of all linear transformations of X into Y is itself a linear space with respect to the linear operations just defined.*

The composition of two functions defined earlier applies in particular to linear transformations. Thus, if $A \in L(Y,Z)$ and $B \in L(X,Y)$, the product AB

---

*Starred sections are not prerequisite to the remainder of Chapter 2, and the reader may choose to bypass this material for the moment.

is the mapping from X into Z defined by

$$(AB)x = A(Bx), \qquad x \in X.$$

It is easy to check that AB is also linear, hence an element of $L(X,Z)$. In particular, if $X = Y = Z$, this shows that $AB \in L(X,X)$ if $A, B \in L(X,X)$. It is easy to prove that this multiplication is associative:

$$A(BC) = (AB)C.$$

Furthermore, multiplication is related to addition by the distributive laws

$$A(B + C) = AB + AC$$

and

$$(A + B)C = AC + BC$$

and to scalar multiplication by

$$\alpha(AB) = (\alpha A)B = A(\alpha B).$$

The proof of these facts is easy. As an illustration, we prove one of the distributive laws by the following computation:

$$[(A + B)C](x) = (A + B)(C(x))$$
$$= A(C(x)) + B(C(x))$$
$$= (AC)(x) + (BC)(x)$$
$$= (AC + BC)(x).$$

The reader is cautioned to observe that the property of commutativity (i.e., $AB = BA$) is *not* generally true under these assumptions. For instance, the $n \times n$ matrices, all of which map R^n into R^n, do not commute. As a further example of this point, let $X = C[0,1]$ and consider the two operators

$$y(s) = (Ax)(x) = \int_0^1 stx(t)dt$$

and

$$z(s) = (Bx)(s) = sx(s).$$

Then

$$ABx = \int_0^1 st \cdot tx(t)dt = s \int_0^1 t^2 x(t)dt$$

$$BAx = s \int_0^1 stx(t)dt = s^2 \int_0^1 tx(t)dt.$$

Therefore $AB \neq BA$.

We have noted specifically so far only the zero transformation 0. A second almost trivial transformation is the identity transformation I, which is defined by $I(x) = x$. We observe that $I \neq 0 \Leftrightarrow X \neq \{0\}$ and that

$$AI = IA = A$$

for every $A \in L(X,X)$. If α is any scalar, then scalar multiplication can be viewed as the linear transformation αI for

$$(\alpha I)(x) = \alpha I(x) = \alpha x.$$

In Theorem G it is shown that if $A \in L(X,X)$ is nonsingular, then A^{-1} exists and is linear; hence $A^{-1} \in L(X,X)$.

DEFINITION D.   *A linear space X is called an algebra if a third element of X, denoted by xy and called the product "x times y," corresponds to every ordered pair (x,y), subject to the following axioms*:

(1) $(xy)z = x(yz)$,
(2) $x(y + z) = xy + xz$,
(3) $(x + y)z = xz + yz$,
(4) $(\alpha x)(\beta y) = (\alpha\beta)(xy)$.

Here it is to be understood that x,y,z are arbitrary elements of X and α, β are arbitrary scalars. The algebra is called real or complex, depending on the real or complex scalar field.

If, in the algebra X, an element i exists such that $ix = xi = x$ for every $x \in X$, i is called the *unit element* of the algebra; it is necessarily unique. If $xy = yx$ for every pair (x,y), the algebra is called *commutative*. If X_0 is a subset of algebra X and $x + y$, αx, and xy are in X_0 whenever (x,y) are any elements of X_0 and α is any scalar, then X_0 is called a subalgebra of X. In other words, a *subalgebra* is a subspace which is also an algebra in its own right.

From this definition and the preceding remarks of this section, it is clear that the set $L(X,X)$ is an algebra. Moreover, this algebra has a unit, namely, the operator I, defined by $Ix = x$ for every x. $L(X,X)$, in general, is not commutative.

*Normed Spaces of Linear Transformations

We have observed that the set $L(X,X)$ of all linear transformations mapping the linear space X into the linear space Y is itself a linear space. If X and Y are Banach spaces, the concept of an operator norm has been defined for the bounded transformations in $L(X,X)$. This dual usage of the term "norm" suggests the possibility that the subset of all bounded transformations in $L(X,X)$ may, under some conditions, be a normed linear space.

Let us denote by $\beta(X,Y)$ the set of all continuous (or bounded) linear transformations of the normed linear spaces X into the normed linear spaces Y. (Here the letter β is intended to suggest the adjective "bounded.") If $A \in \beta(X,Y)$, the function $\|A\|$ of Definition B satisfies the norm axioms. Indeed, assuming

$X \neq \{0\}$, we have

(1) $\|A\| = \sup_{\|x\|=1}\|Ax\| \geq 0$ is self-evident. If $\|A\| = 0$, then $\|Ax\| = 0$ for all x with $\|x\| = 1$. Because of the homogeneity of A, we have $Ax = 0$ for all x, and therefore $A = 0$.

(2) $\|\lambda A\| = \sup_{\|x\|=1}\|\lambda Ax\| = |\lambda|\sup_{\|x\|=1}\|Ax\| = |\lambda| \cdot \|A\|$.

(3) $\|A + B\| = \sup_{\|x\|=1}\|(A + B)x\| \leq \sup_{|x|=1}\|Ax\| + \sup_{\|x\|=1}\|Bx\| = \|A\| + \|B\|$.

We have partially proved the following theorem.

THEOREM F. *If X and Y are normed linear spaces, the set $\beta(X,Y)$ of all continuous linear transformations of X into Y is itself a normed linear space with respect to the pointwise linear operations and the norm induced by X and Y. Further, if Y is a Banach space, then $\beta(X,Y)$ is also a Banach space.*

PROOF. We have already shown that $\beta(X,Y)$ is a normed linear space, and it remains only to prove that when Y is complete this space is also complete; that is, we must show that if $\{A_n\}$ is a Cauchy sequence in $\beta(X,Y)$ it converges to a transformation in $\beta(X,Y)$.

Let $\{A_n\}$ be a Cauchy sequence in $\beta(X,Y)$. If x is an arbitrary vector in X, then, since $\|A_m(x) - A_n(x)\| = \|(A_m - A_n)(x)\| \leq \|A_m - A_n\| \cdot \|x\|$, it follows that $\{A_n(x)\}$ is a Cauchy sequence in Y; and, because Y is complete, there is a vector in Y—we denote it by $A(x)$—such that $A_n(x) \to A(x)$. This, however, defines a mapping A of X into Y.

Is this mapping linear? Since $A(x_1 + x_2) = \lim A_n(x_1 + x_2) = \lim A_n(x_1) + \lim A_n(x_2)$ and $A(\alpha x) = \lim A_n (\alpha x) = \alpha \lim A_n(x) = \alpha A(x)$, it is clear that A is linear. To conclude the proof, we now have to show that A is continuous and that $A_n \to A$ with respect to the norm on $\beta(X,Y)$. Noting that the norms of the terms of a Cauchy sequence in a normed linear space form a bounded set of numbers, we have

$$\|A(x)\| = \|\lim A_n(x)\| = \lim \|A_n(x)\| \leq \sup (\|A_n\| \cdot \|x\|)$$

$$= (\sup \|A_n\|)\|x\|,$$

which shows that A has a bound and therefore is continuous. It remains now only to prove that $\|A_n - A\| \to 0$. Let $\varepsilon > 0$ be given and let n_0 be a positive integer such that $m, n \geq n_0 \Rightarrow \|A_m - A_n\| < \varepsilon$, a property of all Cauchy sequence in normed spaces. If $\|x\| \leq 1$ and $m, n \geq n_0$, then

$$\|A_m(x) - A_n(x)\| = \|(A_m - A_n)(x)\| \leq \|A_m - A_n\| \cdot \|x\| \leq \|A_m - A_n\| < \varepsilon.$$

We now use a classic maneuver by holding m fixed and allow n to approach ∞, so that $\|A_m(x) - A_n(x)\| \to \|A_m(x) - A(x)\|$, from which we conclude that $\|A_m(x) - A(x)\| \leq \varepsilon$ for all $m \geq n_0$ and all x such that $\|x\| \leq 1$. This implies directly that $\|A_m - A\| \leq \varepsilon$ for all $m \geq n_0$ and the proof is complete.

As before, we can expand these results for the case in which the range and domain spaces are the same normed linear space. We call a continuous linear transformation of X into itself simply a *bounded operator* on X, and we identify the normed linear space of all bounded operators on X by $\beta(X)$ instead of the slightly more cumbersome $\beta(X,X)$. Theorem F shows that $\beta(X)$ is a Banach space whenever X is. If A and B are two operators in $\beta(X)$, the compositions AB and BA are defined. Let us show that

$$\|AB\| \leq \|A\| \cdot \|B\|.$$

This relation is readily proved by the following process:

$$\|ABx\| = \|A(Bx)\| \leq \|A\| \cdot \|Bx\| \leq \|A\| \cdot \|B\| \cdot \|x\|.$$

We have shown in an earlier section that in any Banach space addition and scalar multiplication are jointly continuous. If $\beta(X)$ is a Banach space, we conclude (utilizing the foregoing inequality) that multiplication is also jointly continuous; that is, if $A_n \to A$ and $B_n \to B$, then $A_n B_n \to AB$. This follows at once from

$$\|A_n B_n - AB\|$$
$$= \|A_n(B_n - B) + (A_n - A)B\| \leq \|A_n\| \cdot \|B_n - B\| + \|A_n - A\| \cdot \|B\|.$$

When X is not the trivial space $\{0\}$, the identity transformation I is an identity for $\beta(X)$ and we clearly have

$$\|I\| = \sup\{\|I(x)\| : \|x\| \leq 1\} = \sup\{\|x\| : \|x\| \leq 1\} = 1.$$

If T is a transformation, defined on all X with range values in Y, which is one-to-one and onto, then T is nonsingular (invertible). If T is also linear, we have the following additional properties:

THEOREM G.   *Let T denote a linear transformation with $D_T = X$ and $R_T = Y$ in which X and Y are normed linear spaces.*
   (1)   *T^{-1} exists and is bounded if and only if a constant $m > 0$ exists such that $m\|x\| \leq \|Tx\|$ holds for every $x \in X$.*
   (2)   *If (1) holds, $\|T^{-1}\| \leq 1/m$.*
   (3)   *Whenever T^{-1} exists it is linear.*

PROOF.   To prove (2) let $y_1, y_2 \in Y$; then $y_1 = Tx_1$ and $y_2 = Tx_2$, where, in fact, $x_1 = T^{-1}y_1$ and $x_2 = T^{-1}y_2$. Since $(y_1 + y_2) = T(x_1 + x_2)$, we have $T^{-1}(y_1 + y_2) = x_1 + x_2 = T^{-1}y_1 + T^{-1}y_2$. Similarly, $\lambda y_1 = T\lambda x_1$ implies $T^{-1}\lambda y_1 = \lambda x_1 = \lambda T^{-1}y_1$, hence T^{-1} is additive and homogeneous. To prove (1) we note that for $m > 0$, and if $m\|x\| \leq \|Tx\|$ holds, $Tx = 0 \Rightarrow x = 0$, hence T is one-to-one. Moreover, if T^{-1} exists, $y = Tx$ is equivalent to $x = T^{-1}y$. Hence $m\|x\| \leq \|Tx\| \Rightarrow m\|T^{-1}y\| \leq \|y\| \to \|T^{-1}y\| \leq 1/m\|y\|$, for all y in R_T, which is the domain of T^{-1}. This implies by Theorem C that T^{-1} is continuous.

Conversely, if T^{-1} exists and is bounded, then for all $y = Tx \in R_T$ we have

$$\|x\| = \|T^{-1}y\| \le \|T^{-1}\| \cdot \|y\| = \|T^{-1}\| \cdot \|Tx\|$$

and the condition of the theorem holds with $m = 1/\|T^{-1}\|$.

In other words, if T is linear, bounded below (i.e., $m\|x\| \le \|Tx\|$), and $R_T = Y$, then T^{-1} exists and is an element of $\beta(Y, X)$. The reader is referred to Appendix 7 for further discussion of these matters.

It is not usually a simple matter to determine the invertibility of a transformation. The next theorem, however, gives both a criterion for the existence of a bounded inverse and a computational method for approximating the inverse transformation.

THEOREM H.   *If X is a Banach space and $T \in \beta(X)$ with $\|T\| \le \alpha < 1$, the inverse of $I - T$ is bounded and satisfies*

$$\|(I - T)^{-1}\| \le \frac{1}{1 - \alpha} .$$

Furthermore the series in $\beta(X)$

$$(I - T)^{-1} = \sum_{n=0}^{\infty} T^n$$

converges uniformly to the left-hand side of this equality.

The proof of this theorem is not difficult, and is left as an exercise. We shall see in Exercises 7–10, Section 2.5, that it is a useful tool for the study of feedback systems.

*Projections

In this section we mention only briefly two special types of linear transformations. These transformations merit individual attention because they are closely related to the structure of linear spaces and a discussion of their properties will enrich our understanding of this structure. The first transformation is a projection. The notion of a projection was introduced implicitly in Section 1.3 in connection with the direct sum of linear manifolds, and it is at this point that we begin.

Recall that the linear subspaces $\{M_1, \ldots, M_n\}$ decompose the linear space X in a direct-sum manner, $X = M_1 \oplus \cdots \oplus M_n$, if each $x \in X$ has a unique representation of the form $x = x_1 + \cdots + x_n$ with $x_i \in M_i$. This decomposition may be used to define the functions P_i by the expressions

$$P_i x = x_i, \qquad i = 1, \ldots, n,$$

as x takes on all points in X. These operators are apparently linear and satisfy the relations

$$P_i P_j = 0, \qquad i \neq j,$$

$$P_i^2 = P_i, \qquad i = 1, \dots, n,$$

$$I = P_1 + \cdots + P_n.$$

The range of each P_i is the subspace M_i. The null space of P_i is the subspace $X \ominus M_i$ (i.e., $N_{P_i} = M_1 \oplus \cdots \oplus M_{i-1} \oplus M_{i+1} \oplus \cdots \oplus M_n$).

DEFINITION E. *A linear operator P on X is called a projection if $P^2 = P$. If M is the range of P, then P is called the projection of P onto M.*

It is easy to show that if P is a projection

$$X = R_P \oplus N_P.$$

Indeed, since each $x \in X$ can be written in the form

$$x = Px + (I - P)x$$

and $Px \in R_P$, we need show only that $(I - P)x \in N_P$ and $R_P \cap N_P = \varnothing$. The equality chain

$$P[(I - P)(x)] = [P(I - P)](x) = (P - P^2)(x) = (P - P)(x)$$
$$= 0(x) = 0$$

shows that $(I - P)(x)$ is in N_P; hence we find that N_P and R_P span X. To determine whether N_P and R_P are disjoint, we have only to note that if a vector $P(x)$ in R_P is also in N_P, so that $P(P(x)) = 0$, then $P(x) = P^2(x) = P(P(x)) = 0$. This proves that $X = R_P \oplus N_P$, and it follows that P is precisely the projection of X onto R_P.

In a similar manner we can define a projection Q of X onto N_P. It is clear that $Q = I - P$, for if P is a projection on X the equation

$$Q^2 = (I - P)^2 = (I - P)(I - P) = I - P - P + P^2 = I - P = Q$$

shows that Q is a projection; and we know that P is the projection on R_P when $I - P$ is the projection on N_P. We make one further comment. If M_1 is a given linear subspace of X, there exist, in general, many M_2's such that $X = M_1 \oplus M_2$; hence there certainly must be some projection P onto M_2, but the projection P is not unique until the subspace M_2 is specified. (The reader may easily verify this point in R^2.)

So far nothing has been said about continuity. Let us consider a projection P in the Banach X. If P is continuous, the subspace N_P, being the null space of a continuous linear transformation, is closed (see Exercise 1). Since the range of P is the null space of $I - P$, which is also continuous, R_P is also closed. That the converse property is true is pointed out by the next theorem.

THEOREM I. *Every continuous projection P, acting on the Banach space X, defines two closed linear subspaces, N_P and R_P such that $X = N_P \oplus R_P$. Conversely every pair of closed subspaces M, N such that $X = M \oplus N$ defines a continuous projection P such that $R_P = M$ and $N_P = N$.*

It is not true in general that every closed subspace M of a Banach space X has a continuous projection with range M. The difficulty lies in the fact that there may exist no closed linear manifold N complementary to M. It can also happen that $M \oplus N$ is not closed, even though M and N are. In these cases the associated projections are not continuous. (See Remark 1, Section 3.2.)

In the event that X is a Hilbert space, the problems involved in defining a decomposition for X do not arise. Indeed, we recall that according to Theorem D, Section 1.5, every closed linear subspace M has a complement, namely, $M^\perp$ such that $X = M \oplus M^\perp$. For Hilbert spaces we may define without ambiguity an orthogonal projection.

DEFINITION F. *Let H denote a Hilbert space. The linear operator P is called an orthogonal projection in H if P is a projection with $N_P \perp R_P$. If M is a closed subspace of H then the projection P with $R_P = M$ and $N_P = M^\perp$ is called the orthogonal projection of H onto M.*

Orthogonal projections play an important role in the study of the general structure of linear operators. We shall not develop the properties of the orthogonal projection any further at this point except in the exercises.

*Isomorphic and Congruent Spaces

In order to motivate our next definition, let us briefly consider the following example of a linear space X. The vectors in X are the real-ordered pairs (ξ, η). Addition and scalar multiplication are defined in X by the following rules:

$$(\xi_1, \eta_1) + (\xi_2, \eta_2) = (\eta_1 + \eta_2, \xi_1 + \xi_2),$$

$$\lambda(\xi, \eta) = (\lambda \eta, \lambda \xi), \ \lambda \text{ real.}$$

A moment's reflection will show that the axioms of Definition A, Section 1.3, are satisfied so that X is indeed a linear space. Because we have already encountered the space $R \times R = R^2$ it is natural to ask whether X and R^2 are "equal." The set theorist responds "obviously!" The rest of us, however, are a little skeptical. These spaces are both linear and we feel that to be "equal" their computation rules should also be "equal," which is clearly not the case. So we say that they are different. But how different? Certainly not so different as, say, $C(0,1)$ and R^2. In fact, X and R^2 differ in a very trivial respect. Thus, if we define the mapping $T: X \to R^2$ by

$$T(\xi, \eta) = (\eta, \xi),$$

we see immediately that T is linear, one-to-one, and onto R^2. Moreover, any "linear space statement" that is true of R^2 can be translated by T into a true statement about X. For example, X is two-dimensional with a basis consisting of the vectors $T^{-1}(0,1) = (1,0)$ and $T^{-1}(1,0) = (0,1)$. In short, we may obtain the linear space X from the linear space R^2 by simple relabeling points. Certainly this is a trivial change, for as students of linear spaces we do not really care about the nature of vectors anyway. On the other hand, if we had done *more* than change the language of R^2 to obtain X, we would have effected a change in its structure as a *linear space*—a nontrivial change.

The preceding discussion indicates that we ought to regard two linear spaces X and Y as "equal" when they are structurally identical. Since all of our definitions and properties of a linear space derive from its addition and scalar multiplication, this will occur when and only when there is a one-to-one mapping T from X onto Y such that T preserves addition:

$$T(x_1 + x_2) = Tx_1 + Tx_2.$$

Formally, we have the following definition.

DEFINITION G. *Two linear spaces X and Y (with the same scalars) are said to be isomorphic if there exists a one-to-one linear mapping of X onto Y. Such a mapping is called an isomorphism.*

In terms of our definition, the spaces X and R^2 already discussed are isomorphic under the isomorphism T, which sends (ξ,η) into (η,ξ). The initial confusion developed from the fact that the identity mapping i, which sends (ξ,η), regarded as an element of X, into (ξ,η), regarded as an element of R^2, although one-to-one, onto, and homogeneous, is *not* additive:

$$i((\xi_1,\eta_1) + (\xi_2,\eta_2)) = i((\eta_1 + \eta_2, \xi_1 + \xi_2))$$

$$= (\eta_1 + \eta_2, \xi_1 + \xi_2) = (\eta_1,\xi_1) + (\eta_2,\xi_2),$$

whereas

$$i((\xi_1,\eta_1)) + i((\xi_2,\eta_2)) = (\xi_1,\eta_1) + (\xi_2,\eta_2).$$

In paraphrasing this definition, $D_T = X$, $R_T = Y$ and T^{-1} exist. As a consequence of the linearity of T and T^{-1}, the operations of vector addition and scalar multiplication are preserved under the mapping T; that is, if x_1 and x_2 correspond to y_1 and y_2, respectively, then $y_1 + y_2$ corresponds to $x_1 + x_2$ and αy_1 corresponds to λx_1. Also, if X is isomorphic to Y and Y is isomorphic to Z, it is clear that X is isomorphic to Z.

As an exercise, we urge the reader to verify the following propositions.
(1)   If X and Y are isomorphic and finite dimensional, dim $X = $ dim Y.
(2)   If dim $X = $ dim $Y < \infty$, then X and Y are isomorphic.
(3)   If X and Y are isomorphic under T and M is a linear manifold in X, then $T(M)$ is a linear manifold in Y. Moreover, *every* linear manifold N in Y is of the form $N = T(M)$ for a unique linear manifold M of X.

Now that we have agreed to regard two linear spaces as identical if they are isomorphic, it is natural to raise once more the question of "equality" for metric spaces. Recalling that a metric space is simply a set X with a metric ρ and proceeding by analogy with the foregoing, we make it clear that the "metric space" isomorphisms ought to be the isometries (recall Definition I, Section 2.1). More precisely, we call the metric spaces $\{X,\rho_1\}$ and $\{Y,\rho_2\}$ *isometric* if there is a (necessarily) one-to-one mapping T of X onto Y such that

$$\rho_1(x_1,x_2) = \rho_2(Tx_1,Tx_2)$$

for all x_1, $x_2 \in X$. It is clear that if X and Y are isometric the isometry T will carry any metric property of X into the same property of Y and vice versa. To give but one (typical) example, we show that Y is complete if X is complete. The argument is simple: if $\{y_n\}$ is a Cauchy sequence in Y, then because T is one-to-one and onto there is a unique sequence $\{x_n\}$ in X with $Tx_n = y_n$ and because T is isometric the sequence $\{x_n\}$ is Cauchy in X; hence $x_n \to x \in X$. But

$$\rho_2(y_n,Tx) = \rho_1(x_n,x)$$

shows that $y_n \to Tx \in Y$.

The reader is urged to show that any isometry similarly preserves openness, closedness, and our other metric concepts.

Consider now a pair of Banach spaces X and Y. When are X and Y equal as Banach spaces? Because each is a linear space, we want X and Y to be isomorphic as linear spaces. Because each is a metric space, we also require that X and Y be isometric, and because the metric space structure of a Banach space is not entirely independent of its linear space structure ($\|\lambda x\| = |\lambda| \cdot \|x\|$ and $\|x + y\| \leq \|x\| + \|y\|$ relate distance, scalar multiplication, and addition, for example), we require that X and Y be isometric under the same mapping that makes them isomorphic; that is, X and Y are to be regarded as identical Banach spaces if there exists an isometric isomorphism T of X onto Y or, in more detail, a one-to-one linear map of X onto Y such that

$$\|x_1 - x_2\| = \|Tx_1 - Tx_2\|$$

for all x_1 and $x_2 \in X$. A quick review of the definition of a Banach space will show that such a mapping T will indeed preserve the Banach space structure of X and Y and that out intuitive notion of equal Banach spaces is satisfied by the concept of an isometric isomorphism.[1]

Finally, consider the case of two Hilbert spaces X and Y. We would certainly hesitate to identify X and Y if they were not identifiable as Banach spaces (i.e., isometrically isomorphic). On the other hand, the identity

$$\langle x,y \rangle = \tfrac{1}{4}\{\|x + y\|^2 - \|x - y\|^2 + \|x + y\|^2 - \|x - y\|^2\}$$

---

[1] Two isometrically isomorphic Banach spaces are often called *congruent*.

shows that any *linear* mapping that preserves norms will automatically preserve inner products. Because the entire structure of a Hilbert space derives from its inner product, it is clear what the "Hilbert space isomorphisms" are. Two Hilbert spaces X and Y with inner products $\langle\,,\,\rangle_1$ and $\langle\,,\,\rangle_2$ are to be regarded as identical if there exists a one-to-one transformation T from X onto Y satisfying either

$$\langle x_1, x_2 \rangle_1 = \langle Tx_1, Tx_2 \rangle_2, \qquad x_1, x_2 \in X$$

or the (only apparently weaker) condition

$$\|x\|_1 = \|Tx\|_2.$$

In short, X and Y are equal as Hilbert spaces if they are isometrically isomorphic.

To summarize, if we generalize the notion of isomorphism to mean identity of structure, the metric space isomorphisms are the isometries, the linear space isomorphisms are the nonsingular (onto) linear transformations, and the Banach (Hilbert) space isomorphisms are the nonsingular (onto) linear transformations that are also isometric. We now proceed to list examples of the concepts of this section. Additional examples are given in the exercises.

Example 8.   Recall that two real (or complex) polynomials $p(t) = \alpha_0 + \alpha_1 t + \cdots + \alpha_{n-1} t^{n-1}$ and $q(t) = \beta_0 + \beta_1 t + \cdots + \beta_{n-1} t^{n-1}$ are equal if and only if $\alpha_i = \beta_i$, $i = 0, 1, \ldots, n-1$. Thus the mapping T which sends p into the real (complex) n-tuple $(\alpha_0, \alpha_1, \ldots, \alpha_{n-1})$ is well defined and one-to-one into the linear space $R^n(C^n)$ of real (complex) n-tuples. T is also linear and onto so that the space P_n of real (complex) polynomials of degree at most $n-1$ is isomorphic to the space $R^n(C^n)$.

Example 9.   Let H be a separable Hilbert space and let $\{e_n\}_{n=1}^{\infty}$ be a complete orthonormal sequence in H (see Appendix 2). We have already shown that each x in H has an expansion

$$x = \sum_{n=1}^{\infty} \alpha_n e_n,$$

where $\alpha_n = \langle x, e_n \rangle$ and $\sum_{n=1}^{\infty} |\alpha_n|^2 = \|x\|^2$. Moreover, if $y = \sum_{n=1}^{\infty} \beta_n e_n$ is another vector in H and $x = y$ (since the e_i are linearly independent), the coefficients α_n and β_n are identical for $n = 1, 2, \ldots$. Thus each x in H determines a unique vector $(\alpha_1, \alpha_2, \ldots)$ in l_2, and it is easy to see that this correspondence is linear and one-to-one. On the other hand, if $(\alpha_1, \alpha_2, \ldots)$ is any vector in l_2, the series $\sum_i^{\infty} \alpha_n e_n$ is convergent in H (the sequence of partial sums $\sum_{i=1}^{N} \alpha_n e_n$ is Cauchy). We conclude that H is isomorphic to l_2. Parseval's equation $\sum_n |\langle x, e_n \rangle|^2 = \|x\|^2$ shows that this correspondence is also isometric. Every separable Hilbert space is therefore isometrically isomorphic (recongruent) to l_2.

Exercises

1. Prove that the null space of every bounded linear transformation is closed.

2. Give examples of unbounded linear operators with both closed and nonclosed null spaces.) HINT: Form a Cartesian product by using a closed (nonclosed) linear space. Define a linear transformation on the product space.

3. Consider the linear space R^2. Verify that each of the following is a linear operator on R^2:
   (a) $T_1[(\xi_1,\xi_2)] = (\alpha\xi_1,\alpha\xi_2)$, where α is a real number. The effect of T_1 is to multiply each vector in R^2 by the scalar α.
   (b) $T_2[(\xi_1,\xi_2)] = (\xi_2,\xi_1)$. T_2 reflects R^2 about the diagonal line $x_1 = x_2$.
   (c) $T_3[(\xi_1,\xi_2)] = (\xi_1,0)$. T_3 projects R^2 onto the x_1-axis.
   (d) $T_4[(\xi_1,\xi_2)] = (0,\xi_2)$. T_4 projects R^2 onto the x_2-axis.
   Show that these operators have the following matrices.

$$\begin{bmatrix} \alpha & 0 \\ 0 & \alpha \end{bmatrix} \qquad \begin{bmatrix} 0 & 1 \\ 1 & 0 \end{bmatrix} \qquad \begin{bmatrix} 1 & 0 \\ 0 & 0 \end{bmatrix} \qquad \begin{bmatrix} 0 & 0 \\ 0 & 1 \end{bmatrix}.$$

$$\text{(a)} \qquad\qquad \text{(b)} \qquad\qquad \text{(c)} \qquad\qquad \text{(d)}$$

4. If N is an arbitrary normed linear space, show that any linear transformation of a finite-dimensional space X into N is continuous. HINT: Take a basis $\{e_1,e_2,\ldots,e_n\}$ for X. An arbitrary vector x in X can be written uniquely in the form

$$x = \alpha_1 e_1 + \alpha_2 e_2 + \cdots + \alpha_n e_n,$$

and from this we get $A(x) = \alpha_1 A(e_1) + \alpha_2 A(e_2) + \cdots + \alpha_n A(e_n)$. Use the fact that convergence in X implies coordinate convergence.

5. Let N be a finite-dimensional normed linear space with dimension $n > 0$ and let $\{e_1,e_2,\ldots,e_n\}$ be a basis for N. Each vector x in N can be written uniquely in the form

$$x = \alpha_1 e_1 + \alpha_2 e_2 + \cdots + \alpha_n e_n.$$

If T is the one-to-one linear transformation of N onto $l_1(n)$ defined by $T(x) = (\alpha_1,\alpha_2,\ldots,\alpha_n)$, then T^{-1} is continuous by Exercise 4. Prove that T is continuous. HINT: If T is not continuous, then for some $\varepsilon > 0$ there exists a sequence $\{y_n\}$ in N such that $y_n \to 0$ and $\|T(y_n)\| \geq \varepsilon$; if $x_n = y_n\|T(y_n)\|$, then $z_n \to 0$ and $\|T(z_n)\| = 1$; the subset of $l_1(n)$ which consists of all vectors of norm 1 is compact (see Appendix 1) and $\{T(z_n)\} = 1$ has a subsequence which converges to a vector with norm 1; now use the continuity of T^{-1}.

6. In this exercise H denotes a Hilbert space with closed subspaces $\{M_i\}$ which are the ranges of the orthogonal projections P_i, respectively. Prove the following:
   (a) $P_1 P_2$ is a projection if and only if $P_1 P_2 = P_2 P_1$. The range of the projection $P_1 P_2$ is the closed subspace $M_1 \cap M_2$.
   (b) Two subspaces M_1, M_2 are orthogonal if and only if $P_1 P_2 = P_2 P_1 = 0$.
   (c) A finite sum $P = P_1 + \cdots + P_n$ is a projection if and only if $P_i P_j = 0$, $i \neq j$; that is, the subspaces $\{M_i : i = 1, \ldots, n\}$ are pairwise orthogonal. The range of P is the subspace $M = M_1 \oplus \cdots \oplus M_n$.
   (d) The difference $P = P_1 - P_2$ of the two projections is a projection if and only if $M_2 \subset M_1$. The range of P is $M_1 \oplus M_2$.

7. A linear transformation T from a linear space X onto another linear space Y is an isomorphism if and only if one of the following equivalent conditions is satisfied:
   (a) The null space N_T of T consists of 0 alone.
   (b) There exists a linear transformation T' from Y onto X such that $T'T$ and TT' are the identity operators on X and Y, respectively.
   (c) $T(S)$ is a basis for Y whenever $S = \{x_i\}$ is a basis for X.

8. Recall that each function $f(z)$ analytic in the unit disk $|z| < 1$ has a Taylor series expansion

$$f(z) = \sum_0^\infty a_n z^n, \qquad |z| < 1.$$

The series converges uniformly on each closed disk $|z| \leq R < 1$. Let H_2 denote the set of those analytic functions $f(z)$ for which the Taylor coefficients are square-summable:

$$\sum_0^\infty |a_n|^2 < \infty.$$

   (a) H is a linear space.
   (b) $\langle f, g \rangle = \sum_0^\infty a_n b_n$; $(f = \sum a_n z^n, g = \sum b_n z^n)$.
   (c) The mapping which sends $f(z) = \sum_0^\infty a_n z^n$ in H_2 into the sequence $(a_0, a_i, \ldots)$ is an isometric isomorphism from H_2 onto l_2. In particular, H_2 is a (separable) Hilbert space.
   (d) Find a complete orthonormal set in H_2.

9. Let $[a,b]$ be a finite interval and $\mu(t)$ a positive function on $[a,b]$. Then $L_2(a,b;\mu)$ is isometrically isomorphic to $L_2(0,1)$. Prove this by first showing that $f \to f/\mu$ is an isometric isomorphism between $L_2(a,b)$ and $L_2(a,b;\mu)$. Then show that the mapping T defined by

$$(Tf)(s) = \sqrt{b-a}\, f(a + (b-a)s), \qquad 0 \leq s \leq 1$$

is an isometric isomorphism from $L_2(a,b)$ onto $L_2(0,1)$.

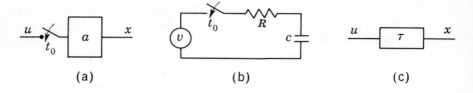

Figure 2.10   Three physical systems.

10.   The system of Figure 2.10(a) consists of a scalar-valued but time-varying multiplication which satisfies the equations

$$x(t) = \begin{cases} a(t)\, u(t), & t \geq t_0, \\ 0, & t < t_0. \end{cases}$$

What conditions on the function a will allow this system to be modeled as an operator on $L_2(\tau)$ or $C(\tau)$ (assume $t_0 \in \tau$)? Is this function linear? With $a(t) = t/\sqrt{1 + t^2}$, $t \in \tau$, and the input and output spaces taken as $B(-\infty,\infty)$ (see Example 7, Section 1.4), determine the Lipschitz norm of this function.

11.   Figure 2.10(b) presents a standard resistance-capacitance circuit with capacitance C satisfying $C(t) = 1 + t^2$, $t \in [0,b]$. With input and output being the voltage across the resistance and initial charge $q(t_0) = q^0$ on the capacitance, under what conditions can this system be modeled as a linear operator on $C(0,b)$ or $L_2(0,b)$?

12.   The system of Figure 2.10(c) is a delay line; that is, $x(t) = u(t - \tau)$. For the function space of a bounded sinusoid on $[-\infty,\infty]$, examine the linearity of this system and determine its norm.

2.3   FIRST–ORDER HOMOGENEOUS SYSTEMS

In Section 2.2 special attention was given to the transformations defined in Examples 6 and 7. This attention is well deserved, for the characteristics of a broad class of physical systems are covered by these two examples. In the remainder of this chapter we shall put aside the general study of functions and spaces to focus attention on two specific classes of systems which fall within the framework of these earlier examples.

The use of differential equations is a classical technique for modeling such physical devices as circuits, mechanisms, and systems in general and no doubt is familiar to the reader. More recently the introduction of digital computers as active system elements has lead to widespread use also of difference equations in specifying system models. Hence it is clear that the topics of the next few sections are of importance in their own right. In taking up these topics at the present point of the development, we shall also have the twofold opportunity to consolidate our understanding of transformations and function spaces and to identify an abundance of physical examples for use in the later sections.

In the differential calculus the derivative of a function $f \in C[a,b]$ is defined in terms of the limit as $h \to 0$ of the ratio

$$\frac{f(t + h) - f(t)}{h}, \qquad t, t + h \in [a,b].$$

The limit is called, respectively, the right derivative of f at t when $h > 0$, the left derivative of f at t when $h < 0$, and when these two limits are equal, simply the derivative of f at t. In the sequel the symbols $f'(t)$, $(df/dt)(t)$, and $(d/dt)f(t)$ are all used on occasion to denote the derivative of f at t.

In the discrete or difference calculus we consider this quotient directly with no intention of allowing h to approach zero. In fact, we define the forward difference operator, denoted by Δ_h, by the relationship

$$\Delta_h f(t) = \frac{f(t + h) - f(t)}{h}, \qquad t, t + h \in [a,b]. \tag{1}$$

It is easy to show that Δ_h is a linear operator. In fact, four of the important operational properties of difference operators are given by

$$\Delta_h c f(t) = c \Delta_h f(t), \tag{2}$$

$$\Delta_h [f(t) + g(t)] = \Delta_h f(t) + \Delta_h g(t), \tag{3}$$

$$\Delta_h [f(t)g(t)] = [\Delta_h f(t)]g(t) + f(t + h)[\Delta_h g(t)], \tag{4}$$

$$\Delta_h \left[\frac{f(t)}{g(t)} \right] = \frac{g(t)\Delta_h f(t) - f(t)\Delta_h g(t)}{g(t)g(t + h)}. \tag{5}$$

In applications dealing with continuously operating dynamic systems—that is, systems for which the independent variable t is continuous—the signals and responses are represented as time functions. For systems operating intermittently, such as sampled data and digital systems, the signals are either time sequences or are important only at particular time instances. The definition of difference operations on time sequences is straightforward.

Let τ be a real time interval which contains subset $\sigma = \{t_0, t_1, \ldots, t_j, \ldots\}$ such that $t_{j+1} > t_j$. If $f(t)$ is a function defined on τ, then f is defined on σ and the image $f(\sigma)$ is the set of points $\{f(t_k)\}$. This set is a time sequence $f = (f(t_0), f(t_1), \ldots, f(t_j), \ldots)$. The difference operator Δ_h can be defined on this sequence. Indeed, if we let $h_k = t_{k+1} - t_k$, then

$$\Delta_k f(t_k) = h_k^{-1} \{f(t_k + h_k) - f(t_k)\}. \tag{6}$$

With this modification in previous definitions, the preceding operational formulas extend to the sequence case.

In the remainder of this section we discuss the theory of systems of first-order linear differential and difference equations of the form

$$\frac{dx_1(t)}{dt} = a_{11}(t)x_1(t) + \cdots + a_{1n}(t)x_n(t)$$

$$\vdots \qquad \vdots \qquad \vdots \qquad t \in \tau$$

$$\frac{dx_n(t)}{dt} = a_{n1}(t)x_1(t) + \cdots + a_{nn}(t)x_n(t)$$

in the continuous case and

$$\Delta_k y_1(t_k) = a_{11}(t_k)y_1(t_k) + \cdots + a_{1n}(t_k)y_n(t_k)$$

$$\vdots \qquad \vdots \qquad \vdots \qquad t_k \in \sigma$$

$$\Delta_k y_n(t_k) = a_{n1}(t_k)y_1(t_k) + \cdots + a_{nn}(t_k)y_n(t_k)$$

in the discrete case. Here we are using the terminology continuous case and continuous system to refer to the type of independent variable involved and *not* to an implied restriction on the continuity of the coefficients a_{ij} and the functions x_j.

First-order equations of this kind are called *normal systems*. It is shown in the exercises of this chapter and Appendix 4 that much more general differential and difference equations can be reduced to normal form by a standard and easily applied change of variables. Thus the properties and results that we shall derive for normal systems can be interpreted directly for the more general case.

In the sequel the independent variable, regardless of its physical manifestation, is called "time" and denoted by t or t_k. In general, the coefficients a_{ij} may be functions of time. If this is the case, the normal system is called a *time-varying* (or *nonstationary*) system. If the coefficients a_{ij} happen to be constant, the system is called *time-invariant* (or *time-stationary*).

In the development of the theory of first-order systems the vector matrix notations are of substantial utility. In addition to the usual vector matrix operations in R^n, the definition of the derivative, the difference, the integral, etc., of these quantities is necessary. If $A = [a_{ij}]$ is a time-varying matrix, we make these definitions in the natural way.

$$\frac{dA(t)}{dt} = \left[\frac{da_{ij}(t)}{dt}\right], \qquad \Delta_k A(t_k) = [\Delta_k a_{ij}(t_k)],$$

whichever is appropriate. Similarly, integration and summation of a matrix are defined, respectively, by

$$\int_0^t A(s)ds = \left[\int_0^t a_{ij}(s)ds\right], \qquad \sum_{k=1}^n A(t_k) = \left[\sum_{k=1}^n a_{ij}(t_k)\right].$$

The differential and difference calculus of matrices is analogous to the calculus of real functions, but a few important differences exist. From the definitions just given it is easily seen that if $A(t)$, $B(t)$ are two square matrices and $C(t_k)$, $D(t_k)$ are two square discrete matrices then

$$\frac{d}{dt}[A(t) + B(t)] = \frac{dA(t)}{dt} + \frac{dB(t)}{dt},$$

$$\Delta_k[C(t_k) + D(t_k)] = \Delta_k C(t_k) + \Delta_k D(t_k). \tag{7}$$

$$\frac{d}{dt}(AB)(t) = \frac{dA(t)}{dt}B(t) + A(t)\frac{dB(t)}{dt},$$

$$\Delta_k[C(t_k)D(t_k)] = [\Delta_k C(t_k)]D(t_k) + C(t_{k+1})[\Delta_k D(t_k)]. \tag{8}$$

Since the multiplication of matrices is not generally commutative, the order of the factors is important. For example, if $A(t)$ has an inverse A^{-1}, then

$$\frac{d}{dt}I = 0 = \frac{d}{dt}(A^{-1}A) = \frac{d(A^{-1}(t))}{dt}A(t) + A^{-1}(t)\frac{dA(t)}{dt}.$$

Hence

$$\frac{d[A^{-1}(t)]}{dt} = -A^{-1}(t)\frac{dA(t)}{dt}A^{-1}(t). \tag{9}$$

Similarly, if $C(t_k)$ is a matrix that is nonsingular at both k and $k + 1$, then

$$0 = \Delta_k I = \Delta_k[C^{-1}(t_k)C(t_k)] = [\Delta_k C^{-1}(t_k)C(t_k) + C^{-1}(t_{k+1})[\Delta_k C(t_k)];$$

hence

$$\Delta_k C^{-1}(t_k) = C^{-1}(t_{k+1})[\Delta_k C(t_k)]^{-1}C(t_k). \tag{10}$$

These formulas are analogous to the formula $(dx^{-1}/dt) = -x^{-2}(dx/dt)$ in elementary calculus but cannot be written in the simpler form unless, for example, A commutes with dA/dt.

Existence and Uniqueness for Differential Systems

Consider first the differential system defined by $t \in \tau = [a, b]$ by

$$\frac{dy(t)}{dt} = A(t)y(t); \qquad y(t_0) = \xi, \qquad t, t_0 \in \tau. \tag{11}$$

Here $y = (y_1, \ldots, y_n)$ and $\xi = (\xi_1, \ldots, \xi_n)$, whereas $A = [a_{ij}]$ denotes an $n \times n$ matrix. Something must be said about the components a_{ij} of A, and we shall assume at first that $a_{ij} \in C(\tau)$, the class of continuous functions on τ, and refer to A as a continuous matrix. By integration on both sides, Eq. 11 can be converted to the equivalent form

$$y(t) = \xi + \int_{t_0}^{t} A(s)y(s)ds, \qquad t \in \tau. \tag{12}$$

Any vector that satisfies either equation is called a solution of the system. The notation $y(t;\xi,t_0)$ is used to denote the value at $t \in \tau$ of the solution to the system satisfying $y(t_0) = \xi$.

THEOREM A. *Let A be continuous on τ. Then, for every t_0, $t \in \tau$ and $\|\xi\| < \infty$ there exists a unique solution to Eq. 11.*

PROOF. To facilitate the proof let the notation $\| \ \|$ denote any norm on R^n and $\|A(t)\|$, the associate matrix norm of $A(t)$, as a mapping on R^n (recall Example 5, Section 2.2). The space X is the product $[C(\tau)]^n$.

Let us introduce a method that is frequently used to prove existence and uniqueness theorems—the celebrated and fundamental method of successive approximations due to Picard. Consider the sequence of (vector) functions defined inductively as follows:

$$\begin{aligned}
y_0(t) \quad &= \xi, &\qquad t, t_0 \in \tau, \\
y_1(t) \quad &= \xi + \int_{t_0}^{t} A(s)y_0(s)ds, \\
&\vdots &\qquad (13) \\
y_{n+1}(t) &= \xi + \int_{t_0}^{t} A(s)y_n(s)ds, &\qquad n = 0, 1, 2, \dots,
\end{aligned}$$

in which we have refrained (for the moment) from using the explicit $y(t;\xi,t_0)$ notation. The subscripts in Eq. 13 refer to the step in the inductive process and not to the component of the vector. This dual use of subscripts is continued in this section whenever there is no danger of confusion.

We wish to show that the sequence of vectoral functions $\{y_j\}$ converges uniformly to a function $y(t)$ for all $t \in \tau$. Succeeding in this, we shall show that this function $y(t)$ satisfies Eq. 12, and finally that $y(t)$ is the *unique* solution to Eq. 12. It is easy to show that each of the Picard iterates is an element of X which, as a finite product of a Banach space, is itself a Banach space. Thus, if we can show that the Picard iterates form a Cauchy sequence, the completeness of X will guarantee that $y_n \to y \in X$.

From the integral recurrence relations we obtain

$$y_{n+1}(t) - y_n(t) = \int_{t_0}^{t} A(s)[y_n(s) - y_{n-1}(s)]ds, \qquad n \geq 1. \tag{14}$$

For convenience we introduce the notation $\bar{A} = \sup_t \|A(t)\|$ and define

$$\Delta_{n+1}(t) = \|y_{n+1}(t) - y_n(t)\|.$$

Then, taking norms on both sides of Eq. 14 and utilizing the easily proved relation $\left\| \int_{t_0}^{t} A(s)y(s)ds \right\| \leq \int_{t_0}^{t} \|A(s)\| \cdot \|y(s)\|ds$, we see that

$$\Delta_k(t) \leq \bar{A} \int_{t_0}^{t} \Delta_{k-1}(s)ds.$$

However, for $k = 1$, we see from Eq. 13 that

$$\Delta_1(t) \leq \int_{t_0}^{t} \|A(s)\| \cdot \|y_0\|ds \leq \bar{A}\|\xi\|(t - t_0);$$

hence by an easy process we deduce from Eq. 14 that

$$\Delta_{n+1}(t) = \|y_{n+1}(t) - y_n(t)\| \leq \frac{\|\xi\| \cdot [\bar{A}(t - t_0)]^{n+1}}{(n + 1)!}, \qquad n = 0, 1, 2, \ldots. \quad (15)$$

With this inequality at our disposal, we now show that the sequence $\{y_n\}$ is a Cauchy sequence with respect to the norm. The proof is as follows:

$$y_{n+p}(t) - y_n(t) = \sum_{j=0}^{p-1} [y_{n+j+1}(t) - y_{n+j}(t)];$$

hence the reader may verify that the following inequalities hold for $t \in \tau$:

$$\|y_{n+p}(t) - y_n(t)\| \leq \sum_{j=0}^{p-1} \Delta_{n+j+1}(t)$$

$$\leq \sum_{j=0}^{p-1} \|\xi\| \frac{[\bar{A}(t - t_0)]^{n+j+1}}{(n + j + 1)!}$$

$$\leq \frac{\|\xi\|[\bar{A}(t - t_0)]^{n+1}}{(n + 1)!} \sum_{j=0}^{p-1} \frac{[\bar{A}(t - t_0)]^j}{j!}$$

$$\leq \frac{\|\xi\|[\bar{A}(t - t_0)]^{n+1}}{(n + 1)!} \exp [\bar{A}(t - t_0)]; \quad (16)$$

hence the sequence converges over any finite interval and we conclude that $y_n(t) \rightarrow \bar{y}(t)$ as $n \rightarrow \infty$. It remains only to show that $\bar{y}(t)$ is unique and, of course, that it satisfies Eq. 11.

Suppose now that the solution to Eq. 11 is actually z; then

$$\frac{dz(t)}{dt} = A(t)z(t), \qquad z(t_0) = \xi, \qquad t_0, t \in \tau.$$

By combining $z(t)$ with the $n+1$ iterate in the foregoing Cauchy sequence, we obtain

$$z(t) - y_{n+1}(t) = \int_{t_0}^{t} A(s)[z(s) - y_n(s)]ds = \int_{t_0}^{t} A(s)[z(s) - y_{n+1}(s)]ds$$

$$+ \int_{t_0}^{t} A(s)[y_{n+1}(s) - y_n(s)]ds, \qquad t \in \tau,$$

and by using earlier relationships we arrive at

$$\|z(t) - y_{n+1}(t)\| \leq \int_{t_0}^{t} \|A(s)\| \cdot \|z(s) - y_{n+1}(s)\| ds + \bar{A}(t - t_0)\Delta_{n+2}.$$

We need now the results of the following lemma.

LEMMA A. *If the functions $y \in C(t_0,t_f)$ and $f \in L_1(t_0,t_f)$ satisfy the inequality*

$$|y(t)| < M[1 + k \int_{t_0}^{t} |y(t)| \cdot | f(t)|dt], \qquad t \in [t_0,t_f],$$

the inequality

$$|y(t)| < M \exp \{kM \int_{t_0}^{t} |f(t)|dt\}, \qquad t > t_0.$$

is satisfied also.

In the case in question we make the identification

$$\|A(t)\| = |f(t)|,$$

$$\|z(t) - y_{n+1}(t)\| = |y(t)|,$$

$$M = \frac{1}{k} = \bar{A}(t_f - t_0)A_{n+2}(t),$$

and conclude that

$$\|z(t) - y_{n+1}(t)\| \leq \bar{A}(t_f - t_0)\Delta_{n+2} \exp \left\{ \int_{t_0}^{t} \|A(s)\| ds \right\}. \tag{17}$$

Since $\Delta_{n+2} \to 0$ as $n \to \infty$ and since $\{y_{n+1}(t)\}$ converges, we see from Eq. 17 that x_n converges uniformly to z. Note that z is an arbitrary solution to Eq. 11; however $\{y_n\}$, being a Cauchy sequence, has a unique limit. Therefore z is the unique solution to Eq. 11 and the Picard iterates converge to this solution.

We have overlooked two points that are easy to miss but should be cleared up before continuing. First, since the solution $y \in X$ is continuous, Eq. 12 may be differentiated to yield Eq. 11, from which it follows that dx/dt is also in X. Generally speaking, dx/dt has the smoothness of the matrix A. The second matter is the proof of Lemma A, which is simple and direct.

PROOF OF LEMMA. Multiplying both sides of the first inequality by $|f(t)|$, we get

$$|y(t)| \cdot |f(t)| < M|f(t)| \left[1 + k \int_{t_0}^{t} |y(t)| \cdot |f(t)| dt \right].$$

Now let $v(t) = \int_{t_0}^{t} |y(t)f(t)| dt$. The inequality may be interpreted in the form

$$\dot{v}(t) < M|f(t)|[1 + kv(t)]$$

or

$$\frac{\dot{v}(t)}{1 + kv(t)} < M|f(t)|.$$

Integration on both sides produces

$$\log(1 + kv(t)) < kM \int_{t_0}^{t} |f(t)| dt,$$

hence

$$1 + k \int_{t_0}^{t} |f(t)y(t)| dt < \exp \left[kM \int_{t_0}^{t} |f(t)| dt \right].$$

By the initial hypothesis

$$\frac{|y(t)|}{M} < 1 + k \int_{t_0}^{t} |f(t)y(t)| dt,$$

which when used in the foregoing yields

$$|y(t)| < M \exp \left[kM \int_{t_0}^{t} |f(t)| dt \right].$$

This result is but a sampling of the body of literature concerning the existence of solutions to the initial-value problem. Indeed, the assumptions of Theorem A are much stronger than necessary. As examples of typical generalizations of this theorem, we state two more without proof.

THEOREM B. *Let A be a matrix such that* $\|A\| \in L_1(\tau)$. *Then a unique absolutely continuous[1] vector function y such that* $y(t_0) = \xi$ *and* $y(t)$ *satisfies Eq. 11.*

REMARK 1. In Theorem B Lebesgue integration is implied, and Eq. 11 is taken to mean equality almost everywhere on τ. The reader with an elementary grasp of measure theory can easily modify all previous arguments to prove this more general result. It is important to note specifically that even under the unrestrictive conditions of Theorem B on the matrix A the unique

---

[1]Roughly a function resulting from the indefinite integration of an L_1 function.

solution y is still an element of the function space X. As a second type of useful extension, we let $\mu = (\mu_1, \ldots, \mu_k)$ be a k-tuplet of parameters. Let $A(t,\mu)$ be a function of t and μ on the $(k + 1)$-dimensional space $\tau \times U$, where U is an open spherical neighborhood of some μ_0.

THEOREM C.   *If $A(t,\mu)$ is a continuous function of μ and satisfies the conditions of Theorem B with respect to t on $\tau \times U$, the equation*

$$\frac{dy}{dt}(t;\zeta,t_0,\mu) = A(t,\mu)y(t;\zeta,t_0,\mu), \qquad y(t_0;\zeta,t_0,\mu) = \zeta, \qquad (t,\mu) \in \tau \times U$$

has a unique solution which is continuous with respect to all parameters t, μ_1, $\ldots$, μ_k for any $t_0 \in \tau$, $\mu \in U$.

In particular, the parameters μ can be the initial conditions at t_0; hence $y(t;\zeta,t_0)$ is continuous with respect to ζ. In fact, if $\{u_k\}$ is a sequence of parameters in U with $u_k \to \bar{u}$, the solutions to Eq. 11 are $y(t,\zeta,t_0,u_k) \to y(t,\zeta,t_0,u)$.

We have shown that for every $\zeta \in R^n$ a unique solution corresponds to Eq. 11. Letting κ denote the set of all such solutions, we now inquire about its properties. It is clear that κ is a linear space. (The reader may take as an exercise the verification that for two solutions y_1, $y_2 \in \kappa$ and scalars α_1, α_2 the vector $\alpha_1 y_1 + \alpha_2 y_2 \in \kappa$.)

THEOREM D.   *The subspace κ is n-dimensional.*

P R O O F.   To show that κ is n-dimensional a set of linearly independent solutions $y_1, \ldots, y_n$ must be exhibited such that every other $y \in \kappa$ is a linear combination (with real or complex coefficients) of the $\{y_i\}$. Let $\{\zeta_i\}$ be n linearly independent constant vectors in the tuplet space R^n. Then, by the existence theorem, for any $t_0 \in \tau$, there are n unique solutions $\{y_j(t;\zeta_j,t_0)\}$ of Eq. 11 such that $y_i(t_0) = \zeta_i$. To prove that these solutions form a basis for κ we begin by showing that the vectors $\{y_j(t;\zeta_j,t_0)\}$ are linearly independent tuplets in R^n for every $t \in \tau$. If this is not so, there must be n scalars $\{c_i\}$ not all zero, such that for at least a single $t' \in \tau$

$$y(t') = \sum_{i=1}^n c_i y_i(t';\zeta_i,t_0) = 0.$$

However, the y so defined is a solution to Eq. 11. If $y(t') = 0$, however, $y(t) = 0$, all $t \in \tau$ for the zero vector satisfies Eq. 11, and the zero initial condition at t' and solution to Eq. 11 for any initial condition is unique. This implies that at $t = t_0$

$$y(t_0) = \sum_{i=1}^n c_i y_i(t_0;\zeta_i,t_0) = \sum_{i=1}^n c_i \zeta_i = 0,$$

and this contradicts the assumption that the ζ_i are linearly independent. Hence we conclude that the $\{y_i(t;\zeta_i,t_0)\}$ is linearly independent for all $t \in \tau$.

If $y(t;\zeta,t_0)$ is any solution to Eq. 11 on τ, then, since the ζ_i span the initial condition tuplet space, there are (unique) constants c_i such that

$$\zeta = \sum_{i=1}^{n} c_i\zeta_i.$$

Hence the function

$$y(t) = \sum_{i=1}^{n} c_i y_i(t;\zeta_i,t_0)$$

is a solution of Eq. 11 on τ which assumes the value ζ at t_0, and, by uniqueness, this must be $y(t;\zeta,t_0)$; that is,

$$y(t;\zeta,t_0) = \sum_{i=1}^{n} c_i y_i(t_0;\zeta_i,t_0).$$

Therefore every solution y of Eq. 11 is a (unique) linear combination of the $\{y_i\}$. The set $\{y_i(t)\}$ is therefore a basis for the space κ.

Fundamental Matrices

If $\Phi(t)$ is a matrix whose n columns consist of any basis $\{(y_i(t;\zeta_i,t_0)\}$ for κ, then $\Phi(t)$ is called a *fundamental matrix* for Eq. 11. Alternatively, we may call $\Phi(t)$ the fundamental matrix of the null space κ. By direct verification it is easily shown that

$$\dot{\Phi}(t) = A(t)\Phi(t), \qquad \Phi(t_0) = Z, \qquad \text{all } t \in \tau. \tag{18}$$

This is the matrix differential equation associated with Eq. 11 on τ; Z is the matrix formed by using the initial condition vectors ζ_i as columns. If the ζ_j correspond to the usual coordinate basis for R^n, then $Z = I$.

Fundamental matrices play an important role in system theory. We now note, for reference purposes, several of their basic properties.

THEOREM E.   *If $|\Phi(t)|$ denotes the determinant of $\Phi(t)$, a fundamental matrix for Eq. 11, then*

$$\frac{d}{dt}|\Phi(t)| = \left[\sum_{i=1}^{n} a_{ii}(t)\right]|\Phi(t)|,$$

or, in integral form,

$$|\Phi(t)| = |\Phi(t_0)| \exp\left\{\int_{t_0}^{t} \sum_{i=1}^{n} a_{ii}(s)ds\right\}.$$

[The quantity $\sum_{i=1}^{n} a_{ii}(t)$ occurs frequently in matrix theory and is therefore dignified by the special name *trace*, written tr (A).]

P R O O F.   The proof, which is left as an exercise, depends on two facts:

(1) $d|\Phi(t)|/dt$ is the sum of the determinants formed by replacing the elements of one row of $|\Phi(t)|$ by their derivatives.
(2) The columns of $\Phi(t)$ are solutions of Eq. 11.

The proof is completed by simplifying the determinants obtained in (1) by use of (2).

COROLLARY. *For a matrix $\Phi(t)$ to be a fundamental matrix for Eq. 11 it is necessary and sufficient that*

(1) $\dot{\Phi}(t) = A(t)\Phi(t)$,   all $t \in \tau$,
(2) $|\Phi(t)| \neq 0$,   all $t \in \tau$.

Both the necessity and sufficiency of conditions (1) and (2) follow directly from the definition and Theorem E. A matrix of column vectors may have a determinant identically zero on an interval τ, although the vectors may be linearly independent as elements of $[C(\tau)]^n$. For example, let $B(t)$ be defined as

$$B(t) = \begin{vmatrix} t & t^2 \\ 0 & 0 \end{vmatrix}$$

for any real interval τ. The content of the corollary, then, is that this cannot occur for vectors that are solutions of Eq. 11.

THEOREM F. *If $\Phi(t)$ is any fundamental matrix of Eq. 11 and H a constant nonsingular matrix, then $\Phi(t)H$ is again a fundamental matrix of Eq. 11. Furthermore, every fundamental matrix of Eq. 11 is of this type for some nonsingular H.*

P R O O F.   If $\Phi(t)$ is a fundamental matrix and H a nonsingular constant matrix, then

$$\frac{d}{dt}[\Phi(t)H] = \dot{\Phi}(t)H = A(t)\Phi(t)H = A(t)[\Phi(t)H],   t \in \tau;$$

hence $\Phi(t)H$ is a solution matrix of Eq. 11. Since

$$|[\Phi(t)H]| = |\Phi(t)| \cdot |H| \neq 0,$$

$\Phi(t)H$ is a fundamental matrix.

Conversely, if $\Phi_1(t)$ and $\Phi_2(t)$ are fundamental matrices, $\Phi_2(t) = \Phi_1(t)H$ for some constant nonsingular matrix H. To show this, let $\Phi_1^{-1}(t)\Phi_2(t) = \Psi(t)$. Then $\Phi_2(t) = \Phi_1(t)\Psi(t)$. Differentiation of this equation gives $\dot{\Psi}_2(t) = \Phi_1(t)\dot{\Psi}(t) + \dot{\Psi}_1(t)\Psi(t)$, and use of Eq. 11 gives $A(t)\Phi_2(t) = \Phi_1(t)\dot{\Psi}(t) + A(t)\Phi_1(t)\Psi(t)$. In light of the fact that $\Phi_2(t) = \Phi_1(t)\Psi(t)$, we have $\Phi_1(t)\dot{\Psi}(t) = 0$. Thus $\dot{\Psi}(t) = 0$ and therefore $\Psi(t) = H$ is a constant. H is nonsingular, since $\Phi_1(t)$ and $\Phi_2(t)$ are nonsingular.

R E M A R K 2.   If it is required only that $\Phi_2(t)$ be a solution matrix, H may be singular. Observe also that if $\Phi(t)$ is a fundamental matrix of Eq. 11 and H is a constant nonsingular matrix, $H\Phi(t)$ is not in general a fundamental matrix.

Finally, two different homogeneous systems cannot have the same fundamental matrix, for in Eq. 11 $A(t) = \dot{\Phi}(t)\Phi^{-1}(t)$. Hence $\Phi(t)$ determines $A(t)$ uniquely, although the converse is not true. In the preceding development it has been convenient to avoid the precise notation $\Phi(t;Z,t_0)$ to denote the unique fundamental matrix $\Phi(t)$ that satisfies the initial condition $\Phi(t_0;Z,t_0) = Z$. In this section we note specifically the properties of the fundamental matrix which corresponds to the coordinate basis for the initial condition space.

DEFINITION A.   *The notation $\Phi(t,t_0)$ designates the fundamental matrix for Eq. 11 which satisfies $\Phi(t_0,t_0) = I$. This matrix is referred to as the system transition matrix.*

The terminology "system transition matrix" stems from the fact that

$$y(t;\zeta,t_0) = \Phi(t,t_0)\zeta, \qquad t \in \tau. \tag{19}$$

Thus the matrix $\Phi(t,t_0)$ maps the initial condition $y(t_0) = \zeta$ onto the present condition $y(t;\zeta,t_0)$ for every $t \in \tau$. It is also easily seen that if $\Phi_1(t)$ is the fundamental matrix satisfying $\Phi_1(t_0) = H$, then

$$\Phi_1(t) = \Phi(t,t_0)H. \tag{20}$$

R E M A R K 3.   Two important computational properties of the transition matrix are the following, the proof of which is again left as an exercise.

$$\Phi(t_1,t_2)\Phi(t_2,t_3) = \Phi(t_1,t_3), \qquad t_1,t_2,t_3 \in \tau,$$
$$\Phi(t_1,t_2)^{-1} \qquad = \Phi(t_2,t_1). \tag{21}$$

R E M A R K 4.   Equation 19 can be viewed in two occasionally useful ways: first, as the linear transformation $\Phi: R^n \to \kappa$ defined by $(\Phi\xi)(t) = y(t;\xi,t_0)$, as t sweeps through τ, and second, as a parameterized family $\{\Phi(t,t_0): t \in \tau\}$ of transformation on R^n.

Example.   To illustrate the preceding developments we consider the linear homogeneous system $\dot{x}(t) = A(t)x(t)$, where $A(t)$ is the matrix[1]

$$A(t) = \begin{bmatrix} 2 & -e^t \\ e^{-t} & 1 \end{bmatrix}.$$

By direct substitution the reader may verify that the two vectors

$$\phi_1(t) = \begin{bmatrix} e^{2t}\cos t \\ e^t \sin t \end{bmatrix} \quad \text{and} \quad \phi_2(t) = \begin{bmatrix} -e^{2t}\sin t \\ e^t \cos t \end{bmatrix}$$

satisfy the differential system. Because $\phi_1(0) = \text{col}\,[1,0]$ and $\phi_2(0) = \text{col}\,[0,1]$,

---

[1]Suggested by Reference [A95], p. 343.

we deduce that the matrix $\Phi(t)$ formed by using ϕ_1 and ϕ_2 as columns satisfies

$$\dot{\Phi}(t) = A(t)\Phi(t), \qquad \Phi(0) = I.$$

If A is constant, $\Phi(t,t_0)$ can be found by substituting $t - t_0$ for t in $\Phi(t)$. Since this is not the case, we shall be a bit more subtle. From the property $\Phi(t,t_0)\Phi(t_0,0) = \Phi(t,0)$, we deduce $\Phi(t,t_0) = \Phi(t,0)\Phi^{-1}(t_0,0)$. The reader may verify that if

$$\Phi(t,0) = \begin{bmatrix} e^{2t}\cos t & -e^{2t}\sin t \\ e^{t}\sin t & e^{t}\cos t \end{bmatrix}$$

then

$$\Phi(0,t) = \Phi^{-1}(t,0) = \begin{bmatrix} e^{-2t}\cos t & e^{-t}\sin t \\ -e^{-2t}\sin t & e^{-t}\cos t \end{bmatrix};$$

hence by direct computation we arrive at

$$\Phi(t,t_0) = \begin{bmatrix} e^{2t}\cos t & -e^{2t}\sin t \\ e^{t}\sin t & e^{t}\cos t \end{bmatrix} \cdot \begin{bmatrix} e^{-2t_0}\cos t_0 & e^{-t_0}\sin t_0 \\ -e^{-2t_0}\sin t_0 & e^{-t_0}\cos t_0 \end{bmatrix}$$

$$= \begin{bmatrix} e^{(-2t-2t_0)}\cos(t-t_0) & -e^{(2t-t_0)}\sin(t-t_0) \\ e^{(t-2t_0)}\sin(t-t_0) & e^{(t-t_0)}\cos(t-t_0) \end{bmatrix}.$$

Exercises

1. Let $\nabla_h f(t)$ denote the quotient $h^{-1}[f(t) - f(t-h)]$. Verify that Eqs. 4 and 5 hold as written as well as when ∇_h is substituted for Δ_h throughout.

2. If E_h denotes the shift operation, $E_h f(t) = f(t+h)$, verify the relations $\Delta_h = h^{-1}(E_h - I)$ and $\nabla_h = h^{-1}(I - E_h)$ and that $\Delta_{-h} = \nabla_h$.

3. By defining the powers of ∇_h, Δ_h, and E_h inductively, $\Delta_h^n f(t) = \Delta_h[\Delta_h^{n-1} f(t)]$, show that $\Delta_h^3 = h^{-3}(E_h^3 - 3E_h^2 + 3E_h - I)$.

4. Using the notation $\binom{n}{k} = n!/[k!(n-k)!]$, show that if n is a positive integer

$$\Delta_h^n y(t) = h^{-n} \sum_{k=0}^{n} \binom{n}{k}(-1)^{n-k} E_h^k y(t).$$

HINT: Use the binomial formula.

5. Let $f(t) = c^t$; c is a positive real number. Apply Exercise 4 to obtain

$$\Delta_h^n c^t = h^{-n} c^t \sum_{k=0}^{n} \binom{n}{k}(-1)^{n-k} c^{-hk}.$$

Note that the sum is the binomial expansion of $(c^h - 1)^n$ and that this result can be written

$$\Delta_h^n c^t = c^t \left(\frac{c^h - 1}{h} \right)^n.$$

6. Verify that $\| \int_0^t A(s)y(s)ds \| \leq \int_0^t \| A(s) \| \cdot \| y(s) \| ds$. HINT: Use the norms of Eq. 4 for specific proof and the equivalence of all norms on finite-dimensional spaces.

7. Complete the proof of Theorem E and its corollary. Verify the properties of Remark 2.

8. Consider the matrix differential equation

$$\dot{X} = \begin{bmatrix} 1 & 2 \\ 2 & 1 \end{bmatrix} \cdot X = AX.$$

Show that $x_1 = \mathrm{col}\ (-e^{-(t-t_0)},\ e^{-(t-t_0)})$ and $x_2 = \mathrm{col}\ (e^{3(t-t_0)}, e^{3(t-t_0)})$ are solutions of the differential equation. Show that

$$\Phi(t,t_0) = \begin{bmatrix} -e^{-(t-t_0)} & e^{3(t-t_0)} \\ e^{-(t-t_0)} & e^{3(t-t_0)} \end{bmatrix}$$

is a fundamental matrix for the system.

Existence and Uniqueness Theorems for Discrete Normal Systems

It is interesting to note that, without exception, the results of the preceding sections have a counterpart in the theory of discrete normal systems. In the present section the precise statement and proof of the most important analogies is undertaken. The opening remarks of this chapter have shown that the difference operator Δ has meaning as an operation on a function $f(t)$, $t \in \tau$ or on a time sequence $f(t_k)$, $t_k \in \sigma$. For purposes of clarity we are concerned here only with difference operators on sequence spaces.

The linear normal discrete system given by

$$\Delta_k y(t_k) = A(t_k)y(t_k); \qquad y(t_0) = \zeta, \qquad t_k \in \sigma, \tag{22}$$

is, in reality, a recursion relation. Indeed, if we recall the definition of the operator Δ_k, it is apparent that Eq. 22 can be written in the alternative form

$$y(t_{k+1}) = [I + h_k A(t_k)]y(t_k); \qquad y(t_0) = \xi, \qquad t_k \in \sigma, \tag{23}$$

which is a precise formula for computing the sequence $\{y(t_k)\}$, $k = 0, 1, \ldots$. Many authors, in fact, prefer the second expression as the basic form for studying discrete linear systems. To begin our examination of such systems we prove the following theorem.

THEOREM G. *Let $A(t_k)$ be an $n \times n$ matrix defined for $t_k \in \sigma = \{t_0, t_1, \ldots, t_k, \ldots\}$. Then there exists a unique sequence of $n \times 1$ vectors $\{y(t_k)\}$ satisfying Eq. 22.*

P R O O F.   We define the vectors $y(t_k)$ as follows: set

$$y(t_0) = y^0.$$

Then, since $y(t_{k+1}) = [I + h_k A(t_k)]y(t_k)$, the sequence

$$y_1 = y(t_1) = [I + h_0 A(t_0)]y_0$$
$$y_2 = [I + h_1 A(t_1)]y_1 = [I + h_1 A(t_1)][I + h_0 A(t_0)]y_0$$
$$\vdots$$

defines a solution to satisfy the theorem. To prove uniqueness, suppose that the sequence $\{z_k\}$ also satisfies the theorem conditions. Then

$$z_0 = y_0$$
$$z_1 = [I + h_0 A(t_0)]y_0 = y_1$$
$$\vdots$$
$$z_n = \qquad \cdots \qquad = y_n;$$

hence the sequences are identical and the solution is unique. The reader no doubt will agree that this proof is much simpler than the corresponding proof for differential equations.

R E M A R K   5.   It is also apparent that if $A(t_k,\mu)$ is a sequence of square matrices, each of which is continuous with respect to the tuplet $\mu = (\mu_1, \ldots, \mu_k)$. for each $t_k \in \sigma$, the solution $y(t_k;y^0,t_0,\mu)$ to Eq. 22 is continuous with respect to μ. Indeed, for each t_k, $y(t_k;y^0,t_0,\mu)$ is a finite product of matrices, each of which is continuous with respect to μ, hence can be differentiated with respect to μ by the standard rule for differentiating a matrix product.

THEOREM H. *The solution space κ of Eq. 22 is n-dimensional. If the matrices $\{[I + h_k A(t_k)]: t_k \in \sigma\}$ are nonsingular, any basic $\{\phi_j\}$ for κ generates tuplets $\{\phi_j(t_k)\}$ which are linearly independent for all $t_k \in \sigma$.*

P R O O F.   We have seen that Eq. 22 has exactly one unique solution satisfying $y(t_0) = \xi^0$ for arbitrary $\xi^0 \in R^n$. Let us choose as a basic set the unique solutions $\phi^1(t_k), \ldots, \phi^n(t_k)$ which satisfy the initial condition $\phi^j(t_0) = e_j$, where $\{e_j\}$ is the coordinate basis for R^n. It is clear from Theorem G that the $\{\phi^j(t_k)\}$ are well defined. Assume now that for some $t_k \in \sigma$ they are linearly dependent; that is, a set of scalars $(\alpha_1, \ldots, \alpha_n)$ not all zero exists such that

$$\alpha_1 \phi^1(t_k) + \cdots + \alpha_n \phi^n(t_k) = 0. \tag{24}$$

Since all ϕ^j satisfy Eq. 22, we have

$$\phi^j(t_k) = [I + h_{k-1}A(t_{k-1})]\phi^j(t_{k-1}), \qquad j = 1, \ldots, n,$$

and on substitution into Eq. 24 we have

$$\sum_{j=1}^{n} \alpha_j[I + h_{k-1}A(t_{k-1})]\phi^j(t_{k-1}) = [I + h_{k-1}A(t_{k-1})]\sum_{j=1}^{n} \alpha_j\phi^j(t_{k-1}) = 0.$$

Because it is hypothesized in the theorem that $[I + h_{k-1}A(t_{k-1})]$ is nonsingular, we have

$$\sum_{j=1}^{n} \alpha_j\phi^j(t_k) = 0 \Rightarrow \sum_{j=1}^{n} \alpha_j\phi^j(t_{k-1}) = 0,$$

and by repeating the process inductively we deduce that

$$\sum_{j=1}^{n} \alpha_j\phi^j(t_0) = \sum_{j=1}^{n} \alpha_j e_j = 0.$$

However, since the e_j are linearly independent, this contradiction shows that the $\phi^j(t_k)$ are linearly independent for all $t_k \in \sigma$.

To show that any solution $z(t_k)$ to Eq. 22 is a linear combination of the $\{\phi^j\}$ we simply note that, at any t_k, $z(t_k)$ is a vector $z(t_k) \in R^n$. Since $\phi^1(t_k), \ldots, \phi^n(t_k)$ are n linearly independent vectors in R^n, they form a basis for R^n; hence scalars $\alpha_1, \ldots, \alpha_n$ exist such that

$$z(t_k) = \sum_{j=1}^{n} \alpha_j\phi^j(t_k).$$

However, because all the sequences involved satisfy Eq. 22, we have

$$z(t_k) = [I + h_{k-1}A(t_{k-1})]z(t_{k-1}) = [I + h_{k-1}A(t_{k-1})]\sum_{j=1}^{n} \alpha_j\phi^j(t_{k-1});$$

hence

$$z(t_{k-1}) = \sum_{j=1}^{n} \alpha_j\phi^j(t_{k-1}),$$

or by using inductive reasoning for all preceding or succeeding $t_j \in \sigma$ we see that

$$z(t_k) = \sum_{j=1}^{n} \alpha_j\phi^j(t_k), \qquad \text{for any } t_k \in \sigma, \tag{25}$$

which completes the proof of the theorem.

REMARK 6.   The condition that the matrix $[I + h_kA(t_k)]$ is nonsingular for all $t_k \in \sigma$ appears at first to have no counterpart in the theory of normal continuous systems. In Theorem H, Section 2.2, it is shown that if $h_k\|A(t_k)\| < 1$, then $I + h_kA(t_k)$ is nonsingular. For small h_k this restriction is automatically satisfied. In a nonrigorous sense the differential dt plays the role of h in the continuous system case. The conditions of Theorem A on $\|A(t)\|$ guarantees that $dt\|A(t)\|$ is arbitrarily small; thus the hypothesis that $I + dtA(t)$ be nonsingular is automatically satisfied. Unless stated otherwise, it is implicitly assumed that the matrices $[I + h_k A(t_k)]$ are all nonsingular. This condition is mentioned on occasion to refresh the reader's memory on this point.

As a particular example of Eq. 25 let $\Phi(t_k,t_0)$ be the matrix whose jth column is the vector $\phi^j(t_0)e_j$. Then, if $z(t_0) = z^o$,

$$z(t_k) = \Phi(t_k,t_0)z^o \tag{26}$$

and the matrix $\Phi(t_k,t_0)$ satisfies the matrix difference equation

$$\Delta_k\Phi(t_k,t_0) = A(t_k)\Phi(t_k,t_0), \qquad \Phi(t_0,t_0) = I. \tag{27}$$

The Properties of $\Phi(t_k,t_0)$

The reader, no doubt, has the intuitive feeling that the matrix sequence $\{\Phi(t_k,t_0)\}$ and the matrix functions $\Phi(t_k,t_j)$ must play a role in the theory of discrete normal systems comparable to that of the state transition matrix $\Phi(t,s)$ in continuous normal systems. In this section we examine the extent to which this intuition is correct. First, we note that by a simple translation of the independent variable our previous analysis indicates that the sequence $\{\Phi(t_k,t_j)\}$ for any $t_j \in \sigma$ is the solution to the equation

$$\Delta_k\Phi(t_k,t_j) = A(t_k)\Phi(t_k,t_j); \qquad \Phi(t_j,t_j)=I, \qquad t_j \in \sigma. \tag{28}$$

In particular, it follows that

$$\Phi(t_{j+1},t_j)= [I +h_j A(t_j)]\Phi(t_j,t_j) = [I + h_j A(t_j)], \qquad \text{any } t_j \in \sigma, \tag{29}$$

from which the semigroup property

$$\Phi(t_k,t_j)\Phi(t_j,t_i) = \Phi(t_k,t_i), \qquad t_k,t_j,t_i \in \sigma, \tag{30}$$

is easily deduced. In particular,

$$\Phi(t_k,t_j) = \Phi^{-1}(t_j,t_k), \qquad t_k,t_j \in T. \tag{31}$$

Any matrix $\Phi(t_k)$ formed from linearly independent solutions to Eq. 22 is called a fundamental matrix for that system; $\Phi(t_k,t_0)$, in particular, is the system transition matrix.

REMARK 7. If $[I + h_i A(t_1)]$ is singular for any $t_i \in \sigma$, then $\Phi(t_k,t_0)$ is singular for $t_k \le t_i$ and Eq. 31 holds only for $t_k,t_j < t_i$. If any of the arguments of Eq. 30 exceed t_i, this equation is true only for $t_k \ge t_j \ge t_i$. As in the continuous case, it can be shown that any fundamental matrix $\Phi(t_k)$ for Eq. 22 has a representation $\Phi(t_k) = \Phi(t_k,t_0)H$ for some nonsingular H.

To summarize these statements, we have the following theorem.

THEOREM I.   *Let $A(t_k)$ be an $n \times n$ matrix defined on σ with $[I + h_k A(t_k)]$ nonsingular on σ. The matrix $\Phi(t_k, t_0)$ which satisfies Eq. 28 is unique and non-singular and satisfies Eqs. 29–31. The unique solution $y(t_k; \xi, t_0)$ to Eq. 22 which satisfies $y(t_0; \xi, t_0) = \xi$ can be expressed as $y(t_k; \xi, t_0) = \Phi(t_k, t_0)\xi$.*

Exercises

9. For the second-order differential equation

$$\frac{d^2x}{dt}(t) + p(t)\frac{dx}{dt}(t) + q(t)x(t) = 0 \tag{a}$$

use the change of variables $y_1(t) = x(t)$ and $y_2(t) = (dx/dt)(t)$ to reduce (a) to the equivalent form

$$\frac{d}{dt}\begin{bmatrix} y_1(t) \\ y_2(t) \end{bmatrix} = \begin{bmatrix} 0 & 1 \\ -q(t) & -p(t) \end{bmatrix} \cdot \begin{bmatrix} y_1(t) \\ y_2(t) \end{bmatrix}. \tag{b}$$

Discuss the initial condition problem in this conversion.

10. Generalize Exercise 9 to the equation

$$\frac{d^n x(t)}{dt^n} + a_n(t)\frac{dx^{n-1}(t)}{dt^{n-1}} + \cdots + a_n(t)x(t) = 0. \tag{c}$$

From the results of this section prove that the solution spaces of (c) form an n-dimensional linear manifold.

11. If y satisfies the scalar equation $y(t_{k+1}) - a(t_k)y(t_k) = 0$, in which $a(t_k) > 0$, show that $y(t_k) = \exp[u(t_k)]$ in which u is the solution of the equation $u(t_{k+1}) - u(t_k) = \log[a(t_k)]$.

12. Reduce the difference equation

$$\Delta_k^2 x(t_k) + a_1(t_k)\Delta_k x(t_k) + a_2(t_k)x(t_k) = 0$$

to an equivalent first-order form by a technique similar to that of Exercise 9.

13. Draw symbolically an analog computer diagram that simulates the differential system

$$\dot{x}(t) = A(t)x(t), \qquad x(t_0) = \xi.$$

Describe how the matrix $\Phi(t, t_0)$ can be computed by using this simulation. Carry it out in detail for the system of Eq. b, Exercise 9. Develop a similar diagram by using delay lines for the system of Eq. 22.

14. Consider the system

$$\dot{y}_1(t) = y_2(t) \qquad y_1(0) = 0,$$
$$\dot{y}_2(t) = -y_1(t) \qquad y_2(0) = 1;$$

show that the Picard iterates converge to the solution tuplet (sin t, cos t).

15. In this problem Theorem A is extended to a class of nonlinear equations. Let (t_0, ξ) be a fixed element in R^{n+1} and $f: R^{n+1} \rightarrow R^n$, a vector-valued function which is Lipschitz and bounded on a neighborhood S:

$$S = \{(t,y): |t - t_0| \le a, \ \|y - \xi\| \le b, \quad t \in R, \ y \in R^n\}.$$

If $\|f(S)\| \le M$, show that the system of differential equations

$$\dot{y}(t) = f(t, y(t)), \qquad y(t_0) = \xi, \qquad t \in \tau,$$

has a unique solution on the interval

$$\tau = \{t: |t - t_0| \le \alpha = \min \{a, b/M\}.$$

HINT: Modify the Picard process for this situation.

16. As a corollary to Exercise 10, prove that the jth Picard iterate y_k is in proximity to the solution y according to the bound relationship

$$\|y(t) - y_j(t)\| \le \frac{M(K\alpha)^{j+1}}{K(j+1)!} e^{\alpha K}, \qquad t \in \tau,$$

where K is the Lipschitz norm of f on the set S.

17. A dynamic system is said to be stable if for every $\delta > 0$ there is an $\varepsilon > 0$ such that $\|x(t_0)\| < \delta \Rightarrow \|x(t)\| < \varepsilon$ for $t \ge t_0$ and asymptotically stable if, in addition, $x(t) \rightarrow 0$ as $t \rightarrow \infty$. Show that Eq. 11 defines a stable system if and only if $\|\Phi(t, t_0)\|$, $t \in [t_0, \infty]$, is bounded and asymptotically stable if and only if, in addition, $\|\Phi(t, t_0)\| \rightarrow 0$ as $t \rightarrow \infty$.

2.4 NONHOMOGENEOUS FIRST–ORDER SYSTEMS

The homogeneous systems of Section 2.3 play an important role throughout the text. In this section the present line of development is brought to fulfillment as attention turns to forced or nonhomogeneous systems. Here, as in Section 2.3, the discrete and continuous versions of the basic problem are treated on an equal footing.

Consider now the forced (or nonhomogeneous) differential system defined by

$$\dot{x}(t) = A(t)x(t) + f(t), \qquad x(t_0) = \zeta, \qquad t, t_0 \in \tau. \tag{1}$$

The matrix A is assumed to have the same properties delineated in Section 2.3. Indeed, Eq. 1 differs from Eq. 11, Section 2.3, only by the appearance of f, a column n-tuplet of forcing functions defined on τ. The solution to Eq. 1, if it exists, is designated $x_f(t;\zeta,t_0)$.

The fact that $x_f(t;\zeta,t_0)$ actually exists and is unique can be established as a consequence of Theorems A and B, Section 2.3. Let us introduce the expanded $2n \times 2n$ matrix

$$\tilde{A}(t) = \left[\begin{array}{c|c} A(t) & F(t) \\ \hline 0 & 0 \end{array}\right], \qquad t \in \tau, \tag{2}$$

in which $F(t)$ is an $n \times n$ diagonal matrix with the components of $f(t)$ on the diagonal. Define now the $2n \times 1$ vector $z(t) = \text{col}\,[z_1(t), \ldots, z_{2n}(t)]$ as the solution to the homogeneous differential system.

$$\dot{z}(t) = \tilde{A}(t)z(t), \qquad z(t_0) = z^0, \qquad t \in \tau. \tag{3}$$

Under the very general conditions of the preceding section z exists and is unique for arbitrary z^0. Let us pick $z^0 = \text{col}(\zeta, 1, \ldots, 1)$. Then, if $z(t)$ is partitioned into the $2n \times 1$ vectors $z_I(t)$ and $z_{II}(t)$, that is, $z(t) = (z_I(t), z_{II}(t))$, we see from Eqs. 2 and 3 that the individual relations

$$\dot{z}_I(t) = A(t)z_I(t) + F(t)z_{II}(t); \qquad z_I(t_0) = \zeta, \qquad t_0, t \in \tau, \tag{4}$$

$$\dot{z}_{II}(t) = 0; \qquad z_{II}(t_0) = \text{col}\,(1, \ldots, 1), \qquad t_0, t \in \tau, \tag{5}$$

must hold simultaneously on τ. The solution to Eq. 5 is obviously $z_{II}(t) = \text{col}(1, \ldots, 1)$ for $t \in \tau$. Use of this result in Eq. 4 with the definition of the matrix $F(t)$ yields $F(t)z_{II}(t) = f(t)$. Thus $z_I(t)$ obeys Eq. 1. This implies that all previous results on the existence and uniqueness of solutions to Eq. 11, Section 2.3, can be carried over to Eq. 1 in an obvious manner.

To summarize we have the following theorem.

THEOREM A. *Let $A(t)$ be an $n \times n$ matrix and $f(t)$ an n-tuple such that $\int_\tau \|A(t)\| dt < \infty$ and $\int_\tau \|f(t)\| dt < \infty$ hold, respectively. A unique vector $x_f(t;\zeta,t_0)$ then exists such that $x_f(t_0;\zeta,t_0) = \zeta$ and $x_f(t;\zeta,t_0)$ satisfies Eq. 1 for every $t \in \tau$. If $A(t)$ is a continuous function of the parameters μ, then, for every $t \in \tau$, $x_f(t;\zeta,t_0)$ is also continuous with respect to these parameters.*

R E M A R K 1.   If $L_1(\tau)$ denotes the usual space of integrable functions on τ, it follows that if $\|f(t)\| \in L_1(\tau)$ then each $f_i(t) \in L_1(\tau)$, $i = 1, \ldots, n$. Thus an alternative condition on $f(t)$ for the purposes of Theorem A is that $\|A(t)\|$ be bounded on τ and $f(t) \in [L_1(\tau)]^n$.

Now that it is established that $x_f(t;\zeta,t_0)$ exists, let us try to pin down the form of this solution. For the present discussion the matrix $A(t)$ and the vector $f(t)$ are considered continuous on τ. The reader with the tools of modern integration at his disposal should feel free to modify the subsequent statements to obtain the more general result.

Let us use the Lagrange variation-of-parameters technique and attempt to find a solution of the form $x_f(t;\zeta,t_0) = \Phi(t,t_0)y(t;f)$. Here $x(t)$, $y(t)$, and $\Phi(t,t_0)$ are continuous with continuous first derivatives; $\Phi(t,t_0)$ is the state transition matrix for Eq. 1 under the condition $f(t) = 0$. Note that in order for x_f to satisfy the initial condition of 1 we must have $y(t_0,f) = \zeta$.

By substituting this expression into Eq. 1 we obtain the equation

$$\dot{\Phi}(t,t_0)y(t,f) + \Phi(t,t_0)\dot{y}(t;f) = A(t)\Phi(t,t_0)y(t;f) + \Phi(t,t_0)\dot{y}(t;f)$$

$$= A(t)\Phi(t,t_0)y(t;f) + f(t).$$

Hence

$$\Phi(t,t_0)\dot{y}(t;f) = f(t), \qquad t \in \tau.$$

Since $\Phi(t,t_0)$ is nonsingular for all $t \in \tau$, we have

$$\dot{y}(t;f) = \Phi^{-1}(t,t_0)f(t), \qquad t \in \tau,$$

or, by integration and use of the fact that $y(t_0,f) = \zeta$, we find that

$$y(t;f) = \zeta + \int_{t_0}^{t}\Phi^{-1}(s,t_0)f(s)ds, \qquad t \in \tau.$$

Consequently, since $x_f(t;\zeta,t_0) = \Phi(t,t_0)y(t;f)$, we have found that the solution of Eq. 4 is

$$x_f(t;\zeta,t_0) = \Phi(t,t_0)\zeta + \int_{t_0}^{t}\Phi(t,t_0)\Phi^{-1}(s,t_0)f(s)ds, \qquad t,t_0,s \in \tau. \tag{6}$$

By utilizing this result and the properties of the state transition matrix, we have the following theorem.

THEOREM B. *If Eq. 1 satisfies the conditions of Theorem A and $\Phi(t,t_0)$ is the state transition matrix for the associated homogeneous system, the solution to Eq. 1 can be expressed in any one of these equivalent forms:*

$$x_f(t;\zeta,t_0) = \Phi(t,t_0)\zeta + \Phi(t,t_0)\int_{t_0}^{t}\Phi^{-1}(s,t_0)f(s)ds, \qquad s,t,t_0 \in \tau$$

$$= \Phi(t,t_0)\zeta + \int_{t_0}^{t}\Phi(t,s)f(s)ds$$

$$= \Phi(t,t_0)\zeta + \Phi(t,t_0)\int_{t_0}^{t}\Phi(t_0,s)f(s)ds.$$

Several comments on the contents of Theorem B are in order at this time. First, it is clear that $x_f(t;\zeta,t_0)$ is the superposition of two terms. The first term, $\Phi(t,t_0)\zeta$, represents the solution to Eq. 1 under the condition $f(t) = 0$ on τ and ζ arbitrary. The second term represents the solution to Eq. 1 under the condition that $\zeta = 0$ and $f(t) \in [L_1(\tau)]^n$ arbitrary. These two factors are frequently called the *free* and the *forced* responses of the nonhomogeneous system.

Consider now the input $\hat{f}$ defined by

$$\hat{f}(t) = \begin{cases} 0, & t_0 \leq t \leq \tau, \\ f(t), & \tau < t < \tau + \Delta\tau, \\ 0, & \tau + \Delta\tau \leq t. \end{cases}$$

According to the properties of the state transition matrix, it follows that the equalities

$$\Phi(t,t_0)\int_\tau^{\tau+\Delta\tau}\Phi(t_0,s)f(s)ds = \Phi(t,\tau)\Phi(\tau,t_0)\left[\int_\tau^{\tau+\Delta\tau}\Phi(t_0,\tau)\Phi(\tau,s)f(s)ds\right]$$

$$= \Phi(t,\tau)\left[\int_\tau^{\tau+\Delta\tau}\Phi(\tau,s)f(s)ds\right] \tag{7}$$

hold. Thus, if the notation

$$\bar{f}_\tau = \int_\tau^{\tau+\Delta\tau}\Phi(\tau,s)f(s)ds \tag{8}$$

is introduced, it is evident that the total system response is given by

$$x_f(t;\zeta,t_0) = \begin{cases} \Phi(t,t_0)\zeta, & 0 \leq t < \tau, \\ \Phi(t,t_0)\zeta + \Phi(t,\tau)\bar{f}_\tau, & \tau < t, \end{cases} \tag{9}$$

where $\Delta\tau$ is assumed to be small and $\tau + \Delta\tau = t$. An alternative form for Eq. 9 is given by

$$x_f(t;\zeta,t_0) = \begin{cases} \Phi(t,t_0)\zeta, & 0 \leq t < \tau, \\ \Phi(t,t_0)[\zeta + \Phi(t_0,\tau)\bar{f}_\tau], & \tau < t, \end{cases} \tag{10}$$

which shows that the responses to the initial condition ζ and the pulselike function $f(t)$ are much the same. Indeed, in Eq. 9 the response appears as if a second initial condition $\hat{f}_\tau$ had been added at time τ without disturbing the first. In Eq. 10 the response appears as that of a homogeneous system with initial condition ζ for $t < \tau$ and with initial $\zeta + \Phi(t_0,\tau)\hat{f}_\tau$ for $t > \tau$.

Let us now consider the nonhomogeneous vectorial difference equation

$$\Delta_k y(t_k) = A(t_k)y(t_k) + f(t_k); \qquad y(t_0) = 0, \qquad t_k \in \sigma. \tag{11}$$

As in Eq. 2, an expanded $2n \times 2n$ matrix $\tilde{A}(t_k)$ can be defined to convert Eq. 11 to a homogeneous form. The existence and uniqueness conditions of Theorem H, Section 2.3, then apply to show that Eq. 11 has a unique solution.

Here we leave the details to the reader and attempt to find this solution by the variation-of-parameters method. As before, $\Phi(t_k,t_0)$ denotes the transition matrix for the homogeneous counterpart of Eq. 11. For convenience we shall assume that $\Phi(t_k,t_0)$ is nonsingular on σ.

If $y(t_k)$ is a solution of Eq. 11, we attempt to determine a vector sequence $u(t_k)$ such that

$$y(t_k) = \Phi(t_k,t_0)u(t_k,t_0).$$

Now, operating with Δ_k on both sides of this equation yields

$$\Delta_k y(t_k) = [\Delta_k \Phi(t_k,t_0)]u(t_k,t_0) + \Phi(t_{k+1},t_0)[\Delta_k u(t_k,t_0)]$$
$$= A(t_k)\Phi(t_k,t_0)u(t_k,t_0) + \Phi(t_{k+1},t_0)[\Delta_k u(t_k,t_0)]$$

However, by invoking Eq. 11 we have

$$A(t_k)\Phi(t_k,t_0)u(t_k,t_0) + f(t_k) = A(t_k)\Phi(t_k,t_0) + \Phi(t_{k+1},t_0)[\Delta_k u(t_k,t_0)],$$

which implies that

$$f(t_k) = \Phi(t_{k+1},t_0)[\Delta_k u(t_k,t_0)].$$

If it is assumed that none of the matrices $[I + h_k A(t_k)]$ is singular, the state transition matrix is always invertible; hence,

$$\Delta_k u(t_k,t_0) = \Phi^{-1}(t_{k+1},t_0)f(t_k);$$

that is,

$$u(t_{k+1}) = u(t_k) + h_k \Phi^{-1}(t_{k+1},t_0)f(t_k) = u(t_k) + h_k \Phi(t_0,t_{k+1})f(t_k).$$

Writing these relations out in detail and utilizing the condition $y(t_0) = 0$, we have

$$u(t_0) = 0$$

$$u(t_1) = h_0 \Phi(t_0,t_1)f(t_0)$$

$$u(t_2) = h_0 \Phi(t_0,t_1)f(t_0) + h_1 \Phi(t_0,t_1)f(t_1)$$

$$\vdots$$

$$u(t_k) = \sum_{i=1}^{k} h_{i-1}\Phi(t_0,t_i)f(t_{i-1}) = \sum_{j=0}^{k-1} h_j \Phi(t_0,t_{j+1})f(t_j).$$

This result leads to the following theorem.

THEOREM C. *If $A(t_k)$ is an $n \times n$ matrix such that $[I + h_k A(t_k)]$ is defined and nonsingular on the set $\sigma = \{t_0, t_1, \ldots, t_n\}$, then the difference equation*

$$\Delta_k y(t_k) = A(t_k)y(t_k) + f(t_k); \qquad y(t_0) = 0, \qquad t_k \in \sigma$$

has the unique vectorial sequence solution defined by

$$y(t_k) = \Phi(t_k,t_0) \sum_{j=0}^{k-1} h_j \Phi(t_0,t_{j+1}) f(t_j), \qquad t_k \in \sigma. \tag{12}$$

REMARK 2.   First, let us note that Eq. 12 has the alternative form

$$y(t_{k+1}) = [I + h_k A(t_k)] y(t_k) + h_k f(t_k)$$

$$= \Phi(t_{k+1},t_k) y(t_k) + h_k f(t_k)$$

$$= \Phi(t_{k+1},t_k)[y(t_k) + H(t_k) f(t_k)]; \qquad H(t_k) = h_k \Phi(t_k,t_{k+1}),$$

which is frequently used as an alternative definition of a discrete dynamic system. Second, using the semigroup property of Eq. 30, Section 2.3, we see that the conclusion of Theorem C of that section can be rewritten as

$$y(t_k) = \sum_{j=0}^{k-1} h_j \Phi(t_k,t_{j+1}) f(t_j). \tag{13}$$

The proof of Theorem C has used the assumed nonsingularity of $\Phi(t_k,t_0)$ on σ in a vital way. This assumption is by no means necessary, however, for Eq. 13 will hold even in the singular case. The proof of this property and that of the following corollary may be established by the rather unelegant but straightforward use of Eq. 11 as an iterative relation.

COROLLARY.   *The vectorial difference equation, defined on σ by*

$$\Delta_k y(t_k) = A(t_k) y(t_k) + f(t_k), \qquad y(t_0) = \xi, \tag{14}$$

has the unique solution y with values on σ given by

$$y_f(t_k;\xi,t_0) = \Phi(t_k,t_0)\xi + \sum_{j=0}^{k-1} h_j(t_k,t_j) f(t_j), \qquad t_k \in \sigma. \tag{15}$$

When $\Phi(t_k,t_0)$ is indeed nonsingular, we may, of course, choose to rewrite Eq. 14 by bringing out a common $\Phi(t_k,t_0)$ factor.

Example 1.   Consider the electronic circuit and its linear equivalent of Figure 2.11. Assuming that the capacitors are initially unchanged at time $t_0 = 0$, the systems equations can be written as

$$\begin{bmatrix} \dot{x}_1(t) \\ \dot{x}_2(t) \end{bmatrix} = \begin{bmatrix} -a & -b \\ -c & -d \end{bmatrix} \begin{bmatrix} x_1(t) \\ x_2(t) \end{bmatrix} + \begin{bmatrix} e \\ f \end{bmatrix} u_1(t), \qquad t \geq 0,$$

where

$$a = (R_0 + R_p)(R_1 + R_2)C_1\Delta, \qquad b = R_1(R_0 + R_p)C_1\Delta,$$

$$c = R_1(R_0 + R_p)C_2\Delta, \qquad d = (R_0 R_1 + R_0 R_p + R_1 R_p)C_2\Delta,$$

$$e = R_0(R_1 + R_2)C_1\Delta, \qquad f = R_0 R_1 C_2\Delta,$$

$$\Delta = R_0 R_1 R_2 + R_0 R_1 R_p + R_0 R_2 R_p + R_1 R_2 R_p.$$

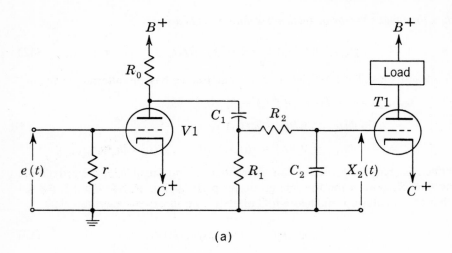

(a)

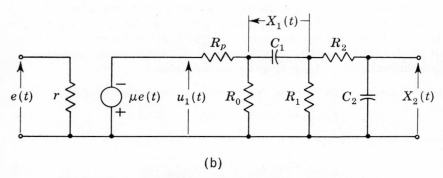

(b)

Figure 2.11   (a) Triggering circuit, (b) equivalent linear model.

In terms of scalars

$$\lambda_1 = -\tfrac{1}{2}(a + d + \sqrt{(a - d)^2 + 4bc}),$$

$$\lambda_2 = -\tfrac{1}{2}(a + d - \sqrt{(a - d)^2 + 4bc}).$$

The system transition matrix may be written

$$\Phi(t,s) = \begin{bmatrix} \Phi_{11}(t,s) & \Phi_{12}(t,s) \\ \Phi_{21}(t,s) & \Phi_{22}(t,s) \end{bmatrix},$$

where the matrix components are given by

$$\Phi_{11}(t,s) = (\lambda_1 - \lambda_2)^{-1}[-(a + \lambda_2)e^{\lambda_1(t-s)} + (a + \lambda_1)e^{\lambda_2(t-s)}],$$

$$\Phi_{21}(t,s) = (\lambda_1 - \lambda_2)^{-1}\{b^{-1}(a + \lambda_1)(a + \lambda_2)[e^{\lambda_1(t-s)} - e^{\lambda_2(t-s)}]\},$$

$$\Phi_{12}(t,s) = (\lambda_1 - \lambda_2)^{-1}\{-b[e^{\lambda_1(t-s)} - e^{\lambda_2(t-s)}]\},$$

$$\Phi_{22}(t,s) = (\lambda_1 - \lambda_2)^{-1}[(a + \lambda_1)e^{\lambda_1(t-s)} - (a + \lambda_2)e^{\lambda_2(t-s)}].$$

Example 2.[1]   Consider now the behavior of a general three-mass system described in Newtonian mechanics by the system of second-order differential equations

$$\begin{bmatrix} m_{11} & m_{12} & m_{13} \\ m_{21} & m_{22} & m_{23} \\ m_{31} & m_{32} & m_{33} \end{bmatrix}\begin{bmatrix} \ddot{x}_1 \\ \ddot{x}_2 \\ \ddot{x}_3 \end{bmatrix} + \begin{bmatrix} f_{11} & f_{12} & f_{13} \\ f_{21} & f_{22} & f_{23} \\ f_{31} & f_{32} & f_{33} \end{bmatrix}\begin{bmatrix} \dot{x}_1 \\ \dot{x}_2 \\ \dot{x}_3 \end{bmatrix}$$

$$+ \begin{bmatrix} k_{11} & k_{12} & k_{13} \\ k_{21} & k_{22} & k_{23} \\ k_{31} & k_{32} & k_{33} \end{bmatrix}\begin{bmatrix} x_1 \\ x_2 \\ x_3 \end{bmatrix} = \begin{bmatrix} f_1(t) \\ f_2(t) \\ f_3(t) \end{bmatrix}.$$

We shall assume that all masses m_{ij}, friction coefficients f_{ij}, and spring constants k_{ij} are independent of t. First we write this system in the vector matrix form

$$M\ddot{x}(t) + F\dot{x}(t) + Kx(t) = f(t), \tag{16}$$

in which the respective matrices are defined by $M = [m_{ij}]$, $F = [f_{ij}]$, and $K = [k_{ij}]$.

Using the procedure suggested by Exercises 9 and 10, Section 2.3, we can write Eq. 16 in normal form. To do so, we consider the velocities of the masses as well as their positions as coordinates. Let $v_i = \dot{x}_i$ and $v = (v_1, v_2, v_3)$. Then Eq. 1 may be replaced by the system of

$$0\dot{v}(t) + I\dot{x}(t) - Iv(t) + 0x(t) = 0,$$

$$M\dot{v}(t) + F\dot{x}(t) + 0v(t) + Kx(t) = f(t), \qquad t \in \tau.$$

On taking advantage of the convenience of the matrix notation, we have

$$\left[\begin{array}{c|c} 0 & I \\ \hline M & F \end{array}\right]\begin{bmatrix} \dot{v}(t) \\ \dot{x}(t) \end{bmatrix} + \left[\begin{array}{c|c} -I & 0 \\ \hline 0 & K \end{array}\right]\begin{bmatrix} v(t) \\ x(t) \end{bmatrix} = \begin{bmatrix} 0 \\ f(t) \end{bmatrix}. \tag{17}$$

Let it be assumed that the matrix

$$\left[\begin{array}{c|c} 0 & I \\ \hline M & F \end{array}\right]$$

is nonsingular. This is clearly so when M is nonsingular. The reader can easily verify that

$$\left[\begin{array}{c|c} 0 & I \\ \hline M & F \end{array}\right]^{-1} = \left[\begin{array}{c|c} -M^{-1}F & M^{-1} \\ \hline I & 0 \end{array}\right]; \tag{18}$$

---

[1]This example was motivated by R. L. Halfman, *Dynamics*, Vol. II, Addison-Wesley, Reading, Mass., Sec. 9.2.

multiplying through by this matrix yields

$$\dot{z}(t) = Az(t) + Bu(t), \qquad t \in \tau, \tag{19}$$

where $u = (0, f)$, $z = (v, x)$, B is the matrix of Eq. 18, and A is given by

$$A = (-1) \left[\begin{array}{c|c} -M^{-1}F & M^{-1} \\ \hline I & 0 \end{array} \right] \cdot \left[\begin{array}{c|c} -I & 0 \\ \hline 0 & K \end{array} \right] = (-1) \left[\begin{array}{c|c} M^{-1}F & MK^{-1} \\ \hline -I & 0 \end{array} \right]. \tag{20}$$

Thus by a simple straightforward process we have brought the general family of second-order differential equations within the framework of the first-order normal system. As a specific example consider Figure 2.12. For

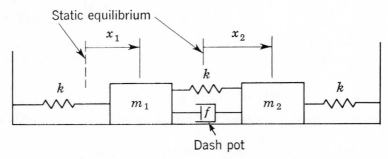

Figure 2.12   A simple mass-spring dash-pot system.

this two-mass system we have the equations of motion

$$\begin{bmatrix} m_1 & 0 \\ 0 & m_2 \end{bmatrix} \begin{bmatrix} \ddot{x}_1(t) \\ \ddot{x}_2(t) \end{bmatrix} + \begin{bmatrix} f & -f \\ -f & f \end{bmatrix} \begin{bmatrix} \dot{x}_1(t) \\ \dot{x}_2(t) \end{bmatrix} + \begin{bmatrix} 2k & -k \\ -k & 2k \end{bmatrix} \begin{bmatrix} x_1(t) \\ x_2(t) \end{bmatrix} = \begin{bmatrix} f_1(t) \\ f_2(t) \end{bmatrix}, \qquad t \in \tau,$$

where the $f(t)$ are external forces positive to the right. In the equivalent first-order form of Eq. 17 this system appears as

$$\begin{bmatrix} 0 & 0 & 1 & 0 \\ 0 & 0 & 0 & 1 \\ m_1 & 0 & f & -f \\ 0 & m_2 & -f & f \end{bmatrix} \begin{bmatrix} \dot{v}_1(t) \\ \dot{v}_2(t) \\ \dot{x}_1(t) \\ \dot{x}_2(t) \end{bmatrix} + \begin{bmatrix} -1 & 0 & 0 & 0 \\ 0 & -1 & 0 & 0 \\ 0 & 0 & 2k & -k \\ 0 & 0 & -k & 2k \end{bmatrix} \begin{bmatrix} v_1(t) \\ v_2(t) \\ x_1(t) \\ x_2(t) \end{bmatrix} = \begin{bmatrix} 0 \\ 0 \\ f_1(t) \\ f_2(t) \end{bmatrix}.$$

Finally, the system is reduced to the standard form of Eq. 19, with A given by

$$A = (-1) \begin{bmatrix} \dfrac{f}{m_1} & \dfrac{-f}{m_1} & \dfrac{2k}{m_1} & \dfrac{-k}{m_1} \\[2mm] \dfrac{f}{m_2} & \dfrac{f}{m_2} & \dfrac{-k}{m_2} & \dfrac{2k}{m_2} \\[2mm] -1 & 0 & 0 & 0 \\[2mm] 0 & -1 & 0 & 0 \end{bmatrix}. \tag{21}$$

Example 3. Consider now the position-control servomechanism of Figure 2.13. For this system the relevant physical parameters are

k_1 = motor constant A = amplifier gain
k_2 = torque constant J = inertia (referred to motor shaft)
k_3 = gear ratio R = armature resistance
k_4 = potentiometer ratio f = viscous damping (referred to motor shaft);

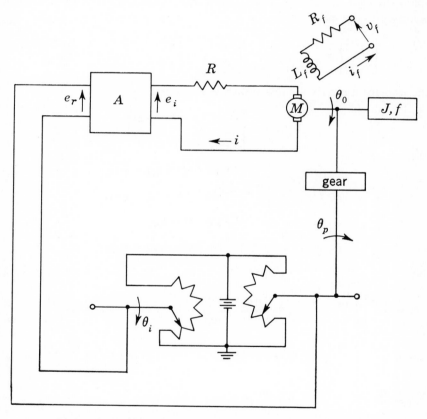

Figure 2.13   A second-order position-control servomechanism.

for fixed i_r and zero initial conditions at $t = t_0$ the governing equations for the system are

$$e_i(t) = Ak_4[\theta_i(t) - \theta_p(t)] = Ri(t) + k_1\theta_0(t),$$

$$T(t) = J\ddot{\theta}_0(t) + f\dot{\theta}_0(t),$$

$$\theta_p(t) = k_3\theta_0(t).$$

Using the constants

$$a_0 = \frac{Ak_2k_3k_4}{JR}, \qquad a_1 = \frac{k_2}{JR}\left(\frac{fR}{k_2} + k_1\right), \qquad k = \frac{Ak_2k_4}{JR},$$

we may reduce the system equations to the form

$$\ddot{\theta}_0(t) + a_1\dot{\theta}_0(t) + a_0\theta_0(t) = k\theta_i(t), \qquad \theta_0(t_0) = \dot{\theta}_0(t_0) = 0,$$

which through the change of variables $x_1(t) = \theta_0(t)$, $x_2(t) = \dot{\theta}_0(t)$, may be expressed in the matrix form

$$\begin{bmatrix} \dot{x}_1(t) \\ \dot{x}_2(t) \end{bmatrix} = \begin{bmatrix} 0 & 1 \\ -a_0 & -a_1 \end{bmatrix}\begin{bmatrix} x_1(t) \\ x_2(t) \end{bmatrix} + \begin{bmatrix} 0 \\ k \end{bmatrix}, \qquad \theta_i(t) = t > t_0.$$

The transform matrix for this system is given by

$$\Phi(t,t_0) = \begin{bmatrix} \phi_{11}(t,t_0) & \phi_{12}(t,t_0) \\ \phi_{21}(t,t_0) & \phi_{22}(t,t_0) \end{bmatrix},$$

where

$$\phi_{11}(t,t_0) = c_1 e^{-b(t-t_0)}\sin\left[\omega(t - t_0) + \psi_1\right],$$

$$\phi_{12}(t,t_0) = c_2 e^{-b(t-t_0)}\sin\left[\omega(t - t_0) + \psi_2\right],$$

$$\phi_{21}(t,t_0) = c_3 e^{-b(t-t_0)}\sin\omega(t - t_0),$$

$$\phi_{22}(t,t_0) = c_4 e^{-b(t-t_0)}\sin\left[\omega(t - t_0) + \psi_2\right]$$

and

$$c_1 = \frac{\sqrt{b^2 + \omega^2}}{\omega}, \qquad c_4 = \sqrt{\frac{(a_1 - b)^2 + \omega^2}{\omega}}, \qquad \psi_1 = \tan^{-1}\frac{-\omega}{b},$$

$$c_2 = \frac{-1}{\omega} \qquad\qquad \omega = a_0 - b^2, \qquad\qquad \psi_2 = \tan^{-1}\frac{\omega}{a_1 - b},$$

$$c_3 = \frac{a_0}{\omega} \qquad\qquad b = \frac{a_1}{2}.$$

REMARK. The reader no doubt has noticed that none of the three examples just given produces difference equations. This, of course, does not imply a scarcity of physical systems that are discrete in nature. On the contrary, discrete dynamic systems occur in many examples as the representation of naturally discrete phenomena. Such is the case with digital computation and digital control systems. In others a continuous physical phenomena is put in discrete form by quantization or sampling. A range tracking pulse radar, for instance, samples the target range at the pulse repetition frequency. Indeed, the preceding three examples can be converted to discrete time systems by the introduction of sampling. Since sampled data systems constitute an important class of applications, we shall investigate the primary connections between discrete time, sampled data, and continuous time systems.

Sampled Data Systems

In modeling physical systems it is often found that a slight generalization of Eqs. 1 and 14 is necessary. To be explicit, the mathematical model of a linear dynamic system may take the form[1]

$$d_t x(t) = A(t)x(t) + B(t)u(t), \qquad x(t_0) = \xi, \qquad t \in v;$$

$$y(t) = C(t)x(t) + D(t)u(t), \qquad\qquad t \in v. \tag{22}$$

Here the tuplet $u = (u^1, \ldots, u_m)$ represents the independent system inputs, the tuplet $y = (y^1, \ldots, y_n)$ represents the independent observable outputs, and $x = (x^1, \ldots, x_r)$ constitutes a minimum set of internal variables (not necessarily unique) sufficient to describe the dynamic behavior of the system. The matrices A, B, C, and D are of compatible dimensions.

The similarity of the continuous and discrete systems suggests that by a judicious choice of notation their individual identities can be almost done away with. In Eq. 22 we have taken a step in this direction. Since σ is discrete, the function x defined on σ may be written $x(t)$, $t \in \sigma$, without ambiguity. Similarly, the notation

$$\Delta_t x(t) = h_k^{-1}[x(t_{k+1}) - x(t_k)], \qquad t = t_k \in \sigma,$$

is just as well defined as the notation $\Delta_k x(t_k)$ used earlier. Thus, when $v = \tau$, the symbol d_t is understood to denote differentiation, and, when $v = \sigma$, then $d_t = \Delta_t$. From Eq. 22 the two system types are indistinguishable until v is specified. Once v is known, however, Eq. 22 is well defined.

Figure 2.14 presents Eq. 22 from a black-box point of view. For obvious reasons D is called the direct transmission matrix and B and C are called the input and output constraint matrices, respectively. For single-output, single-input systems, B is a column vector, whereas C and D are row vectors. In general, we refer to the system in Eq. 22 as *multivariate* and in the single-input or output cases as *single variate*.

With these preliminaries taken care of we proceed to the study of sampled data systems. Our objective is not merely to show that continuous time systems with sampling can be represented as discrete time systems but rather to establish the sampled data system as a two-way link between discrete time and continuous time systems.

To begin, let us assume that the discrete set σ is a subset of the interval τ.

---

[1]Appendix 4 gives examples of systems with mathematical models which require this additional generality.

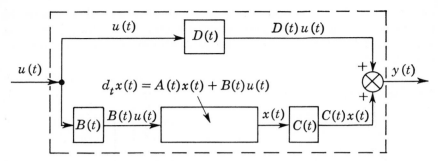

Figure 2.14   A typical multivariate system.

If X denotes the class of all functions defined everywhere on τ and Y, the class of all time sequences defined on σ, then, with $\sigma \subset \tau$, the sampling operation, denoted by S, is the linear transformation $S: X \to Y$ defined by

$$(Sf)(t) = \begin{cases} f(t_k), & t_k \in \sigma, \\ 0, & t_k \in \tau \sim \sigma. \end{cases}$$

The action of the transformation S may be viewed physically as an intermittent switch operation in which the switch is closed instantaneously on the time values $t \in \sigma$. The clamp or linear hold introduced in Example 4, Section 2.1, is useful here and is identified with the linear transformation C, sending Y into X defined by

$$(Cy)(t) = y(t_j), \qquad t \in [t_j, t_{j=1}),$$

with $t \in \tau$ and $t_j, t_{j+1} \in \sigma$.

To be specific in our objectives, let us consider the two systems of Figure 2.15. Continuous and discrete time systems are called *equivalent* if they perform

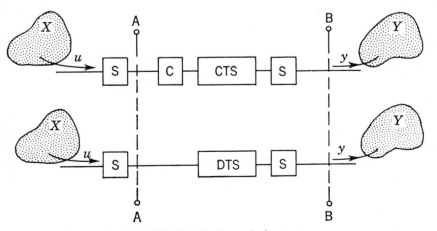

Figure 2.15   Terminally equivalent systems.

identical transformations between terminals A and B. It is apparent that the input sampler may be included to the right of terminal A and that an output sample-hold (i.e., SC) may replace the output sample without disturbing the basic equivalence question.

To formulate the equivalence question analytically, let the discrete dynamic system be described by Eq. 23:

$$
\begin{aligned}
\Delta_k \hat{x}(t_k) &= \hat{A}(t_k)\hat{x}(t_k) + \hat{B}(t_k)u(t_k), & t_k \in \sigma, \\
\hat{y}(t_k) &= \hat{C}(t_k)x(t_k) + \hat{D}(t_k)u(t_k), & t_k \in \sigma.
\end{aligned}
\tag{23}
$$

The continuous system is described by Eq. 24:

$$
\begin{aligned}
\dot{x}(t) &= A(t)x(t) + B(t)\bar{u}(t), & t \in \tau, \\
y(t) &= C(t)x(t) + D(t)\bar{u}(t), & t \in \tau,
\end{aligned}
\tag{24}
$$

where the notation $\bar{u}(t)$ denotes the function $(C\bar{u})(t)$. Let us examine the two-part problem.

Problem 1.   For every continuous system defined by Eq. 24 is it possible to specify a discrete system defined by Eq. 23 in which the values of $\hat{y}$ and y are identical on σ for every function u defined on σ?

Since $u = 0$ is an admissible input the relation $y(t) = \hat{y}(t)$ for $t \in \sigma$ yields immediately that $C(t)x(t) = \hat{C}(t)x(t)$ for $t \in \sigma$. It is sufficient to pick $\hat{C}(t) = (SC)(t)$ and show that the relation $\hat{x}(t) = (Sx)(t)$ can be satisfied. To do this the response equations,

$$
\begin{aligned}
\hat{x}(t) &= \hat{\Phi}(t,t_0)x^0 + \hat{\Phi}(t,t_0)\sum_{j=0}^{k-1} h_j \hat{\Phi}(t_0,t_{j+1})\hat{B}(t_j)u(t_j), & t \in \sigma, \\
x(t) &= \Phi(t,t_0)x^0 + \Phi(t,t_0)\int_{t_0}^{t} \Phi(t_0,s)B(s)\bar{u}(s)ds, & t \in \tau,
\end{aligned}
\tag{25}
$$

will be useful. Again the equivalence of $x(t)$ and $\hat{x}(t)$ on σ with $u = 0$ and all possible x^0 and t_0 specifies immediately that the relationship

$$
\Phi(t_j,t_k) = \hat{\Phi}(t_j,t_k), \qquad t_j, t_k \in \sigma,
$$

must hold.

Since $\hat{\Phi}(t_k,t_0) = \prod_{j=0}^{k-1} [I + h_k\hat{A}(t_k)]$, this in turn defines the matrix sequence $\{\hat{A}(t_k)\}$. By equating the forced responses at the times $t_0, t_1, \ldots, t_k, \ldots$, and setting $\bar{u}(t) = u(t_k)$, for $t \in [t_k, t_{k+1})$, it is not difficult to show that the systems have the same output on σ if and only if

$$
h_k \hat{B}(t_k) = \int_{t_k}^{t_{k+1}} \Phi(t_{k+1},s)B(s)ds, \qquad k = 0, 1, 2, \ldots.
$$

Thus for the continuous system of Eq. 24 an equivalent discrete system is uniquely determined by the relationships

$$\hat{C}(t_k) = C(t_k)$$

$$\hat{D}(t_k) = D(t_k)$$

$$\hat{A}(t_k) = \frac{1}{h_k} [\Phi(t_{k+1}) - I] \tag{26}$$

$$\hat{B}(t_k) = \frac{1}{h_k} \left[\int_{t_k}^{t_{k+1}} \Phi(t_{k+1},s)B(s)ds \right]$$

The converse of Problem 1 is the following.

Problem 2. For every discrete system defined by Eqs. 23, it is possible to specify a continuous system which is equivalent in the sense that, for every $u(t)$ defined on σ, the two systems have identical output values on σ?

This problem is more complicated than the first. It is evident from Eqs. 23 and 24 that it is sufficient to choose any matrices C and D with values $\hat{C}(t_k)$ and $\hat{D}(t_k)$ on σ and prove that matrices A and B can be found such that the continuous system has a total response x with values $\hat{x}(t_k)$ on σ.

LEMMA. *Given a discrete system with transition matrix $\Phi(t_j,t_k)$, suppose that $\Gamma(t)$ is a nonsingular differentiable matrix for which*

$$\|\dot{\Gamma}(t)\Gamma(t)^{-1}\| \le m(t) \in L_1(\tau),$$

$$\Gamma(t_k) = \hat{\Phi}(t_k,t_0), \qquad k = 0, 1, 2, \dots.$$

Define $\Phi(t,s) = \Gamma(t)\Gamma(s)^{-1}$ and let $A(t) = \dot{\Gamma}(t)\Gamma(t)^{-1}$. Then $\Phi(t,t_0)$ is the transition matrix for the differential system

$$\dot{x}(t) = A(t)x(t)$$

and

$$\Phi(t_j,t_k) = \hat{\Phi}(t_j,t_k), \qquad j, k = 0, 1, 2, \dots.$$

PROOF. Let $\Gamma(t)$ satisfy the hypothesis and consider

$$\Phi(t,s) = \Gamma(t)\Gamma(s)^{-1};$$

then

$$\dot{\Phi}(t,s) = \dot{\Gamma}(t)\Gamma^{-1}(s) = \dot{\Gamma}(t)\Gamma^{-1}(t)\Gamma(t)\Gamma^{-1}(s) = \dot{\Gamma}(t)\Gamma^{-1}(t)\Phi(t,s).$$

Furthermore

$$\Phi(t,t) = \Gamma(t)\Gamma^{-1}(t) = I.$$

Hence $\Phi(t,s)$ is the transition matrix for the system and the lemma is proved.

It is apparent from the outset that $\Gamma(t)$ is not unique. We exhibit but one realization out of the many possible constructions.

Given the difference equation $\Delta_k \hat{y}(t_k) = \hat{A}(t_k)\hat{y}(t_k)$ or, alternatively, the discrete transition matrix $\hat{\Phi}(t_k,t_0) = \prod_{i=0}^{k-1} [I + h_i\hat{A}(t_i)]$, let us define a continuous time transition matrix by the equation

$$\Phi(t,t_0) = [I + (t - t_k)\hat{A}(t_k)]\hat{\Phi}(t_k,t_0), \qquad t \in [t_k,t_{k+1});$$

$\Phi(t,t_0)$ is obviously a continuous function for all t and satisfies the condition $\Phi(t_k,t_0) = \hat{\Phi}(t_k,t_0)$ for all $t_k \in \sigma$. Furthermore,

$$\dot{\Phi}(t,t_0) = \hat{A}(t_k)\hat{\Phi}(t_k,t_0) = \hat{A}(t_k)[I + (t - t_k)\hat{A}(t_k)]^{-1}\Phi(t,t_0),$$

which specifies the time-varying system matrix

$$A(t) = A(t_k)[I + (t - t_k)\hat{A}(t_k)]^{-1}, \qquad t \in [t_k,t_{k+1}), \qquad t \in \sigma.$$

Unfortunately, $A(t)$ is not continuous (continuity is not required by our lemma, but it is a desirable feature), for, taking limiting values from the left and right at t_{k+1}, we have

$$A(t_k^-) = A(t_k)\Phi(t_k,t_{k+1})$$

$$A(t_k^+) = A(t_{k+1}).$$

Nonetheless, we may adopt this $\Phi(t,s)$ and, using equality of the forced constraints, find a matrix $B(t)$ that makes the two systems equivalent.

Exercises

1. Consider the linear dynamic system of Eq. 22. Let H denote a time-varying matrix that is used to define a passive feedback law

$$u(t) = H(t)y(t) + v(t), \qquad t \in v.$$

Under the assumption that $\|D(t)H(t)\| < 1$, $t \in v$, bring the closed loop system to the standard form of Eq. 22.

2. Repeat Exercise 1 with the active feedback law:

$$u(t) = Z(t) + v(t), \qquad t \in v,$$

$$d_t Z(t) = H(t)Z(t) + y(t), \qquad t \in v.$$

HINT: Consider the tuplet (x,z) rather than x.

3. Let x, $\hat{x}$ denote two choices for the internal variables of a linear dynamic system. Since the external relationships $u \to y$ are not affected by the choice of the mathematical model (the internal

variables), we expect two equation sets in the form

$$d_t x(t) = A(t)x(t) + B(t)u(t), \qquad t \in v,$$

$$y(t) = C(t)x(t) + D(t)u(t), \qquad t \in v.$$

$$d_t \hat{x}(t) = \hat{A}(t)\hat{x}(t) + \hat{B}(t)u(t), \qquad t \in v,$$

$$y(t) = \hat{C}(t)\hat{x}(t) + \hat{D}(t)u(t), \qquad t \in v.$$

Assume that K is a matrix such that $K(t)$, $K^{-1}(t)$, and $\dot{K}(t)$ all exist for all $t \in v$ and that $\hat{x}(t) = K^{-1}(t)x(t)$ is the relationship between the internal variable sets. Show that in the continuous case the relations

$$\hat{\Phi}(t,s) = K^{-1}(t)\Phi(t,s)K(s),$$

$$\hat{A}(t) = K^{-1}(t)A(t)K(t) - K^{-1}(t)\dot{K}(t),$$

$$\hat{B}(t) = K^{-1}(t)B(t),$$

$$\hat{C}(t) = C(t)K(t)$$

must hold for t, $s \in \tau$ and that these relations hold in the discrete case as well if the substitutions $K^{-1}(t_{k+1})$ for $K^{-1}(t)$ and $\Delta_k K(t_k)$ for $\dot{K}(t)$ are made.

4. A typical electromechanical speaker system obeys a set of differential equations

$$L \frac{di(t)}{dt} + Ri(t) + U \frac{dx(t)}{dt} = v(t),$$

$$m \frac{d^2 x(t)}{dt^2} + kx(t) - Ui(t) = 0,$$

where v, x, and i denote applied voltage, mechanical displacement, and coil current, respectively. Express this behavior as a nonhomogeneous system of first-order differential equations. Using the values $R/L = 6$, $U^2/mL = 10$, obtain the solution of this system in terms of the remaining parameter. Obtain the behavior of x and i as functions of v from the preceding result.

2.5 SOME TRANSFORMATIONS DEFINED BY LINEAR DYNAMIC SYSTEMS

In Sections 2.3 and 2.4 we established several important properties of linear dynamic systems. In this final section these results are reinterpreted from the linear transformation point of view.

Consider Eq. 22 once again. As before, $\Phi(t,s)$ denotes the transition matrix for the system for $t, s \in v$. In the discrete case the set σ is ordered (i.e., $t_{j-1} < t_j$) so that "the greatest t_k function" denoted by $[t]$ may be defined by

$$[t] = \max_{t_k \in \sigma} \{k : t_k \le t\};$$

that is, $[t] = k$ if and only if $t \in [t_k, t_{k-1})$. In terms of this function and by use of Eq. 15, it is clear that the discrete system response $u \to x$ may be written

$$x_u(t;\xi,t_0) = \Phi(t,t_0)\xi + \sum_{j=0}^{[t]-1} h_j \Phi(t,t_{j+1}) B(t_j) u(t_j), \qquad t \in \sigma \qquad (1)$$

or in the nonsingular case as

$$x_u(t;\xi,t_0) = \Phi(t,t_0)\xi + \Phi(t,t_0) \sum_{j=0}^{[t]-1} h_j \Phi(t_0,t_{j+1}) B(t_j) u(t_j), \qquad (2)$$

where t varies over σ. The continuous time system has the analogous relationship

$$x_u(t;\xi,t_0) = \Phi(t,t_0)\xi + \Phi(t,t_0) \int_{t_0}^{t} \Phi(t_0,s) B(s) u(s) ds \qquad (3)$$

as t varies over τ. In both cases the input-output response, $u \to y$, is determined by the additional relationship

$$y(t) = C(t) x_u(t;\xi,t_0) + D(t) u(t), \qquad t \in v.$$

For simplicity we assume that $D = 0$ and $C = I$, leaving the rather minor adjustments in the succeeding statements as an exercise for the interested reader.

Equations 2 and 3 are easily brought within the framework of Section 2.2. For this denote by $l(\sigma)$ the vector space of all real valued functions defined on σ; let $U_m(\sigma)$ be the m-fold Cartesian product of $l(\sigma)$:

$$U_m(\sigma) = l(\sigma) \times l(\sigma) \times \cdots \times l(\sigma) \qquad (m \text{ copies}).$$

We consider first the forced response of Eq. 2. For each u in $U_m(\sigma)$ Theorem C, Section 2.4, states that there is a corresponding unique vector $x_u(t;0,t_0)$ defined on σ and satisfying Eq. 2. Define the transformation F on $U_m(\sigma)$ by requiring that the image of u be this x:

$$(Fu)(t) = x_u(t;0,t_0) = \sum_{j=0}^{[t]-1} W(t,t_j) u(t_j), \qquad t \in \sigma, \qquad (4)$$

where $W(t,t_j) = h_j \Phi(t,t_{j+1}) B(t_j);$

that is, $(Fu)(t)$ denotes the image of the element $u \in U_m(\sigma)$ at the time $t \in \sigma$. It is clear that F is well-defined and linear and that the range of F lies in the space $U_n(\sigma)$. If we restrict σ as finite, $U_m(\sigma)$ is then finite-dimensional and F is bounded relative to any norm on $U_m(\sigma)$. Finally, it is clear that F represents the forced response of the discrete system in the sense that both act on the input u to produce the same output x. These observations are summarized in the following theorem.

THEOREM A. *The forced response of every discrete time, linear dynamic system can be represented as a (bounded if σ is finite) linear transformation F from one Banach space into another.*

In dealing with many control problems, we are often interested in the system output only at certain specified times. Here the system acts on its input space $U_m(\sigma)$ to produce an n-tuple of real numbers at time $t_a \in \sigma$. Thus we are led to consider the system as a linear transformation into R^n, that is, as the mapping F_a defined by

$$F_a u = (Fu)(t_a),$$

where t_a is *fixed* in σ. It is clear that in this way t_a determines a family of mappings $\{F_a\}$. Conversely, these mappings permit the computation of the values of the output function over any subset $E \subset \sigma$ and, in particular, determine F itself. Thus we have the following corollary.

COROLLARY. *The forced response of every discrete linear system can be represented as a family $\{F_a : t_a \in \sigma\}$ of bounded linear transformations F_a, each of which is defined on $U_m(\sigma)$ with range in R^n. These mappings are indexed by the base set σ on which the input functions are defined; F_a acts on the total system input to produce the t_ath sample of the output.*

Returning now to Eq. 3, we first recall that the matrix $\Phi(t,s)$ is continuous on the square $\tau \times \tau$ and thus the matrix $W(t,s) = \Phi(t,s)B(s)$ will be bounded on $\tau \times \tau$ whenever $B(s)$ is bounded on τ. Consider now the forced response. Let $L_p(\tau)$ $(1 \leq p \leq \infty)$ denote the usual Banach space of pth power (Lebesgue) integrable functions on the interval $\tau = [t_0, t_f]$. Let $U_m(\tau)$ denote the Cartesian product

$$U_m(\tau) = L_1(\tau) \times \cdots \times L_1(\tau) \qquad (m \text{ copies}).$$

Define the transformation F on $U_m(\tau)$ by requiring that x, the image of $u \in U_m(\tau)$, be given by

$$(Fu)(t) = x_u(t;0,t_0) = \int_{t_0}^{t} W(t,s)u(s)ds, \qquad t \in \tau; \qquad (5)$$

that is, $(Fu)(t)$ denotes the image of the element $u \in U_m(\tau)$ at the time $t \in \tau$. Since x is continuous and each continuous function on τ is bounded, it is easily verified that with $C(\tau)$ denoting the usual Banach space of continuous functions on τ we have

$$x \in [C(\tau)]^n \subset U_n(\tau).$$

Thus F is a linear transformation on $U_m(\tau)$ with range $C^n(\tau) = C(\tau) \times \cdots \times C(\tau)$ and, in particular, a linear mapping into $U_n(\tau)$. Moreover, by using a technique suggested later in the section we can show that, when τ is finite, F, considered as a mapping from $U_m(\tau)$ equipped with a suitable norm, into any suitably normed version of $C^n(\tau)$ or any of $U_n(\tau)$, is bounded. Our results are summarized in the following theorem.

THEOREM B.   *The forced response of a continuous linear dynamic system can be represented as a (bounded when τ is finite) linear transformation F from one Banach space into another.*

Again, if we are interested in the system output only at certain specified times (here the system acts on its input space to produce an n-tuple of real numbers at time $t_a \in \tau$), the system can be considered as a linear transformation into R^n, that is, as the mapping F_a defined by

$$F_a u = (Fu)(t_a),$$

where t_a is fixed in τ. It is clear that in this way F determines a family of mappings $\{F_a\}$. Conversely, these mappings permit the computation of the values of the output function over any subset $E \subset \tau$ and, in particular, determine F itself. We thus have the following corollary.

COROLLARY.   *The forced response of every continuous time linear dynamic system can be represented as a family $\{F_a : t_a \in \tau\}$ of bounded linear transformations F_a, each of which is defined on a domain $U_m(\tau)$ with range in R^n. These mappings are indexed by the base set τ on which the input functions are defined; F_a acts on the total system input to produce the t_ath sample of the output.*

R E M A R K 1 .   In Chapter 1 and the first two sections of this chapter the development has emphasized the idea that systems of all types should be thought of as mapping between function spaces and that it is not only unnecessary, but often undesirable to distinguish between the specific system categories. The development of the present section reaffirms this idea. Indeed, we have seen in Eqs. 1, 2, and 3 and in Theorems A and B and their corollaries that discrete and continuous linear dynamic systems are distinguishable in only such minor technicalities as the underlying function spaces involved.

R E M A R K 2 .   In the preceding development τ was bounded and σ was finite. These restrictions are not inherent in the analysis, but they do alleviate the need to introduce stability concepts at this point.

R E M A R K 3 .   We have dealt explicitly with only the forced response. However, the free response may be modeled as the linear transformation

$\Phi: R^n \to U_n(v)$, defined for every $\xi \in R^n$ by

$$(\Phi\xi)(t) = \Phi(t,t_0)\xi, \qquad t \in v. \tag{6}$$

Alternatively, the free response may be represented as a parameterized family $\{\Phi_a: t_a \in v)$ of linear operators on R^n, defined by

$$\Phi_a\xi = \Phi(t_a,t_0)\xi, \qquad t_a \in v.$$

It is not difficult to bring the total response within the present framework. Let the augmented input space V be defined (in both continuous and discrete cases) by

$$V = R^n x U_m(v).$$

The elements of V are then of the form $v = (\xi,u)$, and the transform S, defined on V by

$$(Sv)(t) = [S(\xi,u)](t) = \Phi(t,t_0)\xi + (Fu)(t), \qquad t \in v,$$

is obviously linear, well-defined, and bounded whenever F is. Similarly, the parameterized family $\{S_a: t_a \in v\}$, defined by

$$S_av = S_a(\xi,u) = \Phi(t_a,t_0)\xi + (Fu)(t_a), \qquad t_a \in v,$$

is an alternative representation of the total response.

Composite Systems

Although Theorems A and B are arrived at by direct observation of systems of first-order, linear, differential, and difference equations, the conclusion of these theorems can be extended to much larger classes of dynamic systems. In this section a system consisting of intercoupled discrete and continuous subsystems is analyzed (see Figure 2.16). Any such aggregate of continuous-time and discrete-time subsystems, coupled by linear interface elements (i.e., sample or clamp operations), is called a *composite system*.

In Figure 2.16 $u = (u_1, \ldots, u_r)$ denotes an element of the Cartesian product space $U = [l(\sigma)]^r$, whence $v = (v_1, \ldots, v_s)$ is an element of the Cartesian product space $V = [L_1(\tau)]^s$. The tuplet $x = (x_1, \ldots, x_c)$ lies in the product space $[l(\sigma)]^c$, and the tuplet $y = (y_1, \ldots, y_d)$ is found in the product space $Y = [L_1(\tau)]^d$. The free responses $\Phi_1: R^c \to X$ and $\Phi_2: R^d \to Y$ are transformations, as defined in Eq. 6. Similarly, the functions F and G are examples of Eqs. 4 and 5, respectively. Taking into account the first-order clamp $C: X \to V$, we assume that the equations governing the system behavior are the following:

$$x(s) = \Phi_1(s,t_0)x^0 + \sum_{j=0}^{[s]-1} h_j\Phi_1(s,t_{j+1})B_1(t_j)u(t_j), \qquad s \in \sigma, \tag{7}$$

$$y(t) = \Phi_2(t,t_0)y^0 + \int_{t_0}^t \Phi_2(t,\beta)B_2(\beta)[v(\beta) + (Cx)(\beta)]d\beta, \qquad t \in \tau. \tag{8}$$

With the meaning of these equations, we write

$$x(s) = (\Phi_1 x^0)(s) + (Fu)(s), \qquad\qquad s \in \sigma, \qquad (9)$$

$$y(t) = (\Phi_2 y^0)(t) + (Gv)(t) + (GCx)(t), \qquad t \in \tau. \qquad (10)$$

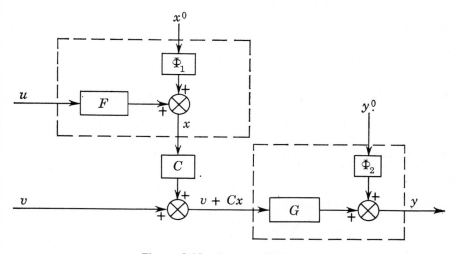

Figure 2.16   A composite system.

If $z^0 = (x^0, y^0) \in R^n = R^c \times R^d$ denotes the total system initial condition, then, from Eqs. 9 and 10, it follows that the system free response is defined by the equation set

$$x(s) = (\Phi_1 x^0)(s), \qquad\qquad s \in \sigma,$$
$$\qquad\qquad\qquad\qquad\qquad\qquad\qquad\qquad\qquad\qquad (11)$$
$$y(t) = (GC\Phi_1 x^0)(t) + (\Phi_2 y^0)(t), \qquad t \in \tau.$$

To be more concise, let the matrix $\Phi_3(t, t_0)$ be defined on τ by

$$\Phi_3(t, t_0) = \int_{t_0}^{t} \Phi_2(t, \beta) B_2(\beta) C \Phi_1(\beta, t_0) d\beta, \qquad t \in \tau. \qquad (12)$$

Then, if $\Theta(r; t_0)$ denotes the matrix defined by

$$\Theta(r; t_0) = \begin{bmatrix} \Phi_1(s, t_0) & 0 \\ \Phi_3(t, t_0) & \Phi_2(t, t_0) \end{bmatrix}, \qquad r = (s, t) \in \sigma \times \tau, \qquad (13)$$

the free response, defined in Eq. 11, may well be written as the linear transformation $\Theta : R^n \to X \times Y$ given by

$$(\Theta z^0)(r) = \Theta(r; t_0) z^0, \qquad r = (s, t) \in \sigma \times \tau. \qquad (14)$$

The forced response of the composite system may be similarly described. We set $z^0 = 0$ in Eqs. 9 and 10, with the result that

$$x(s) = (Fu)(s), \qquad\qquad\qquad s \in \sigma, \qquad\qquad (15)$$

$$y(t) = (GCFu)(t) + (Gv)(t), \qquad t \in \tau. \qquad\qquad (16)$$

By modifying Eq. 12 to read

$$\Phi_3(t,t_j) = \int_{t_j}^t \Phi_2(t,\beta)B_2(\beta)\Phi_1(\beta,t_j)d\beta, \qquad t \in \tau, \quad t_j \in \sigma \qquad (17)$$

we can show that

$$(GCFu)(t) = \sum_{j=0}^{[t]-1} h_j\Phi_3(t,t_{j+1})B_1(t_j)u(t_j), \qquad t \in \tau.$$

Thus, in terms of the matrices

$$W_1(s,t_j) = h_j\Phi_1(s,t_{j+1})B_1(t_j), \qquad s,\, t_j \in \sigma,$$
$$W_2(t,\beta) \;= \Phi_2(t,\beta)B_2(\beta), \qquad\quad t,\, \beta \in \tau, \qquad\qquad (18)$$
$$W_3(t,t_j) \;= h_j\Phi_3(t,t_{j+1})B_1(t_j), \qquad (t,t_j) \in \tau \times \sigma,$$

Eqs. 15 and 16 may be rewritten in concrete form as

$$x(s) = \sum_{j=0}^{[s]-1} W_1(s,t_j)u(t_j), \qquad\qquad\qquad s \in \sigma, \qquad\qquad (19)$$

$$y(t) = \sum_{j=0}^{[t]-1} W_3(t,t_j)u(t_j) + \int_{t_0}^t W_2(t,\beta)v(\beta)d\beta, \qquad t \in \tau. \qquad (20)$$

It is clear from these results that the composite system of Figure 2.16 may be given precisely the same characterization as the discrete-time and continuous-time systems. The forced response may be described as the transformation T which sends elements (u,v) in the Banach space $U \times V$ into elements $(x,y) \in X \times Y$,

$$[T(u,v)](r) = [x(s),y(t)], \qquad r = (s,t) \in \sigma \times \tau, \qquad\qquad (21)$$

according to Eqs. 19 and 20, as $r = (s,t)$ takes on values in the rectangle $\sigma \times \tau$. With the free response transformation Θ defined as in Eq. 14, the total response can be represented as the transformation $(\Theta,T): R^n \times X \times Y \to X \times Y$, defined by

$$[(\Theta,T)(z^0,u,v)](r) = (\Theta z^0)(r) + [T(u,v)](r), \qquad r \in \sigma \times \tau. \qquad (22)$$

By taking fixed points $r_a \in \sigma \times \tau$ we find that a parameterized family of transformations from $R^n \times X \times Y$ into R^n also results.

Continuity in Multivariant Systems

We have seen that a product of two Banach spaces equipped with a suitable definition of norm is a Banach space. For example, we may take

$$\|(u,v)\| = \max \{\|u\|, \|v\|\}$$

$$\|(u,v)\| = (\|u\|^p + \|v\|^p)^{1/p}, \qquad 1 \le p < \infty.$$

It is clear from these examples, and in fact it is true for *any* product norm, that a sequence (u_n, v_n) in $U \times V$ converges to $(u,v) \in U \times V$ in the sense of the norm in $U \times V$ if and only if $u_n \to u$, $v_n \to v$ in U and V, respectively. Stated another way, two vectors (u,v) and (u',v') are close in $U \times V$ if and only if u is close to u' in U and v is close to v' in V.

Consider now the transformation T defined by Eq. 20. Since $x = Fu$, $y = G(v + Cx) = Gv + GCFu$, it follows that T is linear. For example, $\lambda(u,v) = (\lambda u, \lambda v)$ is mapped by T into the vector whose components are

$$F(\lambda u) = \lambda Fu = \lambda x,$$

$$G(\lambda v) + GCF(\lambda u) = \lambda Gv + \lambda GCFu = \lambda y,$$

which shows that

$$T\lambda(u,v) = \lambda T(u,v).$$

This uses the fact that the transformations $F: U \to X$, $C: X \to V$, $G: V \to Y$, are linear. If, in addition, these mappings are bounded, then T is bounded; indeed, if $(u_n, v_n) \in U \times V$ converges to (u,v) in $U \times V$, then

$$u_n \to u,$$
$$v_n \to v;$$

hence by the continuity of F, C, and G

$$Fu_n \to Fu,$$

$$G(v_n + CFu_n) \to G(v + CFu);$$

that is,

$$T(u_n, v_n) \to T(u,v).$$

It is thus clear that the boundedness of the transformation representing the composite system follows from the boundedness of the transformations representing the various subsystems. We are therefore led to determine conditions under which these transformations are bounded. (This conclusion may be generalized open loop combinations of finitely many subsystems. Closed loop subsystems, however, require further analysis. Exercises 7 to 11 give an indication of the difficulties incurred.)

Recall that two norms $\| \ \|$, $\| \ \|'$ on a space X are equivalent if there are constants $0 < \alpha \le \beta$ such that

$$\alpha \|x\| \le \|x\|' \le \beta \|x\|, \qquad \text{all } x \in X.$$

Suppose now that $\| \ \|$ and $\| \ \|'$ are equivalent norms on a space X and that $|\ |$ and $|\ |'$ are equivalent norms on another space Y. If A is a linear mapping from X into Y, we have

$$\|Ax\| \le M\|x\|, \qquad \text{all } x \in X,$$

if and only if

$$\|Ax\|' \le M'\|x\|', \qquad \text{all } x \in X.$$

In other words, a bounded linear mapping from one Banach space into another remains bounded when these spaces are equipped with any equivalent norms.

In particular, if $X = X_1 \times \cdots \times X_n$, and $Y = Y_1 \times \cdots \times Y_m$ are product spaces, then, to prove that a linear transformation A of X into Y is bounded we may choose any convenient pair of norms on X and Y. This observation leads to a further simplification in the computations needed to prove boundedness. Let $Ax = y = (y_1, \ldots, y_m) \in Y$ be the image of the vector $x = (x_1, \ldots, x_n)$ in X. Then A will be bounded if

$$\max_{1 \le j \le m} \{\|y_j\|\} \le M[\max_{1 \le i \le n} \{\|x_i\|\}].$$

In other words, the linear transformation $A: X \to Y$ is bounded if (and only if) each of the mappings $A_j: X \to Y_j \, (j = 1, 2, \ldots, m)$ are bounded, where

$$A_j x = y_j.$$

Consider now the transformation G of Figure 2.16. For $v = (v_1, \ldots, v_s) \in V$, Gv is the vector in Y whose jth component is given by

$$(C_j v)(t) = \int_{t_0}^{t} \sum_{k=1}^{s} W_2^{(j,k)}(t,\beta) v_k(\beta) d\beta, \qquad 1 \le j \le d,$$

where $W_2^{(j,k)}(t,\beta)$ denotes the (j,k) element of the matrix $W_2(t,\beta)$; G is bounded if each transformation $G_j: V \to Y_j$ is bounded, and this in turn follows from the inequalities

$$\left\| \int_{t_0}^{t} W_2^{(j,k)}(t,\beta) v_k(\beta) d\beta \right\| \le M\|v_k\|, \qquad 1 \le k \le s; \ 1 \le j \le d,$$

where the norm on the left is the norm in Y_j and $\|v_k\|$ denotes the norm in V_k.

We cannot go much further without specifying the input space V, and this choice in turn is dictated by physical considerations. For example, we may want to study the behavior of the continuous system G, allowing as much as differentiability of the input vector functions v or as little as integrability, so that the corresponding choices of V vary between $C^1 \times \cdots \times C^1$ and $L_1 \times \cdots \times L_1$. Worse yet (from the general point of view), certain situations may force consideration of inputs $v = (v_1, \ldots, v_s)$, whose various components do not satisfy uniform requirements, so that V may consist of a product involving C, C', C'', $\ldots$, as well as various L_p spaces. Finally, physical considerations dictate the norms (and therefore the choices for Y_j) that are of interest in regard to the output vector $y = Gv$.

We illustrate the technique by examining a special case. Suppose we choose $V_1 = V_2 = \cdots = V_s = L_p(t_0,b)$, where p is fixed ($1 \leq p \leq \infty$). We can then specify a sufficient condition on the functions $W_2^{(i,j)}(t,\beta)$ in the matrix $W_2(t,\beta)$ which guarantees the boundedness of G. This, of course, depends also on the spaces Y_j. With $v_k \in L_p(t_0,b)$ we require $W_2^{(j,k)}(t,\beta)$ to be an $L_q(t_0,b)$ function for each t to guarantee integrability of the product $W_2^{(j,k)}(t,\beta)v_k(\beta)$. (Here $1/p + 1/q = 1$, with the usual convention that if $p = 1$, $q = \infty$.) Let us assume even more, namely that $|W_2^{(j,k)}(t,s)| \leq M_{jk}$ is a bounded function on the rectangle $[t_0,b] \times [t_0,b]$. Then, using the Holder inequality, we have

$$\left| \int_{t_0}^{t} W_2^{(j,k)}(t,\beta)v_k(\beta)d\beta \right| \leq \int_{t_0}^{t} M_{jk}|v_k(\beta)|d\beta$$

$$\leq \int_{0}^{b} M_{jk}|v_k(\beta)|d\beta \leq M'_{jk}\|v_k\|,$$

where

$$M'_{jk} = \begin{cases} b^{1/q}M_{jk}, & \text{if } 1 \leq q < \infty, \\ M_{jk}, & \text{if } q = \infty, \end{cases}$$

and $\|v_k\|$ is the norm of v_k in $L_p(t_0,b)$. Thus the L_∞ norm of the function $\int_0^t W_2^{(j,k)}(t,\beta)v_k(\beta)d\beta$ does not exceed $M\|v_k\|$ where

$$M = \max_{j,k} \{M'_{jk}\}.$$

To summarize, if the matrix W_2 consists of bounded functions, then G will be a bounded linear transformation from $V = L_p(t_0,b) \times \cdots \times L_p(t_0,b)$ into $L_\infty(t_0,b) \times \cdots \times L_\infty(t_0,b)$.

Exercises

1. Does the matrix $\Theta(r,r_0)$ of Eq. 13 have the usual semigroup property and inverse properties of a system transition matrix?

2. Verify the formula for $(GCFu)(t)$ given following Eq. 17.

3. Let $A(t,\mu)$ be a time-varying matrix depending continuously on the

parameter μ. Let $\bar{\mu}$ be a nominal value for μ and $A(t,\mu) = A(t,\bar{\mu}) + d\mu H(t)$ describe functional behavior of A over a neighborhood $\{d\mu: \|d\mu\| < k\}$ with k small. For the system

$$\dot{x}(t) = A(t,\mu)x(t) + B(t)u(t), \qquad t \in \tau,$$

what is the general form of the perturbations in the transformations Φ, Φ_a, F, and F_a in the vicinity of $\bar{\mu}$? For the special case where A and H are diagonal, does the norm of $\delta\Phi$, $\delta\Phi_a$, δF, and δF_a as functions on appropriate Hilbert spaces provide a meaningful measure of system sensitivity to variations in μ?

4. Let B_1, B_2 denote the sets of functions which are defined on an underlying time set v. Let f denote a mapping from B_1 into B_2 and t' an arbitrary point of v. If, for every $u \in B_1$, the values of the functions $y = fu$ for $t \geq t'$ are completely determined by the number

$$y(t') = (fu)(t')$$

and the values of u for $t \geq t'$, then f is said to be a *causal* mapping. Prove that the linear dynamic system

$$d_t x(t) = A(t)x(t) + B(t)u(t), \qquad t \in v,$$
$$y(t) = C(t)x(t) + D(t)u(t) \tag{23}$$

is causal in both the discrete and continuous cases; $v = \sigma$, with $d_t = \Delta_t$ and $v = \tau$, $d_t = d/dt$. Is the composite system of this section causal?

5. The mapping f of Exercise 4 is said to be *nonanticipatory* if for every $t' \in v$ the value

$$y(t') = (fu)(t')$$

is unaffected by the values of u for $t > t'$. Determine if the system of Eq. 23 is nonanticipatory. Is the composite system of this section nonanticipatory? If not, under what conditions is it nonanticipatory?

6. Consider once more the linear dynamic system of Eq. 3. If τ is the interval $[t_a, t_c]$ and if we define the transformation F_a^b by

$$F_a^b u = \int_{t_a}^{t_b} \Phi(t_b, s)B(s)u(s)\,ds$$

show that the total system response satisfies

$$x(t_c) - \Phi(t_c, t_a)x(t_a) = \Phi(t_c, t_b)F_a^b u + F_b^c u$$

for every $t_h \in \tau$.

In the remaining exercises we consider the single loop system of Figure 2.17. In this figure the following transformations are in evidence: $F: B_1 \rightarrow B_2$ represents the internal response of a fixed plant, $G: B_1 \rightarrow B_1$ and $L: B_2 \rightarrow B_1$ are compensation transformations while $K: B_2 \rightarrow B_2$ and $J: B_2 \rightarrow B_2$ are output constraints. The symbols B_1, B_2, and B_3 denote Banach spaces. The system variables are as follows: u and x denote the system input and useful output, respectively, e_4 denotes the observable output, e_3 denotes the internal (state function space) response, e_2 represents the plant input, while the elements ξ and η denote system disturbances.

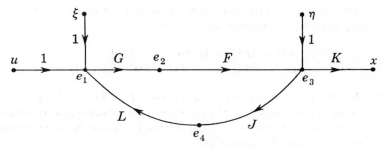

Figure 2.17   A single loop system.

7. Let $M = LJ$ and assuming that $(I + MFG)$ and $(I + FGM)$ are invertible show that

$$e_1 = (I + MFG)^{-1} [u + \xi - M\eta]$$

$$e_3 = (I + FGM)^{-1} [FG(u + \xi) + \eta].$$

If the compensators, $M = LJ$ and G, are required to maintain the uncompensated noise-free ($\xi = 0 = \eta$) plant relationship $e_3 = Fu$, show that

$$G = (I - MF)^{-1}. \tag{24}$$

8. Let all transformations be linear and bounded. Show that if $\|FGM\|$, $\|MF\|$, and $\|FM\|$ are all <1 then

(a) $G = (I - MF)^{-1}$

implies the identities

(b) $(I + FGM)^{-1} = (I - FM)$
(c) $(I + MFG)^{-1} = (I - MF)$
(d) $(I + FGM)^{-1}FG = F$
(e) $I - M(I + FGM)^{-1}FG = I - MF$

HINT: Use Theorem H, Section 2.2, to establish the required invertibility, then clear fractions.) Note that if bounded operators are loosely identified with stable systems these results resemble a well-known stability sufficiency condition. (See references [B105], [B106], [B123] for further elaboration in this direction.)

9. Develop a synthesis technique for realizing G in Eq. 24 based on the Neumann expansion (Theorem H, Section 2.2).

10. Note that the undisturbed system satisfies the equations $\bar{e}_3 = Fu$ and $\bar{e}_1 = u - M\bar{e}_3$. If $\xi, \eta = 0$ and the plant disturbance $F \to F + \delta F$ occurs show that to a first-order approximation the disturbances δe_3 and δe_1 in $\bar{e}_1$ and $\bar{e}_3$, respectively, satisfy

$$e_1 = [I - MF]\,[-M\delta Fu + \xi - M\eta]$$
$$e_3 = [I - FM]\,[\delta Fu + F(I - MF)^{-1}\xi + \eta]$$

11. Assume that F is invertible and defined $M_\lambda = \lambda F^{-1}$, where $0 < \lambda < 1$. What can be said about the limitations on reducing system sensitivity by means of feedback? (What interaction exists between sensitivity reduction and the gain of G?)

2.6 REFERENCES FOR CHAPTER 2

Sections 2.1 and 2.2 continue the development of Chapter 1; hence the texts suggested in that chapter as general references will serve this objective for these two sections as well. Because matrices and determinants are used as a working tool throughout Chapter 2, we add the following to the preceding list: Aitken [A1], Ayres [A7], Cooke [A17], Hoffman and Kunze [A42], and Perlis [A66]. For further examples and results on integral equations, see also Tricomi [A87] and Volterra [A92].

On the theory of differential and differences equations a variety of fine books is available. Several of the general references have chapters on these topics. Suggested reading includes the specialized texts of Bellman [A10], Coddington [A15], Kaplan [A46] and [A47], Miller [A61], Pontryagin [A68], and Spiegel [A80]. On a somewhat higher level Coddington and Levinson [A16] and Lefschetz [A55] are recommended. The theory of difference equations is also well documented. For difference equations consult Goldberg [A34], Miller [A59], and Richardson [A70]. The reader is also referred to Appendices 3 and 4, which supplement Sections 2.3 and 2.4.

Among the several available texts which deal with applications or offer an alternative treatment Tou [A86] and Zadeh and Desoer [A95] are most closely related to Sections 2.3 and 2.4. In a more classical vein are Brown [A13], Horowitz [A43], Jury [A45], Kuo [A53], Peschon [A67], Tou [A85], and Tsypkin [A89].

In the remaining chapters we concentrate on linear systems. It should be noted, however, that many nonlinear system problems can be viewed as natural extensions of the topics of Chapter 2. Specifically the work of Sandberg [B105,B106,B107,B108,B109], Zames [B123,B124], Minty [B84,B85,B86], Browder [B15,B16,B17], and Zarantonello [B125,B126] constitute an important body of nonlinear system theory (see also Anselone [A5], Cronin [A18], Krasnosel'skii [A51,A52], Satty and Braun [A74], and Vainberg [A91]).

3 THE STRUCTURE OF LINEAR SYSTEMS

From the development of Chapter 2 it is now self-evident that the behavior of linear dynamic systems and the properties of linear transformations between Banach spaces are intimately related. In the examples and discussions of Section 2.5, for instance, we have seen that several typical systems can be represented as bounded linear transformations between Cartesian products of L_p and l_p spaces. This knowledge is comforting, for we are now assured that the effort devoted to studying the abstract concepts of Chapter 1 has already paid a dividend of perspective in the modeling of these systems.

If, however, the objectives of the system analyst were limited to modeling the system, his technological contribution would certainly be rather shallow. Such is not the case. Indeed, we usually find that the modeling problem is only the first necessary step in the study of more sophisticated problems such as sensitivity, optimal control, stability, synthesis procedures, and signal filtering. In the remainder of the book we shall take these objectives as our own.

As we turn from answering the question, "What are linear dynamic systems?" to the more interesting problem of what can be done with the answer, we find that attention naturally focuses on the structural properties of linear transformations. Quite a bit of information has already been uncovered in Sections 2.1 and 2.2. This chapter builds on this beginning and brings to partial completion the development of concepts that are vital to our objectives.

164

3.1 LINEAR FUNCTIONALS

With the exception of the identity operator and the zero transformation, a linear functional is the simplest of all linear transformations. As such, their structural properties are more accessible than those of a more general linear transformation. In this section we consider functionals in some detail. This is by no means a process of "getting our courage up" to tackle the more general transformations, for functionals are highly useful tools in a number of later applications.

DEFINITION A.   *A linear functional[1] is a linear transformation which maps its domain X (a normed linear space) into K, the scalars associated with X.*

The spaces K of scalars (i.e., R or C) have been shown to be Banach spaces of dimension 1. Hence a functional is an element of the space $L(X,K)$ of all linear transformations from X into K. If the linear functional f is also bounded, then $f \in \beta(X,K)$, the space of all bounded linear operators from X to K.

The spaces $L(X,K)$ and $\beta(X,K)$ are of such importance in modern analysis that it is standard practice to earmark special symbols to designate these spaces. Although universal acceptance of a standard symbolism has not been achieved, the notation $X' = L(X,K)$ and $X^* = \beta(X,K)$ is frequently used and is adopted throughout the remainder of the present treatment. Thus X^* is the (complete normed) linear subspace of the linear space X' which consists of the *bounded* linear functionals on X. For reasons made apparent later, X^* is called the conjugate space, or the dual space, of the space X. The elements $f \in X^*$ are called real or complex, according to the scalar set being used.

Since the scalars form a Banach space, the properties we have derived for linear transformations hold for functionals. To be specific we summarize these properties for the space X^*.

Properties of Linear Functionals

(1) $f(x_1 + x_2) = f(x_1) + f(x_2)$, $x_1, x_2 \in X$.

(2) $f(\alpha x) = \alpha f(x)$,   all $x \in X$, all scalars α.

(3) $f(x_n) \to f(x)$ if $x_n \to x$, $x_n, x \in X$.

(4) $|f(x)| \le M\|x\|$,   all $x \in X$, some $M \ge 0$.

(5) $\|f\| = \sup_{\|x\|=1} |f(x)| = \sup_{\|x\| \le 1} |f(x)|$.

We emphasize in particular that X^* is a Banach space, whether X is or not. As examples of linear functionals that frequently occur, consider the following:

---

[1]The term functional originated in the theory of integral equations in which it was used to distinguish between a function in the elementary sense defined on a set of numbers and a function (or functional) defined on a set of functions.

Example 1. In the Euclidean space E^3 let $x = (x_1, x_2, x_3)$; then any linear combination $f_0(x) = \bar{\alpha}_1 x_1 + \bar{\alpha}_2 x_2 + \bar{\alpha}_3 x_3$ is a linear functional. Since $\sum_{i=1}^3 \bar{\alpha}_i x_i$ is the inner product of the vectors $x_0 = (\alpha_1, \alpha_2, \alpha_3)$ and x, we can represent this function by $f_0(x) = \langle x, x_0 \rangle$. By changing the vector x_0 we have a family of functionals in R^3 of the form $f_\alpha(x) = \langle x, x_\alpha \rangle$. The Schwarz inequality gives

$$|f_0(x)| \le \left(\sum_i |\alpha_i|^2 \right)^{1/2} \left(\sum_i |x_i|^2 \right)^{1/2};$$

hence f_0 is bounded with norm

$$\|f_0\| \le \left(\sum_i |\alpha_i|^2 \right)^{1/2}.$$

It is easy to see that equality holds in this last relation.

Example 2. Let $X = L_2(0,1)$ and consider $f(x) = \int_0^1 x(t)dt$. This functional assigns to every x a real number (its average value). Since, by the Schwarz inequality,

$$|f(x)| = \left| \int_0^1 x(t)dt \right| \le \int_0^1 |x(t)|dt \le \left[\int_0^1 |x(t)|^2 dt \right]^{1/2} < \infty,$$

it is clear that $f(x)$ is bounded with norm ≤ 1. By use of the definition $\langle x, y \rangle = \int_0^1 x(t)\overline{y(t)}dt$, it is made evident that $f(x) = \langle x, 1 \rangle$. In general, the inner product $f_n(x) = \langle x, h \rangle$, where $h \in L_2(0,1)$ is a bounded linear functional on $L_2(0,1)$.

Example 3. Let $X = C[a,b]$. Let t_0 be any fixed point in the interval $[a,b]$. The formula

$$f(x) = x(t_0)$$

defines an element of X^*, as shown in Example 10 of Section 2.1. A generalization of this linear functional is given by

$$f(x) = \int_a^b x(s)dg(s),$$

where g is an arbitrary function of bounded variation defined on $[a,b]$ and the integral is a Stieltjes integral. For the reader unfamiliar with the Stieltjes integral, the case in which g has a continuous derivative g' can be written as

$$f(x) = \int_a^b x(s)g'(s)ds,$$

this latter integral being a Riemann integral.

Example 4.   Let $X = l_2$. Suppose that $a = \{\alpha_n\}$ is an element of l_2 and define f by

$$f(x) = \langle x,a \rangle = \sum_{i=1}^{\infty} \bar{\alpha}_i \xi_i,$$

where $x = \{\xi_n\}$. The Schwarz inequality shows that the series converges and that f belongs to X^* with norm $\leq (\sum_i |\alpha_i|^2)^{1/2}$.

In Examples 1, 2, and 4 the functional has been expressed as an inner product. Furthermore, each functional of the inner product type is characterized by just one vector; that is, f_0 is determined by x_0 and f_h is determined by h.[1] These two aspects of functionals carry over to much more general situations. Let us restrict our attention at first to Hilbert spaces.

Let y be a fixed vector in a Hilbert space H and consider the functional f_y, which we define on H by the inner product $f_y(x) = \langle x,y \rangle$. It is easy to see that f_y is linear, for

$$f_y(x_1 + x_2) = \langle x_1 + x_2, y \rangle = \langle x_1, y \rangle + \langle x_2, y \rangle = f_y(x_1) + f_y(x_2)$$

and

$$f_y(\alpha x) = \langle \alpha x, y \rangle = \alpha \langle x, y \rangle = \alpha f_y(x).$$

Furthermore, by utilizing

$$|f_y(x)| = |\langle x,y \rangle| \leq \|x\| \cdot \|y\|$$

we see that f_y is continuous, hence $f_y \in H^*$. This also shows that $\|f_y\| \leq \|y\|$.

We can even show that $\|f_y\| = \|y\|$. If $y = 0$, this equality holds. Therefore we assume $y \neq 0$ and choose $x_0 = y/\|y\|$.

$$|f_y(x_0)| = \frac{|\langle y,y \rangle|}{\|y\|} = \|y\|.$$

Since $\|x_0\| = 1$, we have proved our assertion.

We have also shown that each y in H defines a functional f_y in H^*. The equation $\|f_y\| = \|y\|$ shows that the correspondence $y \rightarrow f_y$ is a one-to-one norm-preserving mapping from H into H^*. The following theorem shows that this map is *onto* H^*.

THEOREM A.   *Let H be a Hilbert space and let f be an arbitrary functional in H^*. There then exists a unique vector u in H such that*

$$f(x) = \langle x,u \rangle$$

for every x in H. Furthermore, $\|f\| = \|u\|$.

---

[1] To prove this statement it suffices to observe that if $h, k \in H$ and $f(x) = \langle x,h \rangle = \langle x,k \rangle$, then $\langle x, h - k \rangle = 0$ for all $x \in H$. Choosing $x = h - k$, we have $\|h - k\|^2 = 0 = h = k$.

P R O O F. Consider first the null space N_f of f. If $N_f = H$, we have $f(x) = 0$ for all $x \in H$ and $f(x) = \langle x, 0 \rangle = 0$ and $u = 0$ is the required representation of f. We have already found that N_f is a closed subspace, and for convenience we partition X into the direct sum $H = N_f \oplus N_f^\perp$, as the projection theorem says we can always do. Now for an arbitrary $x \in H$, $x \notin N_f$, we have the representation

$$x = z + w, \qquad z \in N_f^\perp, \qquad w \in N_f, \qquad z \neq 0.$$

Then $f(x) = f(z) + f(w) = f(z) = \alpha \neq 0$. We now define $x_1 = z/\alpha$, so that $f(x_1) = 1$. Let $y \in H$ be a completely arbitrary element with $f(y) = \beta$. Then

$$0 = f(y) - \beta f(x_1) = f(y - \beta x_1).$$

Thus

$$y - \beta x_1 = w_1 \in N_f$$

or

$$y = \beta x_1 + w_1;$$

that is, every y is the sum of a vector from N_f and a vector in the one-dimensional subspace spanned by x_1. Note also that $x_1 \perp w_1$; hence

$$\langle y, x_1 \rangle = \beta \|x_1\|^2,$$

and, since $\beta = f(y)$, we have

$$f(y) = \frac{\langle y, x_1 \rangle}{\|x_1\|^2} = \langle y, u \rangle = f_u(y),$$

where $u = x_1 / \|x_1\|^2$.

Since y is arbitrary, we conclude that the given functional f is the functional f_u. We have already seen, however, that $\|f_u\| = \|u\|$ and that if $f_u = f_r$ then $u = r$. Hence u is the only vector in H satisfying $f = f_u$ and $\|f\| = \|u\|$ as required.

The preceding theorem gives us a great deal of information about the structure of an abstract Hilbert space. We know, for instance, that the functionals in Examples 1, 2, and 4 are the only possible bounded linear functionals on these spaces. More generally, the collection of mappings $x \to \langle x, y \rangle$, y fixed in H, is precisely the set of all bounded linear functionals on any given Hilbert space H.

Another important consequence of the theorem concerns the structure of the space H^*. Recall that if B is a normed linear space, then the set B^* of all bounded linear functionals on B is always a Banach space. In general, we can say little more than this about the structure of B^*. The situation is much simpler when B is in fact a Hilbert space H: we assert that the mapping

$y \rightarrow f_y$ is *conjugate linear*; that is,

$$f_{y_1 + y_2} = f_{y_1} + f_{y_2}, \qquad f_{\alpha y} = \bar{\alpha} f_y.$$

Both of these equations follow easily from the definitions. For example,

$$f_{\alpha y}(x) = \langle x, \alpha y \rangle = \bar{\alpha} \langle x, y \rangle = \bar{\alpha} f_y(x)$$

proves that $y \rightarrow f_y$ is conjugate homogeneous.

We now define a function $(\,,)$ on $H^* \times H^*$ by setting

$$(f_x, f_y) = \langle y, x \rangle.$$

Since each $f \in H^*$ is of the form f_u for some $u \in H$ and there is exactly one u in H for which this is true, it follows that $(\,,)$ is unambiguous and therefore an honest complex-valued function defined on all of $H^* \times H^*$. We assert that $(\,,)$ is actually an inner product on H^*. Before proving this, however, note that by Theorem A the norm of the bounded linear functional f_y agrees with the norm of its representing vector y in H; that is,

$$\|f_y\| \text{ (operator norm)} = \|y\|.$$

Hence

$$\|f_y\| \text{ (inner product norm)} = \|f_y\| \text{ (operator norm)},$$

and it follows that H^*, equipped with the inner product $(\,,)$, is complete and hence a Hilbert space.

The proof that $(\,,)$ is an inner product follows:

$$(f_{x_1} + f_{x_2}, f_y) = \langle y, x_1 + x_2 \rangle = \langle y, x_1 \rangle + \langle y, x_2 \rangle$$
$$= (f_{x_1}, f_y) + (f_{x_2}, f_y)$$

$$(\alpha f_x, f_y) = (f_{\bar{\alpha} x}, f_y) = \langle y, \bar{\alpha} x \rangle = \alpha \langle y, x \rangle = \alpha(f_x, f_y)$$

$$\overline{(f_x, f_y)} = \overline{\langle y, x \rangle} = \langle x, y \rangle = (f_y, f_x)$$

$$(f_x, f_x) = 0 \Rightarrow \|x\|^2 = 0 \Rightarrow x = 0 \Rightarrow f_x = 0.$$

We summarize our results in the following corollary.

COROLLARY. *If H is a Hilbert space, the conjugate space H^* is also a Hilbert space. The inner product on H^* is given by*

$$(f_x, f_y) = \langle y, x \rangle,$$

and the inner product definition of the norm f_y agrees with its previous definition as the norm of a linear transformation on H.

We can state this corollary another way. Let H_0 be the Hilbert space constructed as follows: the vectors of H_0 are to be the vectors of H; addition of two vectors x and y in H_0 is the addition of x and y in H; the H_0-product of the scalar λ with the vector x, however, is defined as the corresponding product of $\bar{\lambda}$ with x in H and the inner product $\langle\ ,\ \rangle$ in H_0 is defined by

$$\langle x,y\rangle_0 = \langle y,x\rangle.$$

The foregoing corollary then asserts that the conjugate space H^* of H is isometrically isomorphic to the Hilbert space H_0.[1]

We therefore identify H^* with H_0. Finally, it is clear that this discussion may be carried out equally well for the Hilbert space H_0 with the result that H_0^* is isometrically isomorphic to H. Since H and H_0 consist of precisely the same vectors with the same algebraic operations and differ only in that the inner product in one is "backward," it is customary to identify H with H_0. When this is done we have the fact that *every Hilbert space is self-conjugate*: $H^* = H$.

We now proceed to examine the content of this discussion in some specific Hilbert spaces.

Example 5.   In the space $l_2(n)$ of real n tuplets the inner product of two tuplets $x = (\xi_1, \ldots, \xi_n)$, $y = (\eta_1, \ldots, \eta_n)$, hence the most general bounded linear functional f, is defined by $f(x) = \langle x,y\rangle = \sum_{i=1}^{n}\xi_i\eta_i$. Furthermore,

$$\|f\|^2 = \sum|\eta_i|^2.$$

This result can be derived directly. The vectors $\{e_i\}_{i=1}^{n}$ with $e_i = (0, 0, \ldots, 0, 1, 0, \ldots, 0)$ form a basis for $l_2(n)$. Thus, if $x = (\xi_1, \ldots, \xi_n) \in l_2(n)$, then $x = \sum_{i=1}^{n}\xi_i e_i$. Now let f be a linear functional on $l_2(n)$ and let $\eta_i = f(e_i)$. Then

$$f(x) = f(\sum_i \xi_i e_i) = \sum_i \xi_i f(e_i) = \sum_i \xi_i\eta_i = \langle x,y\rangle,$$

where

$$y = (\eta_1, \ldots, \eta_n).$$

Example 6.   In much the same way as for the space $l_2(n)$ we can show that the most general bounded linear functional on l_2 is given by

$$f(x) = \langle x,y\rangle = \sum_{i=1}^{\infty} \xi_i\bar{\eta}_i,$$

$$\|f\|^2 = \|y\|^2 = \sum_{i=1}^{\infty} |y_i|^2.$$

[1]Observe that H_0 is the mirror image of H and in analogy to the situation in the complex plane H_0 deserves the designation as the space conjugate to H. The corollary may be interpreted as saying that the Banach space conjugate (dual) of H is the same as its (geometric) conjugate H_0. Note also that in a *real* Hilbert space there is no distinction between H and H_0.

Example 7.   In the space $L_2(0,1)$ the general functional is

$$f(x) = \int_0^1 x(t)\overline{y(t)}dt,$$

$$\|f\|^2 = \int_0^1 |y(t)|^2 dt.$$

The Conjugates of Some Specific Banach Spaces

The representation of linear functionals in terms of an inner product is valid only in a Hilbert space. Linear functionals on other concrete spaces, however, frequently have a familiar form. Our next example is a detailed examination of the linear functionals on a specific Banach space.

EXAMPLE 8.   Every bounded linear functional f on the space c_0 is of the form

$$f(x) = \sum_{i=1}^{\infty} \xi_i \eta_i, \qquad x = (\xi_1, \xi_2, \dots),$$

where

$$(\eta_1, \eta_2, \dots) \in l_1 \text{ and } \|f\| = \sum_{i=1}^{\infty} |\eta_i|.$$

PROOF.   If $(\eta_1, \eta_2, \dots) \in l_1$, then for each $x = (\xi_1, \xi_2, \dots)$ in c_0 we have

$$\sup |\xi_i| = \|x\| < \infty;$$

hence

$$\sum_{i=1}^{n} |\xi_i \eta_i| \le \|x\| \sum_{i=1}^{n} |\eta_i| \le \|x\| \sum_{i=1}^{\infty} |\eta_i| < \infty.$$

This implies that

$$\left| \sum_{i=1}^{\infty} \xi_i \eta_i \right| \le \|x\| \cdot \sum_{i=1}^{\infty} |\eta_i|.$$

It now follows that the function f defined on c_0 by

$$f(x) = \sum_{i=1}^{\infty} \xi_i \eta_i, \qquad x = (\xi_1, \xi_2, \dots) \in c_0,$$

is bounded with norm

$$\|f\| \le \sum_{i=1}^{\infty} |\eta_i|.$$

It is clear that f is linear.

To show that f has norm $\sum_{i=1}^{\infty} |\eta_i|$ it suffices that for each $\varepsilon > 0$ there is a vector $x = (\xi_1, \xi_2, \dots)$ in c_0 with $\|x\| \le 1$ and $|f(x)| > \sum_{i=1}^{\infty}|\eta_i| - \varepsilon$. Now, since $\sum_{i=1}^{\infty}|\eta_i| < \infty$, there is an integer n_0 such that

$$\sum_{i=n_0}^{\infty} |\eta_i| < \varepsilon.$$

Let $x = (\xi_1, \xi_2, \dots)$ be the vector whose coordinates ξ_i are defined by

$$\xi_i = \begin{cases} \dfrac{|\eta_i|}{\eta_i}, & \text{if } \eta_i \ne 0 \text{ and } i = 1, 2, \dots, n_0, \\[2mm] 0, & \text{otherwise.} \end{cases}$$

Clearly $x \in c_0$ and

$$f(x) = \sum_{i=1}^{\infty} \xi_i \eta_i = \sum_{i=1}^{n_0} |\eta_i| > \sum_{i=1}^{\infty} |\eta_i| - \varepsilon.$$

It remains to prove that if f is a bounded linear functional on c_0 there is a vector $(\eta_i, \eta_2, \dots)$ in l_1 such that

$$f(x) = \sum \xi_i \eta_i, \qquad \text{all } x = (\xi_1, \xi_2, \dots) \in c_0.$$

For this we set $\eta_i = f(x_i)$, in which $x_i \in c_0$ is the vector

$$x_i = (0, \dots, 0, 1, 0, \dots),$$

each of whose coordinates is 0 except the ith. If $x = (\xi_1, \xi_2, \dots, \xi_n, 0, \dots)$ has only finitely many nonzero coordinates, it is clear that $f(x) = \sum \xi_i \eta_i$. Now fix an integer n and set $x = (\xi_1, \xi_2, \dots)$, where

$$\xi_i = \begin{cases} \dfrac{|\eta_i|}{\eta_i}, & \text{if } \eta_i \ne 0 \text{ and } i = 1, 2, \dots, n, \\[2mm] 0, & \text{otherwise,} \end{cases}$$

as before. We get

$$\sum_{i=1}^{n} |\eta_i| = \sum_{i=1}^{n} \xi_i \eta_i = f(x) \le \|f\| \cdot \|x\| = \|f\|.$$

Since n is arbitrary, we conclude that $\sum_{i}^{\infty}|\eta_i| < \infty$, hence that

$$(\eta_1, \eta_2, \dots) \in l_1.$$

Finally, if $x = (\xi_1, \xi_2, \dots) \in c_0$ is given, we set $x_n = (\xi_1, \xi_2, \dots, \xi_n, 0, 0, \dots)$ for $n = 1, 2, 3, \dots$. It is clear that $x_n \in c_0$. Now, if $\varepsilon > 0$ is given, there is a n_0 such that $|\xi_i| < \varepsilon$ for $i \ge n_0$, hence

$$\|x - x_n\| = \sup_{i > n} |\xi_i| \le \varepsilon$$

whenever $n \geq n_0$. In other words, $x_n \to x$ in c_0. By the continuity of f, then, $f(x_n) \to f(x)$. On the other hand, $f(x_n) = \sum_{i=1}^{n} \xi_i \eta_i$, and it is easy to see that $\sum_{i=1}^{n} \xi_i \eta_i \to \sum_{i=1}^{\infty} \xi_i \eta_i$ as $n \to \infty$. We conclude therefore that

$$f(x) = \sum_{i=1}^{\infty} \xi_i \eta_i.$$

This completes the proof.

Example 8 is indicative of the situation that exists for several of the familiar Banach spaces. We now summarize the results for the Banach spaces of most interest in the applications.

THEOREM B. *Let* $1 < p < \infty$ *and* $1/p + 1/q = 1$. *Then if* f *is a bounded linear functional defined on the space* $L_p(\tau)$, *there is a uniquely determined element* $y \in L_q(\tau)$ *such that*

$$f(x) = f_y(x) = \int_\tau x(t)y(t)dt$$

and the norm of the functional is the $L_q(\tau)$ *norm of* y:

$$\|f\| = \|y\| = \left(\int_\tau |y(t)|^q dt \right)^{1/q}.$$

This result justifies the assertion that L_q is the conjugate space of L_p. In more detail the theorem asserts that the mapping $f \to f_y$ is a linear isometry from L_p^* onto L_q.

An analogous result for sequence spaces is summarized by Theorem C.

THEOREM C. *Let* $1 < p < \infty$, $1/p + 1/q = 1$. *If* f *is a bounded linear functional defined on the space* l_p, *there exists a unique element* $u \in l_q$ *such that*

$$f(x) = f_u(x) = \sum_{k=1}^{\infty} \xi_k \eta_k,$$

where $x = (\xi_1, \ldots, \xi_k, \ldots)$, $u = (\eta_1, \ldots, \eta_k, \ldots)$, *and* $\|f_u\| = \|u\|_q = (\sum_{i=1}^{n} |\eta_i|^q)^{1/q}$.

R E M A R K 1.   When $p = q = 2$, we have the results for the Hilbert spaces $L_2(\tau)$ and l_2. Since the space $l_2(n) \subset l_2$, Theorem C applies also to $l_2(n)$ in which case the functional takes the form $f(x) = \sum_{i=1}^{n} \xi_i y_i$.

These theorems are valid also when $p = 1$. Here the equation $1/p + 1/q = 1$ hints that we ought to have $L_1^* = L_\infty$ and $l_1^* = l_\infty$. These conjectures in fact are true. Thus every bounded linear functional f on $L_1(\tau)$ has the form

$$f(x) = f_y(x) = \int_\tau x(t)y(t)dt,$$

where

$$y \in L_\infty(\tau) \text{ and } \|f\| = \|y\|_\infty = \operatorname*{ess\ sup}_{t \in \tau} |y(t)|$$

Similarly, the bounded linear functionals on l_1 are of the form

$$f(x) = f_y(x) = \sum_{i=1}^{\infty} \xi_i \eta_i, \qquad x = (\xi_1, \xi_2, \dots) \in l_1,$$

where

$$y = (\eta_1, \eta_2, \dots)$$

belongs to l_∞ and

$$\| \, \|f = \|y\|_\infty = \sup_i |\eta_i|.$$

(The proof that $l_1^* = l_\infty$ follows the development of Example 8 closely.)

Thus Theorems B and C are correct for p in the range $1 \le p \le \infty$. A surprising (and often annoying) fact, however, is that both theorems are *false* for $p = \infty$. The fact that each $y = (\eta_1, \dots, \eta_n, \dots)$ in l_∞ determines a bounded linear functional on l_1 whose norm is $\|y\|_\infty$ gives us the inequality

$$\left| \sum_{i=1}^{\infty} \xi_i \eta_i \right| \le \left(\sum_{i=1}^{\infty} |\xi_i| \right) \left(\sup_i |\eta_i| \right).$$

If $x = (\xi_1, \dots, \xi_n, \dots)$ is fixed in l_1 and y is allowed to vary in l_∞, the mapping that sends y into the number $\sum_i \xi_i \eta_i$ is a bounded linear functional on l_∞; that is, $l_1 \subset l_\infty^*$. The inclusion, however, is a *proper* inclusion. There are not enough vectors in l_1 to represent *every* bounded linear functional on l_∞. The same comments apply to $L_\infty(\tau)$; that is, $L_1 \subset L_\infty^*$.

Perhaps it is worth mentioning that this pathology does not occur in the finite dimensional case; that is, the dual of $l_\infty(n)$ is $l_1(n)$, so that the formula $[l_p(n)]^* = l_q(n)$ holds for $1 \le p \le \infty$. The essential reason is the finite dimensionality of $l_\infty(n)$ or, what amounts to the same thing, the fact that *every* linear functional on $l_\infty(n)$ is bounded.

Finally, observe that if $1 < p < \infty$, then $1 < q < \infty$, and Theorem E (resp F) applied to L_q (resp l_q) shows that the dual of L_q (resp l_q) is L_p (resp l_p). More cryptically, $L_p^{**} = L_p$ and $l_p^{**} = l_p$, provided $1 < p < \infty$. The preceding remarks also show that $[l_p(n)]^{**} = l_p(n)$ for $1 \le p \le \infty$. Thus for $1 > p > \infty$ the spaces $l_p(n)$, l_p, and L_p are *reflexive* (see Section 3.3).

For the reader with a bit stronger background the results of these last two theorems can be more generally phrased in the following manner.

THEOREM D. *Let $1 \le p < \infty$ and $1/p + 1/q = 1$. Then, if f is a bounded linear functional on the Banach space $L_p(\tau, \mu)$ of all measurable functions f defined on τ for which $|f(t)|^p$ is μ-integrable, there is a uniquely determined element $y \in L_q(\tau, \mu)$ such that*

$$f(x) = f_y(x) = \int_\tau x(t)y(t)d\mu(t)$$

and

$$\|f_y\| = \|y\|_q = \left[\int_\tau |y(t)|^q d\mu(t) \right]^{1/q}.$$

The Space *BV*

Before proceeding to the next example we shall pause momentarily to discuss an important Banach space, the space of functions of bounded variation. Let $\{t_1, \ldots, t_{n-1}\}$ denote a subset of points in the interval $[a,b]$ and v, the subdivision of $[a,b]$ according to the rule $a = t_0 < t_1 < \cdots < t_n = b$. Then for every function f defined on $[a,b]$ the number

$$|f|_v = \sum_{i=0}^{n-1} |f(t_{i+1}) - f(t_i)|$$

can be computed. If Ω denotes the set of all possible partitions of the interval, we define the variation of the function f by

$$\operatorname*{var}_{[a,b]} (f) = \sup_{v \in \Omega} |f|_v$$

and if $\operatorname{var}_{[a,b]}(f) < \infty$ we call f a function of *bounded* variation.

We have neither the time nor the inclination to examine in detail this class of functions. We shall, however, summarize several of its important properties. First, we note that if f is nondecreasing [i.e., $f(t_1) \leq f(t_2)$ for $t_1 \leq t_2$], then $\operatorname{var}_{[a,b]}(f) = f(b) - f(a)$; similarly, if f is nonincreasing, then $\operatorname{var}_{[a,b]}(f) = f(a) - f(b)$. Second, if f is differentiable on the interval,

$$\operatorname*{var}_{[a,b]} (f) = \int_a^b |f'(t)| dt,$$

and, if f is a step function (i.e., f is constant except for step discontinuities at a finite number of points), then

$$\operatorname*{var}_{[a,b]} (f) = \sum |f(t_k^+) - f(t_k^-)|,$$

where the sum is taken over the points of discontinuity of f. It is obvious that the variation of a constant function is zero and that

$$\operatorname*{var}_{[a,b]} (\alpha f) = |\alpha| \operatorname*{var}_{[a,b]} (f)$$

$$\operatorname*{var}_{[a,b]} (f + g) \leq \operatorname*{var}_{[a,b]} (f) + \operatorname*{var}_{[a,b]} (g)$$

hold for every scalar α and functions f, g of bounded variation.

In other words, the space $BV[a,b]$ of all functions of bounded variation on $[a,b]$ is a linear space. Furthermore, except for the fact that $\operatorname{var}_{[a,b]}(f) = 0 \Rightarrow f$ is constant, instead of implying that $f = 0$, the "variation operator" satisfies the norm axioms on $BV[a,b]$. This slight deficiency can be patched up by requiring, for instance, that every $f \in BV[a,b]$ also satisfy the condition $f(t') = 0$ for some fixed $t' \in [a,b]$. As an alternative, we may consider any two functions f, $g \in BV[a,b]$ equivalent if they differ by a constant. In this way constant functions are equivalent to the zero function and $BV[a,b]$ becomes a normed linear space consisting of equivalence classes.

The space $L_1(a,b)$ may be embedded in the space $BV[a,b]$ in the following manner: for $f' \in L_1(a,b)$ we associate the function f according to the rule

$$f(t) = \int_a^t f'(s)ds, \qquad t \in [a,b].$$

This clearly defines a linear transformation from $L_1(a,b)$ into $BV[a,b]$. It can be shown that norms are also preserved; that is,

$$\operatorname*{var}_{[a,b]}(f) = \|f'\|_1, \qquad f' \in L_1(a,b).$$

It is not true, however, that every function $f \in BV(a,b)$ can be derived in this manner.

To exhibit a second subset of $BV(a,b)$ let us utilize the familiar (but formal) Dirac delta function notation.[1] We denote by $\delta(t - t_k)$ the generalized function defined by the conditions

$$\delta(t - t_k) = 0, \qquad\qquad t \neq t_k \in [a,b],$$

$$\int_{t_k - \varepsilon}^{t_k + \varepsilon} \delta(t - t_k)dt = 1, \qquad \varepsilon > 0.$$

Now let $\sigma = \{t_k\}$ be a subset of (a,b) which satisfies $t_k < t_{k+1}$ and $\alpha = (\alpha_1, \alpha_2, \dots)$, a tuplet in l_1. We denote by g'_α the function

$$g'_\alpha(t) = \sum_i \alpha_i \delta(t - t_i).$$

It then follows that the function $g_\alpha(t)$, defined by

$$g_\alpha(t) = \int_a^t g'_\alpha(s)ds,$$

is a multiple-step function with discontinuities on the points of σ and incremental step sizes $\{\alpha_i\}$. Furthermore, the variation of g_α is given by

$$\operatorname*{var}_{[a,b]}(g_\alpha) = \|\alpha\| = \sum_i |\alpha_i|.$$

Hence it is clear that we can in a natural way consider $L_1(a,b)$ and the linear spaces of all generalized functions of the foregoing type as proper subspaces of $BV(a,b)$.

---

[1]The delta function can be given a precise meaning within the framework of the theory of distributions. Several excellent treatments (see [A29], [A75], or [A95], for example) are at the disposal of the interested reader.

THEOREM E.   *Every linear functional on the space $C(0,1)$ can be represented by a Stieltjes integral*

$$f(x) = \int_0^1 x(t)dg(t), \qquad x \in C(0,1),$$

where $g(t)$ is of bounded variation on $[0,1]$ and $\|f\|$ is the total variation of g.

It is clear that in these examples the functionals on the Banach spaces involved look quite a bit like functionals on Hilbert spaces. In the examples given each functional f_u on X is formed by choosing an element u from an auxiliary space U and performing the operation $f_u(x) = \langle x,u \rangle$; the symbol $\langle \, , \rangle$ indicates an inner-product-like operation, which, of course, takes concrete forms appropriate to the space X itself.

The spaces X^* and U are in one-to-one correspondence; that is, each and every distinct $u \in l_q$ has a corresponding distinct functional $f_u = \langle \,,u \rangle$ in X^* and vice versa. Furthermore, since $\|f_u(x)\| = \|u\|$, the corresponding u's and f_u's have identical norms. If we just relabel all of the u's by the corresponding f_u so that $f(x) = \langle x,f \rangle$, we eliminate the need for the explicit mention of the auxiliary space U. The space X^*, being an operator space, must then have elements of the form $\langle \,,f \rangle$. In the sequel, however, it is often easier to think of X^* as the elements f with the operation $\langle \, , \rangle$ just understood.

DISCUSSION.   Let us investigate the relation between X and X^* in more detail. We know that if f is a fixed vector from X^* the mapping $x \to f(x)$ is linear:

$$f(\alpha_1 x_1 + \alpha_2 x_2) = \alpha_1 f(x_1) + \alpha_2 f(x_2).$$

Moreover, it is bounded:

$$\|f(x)\| \le \|f\| \cdot \|x\|, \qquad \text{all } x \in X.$$

Suppose, now, that f_1 and f_2 are elements of X^* and α_1, α_2 are scalars. Recall that X^*, regarded as a space of linear transformations from X into the scalar field, is automatically equipped with natural algebraic operations. Thus $\alpha_1 f_1 + \alpha_2 f_2$ has been defined as the linear functional on X whose value at a vector x in X is $\alpha_1 f_1(x) + \alpha_2 f_2(x)$:

$$(\alpha_1 f_1 + \alpha_2 f_2)(x) = \alpha_1 f_1(x) + \alpha_2 f_2(x),$$

and we know that this functional is again bounded, hence, a vector in X^*.

A moment's reflection will show that this last equation asserts that if we fix x in X and let f vary over X^* the mapping $f \to f(x)$ is linear.

We may state these observations more concisely. We agree to write $\langle x,y \rangle$ for the real (or complex) scalar $f(x)$. Then $\langle \, , \rangle$ is a function defined on the product $X \times X^*$, with values in the scalar field, which is *bilinear*:

$$\langle \alpha_1 x_1 + \alpha_2 x_2, f \rangle = \alpha_1 \langle x_1, f \rangle + \alpha_2 \langle x_2, f \rangle,$$

$$\langle x, \alpha_1 f_1 + \alpha_2 f_2 \rangle = \alpha_1 \langle x, f_1 \rangle + \alpha_2 \langle x, f_2 \rangle.$$

Here $\langle \ , \ \rangle$ is the inner-product-like function referred to above. In the sequel we use the notations $\langle x, f \rangle$ and $f(x)$ interchangeably. The fact that $\langle \ , \ \rangle$ has a different meaning when X is a Hilbert space (and, in fact, different properties, notably $\langle x, y \rangle = \overline{\langle y, x \rangle}$) will cause no difficulty, provided we are alert to the context. On the other hand, the notation offers many advantages. For one thing, our original definition of X^* as the space of bounded linear functionals on X suggests that X is somehow more basic than X^*. However, in every concrete Banach space we have studied so far X^* has been identifiable as a Banach space just as basic as X. Thus L_q is not less important than L_p, and l_∞ deserves to be studied just as much as l_1. The notation $\langle x, f \rangle$ places the vectors of X and the vectors of X^* on an equal footing and for this reason alone would be preferable to $f(x)$. The case for $\langle x, f \rangle$ is even stronger: consider the state that each f in X^* is a bounded linear functional on X. In our new notation the boundedness assertion is

$$|\langle x, f \rangle| \le \|f\| \cdot \|x\|, \qquad \text{all } x \in X,$$

an obvious relative of the Cauchy-Schwarz inequality in Hilbert space. The inequality, however, holds for each f in X^*, so that fixing x in X

$$|\langle x, f \rangle| \le \|x\| \cdot \|f\|, \qquad \text{all } f \in X^*.$$

Thus each x in X determines, via the operation of $\langle x, \ \rangle$, a bounded linear functional on X^*. In symbols, $X \subset X^{**}$, in which X^{**} is (by definition) the conjugate space of the Banach space X^*. We study this point in more detail in Section 3.3.

The most useful fact about Hilbert space is the presence of a notion of orthogonality. It is natural to attempt to carry some form of this concept over to Banach spaces. Proceeding by analogy, we would call vectors $x \in X$, $f \in X^*$ orthogonal, provided $\langle x, f \rangle = 0$. We postpone this development until Section 3.2, but we point out an immediate problem concerning the definition. We would certainly hope that a vector f of X^* would not be orthogonal to every vector of X without being the zero vector of X^*; similarly, if $x \in X$ were orthogonal to each f in X^*, then $x = 0$. The first is readily disposed of, for to say that $\langle x, f \rangle = 0$ for all x in X is to say that $f(x) = 0$. The second statement is also true. To prove it, however, we must show that if x is not the zero vector in X there is a bounded linear functional f on X which does not vanish at x. This statement, in turn, depends on (and, in fact, can be viewed as the statement of) the Hahn-Banach theorem (Theorem C) and is, as we shall see, the central result in the theory of Banach spaces.

Table 3.1 summarizes the results of this section.

Table 3.1

X	X^*	Form of Functional	Norm of Functional
$l_2(n)$	$l_2(n)$	$\langle x,f \rangle = \sum_1^n \xi_i \eta_i$	$\|f\| = (\sum |\eta_i|^2)^{1/2}$
l_2	l_2	$\langle x,f \rangle = \sum_1^\infty \xi_i \eta_i$	$\|f\| = (\sum_1^\infty |\eta_i|^2)^{1/2}$
$L_2(0,1)$	$L_2(0,1)$	$\langle x,f \rangle = \int_0^1 x(t)f(t)dt$	$\|f\| = (\int_0^1 |f(t)|^2 dt)^{1/2}$
$L_p(0,1)(1<p<\infty)$	$L_q(0,1)$	$\langle x,f \rangle = \int_0^1 x(t)f(t)dt$	$\|f\| = (\int_0^1 |f(t)|^q dt)^{1/q}$
$L_1(0,1)$	$L_\infty(0,1)$	$\langle x,f \rangle = \int_0^1 x(t)f(t)dt$	$\|f\| = \operatorname*{ess\ sup}_{0 \le t \le 1} |f(t)|$
$l_p\ (1<p<\infty)$	l_q	$\langle x,f \rangle = \sum_1^\infty \xi_i \eta_i$	$\|f\| = \sum_1^\infty (|\eta_i|^q)^{1/q}$
l_1	l_∞	$\langle x,f \rangle = \sum_1^\infty \xi_i \eta_i$	$\|f\| = \sup_i |\eta_i|$
$L(0,1)$	$\{f: f(t)$ is of bounded varia- tion on $[0,1]\}$	$\langle x,f \rangle = \int_0^1 x(t)df(t)$	$\|f\| = \operatorname*{var}_{[a,b]} (f)$

In informal language, this table helps to summarize the fact that every functional $\langle ,f \rangle$ is completely determined by a single element f. Conversely, every element f completely determines a functional $\langle ,f \rangle$. Thus the spaces $\{\langle ,f \rangle\}$ and $\{f\}$ are in one-to-one correspondence and both are Banach spaces in which $\|\langle ,f \rangle\| = \|f\|$.

3.2 SOME USES OF LINEAR FUNCTIONALS

In Section 3.1 we discussed bounded linear functionals on an abstract normed space X, observed that X^* is always a Banach space, and saw that X and X^* are connected in a canonical way by the bilinear form $\langle , \rangle$. We made one glaring omission, however. Although it is true that the concrete Banach spaces (L_p, l_p, C) we examined have a multitude of $\neq 0$ bounded linear functionals, we have not shown that this is true of an arbitrary Banach space. It is entirely possible a priori that a given Banach space X may have no nonzero bounded linear functionals so that our space X^* may consist solely of the vector 0. The fact that X is a complete linear metric space is not enough to guarantee that $X^* \neq \{0\}$.[1] The main theorem of this section shows, however,

---

[1] A readable example may be found in a paper by S. Cater, *American Mathematical Monthly*, **69**, No. 7, 638–640 (August–September 1962).

that this cannot happen if the metric in X arises from a norm (i.e., if X is a Banach space). The significance of the theorem stems not only from the usage in this section but from the vital role that it plays in Chapter 4.

In later sections we need the ability to construct bounded linear functionals with certain specialized properties. In most cases the difficulty in producing these functionals stems from the fact that our Banach space is infinite-dimensional. In a finite-dimensional normed space *every* linear functional is automatically bounded (Section 2.2, Exercise 4), and the problem of the continuity of a specially constructed linear functional does not appear. To avoid the necessity of proving that each functional f of interest in a given situation is bounded, it is natural to hope for a way of reducing the boundedness of f on X to the boundedness of f on a subspace of X. Stated another way, we hope that we can define a functional f on a subspace of X and then assert that f has a continuous linear extension into all of X. This is the course we will follow.

DEFINITION A. *Let $X_1, X,\ Y_1, Y$ be normed linear spaces and A_1, A linear mappings $A_1 : X_1 \to Y_1$, $A : X \to Y$; then A is called a linear extension of A_1 if $X_1 \subset X$ and $Y_1 \subseteq Y$ and $A_1 x = Ax$ for $x \in X_1$. A is called a norm-preserving linear extension of A_1 if in addition $\|A\| = \|A_1\|$.*

THEOREM A. *Let M be a subspace of a Banach space X and let f be a linear functional defined on M and bounded there. Then f has a unique linear norm-preserving extension onto $\overline{M}$.*

  P R O O F.   By hypothesis a constant $C > 0$ exists such that $|f(x)| \le C\|x\|$ whenever $x \in M$. Let x_0 be a given vector in $\overline{M}$. Then a sequence $\{x_n\}$ of vectors in M exists with $\|x_n - x_0\| \to 0$. Since

$$|f(x_n) - f(x_m)| = |f(x_n - x_m)| \le C\|x_n - x_m\|,$$

it follows that $\{f(x_n)\}$ is a Cauchy sequence of scalars, hence is convergent to some scalar α. We assert that α depends only on x_0 and not on the particular approximating sequence $\{x_n\}$. Let $\{x_n'\}$ be another sequence in M which converges to x_0 and let $\beta = \lim f(x_n')$. Then

$$|f(x_n') - f(x_n)| \le C\|x_n' - x_n\| \le C(\|x_n' - x_0\| + \|x_0 - x_n\|),$$

and hence

$$|\beta - \alpha| \le \lim_{n \to \infty} C(\|x_n' - x_0\| + \|x_0 - x_n\|) = 0.$$

Therefore we may unambiguously define a functional F on $\overline{M}$ by setting $F(x) = \lim f(x_n)$ in which $\{x_n\}$ is any sequence in M that converges to x. If x belongs to M, the trivial sequence, each of whose members is x, certainly converges to x and so F agrees with f on M. If $x, x' \in \overline{M}$, $x_n \to x$, and $x_m' \to x'$, the sequence $\{x_n + x_m'\}$ converges to $x + x'$ and hence

$$F(x + x') = \lim f(x_n + x_n') = \lim f(x_n) + \lim f(x_n') = F(x) + F(x').$$

It follows similarly that F is homogeneous. Finally, if $x \in \overline{M}$ and $x_n \to x$, then

$$|F(x)| = \lim_n |f(x_n)| \leq \lim_n C\|x_n\| = C\|x\|,$$

and we conclude that F is bounded with norm $\leq C$.

If F' is any other bounded linear extension of f and $x \in \overline{M}$, by choosing $x_n \in M$ with $\|x_n - x\| \to 0$ we find that the continuity of F' gives

$$F'(x) = \lim_n F(x) = \lim_n f(x_n) = F(x)$$

and it follows that $F' = F$. This proves the uniqueness of F.

We next consider another situation in which the extension problem is easy to solve.

THEOREM B.   *Suppose the Banach space X is the direct sum of the closed subspace M and N. Each bounded linear functional on M has a bounded linear extension to X. The extension is uniquely determined by the requirement that it vanish on N.*

P R O O F.   The hypothesis means that each $x \in X$ has a unique decomposition $x = y + z$ where $y \in M$ and $z \in N$. If F and F' are both extensions of the same linear functional f on M and each vanishes on N, then $F(x) = F(y + z) = F(y) + F(z) = f(y) = F'(y) = f'(x)$, which shows that there is at most one linear extension of f that vanishes on N.

The projection of X onto M along N is defined by $P(x) = y$, where $x = y + z$, $y \in M$, $z \in N$. Recall (Section 2.2) that when M and N are closed P is bounded. Granted this fact, it follows that the composition $F = fP$ is a bounded linear functional on X which vanishes on N. Since P is the identity on M, it is clear that F extends f.

COROLLARY.   *If X is a Hilbert space and M a subspace of X, each bounded linear functional on M has a bounded linear extension on X.*

P R O O F.   By Theorem A the given functional may be extended onto $\overline{M}$, and by the projection theorem we may write $X = \overline{M} \oplus N$, where N is the orthogonal complement of $\overline{M}$. The assertion now follows directly from Theorem B.

R E M A R K 1.   The preceding corollary has a simple direct proof. Thus, if f is a bounded linear functional on $\overline{M}$ then (since $\overline{M}$ is a Hilbert space), a vector $y \in \overline{M}$ exists with $f(x) = \langle x,y \rangle$ for all $x \in \overline{M}$. Setting $F(x) = \langle x,y \rangle$ for $x \in X$, we obtain a bounded linear functional F which extends f onto X. Observe that $\|F\| = \|y\| = \|f\|$ and that F vanishes on the complement of M.

If every closed subspace of a Banach space had a direct sum complement, the preceding theorem would solve every extension problem. This, however, is not the case, even in the relatively nice L_p spaces. The essential reason for this phenomenon is the lack of a projection theorem for Banach spaces. We refer the reader to Murray [B87] and the discussion of Day ([A20], p. 120) for further details.

We turn now to the main theorem of this section.

THEOREM C (Hahn-Banach). *Let M be a proper subspace of a normed linear space X and let f be a bounded linear functional defined on M. Then f can be extended to a bounded linear functional f_0 defined on the whole space X such that $\|f_0\| = \|f\|$.*

The Hahn-Banach theorem is deceivingly simple. Its importance is based in part on its great utility in proving other theorems. To illustrate, let us deduce the following corollary from the Hahn-Banach theorem.

THEOREM D. *If X is a normed linear space and x_0 is a nonzero vector in X, a functional f in X^* exists such that $f(x_0) = \|x_0\|$ and $\|f\| = 1$.*

PROOF. In Hilbert space Theorem D has the following direct proof: let $f(x) = \langle x,y \rangle$, where $y = x_0/\|x_0\|$. Then $\|f\| = \|y\| = 1$ and $f(x_0) = \|x_0\|$ as required. The actual proof of Theorem D is just as simple; $x_0 \neq 0$ is assumed and $L(x_0)$ denotes the one-dimensional subspace spanned by x_0. The vectors in $L(x_0)$ are of the form αx_0, in which α is a scalar. We define a functional f on $L(x_0)$ by $f(\alpha x_0) = \alpha \|x_0\|$. Clearly, f is linear and

$$\|f\| = \sup_{\substack{\|x\|=1 \\ x \in L(x_0)}} |f(x)| = \sup_{\|\alpha x_0\|=1} |\alpha| \cdot \|x_0\| = 1.$$

The desired conclusion follows by an application of the Hahn-Banach theorem.

REMARK 2. The discussion at the end of Section 3.1, together with Theorem D, shows that if X is a Banach space with dual X^* the bilinear form $\langle\,,\,\rangle$ connecting these spaces has these properties.

(1) If $\langle x,f \rangle = 0$ for all $x \in X$, then $f = 0$.
(2) If $\langle x,f \rangle = 0$ for all $f \in X^*$, then $x = 0$.

That is, the only vector in X (or X^*) orthogonal to all the vectors of X^* (or X, respectively) is the zero vector.

REMARK 3. Observe that the Hahn-Banach theorem does not require X to be complete. In his book Banach proves a stronger theorem than the one we stated. He shows that if X is a linear space M is a linear subspace and f is a linear functional on M, which is dominated by a seminorm p on M:

$$|f(x)| \leq p(x), \qquad \text{all } x \in M;$$

f has a linear extension F onto X and F remains below p. (A *seminorm* on a linear space X is a non-negative function satisfying

$$p(x + y) \leq p(x) = p(y), \qquad x, y \in X,$$

$$p(\lambda x) = |\lambda| p(x).$$

Our theorem is the case $p(x) = C\|x\|$, in which C is the norm of f on M.)

As a final development along the current line we have Theorem E.

THEOREM E. *Let M be a linear subspace of the Banach space X. Then, if the element $x_0 \in X$ has a positive distance d from M, a bounded linear functional f on X exists such that f is zero on M, $f(x_0) = 1$ and $\|f\| = 1/d$.*

P R O O F. If X is a Hilbert space, the orthogonal decomposition $X = \overline{M} \oplus \overline{M}^\perp$ holds and x_0 may be uniquely written $x_0 = y_0 + z_0$, where $y_0 \in \overline{M}$, $z_0 \in \overline{M}^\perp$, and $z_0 \neq 0$. The functional

$$f(x) = \langle x, z_0' \rangle, \qquad z_0' = \frac{z_0}{\|z_0\|^2},$$

has the desired properties. As for the general proof, we consider the set M_0 of all elements $x = y + \alpha x_0$, where y runs through M and α runs through the scalars. M_0 is a linear subspace and, since $d > 0$, the representation $x = y + \alpha x_0$ is unique: if $y + \alpha x_0 = y' + \alpha' x_0$, then $(\alpha - \alpha')x_0 = y - y' \in M$. Since $x_0 \notin M$, this implies $\alpha - \alpha' = 0$. Then $y = y'$ follows. Define f by $f(x) = \alpha$. Then f is linear on M_0, $f(x) = 0$ on M, $f(x_0) = 1$. Since $\|x\| = \|y + \alpha x_0\| = \|\alpha\| \cdot \|y'\alpha + x_0\| \geq |\alpha|d$, it follows that $\|f(x)\| = |\alpha| \leq \|x\|/d$, so that $\|f\| \leq 1/d$. On the other hand, the definition of distance from a point to a linear subspace implies that a sequence $\{y_n\}$ in M is such that $\lim \|y_n - x_0\| = d$. Then $|f(y_n - x_0)| = |f(x_0)| = 1 \leq \|f\| \cdot \|y_n - x_0\|$; hence $1 \leq d\|f\|$ or $\|f\| \geq 1/d$. This shows that $\|f\| = 1/d$. The Hahn-Banach theorem may now be used to complete the proof.

Dual Sets

In Hilbert spaces the concept of an orthonormal basis provides the setting for the development of Fourier expansions (see Appendix 2). In Banach spaces the orthogonality concept is not available; yet the concept of an orthonormal basis is so rich in applications that we are hesitant to give it up. The Hahn-Banach theorem is the vehicle for carrying many of the important properties of the Fourier expansion over to the Banach space setting.

THEOREM F. *Let $\{x_1, \ldots, x_n\}$ denote a linearly independent set in the Banach space X. Then there exists a linearly independent set $\{f_1, \ldots, f_n\}$ in X^* such that*

$$f_i(x_j) = \delta_{ij}, \qquad i, j = 1, \ldots, n.$$

P R O O F. Let M_1 denote the manifold spanned by $\{x_2, \ldots, x_n\}$; x_1 is clearly a positive distance from M_1. From Theorem E an $f_1 \in X^*$ exists such that $f_1(x_1) = 1$ and $f(M_1) = 0$. By repeating this process for each x_i we arrive at a set $\{f_1, \dots, f_n\}$ with the desired properties.

THEOREM G. *Let $\{f_1, \dots, f_n\}$ denote a linearly independent subset of X^*. A linearly independent subset $\{x_1, \dots, x_n\}$ of X exists such that*

$$f_i(x_j) = \delta_{ij}, \qquad i, j = 1, \dots, n.$$

PROOF. If X is reflexive, Theorems F and G are the same, with the spaces X and X^* switched.

In the general case we prove the theorem by induction on n. If $n = 1$, then $f_1 \neq 0$, and that an x_1 in X exists with $f_1(x_1) = 1$ is trivial. Suppose then that $n > 1$ and that the theorem has already been proved for $n = 1$. Then there exist elements $y_1, \dots, y_{n-1}$ of X satisfying $f_1(y_1) = 1$, $f_i(y_j) = 0$ for $i \neq j$ $(i, j = 1, 2, \dots, n - 1)$. Let S be the set of all $x \in X$ such that

$$f_1(x) = f_2(x) = \cdots = f_{n-1}(x) = 0.$$

Then for any $x \in X$ the vector $x - \sum_{i=1}^{n-1} f_i(x) y_i$ belongs to S. Consequently, if f_n vanishes identically on S, then for any $x \in X$ we have

$$f(x) = f\left(\left[x - \sum_{i=1}^{n-1} f_i(x) y_i\right] + \sum_{i=1}^{n-1} f_i(x) y_i\right)$$

$$= f\left(\sum_{i=1}^{n-1} f_i(x) y_i\right)$$

$$= \left(\sum_{i=1}^{n-1} f(y_i) f_i\right)(x).$$

Hence $f = \sum_{i=1}^{n-1} f(y_i) f_i$ is linearly dependent on $f_1, \dots, f_{n-1}$. We conclude therefore that there is a vector $y_n \in S$ with $f_n(y_n) = 1$. Since $y_n \in S$, we have

$$f_i(y_n) = 0, \qquad i = 1, 2, \dots, n - 1.$$

By putting

$$x_i = y_i - f_n(y_i) y_n, \qquad i = 1, 2, \dots, n - 1,$$

$$x_n = y_n,$$

we have

$$f_i(x_j) = \delta_{ij}, \qquad i, j = 1, 2, \dots, n.$$

The independence of the x_i is now immediate.

DEFINITION B. *Let $S = \{x_i\} \subset X$ and $S^+ = \{f_i\} \subset X^*$ denote linearly independent sets. If $f_i(x_j) = \delta_{ij}, i, j = 1, 2, \dots$, then S and S^+ are called associated dual sets.*

Let $S = \{x_i\}$ and $S^+ = \{f_i\}$ be associated dual sets. For each x in $L(S)$ unique scalars $\{\alpha_j\}$ exist such that

$$x = \sum_i \alpha_i x_i, \qquad x \in L(S).$$

By direct computation and the linearity of f_j we have

$$f_j(x) = f_j\left(\sum_i \alpha_i x_i\right) = \sum_i \alpha_i f_j(x_i) = \alpha_j, \qquad j = 1, 2, \ldots.$$

Thus we may rewrite the expansion for x as

$$x = \sum_i x_i \langle x, f_i \rangle, \qquad x \in L(S).$$

Similarly, for every $f \in L(S^+)$ we may write

$$f = \sum_i f_i \langle x_i, f \rangle, \qquad f \in L(S^+).$$

When X is a Hilbert space and S is an orthonormal basis for X, $S = S^+$, and these two expansions yield the usual Fourier expansions. When chances of confusion are slight, the notation $S^+ = \{x^+, \ldots, x_n^+\}$ is used to denote the set dual to $S = \{x_1, \ldots, x_n\}$.

Example 1.   Consider the case $X = E^n$ and let $S = \{x_1, \ldots, x_n\}$ be a basis for E^n. Here the x_i are real column vectors. Then any $x \in X$ has the form

$$x = \alpha_1 x_1 + \cdots + \alpha_n x_n,$$

in which the α_j are real numbers. To determine S^+, construct the subspace spanned by $\{x_2, \ldots, x_n\}$ and locate a normal e_1 to this manifold. Then $\langle x_i e_1 \rangle = 0$, $i = 2, \ldots, n$ and $\langle x_1, e_1 \rangle \neq 0$. By adjustment in the length of e_1 we produce an x_1^+ such that $\langle x_1^+, x_1 \rangle = 1$, $\langle x_1^+, x_i \rangle = 0$, $i = 1, \ldots, n$. Repeating the process, we delete a different member of S each time to generate the set

$$S^+ = \{x_1^+, \ldots, x_n^+\}.$$

As an alternative computation for S^+, form the matrix E by using the vectors $x_1, \ldots, x_n$ as columns. Since this set is linearly independent, E is nonsingular. The reader may easily verify that the rows of the inverse matrix E^{-1} are the dual vectors.

The Dyadic Notation

It is convenient at this point to introduce a useful formalism, called the dyadic notation. Two slight modifications are necessary in the present notation. First, we denote the number $f(x)$ by $\langle f, x \rangle$ rather than by $\langle x, f \rangle$, even though in complex spaces the latter is more appropriate. Second, it is necessary to apply a somewhat different shade of meaning to the brackets $\langle$ and $\rangle$. We shall attach the symbol $\rangle$ to vectors and $\langle$ to functionals. Thus $\langle f, u \rangle$ reads formally, the functional $\langle f$ acting on the vector $u \rangle$. As an illustration, let $u \rangle$ denote a column tuplet and $\langle v$ multiplication by a row tuplet. Thus in E^k with $u = (\zeta_1, \ldots, \zeta_k)$ and $v = (\eta_1, \ldots, \eta_k)$ the operation $\langle v, u \rangle$ is defined in the usual manner by

$$\langle v, u \rangle = \sum_{i=1}^{k} \zeta_i \eta_i.$$

Note, however, that by specifying $\langle v$ and $u \rangle$ as row and column vectors, respectively, the expression $u \rangle \langle v$ also has meaning in the conventional sense, namely

$$u \rangle \langle v = \begin{bmatrix} \zeta_1 \\ \vdots \\ \zeta_k \end{bmatrix} \cdot [\eta_1, \ldots, \eta_k] = \begin{bmatrix} \zeta_1 \eta_1 & \cdots & \zeta_1 \eta_k \\ \vdots & & \vdots \\ \zeta_k \eta_k & \cdots & \zeta_k \eta_k \end{bmatrix};$$

that is, $u \rangle \langle v$ is a matrix. All $k \times k$ matrices, however, are linear transforms in $\beta(R^k, R^k)$; thus $A = u \rangle \langle v$ is a linear operator $A: R^k \to R^k$, which is defined by

$$Ax = u \rangle \langle v, x \rangle = u \left(\sum_{i=1}^{n} \eta_i x_i \right),$$

where $x = (x_1, \ldots, x_k)$ is any vector in R^k. The operator A has a one-dimensional range spanned by the vector u and is clearly linear.

Now, if X, Y are linear spaces, we interpret the expression

$$A = e \rangle \langle f,$$

where $f \in X^*$, $e \in Y$, as the linear operator $A \in \beta(X, Y)$, with $R_A = L(e) \subset Y$, and define it for any $x \in X$ by

$$A(x) = e \rangle \langle f, x \rangle.$$

It is evident that the operator $A = e \rangle \langle f$ is linear and bounded. The operator A is called a dyad of rank 1.

Consider now the linearly independent sets $E = \{e_1, \ldots, e_n\} \subset Y$ and $F = \{f_1, \ldots, f_n\} \subset X^*$. The operator $A \in \beta(X, Y)$, written as

$$A = \sum_{i=1}^{n} e_i \rangle \langle f_i$$

and defined by

$$Ax = e_1 \rangle \langle f_1, x \rangle + \cdots + e_n \rangle \langle f_n, x \rangle, \qquad x \in X,$$

is called a dyad of rank n. It is easy to see that A is linear and that it is bounded if the functionals $f_1, \ldots, f_n$ are bounded. The range of A is the linear manifold $R_A = L(e_1, \ldots, e_n) \subset Y$. More generally a dyad of rank n is defined as follows.

DEFINITION C.   *Let X, Y be linear spaces and $\{e_1, \ldots, e_n\} \subset Y$ and $\{f_1, \ldots, f_n\}$ $\subset X^*$ linearly independent subsets. Then, if the square matrix $[a_{ij}]$ is nonsingular, the transformation $A : X \to Y$,*

$$A = \sum_{i,j=1}^{n} e_i \rangle a_{ij} \langle f_j,$$

written with the meaning of the equation

$$Ax = \sum_{i,j=1}^{n} e_i \rangle a_{ij} \langle f_j, x \rangle, \qquad x \in X,$$

is called a dyad of rank n.

The range of A is given by $R_A = L(e_1, \ldots, e_n)$. A is linear and bounded whenever F is a set of bounded functionals.

Example 2.   Suppose that the space X is n-dimensional, with a basis consisting of the vectors $e_1, e_2, \ldots, e_n$ and having the dual set $e_1^+, e_2^+, \ldots, e_n^+$. If y is any vector in X, we can express it in a Fourier expansion as

$$y = e_1 \rangle \langle e_1^+, y \rangle + e_2 \rangle \langle e_2^+, y \rangle + \cdots + e_n \rangle \langle e_n^+, y \rangle.$$

Noting that the identity operator gives $Ly = y$, we have the following expression for the identity operator in terms of dyads:

$$I = e_1 \rangle \langle e_1^+ + e_2 \rangle \langle e_2^+ + \cdots + e_n \rangle \langle e_n^+.$$

Thus any basis S for X and its dual S^+ can be used to decompose the identity on X.

Operators with Finite Rank

Every linear operator A on a finite dimensional domain D_A has a finite dimensional range R_A. In fact, if $E = \{e_1, \ldots, e_n\}$ is any basis for D_A, the vectors $\{Ae_1, \ldots, Ae_n\}$ span R_A and, if A is nonsingular, constitute a basis for R_A. Clearly the converse of this statement is *not* true, for a functional on L_2 has a one-dimensional range and an infinite-dimensional domain. Similarly, the dyad of rank n given in Definition C has a finite-dimensional range and a finite- or infinite-dimensional domain. Transformations with finite-dimensional ranges are said to have *finite rank*.

THEOREM H.   *Every linear transformation with finite rank can be represented as a dyad of the same rank.*

PROOF.   Consider $A : X \to Y$. Since $R_A \subset Y$ is n-dimensional, it has a basis that we denote by $E = \{e_j\}$, $j = 1, \ldots, n$. For any $x \in X$, $A(x) \in R_A$; hence it has the expansion

$$A(x) = c_1 e_1 + c_2 e_2 + \cdots + c_n e_n \tag{1}$$

in terms of the basis set. The coefficients c_j are functions of x and can appropriately be written $c_j = c_j(x)$. Since A is linear,

$$A(\lambda x) = \lambda A(x) = \lambda c_1(x)e_1 + \cdots + \lambda c_n(x)e_n$$

and

$$A(x_1 + x_2) = [c_1(x_1) + c_1(x_2)]e_1 + \cdots + [c_n(x_1) + c_n(x_2)]e_n.$$

Furthermore, continuity of A, if it exists, implies the continuity of the $c_j(x)$. What we have just shown is that the $c_j(x)$ are linear functionals of x; therefore, utilizing the dyadic notation, we write $c_j(x) = \langle f_j, x \rangle$, in which $\langle f_j$ is the appropriate functional from the space X^*. Incorporation of this result into Eq. 1 yields

$$Ax = \sum_{i=1}^{n} e_i \rangle \langle f_i, x \rangle$$

and the theorem is proved.

REMARK 3.   The functionals f_i are independent in X^*. Assume that

$$\sum_{j=1}^{n} d_j f_j = 0.$$

Choose $x_i \in X$ so that $A(x_i) = c_i$. Then, clearly, $f_j(x_i) = \delta_{ij}$. Thus

$$0 = \sum_{j=1}^{n} d_j f_j(x_i) = d_j.$$

REMARK 4.   The dyadic representation for a transformation of finite rank is by no means unique, for the range basis $\{e_i, \ldots, e_n\}$ can be chosen arbitrarily. Let us consider the case in which X is a Hilbert space H. The functionals $f_j \in H^*$ are inner products with the vectors $f_j \in H$. We denote by M the linear manifold spanned by the vectors $(f_1, \ldots, f_n)$. This manifold is n-dimensional as shown in Remark 3.

Let the space H be decomposed into the orthogonal sum of the space M and its complement $M^\perp$. By definition, every $h \in M^\perp$ is orthogonal to the subspace M. In other words, $\langle h, f \rangle = 0$ for all $h \in M^\perp$ and $f \in M$. In particular, for every $h \in M^\perp$, $h \perp f_j$ $(j = 1, \ldots, n)$. Thus $M^\perp \subset N_A$. Also, if $x \in N_A$, then

$$0 = A(x) = \sum_{i=1}^{n} e_i \rangle \langle f_i, x \rangle.$$

By the independence of $\{e_1, \ldots, e_n\}$ we have $\langle f_i, x \rangle = 0$ for all i. Thus $x \in M^\perp$. And, for the transformation $A = \sum_{i=1}^{n} e_i \rangle \langle f_i$, $N_A^\perp = L(f_1, \ldots, f_n)$.

The operator A can thus be described as in Figure 3.1.

REMARK 5.   Since R_A and M have dimension n, it follows that A must map M one-to-one and onto R_A. The restriction of A to M is then a nonsingular linear transformation.

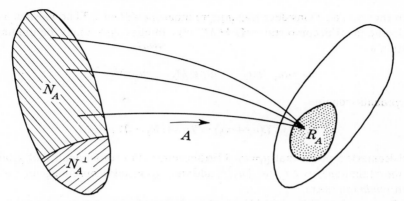

Figure 3.1   Some subspaces defined by a linear transformation.

REMARK 6.   Let $E = \{e_1, \ldots, e_n\}$ and $F = \{f_1, \ldots, f_n\}$ denote arbitrary basis for R_A and M, respectively. The identity on R_A may be written

$$I_R = \sum_{i=1}^{n} e_i \rangle \langle e_i^+,$$

whereas the identity on M is given by

$$I_M = \sum_{j=1}^{n} f_j \rangle \langle f_j^+.$$

From the relation $I_R A I_M = A$, which is self-evident, we have

$$A = \left(\sum_{i=1}^{n} e_i \rangle \langle e_i^+ \right) A \left(\sum_{j=1}^{n} f_j \rangle \langle f_j^+ \right)$$

$$= \sum_{j,i=1}^{n} e_i \rangle (\langle e_i^+, A f_j \rangle) \langle f_j^+.$$

Letting $a_{ij} = \langle e_i^+, A f_j \rangle$, $i, j = 1, \ldots, n$, we have the expansion of A:

$$A = \sum_{i,j=1}^{n} e_i > a_{ij} < f_j^+.$$

The matrix of scalars $[a_{ij}]$ is called the matrix of A with respect to the basis E and F and denoted by $[A]_{E,F}$ or, when the sets themselves are self-evident, simply $[A]$. (When $E = F$ we use $[A]_E$.)

Elementary Minimum Energy Control Problems

Consider the transformation $T : H \to R^n$ of a Hilbert space H *onto* R^n. From Remark 5 it follows that for every $\xi \in R^n$ there is a unique $u_\xi \in M = N_T^\perp$

such that $\xi = Tu_\xi$. Consider now any preimage $u \in H$ of ξ. The existence of the orthogonal decomposition $H = M \oplus N_T$ implies that u may be uniquely written as

$$u = u_1 + u_2, \quad u_1 \in M, \quad u_2 \in N_T.$$

The equality chain

$$\xi = Tu = T(u_1 + u_2) = Tu_1 + Tu_2 = Tu_1 + 0$$

and Remark 5 prove that $u_1 = u_\xi$. Furthermore, the orthogonality of u_ξ and u_2 shows that $\|u\|^2 = \|u_\xi\|^2 + \|u_2\|^2$, and thus u_ξ is also the preimage of $\xi \in R^n$ with *minimum* norm.

This simple problem is the key to the solution of minimum energy problems of considerable complexity. Before presenting examples of its ramifications, let us consider how we might go about computing u_ξ. Let us begin by assuming that T has been decomposed into the form

$$T = \sum_{i=1}^{n} e_i \rangle \langle f_i,$$

where $\{e_1, \dots, e_n\}$ is a basis for R^n.

Given any $\xi \in R^n$, it is clear from the preceding discussion that $u_\xi \in M = L(f_1, \dots, f_n)$. Hence scalars $\{\alpha_i\}$ must exist such that

$$u_\xi = \sum_{i=1}^{n} \alpha_i f_i.$$

Similarly, since $\xi = R^n$ and $\{e_i\}$ is a basis for R^n, unique scalars $\{\beta_i\}$ must exist such that

$$\xi = \sum_{j=1}^{n} \beta_j e_j.$$

Using the assumed form of T, we also have

$$\xi = \sum_{i=1}^{n} \beta_i e_i \rangle = \left[\sum_{i=1}^{n} e_i \rangle \langle f_i \right] \left[\sum_{j=1}^{n} \alpha_j f_j \rangle \right] = \sum_{i=1}^{n} \sum_{j=1}^{n} \alpha_j \langle f_i, f_j \rangle e_i.$$

Since the $\{e_1\}$ are linearly independent, we immediately obtain

$$\beta_i = \sum_{j=1}^{n} \langle f_i, f_j \rangle \alpha_j, \quad i = 1, \dots, n,$$

or, defining $\beta = \mathrm{col}\,(\beta_1, \dots, \beta_n)$, $\alpha = \mathrm{col}\,(\alpha_1, \dots, \alpha_n)$, and letting $\mathscr{F}$ denote the matrix with (i,j) element $\langle f_i, f_j \rangle$, we have the equivalent matrix formulation

$$\beta = \mathscr{F}\alpha.$$

Example 3.   Consider the linear dynamic system defined by

$$\dot{x}(t) = A(t)x(t) + B(t)u(t), \qquad t \in \tau. \tag{2}$$

Let us find the element u that transfers the tuplet $[x(t_0), t_0] \in R^n \times \tau$ to the tuplet $[x(t_f), t_f] \in R^n \times \tau$ while minimizing the functional

$$J(u) = \sum_{i=1}^{m} \int_{t_0}^{t_f} |u_i(s)|^2 ds.$$

As an alternative to Eq. 2 the system at fixed time t_f may be modeled as the transformation sending $R^n \times U$ into R^n and defined by

$$x(t_f) = (\Phi x^0)(t_f) + (Fu)(t_f)$$

$$= \Phi(t_f, t_0)x^0 + \int_{t_0}^{t_f} \Phi(t_f, s)B(s)u(s)ds.$$

Evidently the problem posed is equivalent to finding the element $u \in [L_2(t_0, t_f)]^m = U$ with minimum norm that satisfies

$$\xi = Tu = \int_{t_0}^{t_f} \Phi(t_f, s)B(s)u(s)ds, \tag{3}$$

where $\xi = x(t_f) - \Phi(t_f, t_0)x^0$.

The range of T clearly lies in R^n. Let us take the coordinate basis for that space [i.e., $e_1 = (1, 0, \dots, 0)$, etc.] and, letting $W_{ij}(s)$ denote the (i, j)th element of the matrix $W(s) = \Phi(t_f, s)B(s)$, it is apparent that Eq. 3 may be rewritten as

$$\xi = Tu = \sum_{i=1}^{n} e_i \left(\sum_{j=1}^{m} \int_{t_0}^{t_f} W_{ij}(s)u_j(s)ds \right).$$

Thus, with the functionals on U defined by

$$f_i(u) = \int_{t_0}^{t_f} \left[\sum_{j=1}^{m} W_{ij}(s)u_j(s) \right] ds, \qquad i = 1, \dots, n,$$

the transform $T: U \to R^n$ may be written

$$T = \sum_{i=1}^{n} e_i \rangle \langle f_i.$$

So far we have merely used the finite dimension of R^n to rewrite Eq. 3. The problem is now solved by following the prescribed procedure. First $\mathscr{F}$ is computed. Since $\mathscr{F}_{ij} = \langle f_i, f_j \rangle$, it is easy to see that in the present example $\mathscr{F}$ is the matrix (W^* is the conjugate transpose of W)

$$\mathscr{F}(t_f, t_0) = \int_{t_0}^{t_f} W(s)W^*(s)ds = \int_{t_0}^{t_f} \Phi(t_f, s)B(s)B^*(s)\Phi^*(t_f, s)ds. \tag{4}$$

Furthermore, the basis $\{e_i\}$ is orthonormal and consequently

$$\beta = \xi = x(t_f) - \Phi(t_f, t_0)x^0. \tag{5}$$

Also note that

$$u_\xi(t) = \sum_{i=1}^{n} \alpha_i f_i(t) = W^*(t)\alpha, \qquad t \in \tau. \tag{6}$$

Combining Eqs. 5 and 6 with $\alpha = \mathscr{F}^{-1}(t_f, t_0)\beta$ produces the desired solution:

$$u_\xi(t) = B^*(t)\Phi^*(t_f, t)\mathscr{F}^{-1}(t_f, t_0)[x(t_f) - \Phi(t_f, t_0)x^0], \qquad t \in \tau. \tag{7}$$

Example 4. As a second example, consider the discrete dynamic system defined by

$$\Delta_t x(t) = A(t)x(t) + B(t)u(t), \qquad t \in \sigma.$$

The problem posed is to find the control defined on the set $\sigma = \{t_0, \ldots, t_f, \ldots\}$ such that it transfers the tuplet (x_0, t_0) to the tuplet (x_f, t_f) while minimizing the performance index

$$J = \sum_{i=1}^{m} \sum_{j=0}^{[t]-1} |u_i(t_j)|^2.$$

The similarity with the preceding example makes the present case easy. If $l_2(\sigma)$ denotes the Hilbert space of all functions defined on σ with the inner product,

$$\langle u, v \rangle = \sum_\sigma u(t_\alpha)v(t_\alpha), \qquad u, v \in l_2(\sigma).$$

Then, taking the input space $U = [l_2(\sigma)]^m$ with the inner product

$$\langle u, v \rangle = \sum_{i=1}^{m} \sum_\sigma u_i(t_j)v_i(t_j), \qquad u, v \in U,$$

we find that the present problem is reduced to a direct analog of Example 1. It is easily verified that the matrix $\mathscr{F}$ is given by

$$\mathscr{F}(t_f, t_0) = \sum_{\alpha=[t_0]}^{[t_f]-1} h_\alpha^2 \Phi(t_f, t_{\alpha+1}) B(t_\alpha) B^*(t_\alpha) \Phi^*(t_f, t_{\alpha+1}), \tag{8}$$

whereas the minimizing function u_ξ is computed by the rule

$$u_\xi(t_j) = B^*(t_j)\Phi^*(t_f, t_{j+1})\mathscr{F}^{-1}(t_f, t_0)[x(t_f) - \Phi(t_f, t_0)x^0], \qquad t_j \in \sigma. \tag{9}$$

Example 5. To illustrate these results in a more complicated setting let us return to the composite system of Figure 2.16, Section 2.5. Let $r = (s, t)$ denote a fixed instant in $\sigma \times \tau$ and let $z^0 = (x(s_0), y(t_0))$ and $z^f = (x(s_f), y(t_f))$ denote fixed tuplets in R^n. We wish to find the tuplet $w = (u,v)$ such that z^0 is transferred to z^f while minimizing the functional

$$J(u,v) = \sum_{i=1}^{m_1} \sum_{j=0}^{[s]-1} h_j |u_i(t_j)|^2 + \int_{t_0}^{t} \sum_{j=1}^{m_2} |v_j(\tau)|^2 d\tau.$$

In view of Eqs. 18, 19, and 20 of Section 2.5, it is sufficient to consider the problem of minimizing $J(u,v)$ while satisfying

$$\xi = T(u,v),$$

in which $\xi = z^f - \Theta(r_f,r_0)z^0$ and T are defined by Eqs. 19 and 20 of the earlier section. If $U = [L_2(t_0,t_f)]^{m_1}$ and $V = [l_2(\sigma)]^{m_2}$, then $J(u,v)$ is exactly the norm of $U \times V$ and the present example is precisely the same as the preceding two.

In terms of the matrices defined in Eq. 18, Section 2.5, let us compute the components

$$\mathscr{F}_{11}(r_f;r_0) = \sum_{j=0}^{[s_f]-1} W_1(s_f,t_j)W_1^*(s_f,t_j),$$

$$\mathscr{F}_{12}(r_f;r_0) = \sum_{j=0}^{[s_f]-1} W_1(s_f,t_j)W_3^*(t_f,t_j),$$

$$\mathscr{F}_{21}(r_f;r_0) = \sum_{j=0}^{[s_f]-1} W_3(t_f,t_j)W_1^*(s_f,t_j),$$

$$\mathscr{F}_{22}(r_f;r_0) = \int_{t_0}^{t_f} W_2(t_f,s)W_2^*(t_f,s)ds$$

of the matrix

$$\mathscr{F}(r_f;r_0) = \begin{bmatrix} \mathscr{F}_{11}(r_f;r_0) & \mathscr{F}_{12}(r_f;r_0) \\ \mathscr{F}_{21}(r_f;r_0) & \mathscr{F}_{22}(r_f;r_0) \end{bmatrix}. \tag{10}$$

Then, if $W^*(r;r_0)$ denotes the $m \times n$ matrix

$$W^*(r;r_0) = \begin{bmatrix} W_1^*(s_f,s) & W_3^*(s_f,s) \\ 0 & W_2^*(t_f,t) \end{bmatrix},$$

the solution is written as before by

$$(u_\xi(s),v_\xi(t)) = W^*(r;r_0)\mathscr{F}^{-1}(r_f;r_0)[z^f - \Theta(r_f,r_0)z^0], \qquad r = (s,t) \in \sigma \times \tau.$$

DISCUSSION.   The minimum norm problem of this section illustrates again the clarity of a function space formulation. For emphasis let us note that the basic problem is completely solved in the abstract and that the examples are not concerned with the question "What is the solution?" but rather with the simple matter of what the known solution looks like in the various concrete settings.

The simple Hilbert space minimization problem is a much more general result than it appears to be at first. In later sections it is shown that several seemingly more complex problems can be reduced to the present problem by a suitable choice of Hilbert spaces.

A natural question in regard to the present topic is the possibility of generalizing the setting of the optimization problem to Banach spaces. The Discussion of Section 1.4 suggests a fruitful problem to solve from an applications standpoint: let $T : B \to R$ denote a linear transformation between the Banach spaces B and R. For fixed $\xi \in R$ find the $u \in B$ with minimum norm that satisfies $\xi = Tu$. This question is indeed considerably more difficult than the present problem and the solution takes up most of Chapter 4.

Exercises

1. If X is an n-dimensional Banach space, show that X^* is also of dimension n. If $S = \{x_1, \ldots, x_n\}$ is a basis for X, show that $S^+ = \{x_1^+, \ldots, x_n^+\}$ is a basis for X^*.

2. Let F be the set $\{(0,0,1), (0,1,1), (1,1,1)\}$ and E the set $\{(1,0,0), (1,1,0), (0,0,1)\}$ and define $A : R^3 \to R^3$ by the relations

$$Af_1 = A(0,0,1) = (2,3,5),$$
$$Af_2 = A(0,1,1) = (1,0,0),$$
$$Af_3 = A(1,1,1) = (0,1,-1).$$

Find the matrices $[A]_E$, $[A]_F$, and $[A]_{E,F}$.

3. Let $\{e_1, \ldots, e_n\}$ be a basis in E^n. The projection operator defined by the relations $x = \zeta_1 e_1 + \cdots + \zeta_n e_n$, $Ax = \zeta_1 e_1 + \cdots + \zeta_m e_m$, where $m < n$, has R_A of dimension $m < n$. What does $[A]_E$ look like?

4. Let $S = \{x_1, \ldots, x_n\}$ denote a basis for the Hilbert space X. For every $A : X \to X$ let $[A]$ denote the matrix of A with respect to S (i.e., $a_{ij} = \langle x_i^+, Ax_j \rangle$). Show that the mapping $A \to [A]$ defines a one-to-one and onto correspondence between $\beta(X,X)$ and $\beta(E^n, E^n)$.

5. If A and B are linear operators on X, and α, β scalars, show that
   (a) $[\alpha A + \beta B] = \alpha[A] + \beta[B]$,
   (b) $[0] = $ the zero matrix,
   (c) $[I] = [\delta_{ij}]$,
   (d) $[AB] = [A][B]$,
   (e) $[A^{-1}] = [A]^{-1}$,   when A^{-1} exists.

6. Let $A \in L(X,Y)$ and $B \in L(Y,Z)$. Then if the same basis S for Y is used in defining $[A]$ and $[B]$, show that (d) of Exercise 5 holds as well in this more general setting.

7. Let $P = \{x_1, \ldots, x_n\}$ and $S = \{x_1', \ldots, x_n'\}$ denote two bases for X and

let C denote the matrix $[c_{ij}]$ defined by

$$x_k = \sum_{j=1}^{n} c_{jk} x_j', \qquad k = 1, \ldots, n.$$

Show that for $A \in L(X,X)$ the matrices $[A]_p$, $[A]_S$, and C are related by

$$[A]_p = C^{-1}[A]_S C.$$

8. Let det $([A])$ denote the determinant of the matrix A. Recall that the basic properties of the determinant function are

$$\det ([I]) = 1,$$
$$\det ([A][B]) = \det ([A]) \cdot \det ([B]),$$
$$\det ([A]) \neq 0 \Leftrightarrow [A] \text{ is nonsingular.}$$

Using these properties and Exercise 7, show for a finite rank operator A and any basis S and P that $\det ([A]_S) = \det ([A]_p)$. Thus the determinant of operator A

$$\det [A] = \det ([A]_S)$$

is well defined and independent of S. Show that the characteristic polynomial of A, defined by

$$\Delta(\lambda) = \det (A - \lambda I),$$

is also unique and independent of basis.

9. Let A be a linear operator on X. The rank of A, denoted by $\rho(A)$, has been defined as the dimension of the range of A. Similarly, the nullity of A, denoted by $\nu(A)$, is defined as the dimension of the null space of A. If X is finite-dimensional and $A, B \in L(X,X)$ show that
  (a) $\rho(A) + \nu(A) = \dim (X)$,
  (b) $\rho(A + B) \leq \rho(A) + \rho(B)$,
  (c) $\rho(AB) \leq \min \{\rho(A), \rho(B)\}$,
  (d) $\nu(AB) \leq \nu(A) + \nu(B)$,
  (e) $\rho(AB) = \rho(BA) = \rho(A)$ if B is nonsingular,
  (f) $AB = 0 \Rightarrow \rho(A) + \rho(B) \leq \dim (X)$,
  (g) $\nu(AB) \leq \max \{\nu(A), \nu(B)\}$.

10. Prove that the matrix $[\langle f_i, f_j \rangle]$ is nonsingular if and only if the set $\{f_1, \ldots, f_n\}$ is linearly independent.

11. If $A : B \to R$ is the transformation between Banach spaces defined by

$$A = \sum_{i=1}^{n} e_i \rangle \langle f_i,$$

show that $N_A = \bigcap_{j=1}^{n} N_{f_j}$. Suppose $u_1, u_2, \ldots, u_n \in B$ such that the matrix $Q = [\langle f_i, u_j \rangle]$ is nonsingular. Let S be the subspace of B spanned by $u_1, \ldots, u_n$. Then prove that

$$B = N_A \oplus S$$

is a decomposition of B into a direct sum; that is, $B = N_A + S$, $N_A \cap S = \{0\}$, and the projections of B on N_A along S are continuous.

12. Show that if M is a subspace of a Hilbert space, then $M^{\perp\perp} = M$. HINT: Observe that Theorem E asserts that if S is a subspace of the Banach space B a necessary and sufficient condition that a vector x in B belong to S is that $f(x) = 0$ whenever f is a functional that vanishes on S.

13. Consider once again the minimum energy control problem of this section. Let $W^* : R^n \to (N_T)^{\perp}$ denote any isometry from R^n onto $(N_T)^{\perp}$. Prove that the composition TW^* is a nonsingular matrix and that the optimal control u_ξ is given by

$$u_\xi = W^*(TW^*)^{-1}\xi \tag{11}$$

for every $\xi \in R^n$. Observe that in Examples 3 and 4 multiplication by the matrix $B^*(s)\Phi^*(t_f, s)$ is one such isometry.

14. We direct attention to Example 3 of this section with $\tau = [t_a, t_c]$, W^*, the mapping of Exercise 13, and $\xi = [x(t_c) - \Phi(t_c, t_a)x(t_a)]$. In the spirit of Exercise 6, Section 2.5, we define

$$(FW^*)_a^c = \int_{t_a}^c \Phi(t_c, s)B(s)W^*(s)ds$$

and ask the reader to prove that

$$[(FW^*)_b^c]^{-1}[x(t_c) - \Phi(t_c, t_b)x(t_b)] = [(FW^*)_a^c]^{-1}[x(t_c) - \Phi(t_c, t_a)x(t_a)] \tag{12}$$

holds for every $t_b \in \tau$. HINT: Apply the control of Eq. 11 to show that

$$x(t_b) = \Phi(t_b, t_a)x(t_a) + (FW^*)_a^b[(FW^*)_a^c]^{-1}[x(t_c) - \Phi(t_c, t_a)x(t_a)];$$

then multiply through by $\Phi(t_c, t_b)$ and use the identity

$$\Phi(t_c, t_b)(FW^*)_a^b = (FW^*)_a^c - (FW^*)_b^c.$$

15. Observe that Eqs. 7 and 11 together imply that the system of Eq. 2 may be controlled in an optimal manner by means of the instantaneous feedback law:

$$u_\xi(t) = B^*(t)\Phi^*(t_f, t)\mathscr{F}^{-1}(t_f, t)[x(t_f) - \Phi(t_f, t)x(t)], \qquad t \in \tau.$$

Draw a block diagram that mechanizes this law. Return to one of the examples of Section 2.4 and work out a specific case.

16. Derive the analogous results of Exercises 14 and 15 for the systems of Examples 3 and 4 of this section. NOTE: In Exercises 15 and 16 it is assumed that the matrix $\mathscr{F}(t_f,t)$ is invertible for all $t \in \tau$. In Section 3.6 we shall see that this is not necessarily so. We defer consideration of this problem, however, until this later section.

3.3 THE CONJUGATE AND ADJOINT TRANSFORMATIONS

To proceed with the study of the structure of linear systems we need at our disposal the concepts of the conjugate and adjoint transformations. In addition to advancing the objectives of our present study, these concepts have proved useful in a variety of engineering applications. For example, boundary value problems arising from microwave and electromagnetic field applications represent a specific area in which the adjoint operator plays an important role. Another application is in the study of terminal guidance problems; in fact several of the early missile guidance systems were based on the adjoint principle (see Exercise 8).

We shall see in Chapter 4 that the conjugate transformation concept is prerequisite to the extension of the minimum norm problem of Section 3.2 to Banach spaces. Finally, as an immediate application, the adjoint transformation is used in Section 3.4 to develop two useful canonical forms for linear systems.

The Second Conjugate Space

The Hahn-Banach theorem shows that any Banach space has nontrivial bounded linear functionals; that is, the conjugate space always consists of vectors other than 0. In particular, the dual X^{**} of the Banach space X^* is not the trivial Banach space consisting of the single vector $\{0\}$. We have already found many elements of X^{**}. Indeed, for each x in X we have observed that the mapping $f \rightarrow \langle x,f \rangle$ is a bounded linear functional on X^*. This follows from the equality

$$|\langle x,f \rangle| \leq \|x\| \cdot \|f\|, \qquad x \in X, f \in X^*$$

and the fact that $\langle\ ,\ \rangle$ is linear in its second variable. Let us denote this functional temporarily by F_x so that by definition $F_x(f) = \langle x,f \rangle$ for each f in X^*. It is clear that as we vary x in X the corresponding functionals F_x belong to X^{**}, and the preceding inequality shows that

$$|F_x(f)| \leq \|x\|$$

if f is of norm ≤ 1 in X^*. On the other hand, Theorem D, Section 3.2, shows that there exists a vector f in X^* of norm 1 such that $F_x(f) = \|x\|$. It follows that

$$\|F_x\| = \|x\|.$$

Thus the correspondence $x \to F_x$ is an isometry from X into X^{**}. This mapping is also linear. Thus, if $x_1, x_2 \in X$ and α_1, α_2 are scalars,

$$F_{\alpha_1 x_1 + \alpha_2 x_2}(f) = \langle \alpha_1 x_1 + \alpha_2 x_2, f \rangle = \alpha_1 \langle x_1, f \rangle + \alpha_2 \langle x_2, f \rangle$$

$$= \alpha_1 F_{x_1}(f) + \alpha_2 F_{x_2}(f)$$

$$= (\alpha_1 F_{x_1} + \alpha_2 F_{x_2})(f),$$

and, since f is arbitrary in X^*, this gives

$$F_{\alpha_1 x_1 + \alpha_2 x_2} = \alpha_1 F_{x_1} + \alpha_2 F_{x_2}.$$

In short, $x \to F_x$ is an isometric isomorphism from X onto a (closed) subspace of X^{**}. Less formally, X is indistinguishable (as a Banach space) from a certain piece of X^{**}. If we identify a vector x in X with its image F_x in X^{**} (i.e., with the functional $\langle x, \rangle$), we may write $X \subset X^{**}$ and consider each x in X as a functional on X^*.

We can derive a useful corollary from this result by examining the equation $\|x\| = \|F_x\|$ in more detail. Recalling the definition of the norm of a linear functional on a Banach space, we find that the right member of this equation is given by

$$\|F_x\| = \sup_{\|f\| \le 1, f \in X^*} |F_x(f)|.$$

However, $F_x(f)$ is by definition just $\langle x, f \rangle$, and we have arrived at another means of computing the norm of a vector in X:

$$\|x\| = \sup_{\|f\| \le 1, f \in X^*} |\langle x, f \rangle|.$$

This equation is the precise dual of the *definition* of the norm of an element of X^*:

$$\|f\| = \sup_{\|x\| \le 1, x \in X} |\langle x, f \rangle|.$$

It is natural to expect that the inclusion $X \subset X^{**}$ is really not proper and that the dual space of X^* is just X. In $X = L_p(0,1)$ for $1 < p < \infty$ we have seen that this is true; the bounded linear functionals on L_p can be identified with the vectors of $L_p(0,1)$ ($1/p + 1/q = 1$) and the bounded linear functionals on L_q are the vectors of L_p.

The following definition isolates the good Banach spaces from the bad.

DEFINITION I. *A Banach space X is said to be reflexive if the mapping $x \to F_x$ is onto X^{**}, that is, if $X^{**} = X$.*

We have seen that every Hilbert space is reflexive and that the spaces l_p and L_p are reflexive if $1 < p < \infty$. However, not every Banach space is reflexive, as the following example shows.

Example 1.   The space c_0 is not reflexive.

Recall that c_0 consists of all vectors $x = (\xi_1, \xi_2, \dots)$ with $\lim \xi_n = 0$. The norm is defined as $\|x\| = \sup_i |\xi_i|$. The conjugate space of c_0 may be identified with l_1. In more detail, there is an isometric isomorphism between c_0^* and l_1; under this mapping each $f \in c_0^*$ determines a unique vector $y = (\eta_1, \eta_2, \dots)$ in l_1, and conversely each $y \in l_1$ determines a unique functorial f in c_0^*. The correspondence between f and y is such that

$$f(x) = \sum_{i=1}^{\infty} \xi_i \eta_i$$

or each $x = (\xi_1, \xi_2, \dots)$ in c_0, and

$$\|f\| = \|y\|_1 = \sum_{i=1}^{\infty} |\eta_i|.$$

We also know that l_1^* may be identified with l_∞. Now it is clear that any sequence of scalars $(\xi_1, \xi_2, \dots)$ that converges to 0 must be bounded so that $c_0 \subset l_\infty$. However, it is equally clear that not every bounded sequence converges to 0 so that the inclusion $c_0 \subset l_\infty$ is *proper*. In other words, with $X = c_0$, we see that the second conjugate $X^{**} = (X^*)^* = l^* = l_\infty$ does not coincide with X.

Since the mapping $x \to F_x$ from X into X^{**} is an isometry, the range of this map is closed in X^{**}. Let us check this directly for c_0 by showing that c_0 is a closed subspace of l_∞. The proof is easy. Indeed, if $x_n = (\xi_1^n, \xi_2^n, \dots)$ is a sequence of vectors in c_0 which converges to an $x = (\xi_1, \xi_2, \dots)$ in $\bar{c}_0 \subset l_\infty$, then by definition of the norm in l_∞, given $\varepsilon > 0$, there is an η such that

$$\sup_i |\xi_i^n - \xi_i| < \frac{\varepsilon}{2}$$

whenever $n \geq \eta$. In particular, $|\xi_i^\eta - \xi_i| < \varepsilon/2$ for each $i = 1, 2, \dots$. Since the sequence $(\xi_1^\eta, \xi_2^\eta, \dots)$ converges to 0, we can find i_0 such that $|\xi_i^\eta| < \varepsilon/2$ whenever $i \geq i_0$. It now follows that

$$|\xi_i| \leq |\xi_i^\eta| + |\xi_i - \xi_i^\eta| < \frac{\varepsilon}{2} + \frac{\varepsilon}{2} = \varepsilon$$

whenever $i \geq i_0$. Thus $(\xi_1, \xi_2, \dots)$ converges to 0 and the vector x belongs to c_0.

Our next theorem lists the more common Banach spaces that are reflexive.

THEOREM A.   *Each of the following Banach spaces is reflexive.*

(1) *Any finite dimensional space.*

(2) *Any Hilbert space.*

(3) *The Lebesgue spaces L_p for $1 < p < \infty$.*

(4) *The sequence spaces l_p for $1 < p < \infty$.*

Conjugate and Adjoint Operators

In many areas of analysis the concept of the adjoint operator is extremely useful. The functional concepts that we have just developed are helpful in defining both the conjugate and the adjoint operator. To begin, we consider two normed linear spaces X, Y, and a bounded linear operator $A : X \to Y$.

Let $f \in Y^*$. Then $f(y)$ is defined for every $y \in Y$, hence, in particular, for every $y = Ax$ with $x \in X$; that is, the composition fA maps X into the scalars. Let the composition fA be designated by g.

Being a composition of linear mappings, g is linear. Moreover, since A is bounded,

$$|g(x)| = |f(Ax)| \leq \|f\| \cdot \|Ax\| \leq \|f\| \cdot \|A\| \cdot \|x\|,$$

and hence g is a bounded linear functional on X with norm $\|g\| \leq \|f\| \cdot \|A\|$. So $g \in X^*$.

Thus the correspondence $f \to g = fA$ is a mapping from Y^* into X^*. This mapping is also linear, for, if $f_1, f_2 \in Y^*$ and α_1, α_2 are scalars, then

$$(\alpha_1 f_1 + \alpha_2 f_2)A = \alpha_1(f_1 A) + \alpha_2(f_2 A).$$

Let us call this mapping A^* so that by definition $A^* f = fA$ for each f in Y^*. By rewriting the preceding inequality we have

$$|(A^* f)(x)| = |f(Ax)| \leq \|f\| \cdot \|A\| \cdot \|x\|$$

and the functional $A^* f$ has norm

$$\|A^* f\| \leq \|A\| \cdot \|f\|.$$

Since $f \in Y^*$ is arbitrary, it follows that A^* is a bounded linear transformation with domain Y^* and range in X^*. The bounded linear transformation $A^* : Y^* \to X^*$, defined by $A^* f = g = fA$, is called the *conjugate* of A.

Observe that we do not need to require that A be a map *onto* Y in order to define A^*. For a given f in Y^*, $A^* f$ is the bounded linear functional on X whose value at x in X is given by $(A^* f)(x) = f(Ax)$ (see Figure 3.2).

The important properties of the conjugate transformation are summarized in the following two theorems.

THEOREM B. A^* *is a bounded linear transformation and* $\|A^*\| = \|A\|$.

P R O O F.   In view of the remarks preceding the definition, we need only prove that $\|A^*\| \geq \|A\|$.

Now by definition of the norm $\|A\|$, for every $\varepsilon > 0$ there is a vector $x_0 \in X$ with $\|x_0\| = 1$ and $\|Ax_0\| \geq \|A\| - \varepsilon$. If $Ax_0 = y_0 \in Y$, then Theorem D, Section 3.2, guarantees the existence of a functional $f \in Y^*$ such that $f(y_0) = \|y_0\|$ and $\|f\| = 1$. Then $(A^* f)(x_0) = f(Ax_0) = f(y_0)$ so that

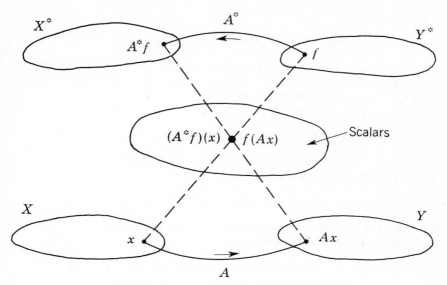

Figure 3.2   A linear transformation and its conjugate.

$\|A^*f\| \geq \|A\| - \varepsilon$. Since f has norm 1, this means that A^* has norm $\|A^*\| \geq \|A\| - \varepsilon$. Since this is true for every $\varepsilon > 0$, it follows that $\|A^*\| \geq \|A\|$.

THEOREM C. *The conjugate transformation has the following properties.*

(1) $0^* = 0$.
(2) $(A_1 + A_2)^* = A_1^* + A_2^*$, $A_i \in \beta(X,Y)$.
(3) $(\alpha A)^* = \alpha A^*$.

If A^{-1} exists and is a bounded linear transformation with domain Y, then

(4) $(A^{-1})^* = (A^*)^{-1}$.

Finally, if $Y = X$, then

(5) $I^* = I$.
(6) $(A_1 A_2)^* = A_2^* A_1^*$, $A_i \in \beta(X,X)$.

P R O O F.   The proofs of the first three properties are simple. To illustrate,

$$[(\alpha A)^*f](x) = f[(\alpha A)x] = \alpha f(Ax) = \alpha(A^*f)(x) = [(\alpha A^*)f](x);$$

hence

$$(\alpha A)^*f = (\alpha A^*)f \quad \text{and} \quad (\alpha A)^* = \alpha A^*.$$

To prove (4), suppose that $A^{-1} \in \beta(Y,X)$. A^{-1} has therefore a conjugate $(A^{-1})^*$ with domain X^* and range in Y^*. Fix f in Y^*, and for all $y = AX \in Y$

we then have

$$(A^{-1})*(A*f)(y) = (A*f)(A^{-1}y) = (A*f)(x) = f(Ax) = f(y).$$

Since every $y \in Y$ is of the form $y = Ax$ for some $x \in X$, it follows that the functional $(A^{-1})*A*f$ agrees with f, and because $f \in Y^*$ is arbitrary this means that $(A^{-1})*A*$ is the identity operator on Y^*.

Similarly, for $g \in X^*$ and $x \in X$,

$$[A*(A^{-1})*g](x) = [(A^{-1})*g](Ax) = (A^{-1})*g(y) = g(A^{-1}y) = g(x);$$

hence $A*(A^{-1})*g = y$, and $A*(A^{-1})*$ is the identity operator on X^*.

It now follows from the equations

$$(A^{-1})*A* = I_{Y*}, \qquad A*(A^{-1})* = I_{X*}$$

that the transformation A^* has inverse $(A^{-1})*$, which proves (4).

To prove (6) we observe that

$$[(A_1 A_2)^*](x) = f(A_1 A_2 x) = (A_1^* f)(A_2 x) = (A_2^* A_1^* f)(x),$$

hence

$$(A_1 A_2)^*(f) = (A_2^* A_1^*)(f).$$

We have already used the notation $\langle x,f \rangle$ for the scalar $f(x)$, in which x and f belong to a normed space and its conjugate space, respectively. In this notation our definition of A^* becomes

$$\langle x,A*f \rangle = \langle Ax,f \rangle, \qquad x \in X, f \in Y^*,$$

when $A : X \to Y$ is a bounded linear transformation. If A is an *operator* on X (i.e., $Y = X$), the conjugate A^* is an operator on X^*. In particular, if $X = H$ is a Hilbert space, each $A \in \beta(H,H)$ determines a unique operator $A^* \in \beta(H^*,H^*)$.

We have seen that H^* may be identified with the Hilbert space H_0 constructed from the set H by introducing a different definition of scalar multiplication and a backward inner product. An equivalent statement is that the correspondence $y \to f_y$, defined by

$$\langle x,y \rangle = f_y(x) = \langle x,f_y \rangle, \qquad \text{all } x \in H,$$

is a conjugate-linear isometry from H onto H^*; that is, every bounded linear functional on H is of the form f_y for some $y \in H$ and the mapping $y \to f_y$ satisfies

$$f_{y_1 + y_2} = f_{y_1} + f_{y_2},$$

$$f_{\lambda y} = \bar{\lambda} f_y,$$

$$\|f_y\| = \|y\|.$$

In a *real* Hilbert space $H_0 = H$, and the mapping $y \to f_y$ is actually linear so that H^* is indistinguishable from H and A^* may be regarded as an operator on H. This situation is useful in the complex case as well and to effect it we introduce another operator.

Let $A \in \beta(H,H)$ be given and fix $y \in H$. Then, by definition of the conjugate A^* of A, we know that $A^*f_y \in H^*$; hence by the representation theorem for bounded linear functionals on H there is a unique $z \in H$ such that

$$A^*f_y = f_z.$$

In other words, there is a well-defined correspondence $y \to z$ from H into itself. Let us write $z = A_* y$ to indicate the dependence of z on y. A_* is a mapping from H into H and, moreover, $A_* \in \beta(H,H)$. To prove this statement we must first obtain another characterization of A_*.

We claim that $A_* y$ is the unique vector in H which satisfies the condition

$$\langle Ax, y \rangle = \langle x, A_* y \rangle, \qquad \text{all } x \in H.$$

That $A_* y$ does satisfy this equation for all $x \in H$ follows from the equation

$$f_y(Ax) = (A^*f_y)(x) = f_z(x), \qquad z = A_* y.$$

That $A_* y$ is the only such vector in H is based on the fact that if a vector $z' \in H$ satisfies

$$\langle x, A_* y \rangle = \langle Ax, y \rangle = \langle x, z' \rangle, \qquad \text{all } x \in H,$$

then

$$\langle x, A_* y - z' \rangle = 0, \qquad \text{all } x \in H;$$

hence $z' = A_* y$.

The proof that A_* is linear and bounded is now immediate. Thus

$$
\begin{aligned}
\langle x, A_*(\alpha_1 y_1 + \alpha_2 y_2) \rangle &= \langle Ax, \alpha_1 y_1 + \alpha_2 y_2 \rangle \\
&= \bar{\alpha}_1 \langle Ax, y_1 \rangle + \bar{\alpha}_2 \langle Ax, y_2 \rangle \\
&= \bar{\alpha}_1 \langle x, A_* y_1 \rangle + \bar{\alpha}_2 \langle x, A_* y_2 \rangle \\
&= \langle x, \alpha_1 A_* y_1 + \alpha_2 A_* y_2 \rangle
\end{aligned}
$$

implies, by the uniqueness of $A_*(\alpha_1 y_1 + \alpha_2 y_2)$, that A_* is linear, and

$$|\langle x, A_* y \rangle| = |\langle Ax, y \rangle| \le \|Ax\| \cdot \|y\| \le \|A\| \cdot \|x\| \cdot \|y\|$$

implies

$$\|A_* y\| = \sup_{\substack{x \in H \\ \|x\| \le 1}} |\langle x, A_* y \rangle| \le \|A\| \cdot \|y\|$$

so that A_* is bounded. (In fact, it is easy to see from the equation

$$A^*f_y = f_z, \qquad z = A_* y$$

that $\omega \leftrightarrow f_\omega$ is an isometry. Since $\|A^*\| = \|A\|$, we actually have $\|A_*\| = \|A\|$. The reader may also follow the chain $y \rightarrow f_y \rightarrow A^*f_y = f_z \rightarrow z$ to check the linearity of A_*.)

Finally, before we summarize our results, let us determine the nature of the mapping $A \rightarrow A_*$ from $\beta(H,H)$ into itself. We have

$$\begin{aligned}
\langle x,(A + B)_*y \rangle &= \langle (A + B)x,y \rangle = \langle Ax,y \rangle + \langle Bx,y \rangle \\
&= \langle x,A_*y + B_*y \rangle, \\
\langle x,(\alpha A)_*y \rangle &= \langle (\alpha A)x,y \rangle + \alpha\langle Ax,y \rangle \\
&= \alpha\langle x,A_*y \rangle = \langle x,\bar{\alpha}A_*y \rangle,
\end{aligned}$$

and

$$\langle x,(AB)_*y \rangle = \langle (AB)x,y \rangle = \langle Bx,A_*y \rangle = \langle x,B_*A_*y \rangle.$$

Since each of these equations is valid for all $x \in H$, we have proved the following theorem.

THEOREM D. *Let H be a Hilbert space. Then to each $A \in \beta(H,H)$ there corresponds a unique operator $A_* \in \beta(H,H)$ which is determined by either of the following definitions.*

(1) A_*y *is the unique* $z \in H$ *for which* $A_*f_y = f_z$.
(2) A_*y *is the unique* $z \in H$ *for which* $\langle Ax,y \rangle = \langle x,z \rangle$ *all* $x \in H$.

The correspondence between A and A_* obeys the following rules:

(1) $0_* = 0, \qquad I_* = I$.
(2) $(A + B)_* = A_* + B_*, \qquad (\alpha A)_* = \bar{\alpha}A_*$.
(3) $(AB)_* = B_*A_*$.
(4) $\|A_*\| = \|A\|$.

If H is a *real* Hilbert space and H^* is identified with H, then A_* coincides with the conjugate A^* of A.

The operator A_* is called the *adjoint* of A. Theorem D tells us that each bounded operator on H has an adjoint[1] and that the process of taking adjoints preserves norms and sums, reverses products, and is conjugate homogeneous. The trivial operators 0 and I are *self-adjoint* in the sense that they agree with their adjoints.

It is clear from the preceding discussion that the adjoint A_* and the conjugate A^* of a bounded operator are logically distinct operators. *In spite of this*, however, we drop the notation A_* and write A^* for both transformations, which is in accord with the usual notation. When it is necessary for clarity, we speak of the "adjoint A^*" or the "conjugate A^*" to isolate the particular meaning at hand. Since the adjoint is defined only for a (bounded linear) mapping of a Hilbert space into itself, the symbol A^* can cause confusion only

---

[1]If $A: H_1 \rightarrow H_2$ is a bounded linear mapping between distinct Hilbert spaces, the conjugate $A^*: H_2^* \rightarrow H_{1*}$ induces a mapping $A_*: H_2 \rightarrow H_1$, which is also called the adjoint of A.

when A is an operator on a complex Hilbert space. As a general rule, the reader should take A^* as the conjugate of A unless the adjoint has meaning, in which case $A \in \beta(H,H)$; the symbol A^* will always mean the adjoint of A.

Example 2.   Let $\{e_n\}_1^\infty$ be an orthonormal system in the Hilbert space l_2. Each $x \in l_2$ has a unique expansion

$$x = \sum_1^\infty \alpha_n e_n, \qquad \alpha_n = \langle x, e_n \rangle.$$

We define the *shift* operator, S on l_2, by specifying that

$$Sx = \sum_{n=1}^\infty \alpha_n e_{n+1}, \qquad \text{if} \quad x = \sum_{n=1}^\infty \alpha_n e_n.$$

Let us determine the adjoint operator S^*. If

$$y = \sum_{n=1}^\infty \beta_n e_n,$$

then

$$\langle Sx, y \rangle = \langle \sum_{n=1}^\infty \alpha_n e_{n+1}, \sum_{n=1}^\infty \beta_k e_k \rangle$$

$$= \sum_{n=1}^\infty \sum_{k=1}^\infty \alpha_n \bar{\beta}_k \langle e_{n+1}, e_k \rangle.$$

Since

$$\langle e_{n+1}, e_k \rangle = \begin{cases} 1, & k = n + 1, \\ 0, & \text{otherwise.} \end{cases}$$

This reduces to

$$\langle Sx, y \rangle = \alpha_1 \bar{\beta}_2 + \alpha_2 \bar{\beta}_3 + \cdots.$$

This, however, we recognize as the inner product of x with the vector z whose coordinates are $(\beta_2, \beta_3, \dots)$; that is, with $z = \sum_{k=1}^\infty \beta_k e_{k-1}$, where e_0 is defined as the zero vector. We conclude therefore that S^* is the operator that sends $y = \sum_1^\infty \beta_k e_k$ into the vector $S^* y = \sum_1^\infty \beta_k e_{k-1}$.

In terms of the coordinate vectors, S sends the vector x with coordinates $(\alpha_1, \alpha_2, \dots)$ into the vector Sx with coordinates $(0, \alpha_1, \alpha_2, \dots)$, whereas S^* sends the same vector x into the vector $S^* x$ whose coordinate vector is $(\alpha_2, \alpha_3, \dots)$.

It is clear from the preceding discussion (and we trust the reader to carry out a formal proof by using the Fourier expansions) that S^*S and SS^* are very different operators. Indeed S^*S sends a vector x with coordinates $(\alpha_1, \alpha_2, \dots)$ into the vector whose coordinates have been shifted one place to the right and then back one; that is, S^*S is the identity operator on l_2, whereas SS^* sends the same vector into one whose coordinates are $(0, \alpha_2, \alpha_3, \dots)$. In other words, SS^* maps the one-dimensional subspace $L(e_1)$ spanned by e_1 into 0 and is the identity operator on the orthogonal compliment of $L(e_1)$.

We cannot in general conclude that an operator on a Hilbert space commutes with its adjoint. Operators A for which $A^*A = AA^*$ are called *normal*; this terminology is used because this condition is precisely the one needed to ensure that a given operator is nice enough to be diagonalized (see Section 3.4).

Example 3. Any $n \times n$ matrix $[a_{ij}]$ defines an operator on a finite-dimensional Banach space. In particular, $[a_{ij}]$ defines an operator A on the Hilbert space $l_2(n)$. Here, if $x = (\xi_1, \xi_2, \dots, \xi_n) \in l_2(n)$, Ax is the vector $y = (\eta_1, \eta_2, \dots, \eta_n)$, with

$$\eta_i = \sum_{j=1}^{n} a_{ij}\xi_j, \qquad i = 1, 2, \dots, n.$$

If $z = (\gamma_1, \gamma_2, \dots, \gamma_n) \in l_2(n)$, then

$$\langle Ax, z \rangle = \langle y, x \rangle = \sum_i \eta_i \bar{\gamma}_i = \sum_i \bar{\gamma}_i \left(\sum_j a_{ij}\xi_j \right).$$

Let $[a_{ij}^*]$ be the matrix of the adjoint operator A^*. Then

$$\langle Ax, z \rangle = \langle x, A^*z \rangle = \sum_i \xi_i \left(\overline{\sum_j a_{ij}^* \gamma_j} \right).$$

By comparing these two equations we see that $a_{ij}^* = \bar{a}_{ji}$; that is, the matrix of A^* is the transpose of the conjugate of the matrix of A.

It follows that the self-adjoint operators on $l_2(n)$ are precisely those whose matrixes $[a_{ij}]$ have the property $a_{ij} = \bar{a}_{ji}$: for example, in the two-dimensional Hilbert space $l_2(2)$ the self-adjoint operators are those with matrices of the form

$$\begin{pmatrix} \alpha & \gamma \\ \bar{\gamma} & \beta \end{pmatrix}$$

for real α, β and some complex scalar γ. In the real Hilbert space $l_2(n)$ the self-adjoint operators occur in matrices that are symmetric about the diagonal (i.e., $a_{ij} = a_{ji}$).

Example 4. The "continuous" analog of the preceding example is the *Fredholm* operator defined in $L_2(0,1)$ by

$$(Ax)(t) = \int_0^1 K(s,t)x(s)ds.$$

[We assume that the kernel function $K(s,t)$ is sufficiently well-behaved for the integral to exist for each $x \in L_2(0,1)$. This is guaranteed for example, by requiring $K(s,t)$ to be bounded, in the square $0 \le s, t \le 1$.]

If $y = Ax$ and $z \in L_2(0,1)$, then

$$\langle Ax, z \rangle = \langle y, z \rangle = \int_0^1 y(t)\overline{z(t)}dt = \int_0^1 \overline{z(t)} \left(\int_0^1 K(s,t)x(s)ds \right) dt$$

$$= \int_0^1 x(s) \left(\int_0^1 K(s,t)\overline{z(t)}dt \right) ds.$$

It follows from this equation that the adjoint A^* sends $z \in L_2(0,1)$ into the function

$$(A^*z)(t) = \int_0^1 \overline{K(t,s)}z(s)ds.$$

Thus the adjoint operator is again a Fredholm operator whose kernel function is obtained from the kernel function of A by forming the "transposed conjugate."

The self-adjoint Fredholm operators arise from a kernel function $K(s,t)$ which satisfies $\overline{K(s,t)} = K(t,s)$.

Example 5.   Consider, now, the continuous-time, linear, dynamic system defined in terms of the system transition matrix $\Phi(t,s)$ by

$$x(t) = (\Phi x^0)(t) + (Fu)(t)$$

$$= \Phi(t,t_0)x^0 + \int_{t_0}^t \Phi(t,s)B(s)u(s)ds, \qquad t \in \tau = [t_0, t_f].$$

Let the domain of the transformation F be taken as $[L_2(\tau)]^m = H_1$ and the range as $[L_2(\tau)]^n = H_2$. Then for every $y \in H_2$ we have[1]

$$\langle y, Fu \rangle = \int_{t_0}^{t_f} [y(t), \int_{t_0}^t \Phi(t,s)B(s)u(s)ds]dt$$

$$= \int_{t_0}^{t_f} \int_{t_0}^t [y(t), \Phi(t,s)B(s)u(s)]dsdt$$

$$= \int_{t_0}^{t_f} \int_{t_0}^t [B^*(s)\Phi^*(t,s)y(t), u(s)]dsdt,$$

where $\Phi^*(t,s)$ denotes the adjoint of $\Phi(t,s)$ as a mapping on E^n. By using the

[1] The notation $[\xi,\eta] = \sum_{i=1}^n \xi_i \overline{\eta}_i$ is frequently useful in dealing with multivariate system problems and is adopted here.

conditions for interchanging order of integration we have

$$\langle y, Fu \rangle = \int_{t_0}^{t_f} \int_s^{t_f} [B^*(s)\Phi^*(t,s)y(t),u(s)]dtds$$

$$= \langle F^*y, u \rangle,$$

where F^* is defined on H_2 by

$$(F^*y)(s) = \int_s^{t_f} B^*(s)\Phi^*(t,s)y(t)dt, \qquad s \in \tau.$$

Several other examples are available within the present setting. For instance, by fixing $t' \in \tau$ the transformation $T : H_1 \to E^n$, defined by $Tu = (Fu)(t')$, is also of interest. For $\xi \in E^n$ we have the equality chain

$$\langle \xi, Tu \rangle = [\xi, \int_{t_0}^{t'} \Phi(t',s)B(s)u(s)ds]$$

$$= \int_{t_0}^{t'} [\xi, \Phi(t',s)B(s)u(s)]ds$$

$$= \int_{t_0}^{t'} [B^*(s)\Phi^*(t',s)\xi,u(s)]ds = \langle T^*\xi, u \rangle,$$

where the conjugate of T is given by

$$(T^*\xi)(t) = B^*(t)\Phi^*(t',t)\xi, \qquad t \in \tau.$$

To deal with the discrete counterpart of the present example let

$$W(t'_k,t_j) = h_j\Phi(t'_k,t_{j+1})B(t_j) \qquad \text{and fix } t'_k \in \sigma.$$

Consider the transformation $T : H_1 \to E^n$, defined by

$$Tu = \sum_{j=0}^{[t_k']-1} W(t'_k,t_j)u(t_j), \qquad u \in H_1,$$

where H_1 is the space $\{l_2(\sigma')\}^m$ and $\sigma' = \{t : t \in \sigma, t < t'_k\}$.
For arbitrary $\xi \in E^n$ we arrive at the relation

$$\langle \xi, Tu \rangle = \sum_{j=0}^{[t_k']-1} [W^*(t'_k,t_j)\xi,u(t_j)].$$

Thus T^*, the conjugate to T, is given by

$$(T^*\xi)(t_j) = h_j B^*(t_j)\Phi^*(t'_k,t_{j+1})\xi, \qquad t_j \in \sigma.$$

R E M A R K 1. The concept of the conjugate transformation is also quite useful in regard to Section 3.2. Consider, for example, the transformation

$T: X \to Y$. Let $S = \{e_1, \dots, e_n\}$ denote a basis for Y. Then, from the decomposition of the identity on Y given by

$$I_y = \sum_{i=1}^{n} e_i \rangle \langle e_i^+,$$

it is immediate from the equality chain

$$Tx = I_y Tx = \sum_{i=1}^{n} e_i \rangle \langle e_i^+, Tx \rangle = \sum_{i=1}^{n} e_i \rangle \langle T^*e_i^+, x \rangle$$

that the functionals $\{f_i = T^*e_i^+ : i = 1, \dots, n\}$ constitute the necessary set to write T in dyadic form

$$T = \sum_{i=1}^{n} e_i \rangle \langle f_i.$$

In the minimum energy problem of Section 3.2 the matrix $\mathscr{F} = [\langle f_i, f_j \rangle]$ associated with T played an important role. Since $f_i = T^*e_i^+$, it is clear that

$$\langle f_i, f_j \rangle = \langle T^*e_i^+, T^*e_j^+ \rangle = \langle e_i^+, (TT^*)e_j^+ \rangle, \qquad i, j = 1, \dots, n.$$

Thus if E denotes the matrix whose ith row is the vector e_i^+, $i = 1, \dots, n$, then by direct multiplication it is readily verified that

$$\mathscr{F} = ETT^*E^*.$$

In particular, if the set S is formed from the coordinate basis for R^n, then $E = I$ and $\mathscr{F} = TT^*$.

R E M A R K 2.   The mapping Φ on E^n defined by $\Phi\xi = \Phi(t',t)\zeta$ has the adjoint $\Phi^*\eta = \Phi^*(t',t)\eta$. The matrix $\Phi^*(t',t)$ as a function of t has some interesting properties which follow from the equality chain:

$$\frac{d}{dt}[\Phi^*(t',t)] = \left[\frac{d}{dt}\Phi^{-1}(t,t')\right]^*$$

$$= [-\Phi^{-1}(t,t')\dot{\Phi}(t,t')\Phi^{-1}(t,t')]^*$$

$$= -\Phi^*(t',t)[A(t)\Phi(t,t')]^*\Phi^*(t',t)$$

$$= -A^*(t)\Phi^*(t',t).$$

In other words, if the two matrices $\Phi(t,t_0)$ and $\Psi(t,t_0)$ are defined by

$$\dot{\Phi}(t,t_0) = A(t)\Phi(t,t_0), \qquad \Phi(t_0,t_0) = I, \tag{1}$$

$$\dot{\Psi}(t,t_0) = -A^*(t)\Psi(t,t_0), \qquad \Psi(t_0,t_0) = I, \tag{2}$$

then

$$\Psi^*(t,t_0) = \Phi^{-1}(t,t_0) = \Phi(t_0,t).$$

Since, for every $t \in \tau$, we have

$$\Psi^*(t,t_0)\Phi(t,t_0) = I,$$

it is clear that the columns of $\Psi(t,t_0)$ move as a function of t in the space R^n in such a way that they are at any instant the dual set to the columns of $\Phi(t,t_0)$. The system of Eq. 2 is frequently called the system adjoint to that of Eq. 1.

Exercises

1. Consider the free response as a mapping $(\Phi\xi)(t) = \Phi(t,t_0)\xi$ of E^n into $[L_2(t_0,t_f)]^n$. Show that Φ^* is given by

$$(\Phi^*y) = \int_{t_0}^{t_f}\Phi^*(s,t_0)y(s)ds, \qquad y \in [L_2(t_0,t_f)]^n.$$

2. Let C denote the clamp operation defined in Eq. 2, Example 4, Section 2.1. If C is a mapping of $l_2(\sigma) \to L_2(\tau)$, show that C^* is defined by

$$(C^*y)(t_k) = \int_{t_k}^{t_{k+1}} y(s)ds, \qquad t_k \in \sigma.$$

3. Verify that the state transition matrix corresponding to the system $\dot{x}(t) = A(t)x(t)$ with

$$A = \begin{bmatrix} 2 & -e^t \\ e^{-t} & 1 \end{bmatrix}$$

is given by

$$\Phi(t,t_0) = \begin{bmatrix} e^{2t-t_0}\cos(t-t_0) & -e^{2t-t_0}\sin(t-t_0) \\ e^{t-2t_0}\sin(t-t_0) & e^{t-t_0}\cos(t-t_0) \end{bmatrix}$$

and then show that the state transition matrix $\Psi(t,t_0)$ of the adjoint system is given by $\Psi(t,t_0) = [\Phi^{-1}(t,t_0)]^* = \Phi^*(t_0,t)$.

4. Let $\mathscr{L}$ denote the linear transformation defined by

$$(\mathscr{L}x)(t) = \dot{x}(t) - A(t)x(t), \qquad t \in [t_0,t_f].$$

Although $\mathscr{L}$ is *not* bounded as an operator on $[L_2(t_0,t_f)]^n$, proceed formally to show that if $\mathscr{L}^*$ is defined by

$$(\mathscr{L}^*y)(t) = -\dot{y}(t) - A^*(t)y(t), \qquad t \in [t_0,t_f],$$

with $\langle \,,\, \rangle$ denoting the usual inner product on $[L_2(t_0,t_f)]^n$, then

$$\langle y,\mathscr{L}x \rangle - \langle \mathscr{L}^*y,x \rangle = [y(t),x(t)]_{t_0}^{t_f}, \qquad (3)$$

where $[\,,\,]$ denotes the inner product in E^n.

5. In Example 5 let $B(s) = I$. The transformation F, defined by

$$x(t) = (Fu)(t) = \int_{t_0}^{t} \Phi(t,s)u(s)ds, \qquad t \in [t_0, t_f]$$

has the conjugate F^* given by

$$q(t) = (F^*y)(t) = \int_{t}^{t_f} \Phi^*(s,t)y(s)ds, \qquad t \in [t_0, t_f].$$

Using Remark 2, show that q satisfies the differential system

$$\dot{q}(t) = -A^*(t)q(t) - y(t), \qquad q(t_0) = \int_{t_0}^{t_f} \Psi(t_0,s)y(s)ds.$$

6. From the expansion $\Delta_k[y(t_k),x(t_k)] = [\Delta_k y(t_k),x(t_k)] + [y(t_{k+1}),\Delta_k x(t_k)]$ prove that

$$\sum_{m}^{N-1} h_k[\Delta_k y(t_k),x(t_k)] = [y(t_k),x(t_k)]_m^N - \sum_{m}^{N-1} h_k[y(t_{k+1}),\Delta_k x(t_k)].$$

By rearranging terms prove also that

$$\sum_{m}^{N-1} h_k[\Delta_k y(t_k),x(t_k)]$$

$$= [y(t_k), x(t_{k-1})]_m^N - \sum_{m}^{N-1} h_k[y(t_k), \left(\frac{h_{k-1}}{h_k}\right)\Delta_{k-1}x(t_{k-1})]. \quad (4)$$

7. Let G denote the operator defined by $(Gx)(t_k) = \Delta_k x(t_k) - A(t_k)x(t_k)$, $t_k \in \sigma$. If $\langle u,v \rangle = \sum_{m}^{N-1} h_k[u(t_k),v(t_k)]$, use Eq. 4 to prove that

$$\langle y,Gx \rangle - \langle G^*y,x \rangle = [y(t_k),x(t_{k-1})]_m^N,$$

where by definition

$$(B^*y)(t_k) = [h_k^{-1}I + A^*(t_k)]y(t_k) - h_k^{-1}y(t_{k-1}).$$

Note that G is defined on $\sigma = \{t_m, \dots, t_N\}$, whereas G^* is defined on $\sigma' = \{t_{m-1}, \dots, t_{N-1}\}$. If $\Phi(t_k,t_0)$ and $\Psi(t_k,t_0)$ are the transition matrices for the systems associated with the operators G and G^*, respectively, show that

$$\Psi(t_{k-1},t_0)\Phi(t_k,t_1) = I, \qquad t_k \in \sigma.$$

If $h_k\|A^*(t_k)\| < 1$, use the expansion

$$[I + h_k A^*(t_k)]^{-1} = I - h_k A^*(t_k) + h_k^2[A^*(t_k)]^2 + \cdots$$

to show that the adjoint system satisfies approximately

$$\Delta_k y(t_k) = - A^*(t_k) y(t_{k-1}).$$

8. Let the vector-valued system of differential equations

$$\dot{x}(t) = f[x(t),u(t),t], \qquad t \in [t_0,t_f],$$

with $x = (x_1, \ldots, x_n)$, $f = (f_1, \ldots, f_n)$, and $u = (u_1, \ldots, u_n)$, describe the motion of a missile system. The tuplet $(\bar{u},\bar{x})$ denotes a nominal control-trajectory pair which satisfies the desired target condition $x(t_f) = \bar{x}(t_f) = \xi$. Assume that disturbance forces necessitate a control perturbation δu. Expand by series the nonlinear system about the point $(\bar{u},\bar{x})$ to arrive at the variational equations

$$\delta \dot{x}(t) = A(t)\delta x(t) + B(t)\delta u(t), \qquad t \in [t_0,t_f].$$

Let $\eta \in E^n$ be a tuplet such that $[\delta x(t_f),\eta]$ is a meaningful measure of the system accuracy. Use Exercise 4 to define a variational control computor. HINT: Note that $(L\delta x)(t) = (B\delta u)(t)$; choose $y \in N_{L^*}$ with $y(t_f) = \eta$. See also Tsien [A88].

9. Show that every closed subspace of a reflexive Banach space is itself a reflexive Banach space.

3.4   CANONICAL FORMS FOR LINEAR SYSTEMS

In this section the current line of theoretical development is brought to completion with the specification of three canonical representations of linear transformations. We have seen for instance in Section 3.2 that transformations with finite rank may be decomposed along any basis for the range of the transformation. The properties of the transformation are independent of the basis chosen. It seems feasible, however, that the structure of the transformation will be more clearly displayed in some coordinates than in others.

It is also apparent that we should not expect a single canonical form to exist for all linear transformations. Indeed, those of finite rank may be expected to differ from those that do not possess this special property. Similarly, we shall find that certain other special classes of transformations have a particularly simple structure that is not possessed in the general case. The discussion of these considerations in the most general framework is far beyond the scope of this book. (This, in fact, is an area of current mathematical research.) We shall be content, therefore, with an exposure to the basic ideas sufficient for the statement and understanding of some of the more general results.

Invariant Manifolds

Let $A : X \to X$ denote a linear operator defined on the linear space X. A linear manifold $M \subset X$ is said to be *invariant* with respect to the operator A if $A(M) \subset M$; that is, for every $x \in M$ we have $Ax \in M$. As examples of invariant manifolds, it is apparent that the whole space X, the null space N_A, and the range R_A are invariant manifolds of any linear operator A.

If M is a proper subspace of X, which is invariant under A, the restriction of A to the domain M can be considered as an operator on M alone; that is, the operation of A on vectors outside M are ignored. If M and N are proper subspaces of X such that $X = M \oplus N$ and M and N are both invariant under A, then M and N are said to *reduce A*. This situation is interesting because it allows us to replace the study of A as a whole by the study of its restrictions to M and N. Hopefully these restrictions will turn out to be operators of some particularly simple type.

In finite dimensional spaces knowledge of the invariance of a subspace under an operator allows specific conclusions about the matrix representing the operator. To be specific, let $M \subset X$ be an m-dimensional invariant subspace under A. Let n be the dimension of X, and N an $n - m$ dimensional subspace such that $X = M \oplus N$. In general, N will not be invariant under A. For this situation we have the following:

THEOREM A. *If M is an m-dimensional invariant subspace of X under A, then a basis S for X exists such that the operator A may be represented by the matrix $[A]_S$ which has only zeros in the lower left-hand $n - m \times m$ corner.*

PROOF. Let $S' = \{x_1, \ldots, x_m\}$ and $S'' = \{x_{m+1}, \ldots, x_n\}$ denote bases for M and N, respectively. Then $S = \{x_1, \ldots, x_n\}$ is a basis for X. Since M is invariant under A, $Ax_j \in L(S')$, $j = 1, \ldots, m$. By the definition of the dual basis $\langle x_i^+, y \rangle = 0$ for every $y \in L(S')$ and $i = m + 1, \ldots, n$. Thus

$$a_{ij} = \langle x_i^+, Ax_j \rangle = 0, \qquad i = m + 1, \ldots, n, \qquad j = 1, \ldots, m,$$

which proves the theorem.

An obvious corollary to Theorem A is that if M and N are both invariant under A the matrix $[A]_S$ will have the form

$$[A]_S = \left[\begin{array}{c|c} A_1 & 0 \\ \hline 0 & A_2 \end{array} \right],$$

in which A_1 and A_2 are $m \times m$ and $(n - m) \times (n - m)$ matrices, respectively. More generally, if $\{M_i : i = 1, \ldots, p\}$ denotes a collection of subspaces of X such that $X = M_1 \oplus \cdots \oplus M_p$ with M_i and $X \ominus M_i$ invariant under A, $i = 1, \ldots, p$, then there exists a basis S for X (composed of sub-basis sets S_i for

M_i, $i = 1, \ldots, p$) such that

$$[A]_S = \begin{bmatrix} A_1 & 0 & \cdots & 0 \\ 0 & A_2 & \cdots & 0 \\ & & & \\ 0 & \cdots & & A_p \end{bmatrix};$$

each matrix A_i, $i = 1, \ldots, p$ represents the action of A on the subspace M_i. We leave it to the reader to construct the set S and verify this conclusion.

One of the more important types of invariant subspaces is one which is one-dimensional; that is, $M = L(x)$; x is a fixed vector. By the definition of invariant subspace it follows that if M is invariant under A

$$Ax = \lambda x, \qquad x \neq 0,$$

in which λ is a scalar. Such a vector x is called a characteristic vector or *eigenvector* of A, and the associated λ is called a characteristic value or *eigenvalue* of A.

Consider now a basis $\{x_1, x_2, \ldots, x_n\}$ for X and let $[a_{ij}]$ be the matrix of A with respect to this basis. To say that a complex number λ is an eigenvalue of A means that there is a vector $x = \sum_{i=1} \alpha_i x_i \neq 0$ such that $Ax = \lambda x$. This, in turn, is equivalent to the following system of equations:

$$(a_{11} - \lambda)\alpha_1 + a_{12}\alpha_2 + \cdots + a_{1n}\alpha_n = 0$$
$$\vdots$$
$$a_{n1}\alpha_1 + a_{n2}\alpha_2 + \cdots + (a_{nn} - \lambda)\alpha_n = 0.$$

Thus λ is an eigenvalue of A if and only if this homogeneous system of equations in the unknowns $\alpha_1, \ldots, \alpha_n$ has a nontrivial solution. From elementary algebra we know that this occurs precisely when the determinant[1] $\det[A - \lambda I]$ of the system vanishes. Observe now that this determinant is a polynomial of degree n in λ. W call it the *characteristic polynomial* of A, and offer the following criterion: a complex number λ is an eigenvalue for A if and only if λ is a zero of the characteristic polynomial of A. This leads us to Theorem B.

THEOREM B.   *Every linear operator on a finite-dimensional complex linear space has an eigenvalue.*

P R O O F.   In view of the preceding remarks, we must show that the characteristic polynomial of such an operator has a zero. This follows from the fundamental theorem of algebra which asserts that every polynomial with complex coefficients has at least one complex zero.

Before proceeding, it is worth observing that Theorem B is by no means elementary. We used one of the deepest facts about the complex number to

---

[1] Recall (see Exercise 8, Section 3.2) that the determinant depends only on the operator and *not* on the basis used to compute it.

prove it, and, indeed, we are forced to, for *every* polynomial $p(\lambda) = \lambda^n + a_1\lambda^{n-1} + \cdots + a_n$ can appear as the characteristic polynomial of a linear operator on a finite-dimensional space. (Consider, for example, the operator on an n-dimensional linear space whose matrix is

$$\begin{bmatrix} 0 & 1 & 0 & 0 \\ 0 & 0 & 1 & 0 \\ \vdots & & & 1 \\ -a_n & -a_{n-1} & \cdots & -a_1 \end{bmatrix}.$$

Thus the theorem is logically *equivalent* to the fundamental theorem of algebra.

Note also that the assumption that X is a *complex* linear space is essential. Indeed, the matrix

$$\begin{bmatrix} 0 & -1 \\ 1 & 0 \end{bmatrix}$$

in a *real* two-dimensional space has no eigenvalues, for its characteristic polynomial never vanishes for real λ.

If A is a linear operator on a finite-dimensional linear space, the *spectrum* of A, denoted by $\sigma(A)$, is the subset of the complex plane consisting of the eigenvalues of A. We have seen that a complex number λ belongs to $\sigma(A)$ if and only if the operator $A - \lambda I$ has a zero determinant. This, in turn, is equivalent to the assertion that $A - \lambda I$ is singular. In other words, $\sigma(A)$ consists of those λ for which $A - \lambda I$ is not invertible.

We know that if A is an operator on an n-dimensional space then $\sigma(A)$ is not empty and consists at most of n distinct points. This general statement is the strongest that can be made, for if $\lambda_1, \lambda_2, \ldots, \lambda_m$ is any set of complex numbers it is clear that a diagonal matrix using only these numbers as its diagonal entries will have a spectrum equal to $\{\lambda_1, \ldots, \lambda_m\}$. A triangular matrix with this λ_i on its diagonal will also have the same spectrum. Thus quite different operators may have the same spectrum.

Suppose now that A is a linear operator on a finite-dimensional complex space X.

LEMMA A.   *The eigenvectors $x_1, x_2, \ldots, x_m$ of an operator A corresponding to distinct eigenvalues $\lambda_1, \lambda_2, \ldots, \lambda_m$ are linearly independent.*

P R O O F.   Assume that the vectors $x_1, \ldots, x_m$ are dependent and that a maximal independent subset $x_1, \ldots, x_{j-1}$ (reorder the vectors if necessary) exists. There is also a dependence relation

$$\gamma_1 x_1 + \gamma_2 x_2 + \cdots + \gamma_j x_j = 0$$

between j eigenvectors of the operator A, in which at least one γ, say γ_1, is nonzero. Applying the operator A to this relation gives

$$\gamma_1 \lambda_1 x_1 + \gamma_2 \lambda_2 x_2 + \cdots + \gamma_j \lambda_j x_j = 0.$$

By multiplying the first equation by λ_j and subtracting it from the second equation we obtain

$$\gamma_1(\lambda_1 - \lambda_j)x_1 + \lambda_2(\lambda_2 - \lambda_j)x_2 + \cdots + \gamma_{j-1}(\lambda_{j-1} - \lambda_j)x_{j-1} = 0,$$

but because $x_1, \ldots, x_{j-1}$ are linearly independent this result implies that all the coefficients

$$\gamma_1(\lambda_1 - \lambda_j), \ldots, \gamma_{j-1}(\lambda_{j-1} - \lambda_j)$$

will vanish. However, $\gamma_1(\lambda_1 - \lambda_j) = 0$ contradicts the assumed conditions $\gamma_1 \neq 0$ and $\lambda_1 \neq \lambda_j$. Therefore our assumption of linear dependence between $x_1, x_2, \ldots, x_j$ is false.

An immediate consequence of Lemma A is that if A is an operator whose eigenvalues are *distinct* we will have a basis $x_1, x_2, \ldots, x_n$ with respect to which A has a diagonal matrix. Indeed, if $x_1, x_2, \ldots, x_n$ is chosen as the eigenvectors of A, Lemma A ensures that this set will be a basis, and for any $x = \sum \alpha_i x_i$ in X we have

$$Ax = \sum_i \alpha_i A x_i = \sum_i \alpha_i \lambda_i x_i.$$

Therefore, relative to the basis $x_1, \ldots, x_n$, A has the matrix

$$\begin{bmatrix} \lambda_1 & 0 & \cdots & 0 \\ 0 & \lambda_2 & \cdots & \\ & & \ddots & \\ \vdots & & & \ddots \\ 0 & & & \lambda_n \end{bmatrix}.$$

If the eigenvalues are distinct, we can choose n independent vectors $x_1, x_2, \ldots, x_n$, so that in each direction x_i the operator A is just multiplication by λ_i.

REMARK 1.   We shall say that a linear operator A on an n-dimensional space is *simple* if A has a full complement of n eigenvectors. In other words, an operator is simple if the matrix of the operator can be put in diagonal form. We have just seen that operators with distinct eigenvalues $\lambda_1, \ldots, \lambda_n$ are simple. This condition, however, is by no means essential. For example, the identity operator has only one eigenvalue, $\lambda = 1$, but it also has a diagonal matrix (namely, the identity matrix) when decomposed along any basis.

Let $\Delta(\lambda) = (\lambda - \lambda_1)^{p_1} \cdot (\lambda - \lambda_2)^{p_2} \cdots (\lambda - \lambda_m)^{p_m}$ denote the characteristic polynomial of the operator A. Here $\lambda_1 \cdots \lambda_m$ are distinct and $\sum_j p_j = n$. The multiplicity p_j of the root λ_j is called the *algebraic multiplicity* of the eigenvalue $\lambda_j, j = 1, \ldots, m$. For each λ_j the operator $A - \lambda_j I$ is singular and has a null space consisting of the eigenvectors associated with this eigenvalue. The dimension of the null space (i.e., the nullity) of $A - \lambda_j I$ is called the *geometric multiplicity* of the eigenvalue λ_j. In view of the earlier remarks, it is clear that simple operators are exactly those for which the algebraic and geometric multiplicities of each eigenvalue are the same.

As a comparison of the two possibilities, consider, in the spirit of Example 3, Section 3.3, the operators on a two-dimensional space with the respective matrices

$$[I] = \begin{bmatrix} 1 & 0 \\ 0 & 1 \end{bmatrix} \qquad [T] = \begin{bmatrix} 1 & 1 \\ 0 & 1 \end{bmatrix}.$$

Notice that both operators have only the eigenvalue $\lambda = 1$. The reader may verify, as an exercise, that the operator T is *not* simple.

Functions of an Operator

Let the linear space X be the direct sum $X = X_1 \oplus X_2 \oplus \cdots \oplus X_n$ of the linear manifolds $\{X_i\}$. Recall from Section 2.1 that the projection P_i of X onto the subspace X_i was defined as the linear transformation satisfying

$$P_i x = 0, \qquad x \in X_j, \qquad i \neq j,$$
$$P_i x = x, \qquad x \in X_i.$$

Observe that $P_i P_j = 0$ if $i \neq j$, $P_i^2 = P_i$ and that the sum $P_1 + P_2 + \cdots + P_n$ is an identity operator on X. Moreover, $X_i = P_i(X)$ is the range of P_i.

Suppose now that dim $(X) = n$ and let A be a simple operator on X. We assert that there is a unique family of $\{P_i\}$ projections on X with the following properties:

$$P_i P_j = 0, \qquad \text{if } i \neq j, \tag{1a}$$

$$\sum_i P_i = I, \tag{1b}$$

$$A = \sum_i \lambda_i P_i. \tag{1c}$$

The λ's are the eigenvalues of A. Indeed, because A is simple, we may choose a basis $\{e_1, e_2, \ldots, e_n\}$ for X, which consists of eigenvectors of A. The fact that the e_i form a basis for X means that $X = L(e_1) \oplus L(e_2) \oplus \cdots \oplus L(e_n)$, which in turn is equivalent to Eqs. 1a and 1b, where P_i is the projection of X onto $L(e_1)$. Eq. 1c is equivalent to the n equations $Ae_i = \lambda_i e_i$. If $\{Q_i\}$ is any other set of n projections on X with the properties of Eqs. 1a and 1b then $X = Q_1(X) \oplus Q_2(X) \oplus \cdots \oplus Q_n(X)$. This implies that each $Q_i \neq 0$; in fact, dim $Q_i(X) = 1$. If we also have

$$A = \sum_i \mu_i Q_i$$

for some scalars μ_i, it follows that

$$AQ_jx = \left(\sum_{i=1}^{n} \mu_i Q_i\right)(Q_jx) = \mu_j Q_jx;$$

that is, the scalars $\{\mu_i\}$ are a rearrangement of the eigenvalues $\{\lambda_i\}$ of A and the Q's are the projections onto the corresponding eigenspaces $L(e_i) = P_i(X)$. This proves the uniqueness of the family $\{P_i\}$ of projections associated with the simple operator A.

It is easy to identify the projections P_i. Indeed

$$P_i = e_i\rangle\langle e_i^+$$

and the matrix of P_i (in relation to the basis $\{e_1, e_2, \ldots, e_n\}$) consists of zeros everywhere except for a one in the ith diagonal position. Eq. 1c then has the form

$$A = \sum_{i=1}^{n} e_i\rangle\lambda_i\langle e_i^+$$

and states that the matrix of A is diagonal.

If A is simple, we may use the preceding *spectral representation* of A or, equivalently, the representation of A as a diagonal matrix relative to the basis $\{e_1, e_2, \ldots, e_n\}$ to study "functions" of A. If k is a positive integer, the power A^k is defined inductively by $A^{k+1} = A(A^k), k = 1, 2, \ldots$. For the simple operator A of Eq. 1c it follows by a direct computation that

$$A^k = \sum_{i=1}^{n} (\lambda_i)^k P_i = \sum_{i=1}^{n} e_i\rangle(\lambda_i)^k\langle e_i^+.$$

Similarly, for any polynomial

$$\psi(z) = \sum_{k=0}^{N} \alpha_k z^k$$

the operator

$$\psi(A) = \sum_{k=0}^{N} \alpha_k A^k$$

will have the representation

$$\psi(A) = \sum_i \psi(\lambda_i)P_i = \sum_i e_i\rangle\psi(\lambda_i)\langle e_i^+.$$

If A is an invertible operator [i.e., if $0 \notin \sigma(A)$], it is clear that A^{-1} is given by

$$A^{-1} = \sum_i \lambda_i^{-1} P_i;$$

that is, A^{-1} is the operator whose matrix relative to the basis $\{e_1, \ldots, e_n\}$ is diagonal with entries $\{\lambda_1^{-1}, \ldots, \lambda_n^{-1}\}$. In fact, if $f(z)$ is any function of a complex variable that is analytic on an open set containing the spectrum of the simple operator A, it can be shown that the function $f(A)$ is well defined (e.g., by a Taylor series) and

$$f(A) = \sum_i f(\lambda_i)P_i = \sum_i e_i\rangle f(\lambda_i)\langle e_i^+.$$

Note also that it is easy to compute the spectrum of a function of A from the spectral representation of A. Indeed, for the functions $z \to z^n$, $z \to \psi(z)$, and $z \to z^{-1}$ it follows by inspection of the corresponding matrices that the operators A^n, $\psi(A)$, and A^{-1} have spectra equal to $[\sigma(A)]^n$, $\psi[\sigma(A)]$, and $[\sigma(A)]^{-1}$, respectively. More generally, if f is a function for which $f(A)$ makes sense as an operator, we have[1]

$$\sigma[f(A)] = f[\sigma(A)],$$

where the set on the right is by definition the range of f:

$$f[\sigma(A)] = \{v : v = f(\lambda), \lambda \in \sigma(A)\}.$$

Normal Operators

So far we have used only the fact that X is a linear space. Let us now suppose that $X = H$ is also endowed with an inner product so that it is a finite-dimensional Hilbert space. We still have the notion of an invariant linear manifold under an operator A on H, and, since H is finite-dimensional, it will always be closed and therefore a subspace of A. In the general infinite-dimensional case it is easy to see that if M is an invariant linear manifold of an operator A its closure $\overline{M}$ is an invariant subspace of A. In analogy with the algebraic case we say that an invariant subspace M of A *reduces* A if $M^\perp$ is also invariant under A.

It is easy to construct examples to show that an invariant subspace of an operator need not reduce that operator. For instance, consider the Hilbert space l_2 of vectors $(\alpha_1, \alpha_2, \ldots)$, with $\sum_1^\infty |\alpha_k|^2 < \infty$, and the shift operator S on that space (see Example 2, Section 3.3). The subspace M, which consists of vectors of the form $(0, 0, \alpha_3, \ldots)$ is then invariant under S but does not reduce S. Indeed, $M^\perp$ consists of the vectors of the form $(\alpha_1, \alpha_2, 0, \ldots)$, and it is clear that the image $(0, \alpha_1, \alpha_2, 0, \ldots)$ of such a vector under S need not belong to $M^\perp$.

The relation $\langle Ax,y \rangle = \langle x, A^*y \rangle$ between an operator and its adjoint shows that a subspace M is invariant under A if and only if $M^\perp$ is invariant

---

[1]This equation is the statement of the spectral mapping theorem, which, although more or less trivial for simple operators, remains true for nonsimple operators as well.

under A^*. Thus, if $A(M) \subset M$, the above relation shows that if $y \perp M$, then for all $x \in M$ we have $A^*y \perp x$. That is, $A^*(M^\perp)^\perp \subset M^\perp$. Conversely, if $M^\perp$ is invariant under A^*, then $M = (M^\perp)^\perp$ is invariant under $(A^*)^* = A$.

It follows from this that a subspace M *reduces* A if and only if it is invariant under *both* A and A^*.

Let us now consider an operator A on the finite-dimensional Hilbert space H. Our preceding results show that the matrix of A, at least when A is simple, can be put into a diagonal form by a suitable choice of a not necessarily orthogonal basis for H. If we orthonormalize the x_i's by the Gram-Schmidt process to obtain an orthonormal basis $\{y_1, y_2, \ldots, y_n\}$, it is not difficult to see that the matrix of A relative to the new basis will be triangular. We do not, however, need the hypothesis that A is simple, as Theorem C shows.

THEOREM C.   *Let A be a linear operator on a finite-dimensional complex Hilbert space H. There is then an orthonormal basis $\{x_1, x_2, \ldots, x_n\}$ of M, with respect to which the matrix of A has the form*

$$\begin{bmatrix} \lambda_1 & \alpha_{12} & \alpha_{13} & \cdots & \alpha_{1n} \\ 0 & \lambda_2 & \alpha_{23} & \cdots & \alpha_{2n} \\ 0 & 0 & \lambda_3 & \cdots & \alpha_{3n} \\ \vdots & & & & \vdots \\ 0 & 0 & \cdot & \cdot & \cdot & \lambda_n \end{bmatrix}.$$

The diagonal elements $\lambda_1, \lambda_2, \ldots, \lambda_n$ are precisely the eigenvalues of A counted according to their multiplicity as zeros of the characteristic polynomial of A (i.e., their algebraic multiplicity).

P R O O F.   We need only prove the first assertion. The second follows immediately from the fact that the determinant of a triangular matrix is just the product of the diagonal elements.

By Theorem B, A has an eigenvalue λ_1, hence a unit eigenvector x_1:

$$Ax_1 = \lambda_1 x_1.$$

Let H_1 denote the manifold $L(x_1)$ and consider now the orthogonal complement $H_2 = H_1^\perp$. This again is a finite-dimensional Hilbert space. If H_1 reduces A, then H_2 is invariant under A, and so we may legitimately regard A as an operator on H_2. By applying Theorem B to the restriction of A to H_2 we would then obtain a vector $x_2 \perp x_1$ and a λ_2 such that $Ax_2 = \lambda_2 x_2$. However, H_1 need not reduce A, so we consider instead the operator P_2A, in which P_2 is the projection of H onto H_2. This *does* leave H_2 invariant, and hence we have λ_2 and $x_2 \perp x_1$ such that

$$P_2Ax_2 = \lambda_2 x_2.$$

Hence for some scalar α_{12}

$$Ax_2 = \alpha_{12}x_1 + \lambda_2 x_2; \qquad x_2 \perp x_1, \qquad \|x_2\| = 1.$$

This done, we consider the space $H_3 = L(x_1,x_2)^\perp$ and the operator P_3A on H_3, where P_3 is the projection of H onto H_3. Theorem B gives λ_3 and $x_3 \in H_3$ such that

$$P_3Ax_3 = \lambda_3x_3, \qquad \|x_3\| = 1,$$

and since $(I - P_3)Ax_3$ belongs to $L(x_1,x_2)$ it has the form

$$(I - P_3)Ax_3 = \alpha_{13}x_1 + \alpha_{23}x_2.$$

Hence

$$Ax_3 = \alpha_{13}x_1 + \alpha_{23}x_2 + \lambda_3x_3; \qquad x_3 \perp x_1,x_2 \text{ and } \|x_3\| = 1.$$

Continuing in this way, we arrive at the assertion of the theorem.

THEOREM D.   *A linear operator A on H has a diagonal matrix with respect to some orthonormal basis of H if and only if A commutes with A*.*

P R O O F.   If the matrix of A is diagonal relative to some orthonormal basis, so is the matrix of A^*, and it is trivial that any two diagonal matrices commute. Hence the condition $AA^* = A^*A$ is necessary.

Now suppose that $AA^* = A^*A$. We may also suppose that the matrix A is triangular. A^* then has the matrix

$$\begin{bmatrix} \bar{\lambda}_1 & 0 & 0 & \cdots & 0 \\ \bar{\alpha}_{12} & \bar{\lambda}_2 & 0 & \cdots & 0 \\ \bar{\alpha}_{13} & \bar{\alpha}_{23} & \bar{\lambda}_3 & \cdots & 0 \\ \vdots & & & & \\ \bar{\alpha}_{1n} & \bar{\alpha}_{2n} & \bar{\alpha}_{3n} & \cdots & \bar{\lambda}_n \end{bmatrix},$$

and direct computation shows that the off-diagonal elements must vanish.

We may also prove sufficiency by observing that if $AA^* = A^*A$ then $Ax = \lambda x$ implies $A^*x = \bar{\lambda}x$; hence the spaces $H_1, H_2, H_3, \ldots$ in the proof of Theorem C reduce A, and the scalars α_{ij} do not appear.

An operator A on an arbitrary Hilbert space is *normal* if it commutes with its adjoint. Theorem D asserts that the normal operators on a finite-dimensional Hilbert space are precisely those which, relative to a suitable orthonormal basis $\{e_1, e_2, \ldots, e_n\}$, have a diagonal matrix. If A is normal on the finite-dimensional Hilbert space H, we can choose an orthonormal basis $\{e_1, e_2, \ldots, e_n\}$ for H, which consists of eigenvectors of A. By writing P_i for the projection of H onto $L(e_i)$, we have $P_iP_j = 0$ for $i \neq j$, $P_i^2 = P_i$, and $\sum_{i=1}^n P_i = I$ just as before. However, in the present situation the P_i have the additional property that $P_i^* = P_i$. Indeed, if $x = (x_1, x_2, \ldots, x_n)$ and $y = (y_1, y_2, \ldots, y_n)$, then $\langle x, P_i^*y \rangle = \langle P_ix, y \rangle = \langle x_i, y_i \rangle = \langle x, P_iy \rangle$, which states that the subspaces $L(e_i)$ are pairwise orthogonal. We may again write A in terms of the P_i as $A = \sum_{i=1}^n \lambda_iP_i$, and, in terms of dyads, P_i is the operator $e_i\rangle\langle e_i$.

In other words, we have associated with the normal operator A a *spectral family* $\{P_i\}$ of projections satisfying

$$P_i^2 = P_i = P_i^*, \qquad P_i P_j = 0, \quad \text{if } i \neq j, \tag{2a}$$

$$\sum_i P_i = I, \tag{2b}$$

$$A = \sum_i \lambda_i P_i. \tag{2c}$$

We refer to Eq. 2c as the *spectral decomposition* of A.

We leave it to the reader to show that if $\{Q_i\}$ is any other family of projections that satisfies Eqs. 2a, 2b, and 2c for some scalars $\{\mu_i\}$ the μ_i are a rearrangement of the λ_i and the Q's are the corresponding P's. Conversely, it is easy to see that if $\{P_i\}$ is a family of projections that satisfies Eqs. 2a and 2b, then Eq. 2c defines a normal operator A on H for each choice of scalars $\lambda_1, \lambda_2, \ldots$.

So far our treatment of normal operators is much the same as the situation for simple operators and indeed would be identical except for the apparently innocuous fact that $P_i^* = P_i$. This, however, is the basic distinction that allows us to connect the behavior of A with the metric structure of H, as we now proceed to do. Note first that it follows from Eq. 2c that for any vector x in H we have $Ax = \sum_{i=1}^n \lambda_i P_i x$; hence for any $y \in H$

$$\langle Ax, y \rangle = \langle \sum_i \lambda_i P_i x, y \rangle = \sum_i \lambda_i \langle P_i x, y \rangle.$$

Taking complex conjugates, we obtain

$$\langle A^* y, x \rangle = \langle \overline{Ax, y} \rangle = \sum_i \bar{\lambda}_i \langle y, P_i x \rangle = \sum_i \bar{\lambda}_i \langle P_i y, x \rangle$$

$$= \langle \sum_i \bar{\lambda}_i P_i x, y \rangle. \tag{3}$$

This shows that $\{P_i\}$ is also the spectral family associated with A^* and moreover that the spectrum of A^* is the complex conjugate of the spectrum of A: $\sigma(A^*) = \overline{\sigma(A)}$. In particular, this shows that the spectrum of a normal operator is real if and only if A is *self-adjoint*; that is, $A^* = A$.

Again returning to Eq. 2c we have

$$\|Ax\|^2 = \langle Ax, Ax \rangle = \langle \sum_i \lambda_i P_i x, \sum_j \lambda_j P_j x \rangle$$

$$= \sum_{i,j} \lambda_i \bar{\lambda}_j \langle P_i x, P_j x \rangle = \sum_i |\lambda_i|^2 \cdot \|P_i x\|^2. \tag{4}$$

This yields the fact that, if A is normal, $\|A\|$ is the radius of the spectrum of A:

$$\|A\| = \max \{|\lambda| : \lambda \in \sigma(A)\}.$$

R E M A R K 2.   An operator U for which $U^*U = I = UU^*$ is called *unitary*. Clearly, each unitary operator is normal and from Eq. 4 it follows that a normal operator is unitary if and only if $\| Ux \| = \| x \|$ for all $x \in H$. This in turn holds if and only if $\sigma(U)$ lies on the unit circle.

R E M A R K 3.   Let us call a self-adjoint operator A positive $(A \geq 0)$ if its spectrum lies on the non-negative real axis. If A is positive, then for any $x \in H$

$$\langle Ax,x \rangle = \sum_i \lambda_i \langle P_i x, x \rangle = \sum_i \lambda_i \langle P_i x, P_i x \rangle,$$

so that $\langle Ax,x \rangle \geq 0$. Conversely, if A is a self-adjoint operator for which $\langle Ax,x \rangle \geq 0$ for all $x \in H$, then

$$0 \leq \langle AP_j x, P_j x \rangle = \sum_i \lambda_i \langle P_i(P_j x), P_j x \rangle = \lambda_j \| P_j x \|$$

and consequently $\lambda_j \geq 0$. Thus positive operators are those self-adjoint operators A for which the quadratic form $\langle Ax,x \rangle$ is non-negative.

In particular, for any operator B the operator $A = B^*B$ is positive, for $\langle Ax,x \rangle = \langle B^*Bx,x \rangle = \| Bx \|^2$. Conversely, if $A \geq 0$ with spectral decomposition

$$A = \sum_{i=1}^{n} \lambda_i P_i,$$

each λ_i is non-negative; hence it has a unique positive square root and

$$\left(\sum_i \lambda_i^{1/2} P_i \right) \cdot \left(\sum_j \lambda_j^{1/2} P_j \right) = \left(\sum_i \lambda_i^{1/2} P_i^* \right) \left(\sum_j \lambda_j^{1/2} P_j \right)$$

$$= \sum_{i,j} \lambda_i^{1/2} \lambda_j^{1/2} P_i P_j = \sum_i \lambda_i P_i = A.$$

Thus positive operators A have a square root $A^{1/2}$ whose spectral decomposition is $A^{1/2} = \sum_i \lambda_i^{1/2} P_i$. It is not difficult to show that the conditions $A^{1/2} \geq 0$, $(A^{1/2})^2 = A$ uniquely determine this square root; that is, if $B^2 = A$, $B \geq 0$, then B must agree with the operator $\sum_i \lambda_i^{1/2} P_i$.

R E M A R K 4.   With the aid of the spectral decomposition $A = \sum_{i=1}^{n} \lambda_i P_i$ of the normal operator A, it is easy to develop a functional calculus. Thus for the function $\psi_n(\lambda) = \lambda^n$ $(n \geq 1)$ we have $\psi(A) = A^n$ by definition of A^n and $\psi_n(A)^* \psi_n(A) = A^{n*} A^n = A^{*n} A^n = A^n A^{*n} = \psi_n(A) \psi_n(A)^*$ so that $\psi_n(A)$ is again normal. Also, since the projections P_i are pairwise orthogonal,

$$\psi_n(A) = \left(\sum_{i=1}^{n} \lambda_i P_i \right)^n = \sum_{i=1}^{n} \lambda_i^n P_i = \sum_{i=1}^{n} \psi_n(\lambda_i) P_i.$$

Also, by choosing A^0 as I, we have $\psi_0(A) = I = \sum_i P_i = \sum_i \psi_0(\lambda_i) P_i$, and we conclude that for any polynomial $\psi(z) = \sum_0^n a_n z_n$ the operator $\psi(A) = \sum_0^n a_n A^n$ has spectral decomposition

$$\psi(A) = \sum_i \psi(\lambda_i) P_i.$$

This last result expresses the elementary fact that if A is a diagonal matrix then $\psi(A)$ for any polynomial $\psi(\lambda)$ is also a diagonal matrix with entries $\psi(\lambda_1), \psi(\lambda_2), \dots, \psi(\lambda_n)$.

R E M A R K 5. Knowing the spectral decomposition of $\psi(A)$, we can compute its norm. Thus

$$\|\psi(A)x\|^2 = \langle \psi(A)x, \psi(A)x \rangle = \langle \sum_i \psi(\lambda_i)P_i x, \sum_i \psi(\lambda_j)P_j x \rangle$$

$$= \sum_{i,j} \psi(\lambda_i)\overline{\psi(\lambda_j)}\langle P_i x, P_j x \rangle$$

$$= \sum_i |\psi(\lambda_i)|^2 \cdot \|P_i x\|^2$$

$$\leq \max_i |\psi(\lambda_i)|^2 \sum_i \|P_i x\|^2 = \max_i |\psi(\lambda_i)|^2 \cdot \|x\|^2.$$

Now choose k so that $\max_i |\psi(\lambda_i)| = |\psi(\lambda_k)|$ and $y = P_k x \neq 0$. We then have

$$\|\psi(A)y\|^2 = \sum_i |\psi(\lambda_i)|^2 \cdot \|P_i P_k x\|^2 = |\psi(\lambda_k)|^2 \|y\|^2.$$

Thus for any polynomial $\psi(\lambda)$ the operator $\psi(A)$ has the norm

$$\|\psi(A)\| = \sup \{|\psi(\lambda)| : \lambda \in \sigma(A)\}.$$

Observe that we can also obtain this last result by using the fact that because $\psi(A) = \sum_i \psi(\lambda_i)P_i$ the spectrum of $\psi(A)$ consists of the numbers $\psi(\lambda_1), \dots, \psi(\lambda_n)$, and as we have already seen the norm of any normal operator equals its spectral radius.

R E M A R K 6. As a final illustration of the use of the spectral decomposition of a normal operator, let us investigate the *numerical range* $W(A)$ of such an operator. Here $W(A)$ is defined as the range of the quadratic form $\langle Ax, x \rangle$ on the unit sphere of H:

$$W(A) = \{\langle Ax, x \rangle : \|x\| = 1\}.$$

If $A = \sum_i \lambda_i P_i$ is normal, then, for any $\|x\| = 1$,

$$\langle Ax, x \rangle = \sum_i \lambda_i \langle P_i x, x \rangle = \sum_i \|P_i x\| \lambda_i,$$

$$\sum_i \|P_i x\|^2 = \|x\|^2 = 1.$$

In other words, $\langle Ax, x \rangle$ belongs to the convex hull of the set $\{\lambda_1, \lambda_2, \ldots, \lambda_n\}$. Conversely, if $\lambda = \sum_i \alpha_i \lambda_i$, $(\alpha_i \geq 0, \sum_i \alpha_i = 1)$ belongs to the convex hull of $\{\lambda_1, \lambda_2, \ldots, \lambda_n\}$, put $x = \sum_i \alpha_i^{1/2} e_i$. Then $\|x\|^2 = \sum_i \alpha_i = 1$ and

$$\langle Ax, x \rangle = \langle \sum_i \alpha_i^{1/2} A e_i, \sum_j \alpha_j^{1/2} e_j \rangle$$

$$= \sum_i \alpha_i^{1/2} \alpha_j^{1/2} \lambda_i \langle e_i, e_j \rangle = \lambda.$$

We conclude that if A is normal then $W(A)$ is the convex hull of the spectrum of A.

As an example, the reader may show that the operator U in three-dimensional Euclidean space, whose matrix relative to the natural basis is

$$\begin{bmatrix} 0 & 0 & 1 \\ 1 & 0 & 0 \\ 0 & 1 & 0 \end{bmatrix},$$

is unitary and has a spectrum consisting of the three cube roots of unity; $W(U)$ consists of the equilateral triangle constructed with those roots as vertices. By way of contrast we see that $T = \begin{bmatrix} 0 & 0 \\ 1 & 0 \end{bmatrix}$ defines an operator of norm 1 in two-dimensional Euclidean space with $\sigma(T) = \{0\}$ and $W(T)$ is the disk of radius $1/2$ about the origin.

Canonical Forms

In the study of linear systems three particular forms for the representation of linear transformations are most often useful. The first form to which we turn our attention is the *spectral representation for normal operators* on a Hilbert space. For normal operators on finite-dimensional Hilbert spaces the spectral representation has already been given in Eq. 1. An analogous result holds for every bounded normal operator on an infinite-dimensional Hilbert space. Because it presupposes some knowledge of measure theory, a derivation of this more general result is not included. The interested reader will find in Appendix 5 a discussion that contains the statement of the general spectral representation for bounded normal operators.

A second representation of substantial usefulness is the *Jordan canonical form*, which is valid for arbitrary linear operators on finite-dimensional linear (not necessarily Hilbert) spaces. For simple operators the Jordan form also coincides with the spectral representation of Eq. 1. If the operator in question is not simple, the Jordan representation may be thought of as the closest possible representation to diagonal form.

To be explicit, we consider the operator A on R^n with distinct eigenvalues $\{\lambda_1, \dots, \lambda_m\}$, $m \le n$. Let $\lambda_j \in \sigma(A)$ be an eigenvalue with algebraic multiplicity p_j and geometric multiplicity q_j. Then, associated with each λ_j is a subspace X_j of dimension p_j which is invariant under A. There are q_j linearly independent eigenvectors associated with λ_j, all of which lie in the subspace X_j. The subspaces $\{X_j\}$ decompose X, $X = X_1 \oplus X_2 \oplus \cdots \oplus X_n$. Two possibilities now exist.

If $p_j = q_j$, the eigenvectors associated with λ_j constitute a basis for X_j, the operator A_j, which is the restriction of A to X_j, is simple, and consequently the matrix of this restriction is diagonal. If $p_j > q_j$, the eigenvectors form only a partial basis for X_j and A_j cannot be diagonalized. The Jordan theorem ensures the existence of certain vectors $\{e_{ji} : i = q_{j+1}, \dots, p_j\}$, which when combined with the eigenvectors $\{e_{ji} : i = 1, \dots, q_j\}$ form a basis $E_j = \{e_{j1}, \dots, e_{jp_j}\}$ for X_j. Furthermore, the matrix of A_j with respect to this basis has the form

$$[A_j]_{E_j} = \qquad\qquad\qquad\qquad\qquad\qquad (5)$$

$\leftarrow (q_j + 1)$st row.

$\llcorner\!(q_j + 1)$st column

The set E_j is called a Jordan basis for X_j and the matrix $[A_j]_{E_j}$ is called a Jordan matrix.

To obtain the Jordan canonical representation of the operator A we obtain first the Jordan basis $E_j, j = 1, \dots, m$ associated with each distinct $\lambda_j \in \sigma(A)$. The Jordan basis E for the space X is then the union $E = \cup_j E_j = \{e_{11}, \dots, e_{1p_1}, e_{21}, \dots, e_{mp,m}\}$. The reader may verify that the matrix $[A]_E$ has nonzero elements only among a diagonal of blocks:

$$[A]_E = \qquad\qquad\qquad\qquad . \qquad\qquad (6)$$

In other words, the diagonal of $[A]_E$ consists of the numbers $\{\lambda_1, \dots, \lambda_m\}$, each counted according to their algebraic multiplicity. The first subdiagonal above and to the right has zeros or ones in proportions determined by the algebraic and geometric multiplicities of each eigenvalue. For example, an operator with the characteristic polynomial $\Delta(\lambda) = (\lambda - \lambda_1)^3(\lambda - \lambda_2)(\lambda - \lambda_3)$ may have any one of the following Jordan forms:

$$
\begin{bmatrix}
\lambda_1 & 1 & 0 & 0 & 0 \\
0 & \lambda_1 & 1 & 0 & 0 \\
0 & 0 & \lambda_1 & 0 & 0 \\
0 & 0 & 0 & \lambda_2 & 0 \\
0 & 0 & 0 & 0 & \lambda_3
\end{bmatrix},
\begin{bmatrix}
\lambda_1 & 0 & 0 & 0 & 0 \\
0 & \lambda_1 & 1 & 0 & 0 \\
0 & 0 & \lambda_1 & 0 & 0 \\
0 & 0 & 0 & \lambda_2 & 0 \\
0 & 0 & 0 & 0 & \lambda_3
\end{bmatrix},
\begin{bmatrix}
\lambda_1 & 0 & 0 & 0 & 0 \\
0 & \lambda_1 & 0 & 0 & 0 \\
0 & 0 & \lambda_1 & 0 & 0 \\
0 & 0 & 0 & \lambda_2 & 0 \\
0 & 0 & 0 & 0 & \lambda_3
\end{bmatrix}.
$$

The final canonical form to be discussed in this section is the *polar decomposition*.[1] As the setting for this discussion, we consider an arbitrary Hilbert space H, the n-dimensional Hilbert space E^n, and the linear transformation $T: H \to E^n$. The central result is Theorem E.

THEOREM E.   *Let T denote a linear transformation $T: H \to E^n$. Then there exist orthonormal sets $\{e_1, \ldots, e_n\} \subset E^n$ and $\{f_1, \ldots, f_n\} \subset H$ and non-negative real scalars $\{\mu_1, \ldots, \mu_n\}$ such that*

$$T = \sum_{i=1}^{n} e_i\rangle\mu_i\langle f_i. \tag{7}$$

P R O O F.   Assume an expansion for T of the prescribed form. A simple computation shows that the transformation adjoint to T is given by

$$T^* = \sum_{j=1}^{n} f_j\rangle\mu_j\langle e_j. \tag{8}$$

If we use the orthonormality of the set $\{f_i\}$, it will follow directly from Eqs. 7 and 8 that

$$TT^* = \sum_{i=1}^{n} e_i\rangle\mu_i^2\langle e_i.$$

It is thus clear that the scalars $\{\mu_i^2\}$ must constitute the spectrum of TT^*. Similarly, the elements $\{e_i\}$ are eigenvectors of TT^*.

These initial observations indicate how we may find the vectors $\{e_i\}$ and $\{f_i\}$ and the scalars $\{\mu_i\}$ to satisfy the theorem. For any $T: H \to E^n$ we form TT^*, which is a non-negative self-adjoint operator on E^n. Therefore it has non-negative eigenvalues $\lambda_1, \lambda_2, \ldots, \lambda_n$ (each counted according to its algebraic multiplicity) and an associated set of orthonormal eigenvectors $e_1, e_2, \ldots, e_n$. We may suppose that the λ's are lettered so that the

[1]The motivation for this terminology is discussed in Appendix 5.

nonzero ones occur first, say $\lambda_j > 0$ for $j = 1, 2, \ldots, k$ and $\lambda_j = 0$ for $j = k + 1, \ldots, n$. We define the sequence $\{f_i\}$ as follows: set $f_1 = \lambda_i^{-1/2} T^* e_i$ for $1 \leq i \leq k$; for f_{k+1} take any unit vector orthogonal to the linear manifold $L(f_1, \ldots, f_k)$; for f_{k+2} choose any unit vector orthogonal to the manifold $L(f_1, \ldots, f_k, f_{k+1})$, and so on. Since $T^* e_i = 0$ for $i = k + 1, \ldots, n$, the set so defined satisfies

$$\lambda_i^{1/2} f_i = T^* e_i, \qquad i = 1, 2, \ldots, n. \tag{9}$$

It is clear that by this process every linear transformation $T : H \rightarrow E^n$ defines (not necessarily uniquely) the orthonormal set $\{e_i\} \subset E^n$, the set $\{f_i\} \subset H$, and the non-negative scalars $\{\lambda_i^{1/2}\}$. It remains only to show that these sets satisfy the theorem. First, from the orthonormality of the set $\{e_i\}$, the identity on E^n may be expanded in the form

$$I = \sum_{i=1}^{n} e_i \rangle \langle e_i.$$

Equation 7 then follows from the equalities

$$T = (I)T = \left(\sum_{i=1}^{n} e_i \rangle \langle e_i \right) T$$

$$= \sum_{i=1}^{n} e_i \rangle \langle T^* e_i = \sum_{i=1}^{n} e_i \rangle \lambda_i^{1/2} \langle f_i.$$

The fact that the set $\{f_i\}$ is orthonormal follows from the relations

$$\langle f_i, f_j \rangle = \langle \lambda_i^{-1/2} T^* e_i, \lambda_j^{-1/2} T^* e_j \rangle = (\lambda_i \lambda_j)^{-1/2} \langle TT^* e_i, e_j \rangle$$

$$= (\lambda_i \lambda_j)^{-1/2} \lambda_i \langle e_i, e_j \rangle = \delta_{ij}, \qquad i = 1, \ldots, n,$$

which completes the proof.

The polar expansion (Eq. 7) tells quite a bit about the transformation T. The rank of T is equal to the number of nonzero μ_i's. The range of T is equal to the linear manifold spanned by the e_i's associated with nonzero μ_i's. The orthogonal complement of the null space of T is spanned by the elements f_i associated with nonzero μ's; furthermore, $\|T\| = \max_i \{\mu_i\}$ (see Exercise 7).

The polar form for T is unique when the spectrum of TT^* is distinct. When multiple values occur, a nonuniqueness exists in the choice of the basis set within the eigenspace; in short, Eq. 7 is unique to within a rotation within each of the distinct eigenspaces. It is also noteworthy that the computation of the canonical decomposition takes place in the simplest space involved, namely E^n. Indeed, TT^* is a matrix, and the elements $\{e_i\}$ are n-tuples. The Hilbert space vectors $\{f_i\}$ are computed in terms of the e_i, as indicated in the preceding proof.

REMARK 7. The three canonical representations share these common factors: linearity of the transformation, finite rank of the transformation, and dependence in an essential way on the spectrum and eigenspaces of an operator. Except for this common ground, they are independent and should be considered completely distinct. The spectral representation of normal operators is naturally framed in a functional analysis setting and depends on the Hilbert space structure, the adjoint operator and commutative properties (finite dimensionality of the spaces playing absolutely no role at all in the statement of the basic theorems). In contrast, the Jordan canonical form is a topic of linear algebra. It depends on the finite dimensionality of the space in an essential way and the metric structure, that is, the norm or inner product, not at all. The polar canonical form is valid for transformations as well as operators. Here, again, the proper setting is the Hilbert space. In Appendix 5 the extension of the polar form to infinite dimensions shows clearly that conceptually the polar form is in the same spirit as the normal spectral representation.

Since the spectral representation of normal operators is given additional exposure in Appendix 5 and the exercises and the Jordan canonical form is used in Section 3.5, we shall pass, at this point, directly to an application of the polar canonical form. As we shall see in this example, the use of a canonical form provides a rich harvest of insight into the structure of the transformation in question.

Example. In this example we reconsider the minimum energy problem posed and solved in Section 3.2. First, however, let us recall some definitions from Euclidean geometry.

Consider the subset D_2 of the real space E^2 defined by

$$D_2 = \{(x_1, x_2) = (\alpha_1 \mu_1, \alpha_2 \mu_2) : \alpha_1^2 + \alpha_2^2 = 1\},$$

where μ_1, μ_2 are fixed nonzero scalars. It is not difficult to show that D_2 is an ellipse, centered at the origin, and with semimajor and semiminor axis lying along the coordinate directions $(1,0)$ and $(0,1)$, respectively. Indeed, for every tuplet $(x_1, x_2) \in D_2$ we have

$$x_1^2 / \mu_1^2 + x_2^2 / \mu_2^2 = \alpha_1^2 + \alpha_2^2 = 1,$$

which is perhaps a more familiar form for an ellipse.

In the real space E^n we may define a generalized ellipse in the following natural manner. Let $\{e_1, \ldots, e_n\}$ be an orthonormal basis for E^n. Let $\{\mu_1, \ldots, \mu_n\}$ be real scalars. The set D_n defined by

$$D_n = \{x : x = \sum_{i=1}^{n} (\mu_i \alpha_i) e_i, \text{ with } \sum_{i=1}^{n} \alpha_i^2 = 1\} \tag{10}$$

is called an ellipsoid. The principle axis of the ellipsoid lies along the one-dimensional subspaces $L(e_1), \ldots, L(e_n)$. When $n = 2$ and $e_1 = (1,0)$, $e_2 = (0,1)$, set D_n is evidently identical with set D_2.

Consider now the linear transformation $T: H \to E^n$. The polar canonical form for T is given by

$$T = \sum_{i=1}^{n} e_i \rangle \mu_i \langle f_i. \tag{11}$$

Assuming that $\mu_i \neq 0$, $i = 1, \ldots, n$, the subspace $M = (N_T)^{\perp}$ is evidently the manifold $L(f_1, \ldots, f_n)$.

Let ∂U_M denote the set

$$\partial U_M = \{u : u \in M, \|u\| = 1\}.$$

Since $\{f_i\}$ is an orthonormal basis for M, it is easily verified that as an alternative we may write

$$\partial U_M = u : \{u = \sum_{i=1}^{n} \alpha_i f_i, \sum_{i=1}^{n} \alpha_i^2 = 1\}.$$

Geometrically speaking, ∂U_M is a sphere about the origin of radius 1 and lying in M. Using Eq. 11, we obtain

$$T(\partial U_M) = \{y : y = Tu, u \in \partial U_M\}$$

$$= \{y : y = \sum_{i=1}^{n} e_i(\mu_i \alpha_i), \sum_{i=1}^{n} \alpha_i^2 = 1\}.$$

Comparing the set $T(\partial U_M)$ with D_n we make clear that the transformation T sends the unit sphere in M onto an ellipsoid of E^n.

A completely geometric viewpoint of the transformation T is now possible. The vectors $\{e_i, \ldots, e_n\}$ are the principle axis of the ellipse D_n. The scalars $\{\mu_i\}$ are the "gains" of the transformation along its canonical directions. Since $\|T\| = \max \{\mu_i\}$, the normalized form for T is

$$T = \|T\| \left(\sum_{i=1}^{n} e_i \rangle \mu_i' \langle f_i \right), \tag{12}$$

where $0 \leq \mu_i' = \mu_i / \|T\| \leq 1$, $i = 1, \ldots, n$. The μ_i' may be used as a measure of the eccentricity of the transformation. From the linearity of T it is apparent that any multiple $\alpha \partial U_M$ of the unit sphere is carried into the multiple αD_n of the associated ellipse.

Let $\xi \in E^n$ and consider once again the problem of finding the element u_ξ of minimum norm that satisfies $\xi = Tu_\xi$. Geometrically, the problem is one of finding the multiple αD_n which contains ξ and then locating the unique preimage of ξ in $\alpha \partial U_M$. The polar form allows us to be much more direct, however. If we denote by $T^\dagger$ the function that sends $\xi \in u_\xi$ for every $\xi \in E^n$, it follows by inspection, from the fact that the range of $T^\dagger$ is M and that the composition $TT^\dagger$ must be the identity on E^n, that

$$T^\dagger = \sum_{i=1}^{n} f_i \rangle \frac{1}{\mu_i} \langle e_i, \tag{13}$$

which explicitly solves the minimum energy problem.

To outline the steps necessary to compute the polar form for a physical problem consider the electromechanical system of Figure 2.13. In Example 3, Section 2.4, the equations of motion and the transition matrix for this system have been computed and we take these results as our starting point; T is the transformation which sends $H = L_2(t_0, t_f)$ into E^2, defined by

$$Tu = \int_{t_0}^{t_f} \Phi(t_f, s) B(s) u(s) ds.$$

We have seen that $T^* : E^2 \to H$ may be identified with multiplication by the time-varying matrix $B^*(t)\Phi^*(t_f, t)$. In the present example, B is the column vector $(0, k)$; hence by direct multiplication we may verify that

$$TT^* = \int_{t_0}^{t_f} \Phi(t_f, s) B(s) B^*(s) \Phi^*(t_f, s) ds = \begin{bmatrix} t_{11} & t_{12} \\ t_{21} & t_{22} \end{bmatrix},$$

where

$$t_{11} = \int_{t_0}^{t_f} d^2 \phi_{12}^2(t_f, s) ds, \qquad\qquad t_{12} = \int_{t_0}^{t_f} d^2 \phi_{12}(t_f, s) \phi_{22}(t_f, s) ds,$$

$$t_{21} = \int_{t_0}^{t_f} d^2 \phi_{22}(t_f, s) \phi_{12}(t_f, s) ds, \qquad t_{22} = \int_{t_0}^{t_f} d^2 \phi_{22}^2(t_f, s) ds.$$

The components of $\Phi(t, t_0)$ were explicitly determined in Example 3, Section 2.4. Thus it is apparent that for any interval $[t_0, t_f]$ the matrix TT^* can be explicitly computed. The spectrum of TT^* and an orthonormal set of eigenvectors is also easily computed. The polar expansion follows immediately and the problem is complete.

Exercises

1. If A and B are normal operators and $AB^* = B^*A$, show that $A + B$ and AB are normal. (For a deeper result see [A23], p. 934.)

2. If $\xi \in E^n$ is a fixed vector, $T : H \to E^n$ is defined by Eq. 11 and $\xi_i = \langle e_i, \xi \rangle$ $i = 1, \ldots, n$; use Eq. 13 to show that the minimum energy necessary to reach ξ is given by

$$\|u_\xi\| = \left[\sum_{i=1}^{n} \left(\frac{\xi_i}{\mu_i} \right)^2 \right]^{1/2}.$$

3. In this problem K denotes an operator on the Hilbert space E^n. Let $\lambda_i \in \sigma(K)$ be a point of the spectrum with eigenvector e_i. $K' = K + \delta K$ will denote a perturbed form of K. If $\|\delta K\|$ is small, the eigenvectors and spectrum of K' are close to the eigenvectors and spectrum of K, respectively. Show that

$$\delta \lambda_i = \langle e_i^+, \delta K e_i \rangle, \qquad i = 1, \dots, n.$$

Express the variations $\{\delta e_i\}$ as functions of δK. HINT: Substitute $K \to K + \delta K$, $\lambda_i \to \lambda_i + \delta \lambda_i$, and $e_i \to e_i + \delta e_i$ into $(K - \lambda_i I)e_i = 0$ and use the fact that $(K - \lambda_i I)e_i^+ = 0$.

4. For the transformation of Eq. 13 the norm $\|T\| = \max\{\mu_i\}$ is only one of several measures of operator gain. Consider the volume V_n of the smallest hyperrectangle enclosing the ellipsoid D_n. Evidently

$$V_n = 2 \prod_i \mu_i = 2 \left(\prod_i \lambda_i \right)^{1/2}.$$

Using Exercise 3, show that when $V_n \neq 0$ the variation δV_n, due to a change δK, satisfies

$$\frac{\delta V_n}{V_n} = \sum_{i=1}^n \frac{\delta \lambda_i}{\lambda_i} = \sum_{i=1}^n \frac{\langle e_i^+, \delta K e_i \rangle}{\langle e_i^+, K e_i \rangle}.$$

5. Let α denote a parameter of matrix $A(t,\alpha)$ of Example 3, Section 3.2. From Theorem B, Section 2.1, it follows that the transform T of Example 3 depends continuously on α whenever $A(t,\alpha)$ does. Use Exercise 4 to investigate the sensitivity of T with respect to α.

6. If $Q(t)$ is a positive, definite, self-adjoint, continuous matrix for every $t \in \tau$, prove that the function $\langle x,y \rangle_Q$ on the tuplets of $[L_2(\tau)]^n$ defined by

$$\langle x,y \rangle_Q = \int_\tau [x(s), Q(s)y(s)] ds$$

is an inner product.

7. Prove for the transformation T of Eq. 8 that $\|T\| = \max\{\mu_i\}$. HINT: Use $\|T^*x\|^2 = \langle x, TT^*x \rangle$ and the fact that $\|T\| = \|T^*\|$.

3.5 MODES IN STATIONARY SYSTEMS

We show in Appendix 3 that the transition matrix for the system

$$\dot{x}(t) = Ax(t), \qquad t \in \tau, \tag{1}$$

where A is a time-invariant matrix, may be written

$$\Phi(t,t_0) = \exp[A(t-t_0)], \qquad t,t_0 \in \tau.$$

By utilizing the canonical form of the matrix A we may sharpen this expression considerably. The result is a decomposition of the transition matrix Φ, which yields valuable insight into the behavior of stationary systems.

Assume first that A is a simple matrix. The set $S = \{e_1, \ldots, e_n\}$ of eigenvectors for A is a basis for R^n and in terms of this basis and its dual A may be written

$$A = \sum_{i=1}^{n} e_i \rangle \lambda_i \langle e_i^+.$$

Recall from Section 3.4 that if $f(z)$ is any function, analytic on an open disk containing the spectrum of A, the expression

$$f(A) = \sum_{i=1}^{n} e_i \rangle f(\lambda_i) \langle e_i^+ \tag{2}$$

is valid and, in particular,

$$\exp [A(t - t_0)] = \sum_{i=1}^{n} e_i \rangle \exp [\lambda_i(t - t_0)] \langle e_i^+. \tag{3}$$

From Eq. 3 it is immediate that the free response of the system is given by

$$x(t) = \sum_{i=1}^{n} e_i \rangle \exp [\lambda_i(t - t_0)] \langle e_i^+, x^0 \rangle, \qquad t \geq t_0. \tag{4}$$

The invariant subspaces of the matrix A (in this case, the eigenspaces) are called the *modes* of the system. The functions $\alpha_j(t) = \exp [\lambda_j(t - t_0)] \langle e_j^+, x^0 \rangle$ represent the motion of the system in the jth mode. Equations 3 and 4 are the spectral (or the modal) decomposition of the transition matrix and free response, respectively.

R E M A R K 1.   From Eq. 3 it is clear that each mode is excited independently of the other modes; that is, the excitation of the ith mode is computed directly by $\langle e_i^+, x^0 \rangle$ and is independent of the values $\langle e_k^+, x^0 \rangle$ for $k \neq i$. If the initial condition x^0 lies in any subset of modes, the system trajectory remains in this subset for all $t \geq t_0$; that is, if $\langle e_j^+, x^0 \rangle = 0$ for any j, the coefficient of e_j is zero for all time $i \geq t_0$.

Phase Plane Plots

A phase plane plot is the tracing of the motion of the free response of a discrete or continuous system as it moves through the space R^n. The results and remarks of Section 2.4 have a particularly simple form when described on a phase plane plot. To simplify matters, let us consider the case in which A is a real 2×2 matrix with eigenvalues $\{\lambda_1, \lambda_2\}$ and eigenvectors $\{e_1, e_2\}$ which are also real.

CASE 1 (NODE). Let us assume that λ_1 and λ_2 are nonzero and have the same sign and that

$$|\lambda_1| < |\lambda_2|. \tag{5}$$

Consider first

$$\lambda_1 < 0, \qquad \lambda_2 < 0.$$

Since the motion in each node is proportional to $\exp[\lambda_j(t - t_0)]$, it is clear that the motion in each mode approaches the origin as t increases. Since $\lambda_2 < \lambda_1 < 0$, the ratio of the magnitudes of the mode motions, given by

$$\frac{\langle e_2^+, \zeta \rangle}{\langle e_1^+, \zeta \rangle} \cdot \frac{\exp[\lambda_2(t - t_0)]}{\exp[\lambda_1(t - t_0)]},$$

approaches zero as $t \to \infty$; hence the system trajectory must become asymptotic to the mode e_1 as it approaches the origin. This phase picture is called a *stable node* (Figure 3.3). If the inequalities

$$\lambda_1 > 0, \qquad \lambda_2 > 0,$$

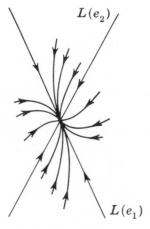 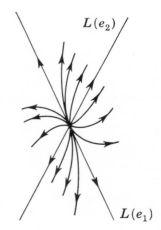

Figure 3.3 Stable node: $\lambda_2 < \lambda_1 < 0$.   **Figure 3.4** Unstable node: $\lambda_2 > \lambda_1 > 0$.

together with inequality 5, hold, the trajectories remain as before, but the motion along them is in the opposite direction, and we have an *unstable node* (Figure 3.4). If $\lambda_1 = \lambda_2$ and e_1 and e_2 are still linearly independent, the phase plane diagram reduces the straight lines running through the origin. For a stable node case we have Figure 3.5.

CASE 2 (SADDLE POINT). Let us assume that the eigenvalues λ_1 and λ_2 have opposite signs. To be definite we assume that

$$\lambda_1 < 0 < \lambda_2.$$

In this case the motion in the first eigenspace is stable, whereas the motion in the second eigenspace is unstable. The forms of the trajectories resemble hyperbolas, and motions along these trajectories proceed toward the origin along the first eigenspace and away from the origin along the second eigen-space. This phase portrait (Figure 3.6) is called a *saddle point*.

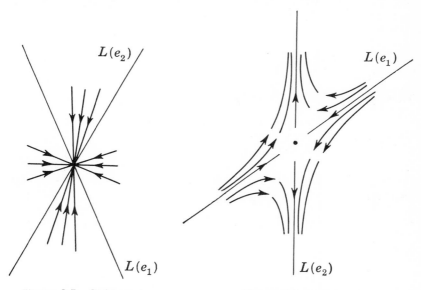

Figure 3.5   Stable node:
$\lambda_1 = \lambda_2 < 0.$

Figure 3.6   Saddle point:
$\lambda_1 < 0 < \lambda_2.$

CASE 3 (COMPLEX EIGENVALUES). The case in which complex eigenvalues occur is sufficiently interesting to merit detailed consideration. Let $\lambda_1 = \alpha_1 + j\omega_1$ be a complex eigenvalue of A. Since the characteristic equation has real coefficients, $\lambda_2 = \alpha_1 - j\omega_1$ is also an eigenvalue. The eigen-vectors e_1 and e_2 corresponding to λ_1 and λ_2, respectively, have complex elements. It is also apparent that they can be chosen as conjugate so that they can be denoted by

$$e_1 = \mu_1 + j\mu_2,$$

$$e_2 = \mu_1 - j\mu_2,$$

where μ_1 and μ_2 are real linearly independent vectors. (If this were not so,

e_1 and e_2 would be dependent). The duals e_1^+ and e_2^+ can also be shown to be complex conjugates of one another.

To find the duals we put

$$e_1^+ = \tfrac{1}{2}v_1 + j\tfrac{1}{2}v_2, \qquad e_2^+ = \tfrac{1}{2}v_1 - j\tfrac{1}{2}v_2.$$

By using the distributive property of the inner product and the four relations

$$\langle e_i^+, e_j^+ \rangle = \delta_{ij}, \qquad i, j = 1, 2,$$

the reader can verify the four scalar relations involving real vectors μ_1, v_1, μ_2, and v_2:

$$\langle v_1, \mu_1 \rangle = 1; \qquad \langle v_2, \mu_1 \rangle = 0;$$

$$\langle v_1, \mu_2 \rangle = 0; \qquad \langle v_2, \mu_2 \rangle = 1.$$

Thus $v_1 = \mu_1^+$, $v_2 = \mu_2^+$. In all we have the four equations

$$e_1 = \mu_1 + j\mu_2, \qquad e_1^+ = \tfrac{1}{2}\{\mu_1^+ + j\mu_2^+\},$$

$$e_2 = \mu_1 - j\mu_2, \qquad e_2^+ = \tfrac{1}{2}\{\mu_1^+ - j\mu_2^+\}.$$

In terms of these quantities, the reader can verify that for any x^0 the free response

$$x(t) = e_1 \rangle \langle e_1^+, x^0 \rangle \exp [\lambda_1 (t - t_0)] + e_2 \rangle \langle e_2^+, x^0 \rangle \exp [\bar{\lambda}_1 (t - t_0)]$$

can be reduced to

$$x(t) = \exp [\alpha_1 (t - t_0)](\langle u_1^+, x^0 \rangle \cos \omega_1 t + \langle \mu_2^+, x^0 \rangle \sin \omega_1 t) \mu_1$$

$$+ \exp [\alpha_1 (t - t_0)](\langle \mu_2^+, x^0 \rangle \cos \omega_1 t - \langle \mu_1^+, x^0 \rangle \sin \omega_1 t) \mu_2$$

or, in its equivalent polar form,

$$x(t) = \exp [\alpha_1 (t - t_0)][\gamma \cos (\omega_1 t - \phi) \mu_1 - \gamma \sin (\omega_1 t - \phi) \mu_2],$$

where γ and ϕ are given by

$$\gamma \cos \phi = \langle \mu_1^+, x^0 \rangle, \qquad \gamma \sin \phi = \langle \mu_1^+, x^0 \rangle.$$

The bracketed quantity is the superposition of two sinusoidal oscillations along the directions μ_1, μ_2. The amplitude and phase of the oscillations depend only on the initial state x^0. For $\alpha_1 \neq 0$ every trajectory turns out to be a logarithmic spiral. The corresponding picture on the phase plane is called a *focus*. If $\alpha_1 < 0$, the trajectories approach the origin asymptotically as t increases, describing a logarithmic spiral. This is a *stable focus* (Figure 3.7).

If $\alpha_1 > 0$, then the point moves toward infinity and the focus is *unstable* (Figure 3.8). If the number α_1 is zero, every phase trajectory closes on itself, and we have the *center* (Figure 3.9).

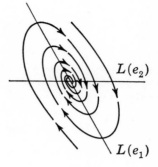

Figure 3.7 Stable focus: Re $(\lambda) < 0$.

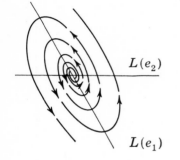

Figure 3.8 Unstable focus: Re $(\lambda) > 0$.

Figure 3.9 Center: Re $(\lambda) = 0$.

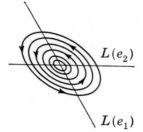

The General Case

Let A be an $n \times n$ matrix that is not necessarily simple. Then, from Section 3.4, we know a basis $E = \{e_1, \ldots, e_n\}$ can be found that reduces A to its associated Jordan form, which we denote by $J_A = [A]_E$. The concept of a function of a matrix A does not require that A be simple. Hence we need only consider the distinctions in computational methods for simple matrices and the present case. If γ is the (i,j) element of J_A such that

$$A = \sum_{i,j=1}^{n} e_i \rangle \gamma_{ij} \langle e_j^+$$

it can be shown that $f(A)$ has the expansion

$$f(A) = \sum_{i,j=1}^{n} e_i \rangle \gamma'_{ij} \langle e_j^+,$$

where γ'_{ij} is the (i, j) element of the matrix $f(J_A)$. Thus the problem reduces to the computation of a function of a Jordan matrix.

Consider the Jordan matrix J which consists of nonzero elements only in the partitioned diagonal blocks $J = \text{diag}[J_1, \ldots, J_p]$ (see Eq. 7, Section 3.4). Because of the partitioned diagonal form of J, a function f on the matrix J produces the effect $f(J) = \text{diag}[f(J_1), \ldots, f(J_p)]$ (the reader may wish to test a polynomial case). Thus the problem reduces finally to a computation of the function of a Jordan block. The key to this problem is Theorem A.

THEOREM A.   *Let f be an analytic function on an open neighborhood of λ and D a Jordan block of rank p. Then $f(D)$ is the upper triangular matrix.*

$$D = \begin{bmatrix} \lambda & 1 & 0 & 0 \\ 0 & \ddots & \ddots & 0 \\ & & \ddots & 1 \\ 0 & & 0 & \lambda \end{bmatrix}, f(D) = \begin{bmatrix} f(\lambda) & f'(\lambda) & \cdots & \dfrac{f^{p-1}(\lambda)}{(p-1)!} \\ 0 & \ddots & \ddots & \\ & & \ddots & f'(\lambda) \\ 0 & & 0 & f(\lambda) \end{bmatrix}.$$

The proof of this theorem is left as an exercise. In particular, let us note that

$$\exp\{Dt\} = \exp(\lambda t) \begin{bmatrix} 1 & t & \cdots & t^{p-1}/(p-1)! \\ 0 & \ddots & & \vdots \\ & & \ddots & t \\ 0 & & & 1 \end{bmatrix}. \tag{6}$$

CASE 4 (DEGENERATE NODES).   To complete the phase portrait discussion of Section 3.4 let us now consider the two-dimensional cases in which the basis vectors $\{e_1, e_2\}$ for R^2 are such that A is brought to Jordan form. Then from Eq. 6 it follows that

$$\exp[A(t - t_0)] = e_1 \rangle \exp[\lambda(t - t_0)] \langle [e_1^+ + (t - t_0)e_2^+] + e_2 \rangle \exp[\lambda(t - t_0)] \langle e_2^+.$$

Thus, if $x^0 \in R^2$, the free response is the sum

$$x(t) = \alpha_1(t)e_1 + \alpha_2(t)e_2,$$

in which

$$\alpha_1(t) = \exp\left[\lambda(t - t_0)\right]\langle e_1^+, x^0\rangle + (t - t_0)\langle e_2^+, x^0\rangle],$$

$$\alpha_2(t) = \exp\left[\lambda(t - t_0)\right]\langle e_2^+, x^0\rangle.$$

First, let $\lambda < 0$. It is evident that by changing the sign of $t - t_0$ a reflection of the phase plane is obtained; thus it is sufficient to consider positive $t - t_0$.

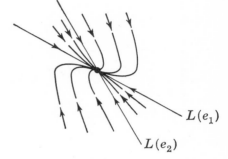

Figure 3.10   Stable degenerate node.

If $\langle e_2^+, x^0\rangle = 0$, the two trajectories along the e_1-direction are obtained, both directed toward the origin. For $\langle e_1^+, x^0\rangle = 0$ we have

$$\alpha_1(t) = (t - t_0)\langle e_2^+, x^0\rangle \exp\left[\lambda(t - t_0)\right],$$

$$\alpha_2(t) = \langle e_2^+, x^0\rangle \exp\left[\lambda(t - t_0)\right].$$

For $t = t_0$ the trajectory is on the e_2-axis. As t increases, the point moves toward the e_1-axis, coming asymptotically toward the origin along that axis. It is not difficult to complete the phase plane picture (Figure 3.10). If $\lambda > 0$,

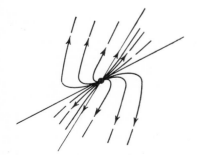

Figure 3.11   Unstable degenerate node.

the motion of the trajectory is obtained by a mirror reflection and proceeds along the trajectories away from the origin (Figure 3.11). These two cases are *stable* and *unstable degenerate nodes*, respectively.

Finally, the case in which one of the eigenvalues is zero can be deduced from the preceding paragraphs. Indeed, if $\lambda_1 = 0$ and $\lambda_2 \neq 0$, we have immediately from Eq. 4

$$x(t) = e_1\rangle\langle e_1^+, x^0\rangle + e_2\rangle \exp[\lambda_2(t - t_0)]\langle e_2^+, x^0\rangle, \qquad t \geq t_0,$$

which is shown in Figure 3.12 for $\lambda_2 < 0$ and also for $\lambda_2 > 0$ if the arrows are reversed.

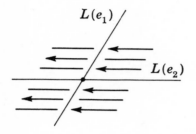

$L(e_1)$

$L(e_2)$

Figure 3.12   Degenerate node:
$\lambda_1 = 0, \lambda_2 < 0$.

If $\lambda_1 = \lambda = 0$, either

$$x(t) = e_1\rangle\langle e_1^+, x^0\rangle + e_2\rangle\langle e_2^+, x^0\rangle$$

holds and every point in the phase plane is an equilibrium point or

$$x(t) = e_1\rangle[\langle e_1^+, x^0\rangle + t\langle e_2^+, x^0\rangle] + e_2\rangle\langle e_2^+, x^0\rangle,$$

in which case the motion takes place along the straight lines parallel to e_2. All points on $\langle e_2^+, x^0\rangle = 0$ are equilibrium points (Figure 3.13).

Figure 3.13   Degenerate node:
$\lambda_1 = \lambda_2 = 0$.

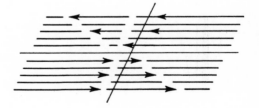

R E M A R K   2.   The graphical generalization of the phase plane diagram to dimensions higher than 2 is not productive. The generalization of the ideas described by this technique can, however, be concisely made. Remark 1 is precisely such an extension if it is also noted that the motion within each individual mode can be visualized as a separate phase plot, the total motion being the superposition of the individual plots.

The properties and concepts of the present section provide ample opportunity for a variety of illustrations. For the present two examples are given to illustrate the various properties.

Example 1. Consider the homogeneous differential system defined by

$$\begin{bmatrix} \dot{x}_1(t) \\ \dot{x}_2(t) \end{bmatrix} = \begin{bmatrix} 1 & \alpha \\ \alpha & 1 \end{bmatrix} \begin{bmatrix} x_1(t) \\ x_2(t) \end{bmatrix} \qquad \begin{bmatrix} x_1(t_0) \\ x_2(t_0) \end{bmatrix} = \begin{bmatrix} x_1^0 \\ x_2^0 \end{bmatrix}.$$

It is easy to determine the eigenvalues of A which are $\lambda_1 = 1 + \alpha$ and $\lambda_2 = 1 - \alpha$. The state transition matrix $\Phi(t,t_0) = \exp[A(t - t_0)]$ is computed in Exercise 6 of this section. The result can be written in the form

$$\Phi(t - t_0) = \tfrac{1}{2} \exp[\lambda_1(t - t_0)] \begin{bmatrix} 1 & 1 \\ 1 & 1 \end{bmatrix} + \tfrac{1}{2} \exp[\lambda_2(t - t_0)] \begin{bmatrix} 1 & -1 \\ -1 & 1 \end{bmatrix}$$

as the reader can easily verify by substituting this matrix back into the differential equation. The solution $x(t;x^0,t_0)$ is thus given by

$$x(t;x^0,t_0) = \tfrac{1}{2} \begin{bmatrix} \exp[\lambda_1(t - t_0)](x_1^0 + x_2^0) + \exp[\lambda_2(t - t_0)](x_1^0 - x_2^0) \\ \exp[\lambda_1(t - t_0)](x_1^0 + x_2^0) + \exp[\lambda_2(t - t_0)](-x_1^0 + x_2^0) \end{bmatrix}.$$

Example 2. Consider now the stationary homogeneous differential system

$$\begin{bmatrix} \dot{x}_1(t) \\ \dot{x}_2(t) \end{bmatrix} = \begin{bmatrix} -15 & 12 \\ -24 & 19 \end{bmatrix} \begin{bmatrix} x_1(t) \\ x_2(t) \end{bmatrix}.$$

In Appendix 3 the matrix $\exp[A(t - t_0)] = \Phi(t - t_0)$ is found to be

$$\Phi(t - t_0) = \exp(t - t_0) \begin{bmatrix} 9 & -6 \\ 12 & -8 \end{bmatrix} + \exp[3(t - t_0)] \begin{bmatrix} -8 & 6 \\ -12 & 9 \end{bmatrix}.$$

The reader may verify that $\Phi(0) = I$ and $\Phi(t - t_0)$ satisfies the differential equation. To derive this result by the spectral decomposition technique we must first find the eigenvectors e_1 and e_2. It is easily verified that the eigenvalues for A are $\lambda_1 = 1$ and $\lambda_2 = 3$. To find e_1 we solve

$$[A - \lambda_1 I]e_1 = \begin{bmatrix} -16 & 12 \\ -24 & 18 \end{bmatrix} \cdot \begin{bmatrix} e_{11} \\ e_{12} \end{bmatrix} = \begin{bmatrix} 0 \\ 0 \end{bmatrix}$$

which yields the solution $e_1 = k$ col $(3,4)$. Here k is an arbitrary scale factor and we shall choose $k = 1$. Similarly, we find that $e_2 = $ col $(2,3)$.

The duals e_1^+ and e_2^+ are row vectors. Let $e_1^+ = (\alpha,\beta)$; then from $\langle e_1^+,e_1 \rangle = 1$ we have $3\alpha + 4\beta = 1$ and from $\langle e_1^+,e_2 \rangle = 0$ we have $2\alpha + 3\beta = 0$.

Solving for α and β yields

$$e_1^+ = (3, -2).$$

Similarly, e_2^+ can be shown to be

$$e_2^+ = (-4, 3).$$

The spectral decomposition says that $A = \sum_{i=1}^n e_i \rangle \lambda_i \langle e_i^+$; hence

$$A = \begin{bmatrix} 3 \\ 4 \end{bmatrix} \cdot (1) \cdot [3, -2] + \begin{bmatrix} 2 \\ 3 \end{bmatrix} \cdot (3) \cdot [-4, 3]$$

$$= \begin{bmatrix} 9 & -6 \\ 12 & -8 \end{bmatrix} + 3 \begin{bmatrix} -8 & 6 \\ -12 & 9 \end{bmatrix} = \begin{bmatrix} -15 & 12 \\ -24 & 19 \end{bmatrix}.$$

In addition, the matrix function $\exp [A(t - t_0)] = \sum_{i=1}^n e_i \rangle \exp [\lambda_i(t - t_0) \langle e_i^+$, reduces to

$$\exp [A(t - t_0)] = \exp (t - t_0) \begin{bmatrix} 3 \\ 4 \end{bmatrix} \cdot [3, -2] = \exp [3(t - t_0)] \begin{bmatrix} 2 \\ 3 \end{bmatrix} \cdot [-4, 3]$$

$$= \exp (t - t_0) \begin{bmatrix} 9 & -6 \\ 12 & -8 \end{bmatrix} + \exp [3(t - t_0)] \begin{bmatrix} -8 & 6 \\ -12 & 9 \end{bmatrix}.$$

Both results check with previous derivations. If the system has an initial condition of the form $x(t_0) = \text{col } (x_1^0, x_2^0)$, the projection of the trajectory on the first mode is given by

$$\langle e_1^+, x(t) \rangle = \langle e_1^+, x(t_0) \rangle \exp [\lambda_1(t - t_0)] = \exp (t - t_0)\{3x_1^0 - 2x_2^0\}.$$

Similarly, for the second mode

$$\langle e_2^+, x(t) \rangle = \langle e_2^+, x(t_0) \rangle \exp [\lambda_2(t - t_0)] = \exp [3(t - t_0)] \{-4x_1^0 + 3x_2^0\}.$$

The system trajectory is then given by

$$e_1 \rangle \langle e_1^+, x(t) \rangle + e_2 \rangle \langle e_2^+, x(t) \rangle = \exp (t - t_0)(3x_1^0 - 2x_2^0) \cdot \text{col } (3, 4)$$

$$+ \exp [3(t - t_0)](-4x_1^0 + 3x_2^0) \cdot \text{col } (2, 3)$$

which is identical to the expression $\Phi(t - t_0)x(t_0)$. Since both eigenvalues are real and positive, the phase plane plot of the free response is that of an unstable node.

R E M A R K 3.   A discrete system on the set $\sigma = \{t_0, t_1, \ldots, t_k, \ldots\}$

$$\Delta_t x(t) = A(t)x(t), \qquad t \in \sigma,$$

is called stationary whenever the matrix $\Phi(t_{k+1},t_k) = [I + h_k A(t_k)]$, $t_k \in \sigma$, is constant. Since

$$\Phi(t_k,t_0) = \prod_{j=0}^{k} [I + h_j A(t_j)], \qquad t_k,t_0 \in \sigma,$$

it is clear that in the stationary case $\Phi(t_k,t_0) = [\Phi(t_1,t_0)]^k$.

Consider the case in which A is a simple matrix with spectrum $\sigma(A) = \{\lambda_1, \ldots, \lambda_n\}$. It follows immediately that J_Φ, the Jordan form for the matrix $\Phi(t_1,t_0) = [I + hA]$, is given by $J_\Phi = \text{diag} [(1 + h\lambda_1), \ldots, (1 + h\lambda_n)]$. Let the scalars $\{\lambda_i'\}$ be defined by $\lambda_i' = h^{-1} \ln (1 + h\lambda_i)$, $i = 1, \ldots, n$ [$\ln (x)$ denotes the natural logarithm of x]. Then, since $t_k - t_0 = kh$, it can be verified that

$$(J_\Phi)^k = \exp [J_\Phi'(t_k - t_0)],$$

where $J_\Phi = \text{diag} [\lambda_1', \ldots, \lambda_n']$. Hence, if A' is the matrix whose eigenvectors are identical with those of the matrix A and whose spectrum is the function $\lambda_i \to \lambda_i'$ of $\sigma(A)$, it follows that we may write

$$\Phi(t,t_0) = [I + hA]^{(t-t_0)} = \exp [A'(t - t_0)], \qquad t,t_0 \in \sigma \qquad (7)$$

in the discrete, as well as the continuous, case. Hence Figures 3.1–3.11, if time-sampled on σ, describe the discrete case as well.

The Forced Response

From Remark 3 it is clear that the forced response of a stationary system may be written

$$(Fu)(t) = \exp [A(t - t_0)] \int_{t_0}^{t} \exp [A(t_0 - s)]Bu(s)ds, \qquad t \in \tau,$$

$$(Fu)(t) = \exp [A(t - t_0)] \sum_{j=0}^{[t]-1} \exp [A(t_0 - t_j)]Bu(t_j), \qquad t \in \sigma$$

in the continuous and discrete cases, respectively.

Here B is a constant matrix with columns denoted by $b_1, \ldots, b_m$. Consider first the single variable case $Bu(t) = b_1 u_1(t)$. Let us set $t_0 = 0$ and assume that A is a simple matrix. Using the spectral representation for $\exp (At)$, we have the respective equations

$$x(t) = \sum_{i=1}^{n} e^{\lambda_i t} e_i \rangle [\langle e_i^+, x^0 \rangle + \int_{t_0}^{t} e^{-\lambda_i s} \langle e_i^+, b_1 \rangle u_1(s)ds], \qquad t \in \tau, \qquad (8)$$

$$x(t) = \sum_{i=1}^{n} e^{\lambda_i t} e_i \rangle \left[\langle e_i^+, x^0 \rangle + \sum_{j=0}^{[t]-1} e^{-\lambda_i t_j} \langle e_i^+, b_1 \rangle u(t_j) \right], \qquad t \in \sigma, \qquad (9)$$

where $\{e_1\}_1^n$ is the set of eigenvectors for A. Thus, for any t, the response $x(t)$ is a linear combination of the modes of the system; however, the time behavior of the coefficient of the linear combination is more complicated than before. The excitation of the ith mode due to the input $u_1(t)$ is given respectively by

$$e^{\lambda_i t}\langle e_i^+, b_1 \rangle \int_0^t e^{-\lambda_i s} u_1(s)\,ds, \qquad t \in \tau,$$

$$e^{\lambda_i t}\langle e_i^+, b_1 \rangle \sum_{j=0}^{[t]-1} e^{\lambda_i t_j} u_1(t_j), \qquad t \in \sigma;$$

for all $t \in v$ this term is proportional to the constant $\langle e_i^+, b_1 \rangle$, which is the component of b_1 along e_i in the basis $\{e_k\}$. The foregoing expression suggests the following comments:

(1) Irrespective of b_1, the response of each mode is independent of the others; that is, the amount of excitation in any particular mode does not depend on the amount of excitation of the other modes.

(2) If the vector b_1 is orthogonal to any of the eigenspaces [i.e., $\langle e_i^+, b_1 \rangle = 0$], the motion in that eigenspace, regardless of $u_1(t)$, is never affected by the input.

(3) As a consequence of (1) and (2), if both vectors b_1 and x^0 lie in an invariant subspace of A, the motion lies in that subspace for all $t \geq t_0$.

These results have a natural generalization in the multivariate case. Here B is an $n \times m$ constant matrix, with columns $b_1, \ldots, b_m$ and $u = [u_1(t), \ldots, u_m(t)]$ is the usual element of a Cartesian product space. Consider the weighting matrix $Z(t) = \Phi(t_0,t)B(t)$. Assuming that A is simple, it follows immediately that

$$Z(t) = \Phi(t_0 - t)B = \{\sum_{i=1}^n e_i\rangle \exp[\lambda_i(t_0 - t)]\langle e_i^+\}B, \qquad t \in v.$$

This equation can be expressed more simply if two new matrices are introduced. Let $\Lambda(t_0 - t)$ denote the diagonal matrix with elements $\exp[\lambda_i(t_0 - t)]$, $i = 1, \ldots, n$ along the diagonal

$$\Lambda(t_0 - t) = \operatorname{diag}\{\exp[\lambda_1(t_0 - t)], \ldots, \exp[\lambda_n(t_0 - t)]\}$$

and H the matrix with *columns* $e_1, \ldots, e_n$

$$H = \begin{bmatrix} \uparrow & & \uparrow \\ e_1 & \cdots & e_n \\ \downarrow & & \downarrow \end{bmatrix}.$$

It is immediate that H is nonsingular ($e_1, \ldots, e_n$ are linearly independent) and its inverse is given by the matrix whose *rows* are the dual vectors $e_1^+, \ldots, e_n^+$

$$H^{-1} = \begin{bmatrix} \leftarrow e_1^+ \rightarrow \\ \vdots \\ \leftarrow e_n^+ \rightarrow \end{bmatrix}.$$

It is also apparent that

$$\exp\left[A(t_0 - t)\right] = H\Lambda(t_0 - t)H^{-1}, \qquad t \in v.$$

In light of these developments, it follows that

$$Z(t) = \Phi(t_0 - t)B = H\Lambda(t_0 - t)H^{-1}B, \qquad t \in v.$$

This form holds for the general case if $\Lambda(t_0 - t)$ is modified according to Theorem A for the Jordan canonical form.

Since the forced response can be written in the respective forms

$$x(t) = H\Lambda(t - t_0)H^{-1} \int_{t_0}^{t} H\Lambda(t_0 - s)H^{-1}Bu(s)\,ds, \qquad t \in \tau,$$

$$x(t) = H\Lambda(t - t_0)H^{-1} \sum_{j=0}^{[t]-1} H\Lambda(t_0 - t)H^{-1}Bu(t_j), \qquad t \in \sigma,$$

which reduce immediately to

$$x(t) = H \int_{t_0}^{t} \Lambda(t - s)H^{-1}Bu(s)\,ds, \qquad t \in \tau,$$

$$x(t) = H \sum_{j=0}^{[t]-1} \Lambda(t - t_j)H^{-1}Bu(t_j), \qquad t \in \sigma,$$

it follows that the instantaneous influence of the kth input $u_k(t)$ on the ith mode motion is determined by the (i,j)th element of $H^{-1}B$ (which is the constant $\langle e_i^+, b_k \rangle$) and the weighting factor $\exp\left[\lambda_i(t_0 - s)\right]$. Thus the columns of $H^{-1}B$ are the coupling constants between a fixed input and all modes. The rows are the coupling constants for a fixed mode and the various inputs. The accumulated influence is the integral (or summation) of the instantaneous influences after being weighted by the matrix $\Lambda(t_0 - t)$.

The picture is not quite so simple if A has a nondiagonal canonical form. Here $\Lambda(t_0 - t)$ is the exponent of the Jordan form for A and as such consists of diagonal Jordan blocks. Considering each total invariant subspace as a mode, however, we find that the previous statements remain true.

To conclude the present section, let us consider in detail a specific example.

Example 3. For the network of Figure 3.14 the loop voltage equations are given by

$$u(t) = L_1 \frac{di_1}{dt} + R_1 i_1 - R_1 i_2,$$

$$R_1 i_1 = L_2 \frac{di_2}{dt} + (R_1 + R_2) i_2.$$

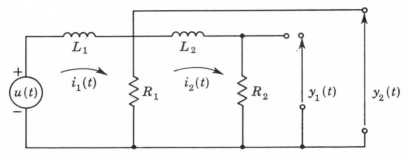

Figure 3.14   A simple network.

By rearrangement these equations become

$$\frac{di_1}{dt} = \left(\frac{R_1}{L_1}\right) i_1 + \left(\frac{R_2}{L_1}\right) i_2 + \left(\frac{1}{L_1}\right) u(t),$$

$$\frac{di_2}{dt} = \left(\frac{R_1}{L_2}\right) i_1 - \left(\frac{R_1 + R_2}{L_2}\right) i_2.$$

We introduce the notation $x(t) = \text{col}\,[i_1(t), i_2(t)]$ and write these equations in the normal system form

$$\dot{x}(t) = Ax(t) + bu(t), \qquad x(t_0) = x^0,$$

where the matrix A and the vector b are stationary.

$$A = \begin{bmatrix} -\dfrac{R_1}{L_1} & \left(\dfrac{R_2}{L_1}\right) \\[2ex] \dfrac{R_1}{L_2} & \dfrac{R_1 + R_2}{L_2} \end{bmatrix},$$

$$b = \frac{1}{L_2} \begin{pmatrix} 1 \\ 0 \end{pmatrix}.$$

To be specific, let the particular element values $R_1 = 30$, $R_2 = 6$, $L_1 = 10h$, and $L_2 = 9h$ be chosen. The reader can verify that the eigenvalues of A are then given by $\lambda_1 = -2$, $\lambda_2 = -5$, and a suitable set of corresponding eigenvectors is

$$e_1 = (1, \tfrac{5}{3})$$

$$e_2 = (\tfrac{3}{10}, -1)$$

and the dual set to this choice of eigenvectors is given by

$$e_1^+ = (\tfrac{2}{3}, \tfrac{1}{5})$$

$$e_2^+ = (\tfrac{10}{9}, -\tfrac{2}{3}).$$

From these quantities we can write the transition matrix for the system:

$$\Phi(t,t_0) = \exp\left[A(t - t_0)\right] = \sum_{i=1}^{2} e_i \rangle \exp\left[\lambda_i(t - t_0)\right]\langle e_i^+ .$$

By substituting in the numerical values just determined, we have

$$\Phi(t,t_0) = (1,\tfrac{5}{3})\rangle\exp\left[-2(t - t_0)\right]\langle(\tfrac{2}{3},\tfrac{1}{5}) + (\tfrac{3}{10},-1)\rangle\exp\left[-5(t - t_0)\right]\langle(\tfrac{10}{9},-\tfrac{2}{3}).$$

The matrix H, whose columns are e_1 and e_2, and its inverse (which has row vectors e_1^+ and e_2^+) are easily located. If $\Lambda(t,t_0)$ is defined by

$$\Lambda(t,t_0) = \begin{bmatrix} \exp\left[-2(t - t_0)\right] & 0 \\ 0 & \exp\left[-5(t - t_0)\right] \end{bmatrix},$$

the reader may verify that an alternative form for $\Phi(t,t_0)$ is given by $\Phi(t,t_0) = H\Lambda(t - t_0)H^{-1}$, which in this example has the numerical value

$$\Phi(t,t_0) = \begin{bmatrix} 1 & \tfrac{3}{10} \\ \tfrac{5}{3} & -1 \end{bmatrix} \cdot \begin{bmatrix} \exp\left[-2(t - t_0)\right] & 0 \\ 0 & \exp\left[-5(t - t_0)\right] \end{bmatrix} \cdot \begin{bmatrix} \tfrac{2}{3} & \tfrac{1}{5} \\ \tfrac{10}{9} & -\tfrac{2}{3} \end{bmatrix}.$$

As a final alternative, consider the parameterized family of functionals $\{g_i^t : t \in \tau\}$ on R^n, defined by

$$\langle g_1^t, \zeta \rangle = \exp\left[-2(t - t_0)\right][e_1^+,\zeta] = (\tfrac{2}{3}\zeta_1 + \tfrac{1}{5}\zeta_2)\exp\left[-2(t - t_0)\right],$$

$$\langle g_2^t, \zeta \rangle = \exp\left[-5(t - t_0)\right][e_2^+,\zeta] = (\tfrac{10}{9}\zeta_1 - \tfrac{2}{3}\zeta_2)\exp\left[-5(t - t_0)\right].$$

In terms of these functionals, an expansion of $\Phi(t,t_0)$ may be given by

$$\Phi(t,t_0) = e_1 \rangle\langle g_1^t + e_2 \rangle\langle g_2^t, \qquad t \in \tau.$$

The forced response is also easily obtained and is, in fact,

$$(Fu)(t) = \int_{t_0}^{t} \Lambda(t,s)H^{-1}bu(s)ds.$$

For the present numerical values and the particular form of b this expression becomes

$$(Fu)(t) = \begin{bmatrix} 1 & \frac{3}{10} \\ \frac{5}{8} & -1 \end{bmatrix} \int_{t_0}^{t} \begin{bmatrix} \exp[-2(t-s)] & 0 \\ 0 & \exp[-5(t-s)] \end{bmatrix} \cdot \begin{bmatrix} \frac{1}{15} \\ \frac{1}{9} \end{bmatrix} u(s)ds.$$

We let F^t denote the transformation defined by $F^t u = (Fu)(t)$ and use the functionals defined by

$$\langle f_1^t, u \rangle = \frac{1}{15} \int_{t_0}^{t} \exp[-2(t-s)]u(s)ds, \qquad t \in \tau,$$

$$\langle f_2^t, u \rangle = \frac{1}{9} \int_{t_0}^{t} \exp[-5(t-s)]u(s)ds, \qquad t \in \tau,$$

to form the dyadic decomposition

$$F^t = \mu_1 \rangle \langle f_1^t + \mu_2 \rangle \langle f_2^t$$

for F^t. If $v(t) = (x_1^0, x_2^0, u(t))$, the total system response T can be represented as

$$(Tv)(t) = (\Phi x^0)(t) + (Fu)(t)$$

$$= \begin{bmatrix} 1 & \frac{3}{10} \\ \frac{5}{8} & -1 \end{bmatrix} \cdot \left\{ \begin{bmatrix} \exp[-2(t-t_0)] & 0 \\ 0 & \exp[-5(t-t_0)]) \end{bmatrix} \begin{bmatrix} \frac{2}{3} & \frac{1}{3} \\ \frac{10}{9} & -\frac{2}{3} \end{bmatrix} \cdot \begin{bmatrix} x_1^0 \\ x_2^0 \end{bmatrix} \right.$$

$$+ \int_{t_0}^{t} \begin{bmatrix} \exp[-2(t-s)] & 0 \\ 0 & \exp[-5(t-s)] \end{bmatrix} \cdot \begin{bmatrix} \frac{1}{15} \\ \frac{1}{9} \end{bmatrix} u(s)ds \Big\},$$

or, by defining the functionals $\langle h_1^+$ and $\langle h_2^+$ on $R^2 \times U$, by

$$\langle h_1^t, v \rangle = \langle g_1^t, x^0 \rangle + \langle f_1^t, u \rangle, \qquad t \in \tau,$$

$$\langle h_2^t, v \rangle = \langle g_2^t, x^0 \rangle + \langle f_2^t, u \rangle, \qquad t \in \tau.$$

The total response, at time t, has the decomposition

$$T^t = \mu_1 \rangle \langle h_1^t + \mu_2 \rangle \langle h_2^t, \qquad t \in \tau,$$

which has the numerical form

$$T^t v = \begin{bmatrix} 1 \\ \frac{5}{3} \end{bmatrix} \{\exp[-2(t-t_0)][(\tfrac{2}{3})x_1^0 + (\tfrac{1}{3})x_2^0] + \frac{1}{15} \int_{t_0}^{t} \exp[-2(t-s)]u(s)ds\}$$

$$+ \begin{bmatrix} \frac{3}{10} \\ -1 \end{bmatrix} \{\exp[-5(t-t_0)][(\tfrac{10}{9})x_1^0 - (\tfrac{2}{3})x_2^0] + \frac{1}{9} \int_{t_0}^{t} \exp[-5(t-s)]u(s)ds\}.$$

A factor of considerable practical interest can be illustrated at this point. We note that $x(t) = (i_1(t), i_2(t))$ and that the individual loop currents can be obtained directly from these results by recognizing that

$$i_1(t) = ((1,0), x(t)),$$

$$i_2(t) = ((0,1), x(t)).$$

We use this fact as a computational tool. To illustrate, we determine $y_1(t)$ of Figure 3.14.

$$y_1(t) = R_2 i_2(t) = R_2((0,1), x(t))$$

$$= 6 \left(\frac{5}{3} \left\{ \exp\left[-2(t - t_0)\right] \left[\left(\frac{2}{3}\right) x_1^0 + \left(\frac{1}{5}\right) \right] + \frac{1}{15} \int_{t_0}^{t} \exp\left[-2(t - s)\right] u(s) ds \right\} \right.$$

$$\left. - \left\{ \exp\left[-5(t - t_0)\right] \left[\left(\frac{10}{9}\right) x_1^0 - \left(\frac{2}{3}\right) x_2^0 \right] + \frac{1}{9} \int_{t_0}^{t} \exp\left[-5(t - s)\right] u(s) ds \right\} \right).$$

Indeed, it is apparent that when the behavior of physical systems is formulated as a normal system of equations, the behavior of all primary system variables can be obtained from the solution of the normal system by taking an appropriate inner product.

Exercises

1. Determine the eigenvalues and eigenvectors for the matrix

$$M = \begin{bmatrix} h & k - 1 \\ k + 1 & h \end{bmatrix}.$$

Under what conditions on k and h would the eigenvalues be real? Compute $\exp(Mt)$.

2. Let N denote the raised diagonal matrix of degree n

$$N = \begin{bmatrix} 0 & 1 & 0 & \cdots & 0 \\ & & \ddots & & 0 \\ \vdots & & & \ddots & \vdots \\ & & & & 1 \\ 0 & & & & 0 \end{bmatrix}.$$

Compute $N^2, N^3, \ldots, N^{n-1} = 0$. Let $f(s)$ denote a function, analytic in a neighborhood of the point $s = \lambda$ and with the convergent Taylor expansion

$$f(s) = \sum_{n=0}^{\infty} \frac{(s - \lambda)^n}{m} \left. \frac{d^n f}{ds^n} \right|_{s = \lambda}.$$

Let D denote the Jordan block $D = \lambda I + N$. Verify directly that $f(D)$ is completely determined by the first n terms of this series.

3. Let $f(s)$ denote a function, analytic on an open disk enclosing the spectrum of the $n \times n$ matrix A. It can be shown that if A has a distinct spectrum

$$f(A) = v^{-1}[v_0 I + v_1 A + \cdots + v_{n-1} A^{n-1}],$$

where v is the Vandermonde determinant

$$v = \begin{vmatrix} 1 & \cdots & \cdots & 1 \\ \lambda_1 & \cdots & \cdots & \lambda_n \\ \lambda_1^2 & \cdots & \cdots & \lambda_n^2 \\ \lambda_1^{n-1} & \cdots & \cdots & \lambda_n^{n-1} \end{vmatrix}$$

and v_k is identical to v except for the substitution of the tuplet $[f(\lambda_1), f(\lambda_2), \ldots, f(\lambda_n)]$ in the $(k + 1)$th row of v. Use this formulation to check the first two exercises.

4. Let A denote the matrix

$$A = \begin{bmatrix} -\sqrt{2} & \sqrt{2} \\ 3 - 2\sqrt{2} & -3 + 2\sqrt{2} \end{bmatrix}.$$

Show that $\lambda_1 = -1$ and $\lambda_2 = -2$ and by two different methods that

$$\exp(At) = e^{-t} \begin{bmatrix} 2 - 2\sqrt{2} & \sqrt{2} \\ 3 - 2\sqrt{2} & \sqrt{2} - 1 \end{bmatrix} + e^{-2t} \begin{bmatrix} 2\sqrt{2} - 1 & -\sqrt{2} \\ 2\sqrt{2} - 3 & 2 - \sqrt{2} \end{bmatrix}.$$

5. Let A denote the matrix

$$A = \begin{bmatrix} 1 & \alpha \\ \alpha & 1 \end{bmatrix}.$$

Show that $\lambda_1 = 1 + \alpha$, $\lambda_2 = 1 - \alpha$. Compute by two different methods the exponent $\exp[A(t - t_0)]$ of this matrix.

6. One of the few distinctions between continuous and discrete systems is that the free response may become zero in a finite number of steps. This happens if and only if $\Phi(t_k, t_0)$ becomes singular. Discuss this situation.

7. Let A denote a fixed normal matrix with distinct spectrum $\sigma(A) = \{\lambda_1, \ldots, \lambda_n\}$ such that $\lambda_i < 0$, $i = 1, \ldots, n$. Design a sample spacing set

$\{t_1, t_2, \ldots, t_n\}$ such that $\Phi(t_n, t_0) = 0$ and each of the numbers $\{\|\Phi(t_k, t_0)\| : k = 1, 2, \ldots, n\}$ is a minimum.

8. In the stationary system of Eq. 8 assume that $x^0 = 0$, $t_0 = -\infty$, and $u(t) = e^{j\omega t}$. Verify that

$$[u(t)]^{-1} x(t) = \sum_{i=1}^{n} e_i \frac{\langle e_i^+, b \rangle}{j\omega - \lambda_i}. \tag{$*$}$$

Use this expression to interpret geometrically the frequency response of stationary systems. Consider specifically the system $D^n y(t) + a_{n-1} D^{n-1} y(t) + \cdots + a_0 y(t) = u(t)$. Write the frequency response of the system by utilizing a partial fraction expansion of the system tranfer function. Compare this expression with $(*)$ after reducing the equation to first-order form. In particular, what corresponds to the residues and poles of the transfer function?

9. Consider the first-order vectorial system

$$\dot{x}(t) = Ax(t) + bu(t), \qquad t \in \tau,$$
$$y(t) = \langle c, x(t) \rangle, \tag{$\dagger$}$$

which is the usual equivalent (see Appendix 4) of the equation

$$x_1^{(n)}(t) + a_{n-1} x_1^{(n-1)}(t) + \cdots + a_0 x_1(t) = u(t), \qquad t \in \tau. \tag{$\ddagger$}$$

[Here $b = (0, \ldots, 0, 1)$ and $c = (1, 0, \ldots, 0)$.] Let the function u be determined in both cases by an input θ and the linear feedback law

$$u(t) = \theta(t) - kx_1(t) = \theta(t) - k\langle c, x(t) \rangle, \qquad t \in \tau;$$

the nth-order equation $u(t)$ becomes $\theta(t)$ and a_0 becomes $a_0 - k$. Show that the feedback induces the change $u \to \theta$ and that

$$A \to A' = A - k[b\rangle\langle c]$$

in the first-order system. Prove that the poles of the nth-order equation and the eigenvalues of A' coincide for every value of k. Show how the root locus technique, ordinarily used for stability considerations of the nth-order equation, may be employed as a tool to determine the spectrum of A' as k varies.

10. Consider the system in $(\dagger)$ and $(\ddagger)$ with $k = 1$ and $b = (0, \ldots, 0, 1)$. Show that if $c = (c_0, \ldots, c_{n-1})$ the characteristic polynomial of A' is given by

$$p(\lambda) = \lambda^n + (a_{n-1} + c_{n-1})\lambda^{n-1} + \cdots + (a_1 + c_1)\lambda + (a_0 + c_0).$$

Prove that for every set $(a_0, \ldots, a_{n-1})$ of coefficients in $(\ddagger)$ scalars

$(c_0, \ldots, c_{n-1})$ can be found such that the spectrum of A' may be forced to take on any predetermined values $\{\lambda_1, \ldots, \lambda_n\}$. Complex scalars occur only in conjugate pairs.

11. Let A be a simple matrix whose eigenvalues have negative real parts. Show that scalars $K > 0$, $\mu < 0$ exist such that

$$\|\exp [A(t - t_0)]\| \leq K \exp [\mu(t - t_0)].$$

Is this result true if A is not simple?

12. Let $A(t) = A_1 + A_2(t)$, where A_1 satisfies the conditions of Exercise 11 and where $\|A_2(t)\| \in L_1(0,\infty)$. Prove that scalars $M > 0$ and $\mu < 0$ exist such that $\|\Phi(t,t_0)\| \leq M \exp [\mu(t - t_0)]$ also holds. HINT: Show first that

$$\|\Phi(t,t_0)\| \leq K \exp [\mu(t - t_0)]$$
$$\left[1 + \int_{t_0}^{t} \exp [\mu(t_0 - s)] \cdot \|A_2(s)\| \cdot \|\Phi(s,t_0)\| ds \right]$$

and apply Lemma A of Section 2.3.

3.6 SOME PROBLEMS RELATED TO SYSTEM STRUCTURE

In this section attention is focused on certain problems related to the linear dynamic system defined by the equations

$$d_t x(t) = A(t)x(t) + B(t)u(t), \qquad t \in v, \tag{1}$$

$$y(t) = C(t)x(t) + D(t)u(t), \qquad t \in v. \tag{2}$$

Here the formal notation introduced in Section 2.5 is being used to incorporate both differential systems ($v = \tau$ and $d_t = d/dt$) and difference systems ($v = \sigma$ and $d_t = \Delta_t$). For conciseness differential systems are used as the main vehicle for the development. It is apparent that discrete systems and composite systems exhibit analogous properties; the details, however, are left to the reader as exercises.

In Exercise 3, Section 2.4, the concept of equivalence for systems that satisfy Eq. 1 is introduced. This exercise plays an important role in this section. Therefore we shall discuss the situation briefly before proceeding. Let us consider first the simple homogeneous system

$$\dot{x}(t) = A(t)x(t). \tag{3}$$

Let $K(t)$ denote any matrix, nonsingular on τ, and $\hat{x}(t)$ a vector, such that

$$x(t) = K(t)\hat{x}(t). \tag{4}$$

The question of the existence and form of a homogeneous dynamic system for which $\hat{x}(t)$ is a solution naturally arises. This question is easily settled, for by differentiating Eq. 4, substituting into Eq. 3 and collecting terms, we see that $\hat{x}$ satisfies another linear homogeneous system

$$\dot{\hat{x}}(t) = \hat{A}(t)\hat{x}(t), \tag{5}$$

where $\hat{A}(t)$ is given by

$$\hat{A}(t) = K^{-1}(t)A(t)K(t) - K^{-1}(t)\dot{K}(t).$$

Clearly the transformation $x(t) = K(t)\hat{x}(t)$ has set up a one-to-one relationship between the solutions of Eqs. 3 and 5.

Thus it is apparent that linear dynamic systems can be converted by a change in variables to many diverse forms. We have the feeling, however, that the different formulations are equivalent in some sense. To be precise about this feeling we shall agree on the definition.

DEFINITION A.   *The two homogeneous dynamic systems of Eqs. 3 and 5 are said to be equivalent if there exists a matrix $K(t)$ such that*
  (1) $K(t)$ and $\dot{K}(t)$ are defined on v,
  (2) $\sup_v \| K(t) \| < \infty$, $\sup_v \| K^{-1}(t) \| < \infty$,
  (3) $\hat{x}(t) = K^{-1}(t)x(t)$, $t \in v$.

Conditions (1) and (3) appear naturally as a consequence of the opening remarks of this section. Condition (2) is included to guarantee that the stability properties of the solutions $x(t)$ and $\hat{x}(t)$ will be preserved under the mapping $K(t)$. It is apparent that the specific norm used in condition (2) is irrelevant.

The definition of equivalent systems can be extended to the nonhomogeneous case. Consider the two nonhomogeneous dynamic systems

$$\begin{aligned} \dot{x}(t) &= A(t)x(t) + B(t)u(t), \quad t \in v, \\ y(t) &= C(t)x(t) + D(t)u(t), \quad t \in v, \end{aligned} \tag{6}$$

$$\begin{aligned} \dot{\hat{x}}(t) &= \hat{A}(t)\hat{x}(t) + \hat{B}(t)u(t), \quad t \in v, \\ \hat{y}(t) &= \hat{C}(t)\hat{x}(t) + \hat{D}(t)u(t), \quad t \in v. \end{aligned} \tag{7}$$

DEFINITION B.   *The two linear dynamic systems of Eqs. 6 and 7 are said to be equivalent if, for every $u(t)$, $y(t) = \hat{y}(t)$ on v and $x(t)$ and $\hat{x}(t)$ are equivalent (satisfy Definition C) under the conditions $u(t) = 0$.*

R E M A R K 1.   Consider the usual black-box problem in which u and y are the physical external input and output variables. Definition B then states the conditions for which two choices $x, \hat{x}$ of internal variables are equivalent. From previous results the reader can verify that the equivalence of the systems of Eqs. 6 and 7 implies the following relations between the system matrices[1]:

$$\begin{aligned}
\hat{\Phi}(t,\tau) &= K^{-1}(t)\Phi(t,\tau)K(\tau), \\
\hat{A}(t) &= K^{-1}(t)A(t)K(t) - K^{-1}(t)\dot{K}(t), \qquad t \in v, \\
\hat{B}(t) &= K^{-1}(t)B(t), \\
\hat{C}(t) &= C(t)K(t).
\end{aligned} \tag{8}$$

Proper Systems

In this section implications of the polar decomposition (Theorem E, Section 3.4) of linear dynamic systems are developed in some detail. The results derived will depend only on the properties of a linear transformation $T: B \to R^n$ defined on an arbitrary Hilbert space H and with values in R^n. Thus we shall be able to interpret these results for the continuous, discrete, and composite system on an equal footing.

DEFINITION C. *Let T denote a linear transformation $T: H \to R^n$ with the polar form*

$$T = \sum_{i=1}^{n} e_i \rangle \mu_i \langle f_i.$$

The transformation T is called proper if $\mu_i \neq 0$ for $i = 1, \ldots, n$.

Since all transformations from H into R^n have a polar form, it follows easily from the definition that proper transformations are exactly those transformations that are *onto* R^n.

Consider first the plant with $D(t) \equiv 0$, $C(t) \equiv I$. Without distinguishing between the several system types, we let $F: H \to B$ and $\Phi: R^n \to B$ denote the transformations defined by the systems forced and free response, respectively. Thus for any $u \in H$ and $x^0 \in R^n$ the response x at time $t \in v$ is given by

$$x(t) = (\Phi x^0)(t) + (Fu)(t), \qquad t \in v. \tag{9}$$

For linear dynamic systems the concept of controllability has received much attention.

DEFINITION D. *A linear dynamic system is said to be controllable (on v) if for every tuplet (x^0, t_0) a control $u \in H$ and a time $t_\alpha \in v$ exist such that the condition*

$$x_u(t_\alpha; x^0, t_0) = 0$$

may be attained.

---

[1]Definitions A and B and equation sets (6), (7), and (8) hold for the analogous discrete system if $t \in \sigma$ and if the substitutions $K^{-1}(t_{k+1})$ for $K^{-1}(t)$ and $\Delta_k K(t_k)$ for $\dot{K}(t)$ are made.

In other words a controllable system is one for which, given enough time, every initial condition can be brought to the origin. Let the transformation $T_\alpha : H \to R^n$ be defined by $T_\alpha u = (Fu)(t_\alpha)$, $t_\alpha \in v$, for every $u \in H$. The essential relationship between controllability and proper transformations is given by Lemma A.

LEMMA A.   *A linear dynamic system is controllable if and only if $t_\alpha \in v$ exists such that T_α is proper.*

P R O O F.   Since $\Phi(t_\alpha, t_0)$ is nonsingular on R^n, the vector $\xi = \Phi(t_\alpha, t_0)x^0$ is arbitrary when x^0 is also. From the condition $0 = x_u(t_\alpha; x^0, t^0) = \Phi(t_\alpha, t_0)x^0 + T_\alpha u$ it follows that u must satisfy $T_\alpha u = -\xi$. Since ξ is arbitrary, this condition may be satisfied if and only if the range of T_α is all of R^n, which happens if and only if T_α is proper.

In the form of Definition D the term controllable may seem to some readers aesthetically objectionable. A technical term that utilizes the root "control" suggests in the mind's eye a concept related to purposeful excitation of a system. In its present form, however, it is essentially a statement about the structure of the system and not at all related to control action. In fact, from the proof of Lemma A we see that although Definition C is a precise statement about the structure of any linear, discrete, continuous or composite, dynamic system, for which at any time t the system is a mapping *onto* R^n, Definition D is essentially the statement that, when this map is onto, the term controllable rather than simply onto or proper should be used.

LEMMA B.   *The transformation $T : H \to R^n$ is proper if and only if the matrix TT^* is nonsingular.*

Since the scalars $\{\mu_i\}$ in the polar form for T are the positive square roots of the eigenvalues of TT^*, this lemma is obviously true. Because of its simplicity it is a useful tool for determining the rank of T. For example, the continuous linear dynamic system

$$\dot{x}(t) = A(t)x(t) + B(t)u(t), \qquad t \in \tau, \tag{10}$$

has the associated matrix

$$T_\alpha T_\alpha^* = \int_{t_0}^{t_\alpha} \Phi(t_\alpha, s)B(s)B^*(s)\Phi^*(t_\alpha, s)ds,$$

whereas its discrete time counterpart ($\tau \to \sigma$) takes the form

$$T_\alpha T_\alpha^* = \sum_{j=0}^{[t_\alpha]-1} h_j \Phi(t_\alpha, t_j)B(t_{j+1})B^*(t_{j+1})\Phi^*(t_\alpha, t_j).$$

In both cases, once the system transition matrix has been determined, these computations are straightforward.

For the next theorem we restrict attention to the continuous-time, linear, dynamic system of Eq. 10. Let us assume, in addition, that the elements $\{b_{ij} : i = 1, \ldots, n, j = 1, \ldots, m\}$ of the matrix B and the elements $\{a_{ij} : i, j = 1, \ldots, n\}$ of the matrix A have at least $n - 1$ derivatives. The symbol $\mathscr{L}$ denotes the linear differential operator, defined on the interval τ by

$$(\mathscr{L}x)(t) = \dot{x}(t) - A(t)x(t), \qquad t \in \tau.$$

The transformation T_α is defined as usual by

$$T_\alpha u = (Tu)(t_\alpha) = \int_{t_0}^{t_\alpha} \Phi(t_\alpha,s)B(s)u(s)ds, \qquad t_0, t \in \tau.$$

THEOREM A. *If the rank of T_α is less than n then for every fixed time $t_\alpha \in \tau$ the columns of the n matrices*

$$B(t),(\mathscr{L}B)(t), \ldots, (\mathscr{L}^{n-1}B)(t),$$

all together, lie in a subspace of dimension less than n.

P R O O F.   Assume that T_α has a rank less than n; that is, T_α is not proper. The spectrum of $T_\alpha T_\alpha^*$ contains zero or, equivalently, a nonzero $\lambda \in R^n$ exists such that $T_\alpha^* \lambda = 0$. In the present case this means that

$$B^*(t)\Phi^*(t_\alpha,t)\lambda = 0, \qquad t \in \tau.$$

Let us recall from Section 3.3 that $\Phi^*(t_\alpha,t) = \Psi(t,t_\alpha)$, the transition matrix of the adjoint system, and that $\psi(t) = \Phi^*(t_\alpha,t)\lambda$ satisfies the equation

$$\dot{\psi}(t) + A^*(t)\psi(t) = 0, \qquad t \in \tau.$$

Now by the continuity of ψ and B it follows that if

$$B^*(t)\psi(t) = 0, \qquad t \in \tau,$$

then

$$0 = \frac{d}{dt} B^*(t)\psi(t), \qquad t \in \tau$$

$$= \dot{B}^*(t)\psi(t) + B^*(t)\dot{\psi}(t)$$

$$= \dot{B}^*(t)\psi(t) - B^*(t)A^*(t)\psi(t)$$

$$= [\dot{B}^*(t) - B^*(t)A^*(t)]\psi(t)$$

$$= [(\mathscr{L}B)(t)]^*\psi(t).$$

Since $\psi \not\equiv 0$, it spans at any time t a one-dimensional subspace of R^n. These relations show that the columns of $B(t)$, $(\mathscr{L}B)(t) \cdots (\mathscr{L}^{n-1}B)(t)$ are in the orthogonal complement of the manifold $L(\psi(t))$ and the theorem is proved.

COROLLARY.   *If A and B are stationary, the $n \times mn$ matrix*

$$[B, AB, A^2B, \ldots, A^{n-1}B]$$

has rank $\leq n - 1$.

Since the stationary case $\mathscr{L}B = AB$, this corollary is an obvious consequence of the theorem. If the columns of B do *not* satisfy the condition of Theorem A, these columns are said to be in *general position,* a choice of terminology that stems from consideration of the system impulse response matrix

$$W(t,s) = \Phi(t,s)B(s)$$

$$= \Phi(t,t_0)\Psi^*(t_0,s)B(s).$$

If the columns of B are not in general position, a row of $\Psi^*(t_0,s)B(s)$ is identically zero on τ and consequently no control can be exerted over the corresponding column of $\Phi(t,t_0)$.

R E M A R K 2.   We have specifically treated only the differential system with zero direct transmission and unconstrained output (i.e., $y = x$). To take into account an output constraint and direct transmission only minor modifications in the preceding development are necessary. In particular, the output constraint can be accounted for by replacing transformation T_α by $T'_\alpha = C(t_\alpha)T_\alpha$. The direct transmission can be handled by viewing the system as a mapping which carries the tuplet $[u(t_\alpha),u]$ into $y(t_\alpha)$ by the rule

$$y(t_\alpha) = D(t_\alpha)u(t_\alpha) + T'_\alpha u.$$

Lemmas A and B now hold, with $D(t_\alpha) \oplus T'_\alpha$ replacing T_α. The matrix $T_\alpha T^*_\alpha$ becomes $T'_\alpha T'^*_\alpha + D(t_\alpha)D^*(t_\alpha)$. Other variations on the central result are suggested in the exercises.

R E M A R K 3.   A linear plant is said to be completely observable on an interval $[t_0,t']$ if every initial condition x^0 [and $u(t) \equiv 0$] can be uniquely determined from the values of the output on this interval. Since the transition matrix for the system of Eq. 1 is nonsingular for all t, it is trivial that plants with $C(t) \equiv I$ are completely observable. More generally speaking, the plants of Eqs. 1 and 2 are completely observable if and only if the mapping $C\Phi$: $R^n \to L^m_2(\tau)$, defined by

$$(C\Phi\xi)(t) = C(t)\Phi(t,t_0)\xi, \qquad t \in \tau,$$

is proper. From the equality

$$\langle y, C\Phi\xi \rangle = \int_{t_0}^{t_f} [y(s), C(s)\Phi(s,t_0)\xi] ds = \int_{t_0}^{t_f} [\Phi^*(s,t_0)C^*(s)y(s),\xi] ds$$

it is clear that

$$(C\Phi)^* y = \int_{t_0}^{t_f} \Phi^*(s,t_0)C^*(s)y(s) ds$$

and that the plant with output constraint C will be completely observable if and only if the matrix

$$(C\Phi)^* C\Phi = \int_{t_0}^{t_f} \Phi^*(s,t_0)C^*(s)C(s)\Phi(s,t_0) ds$$

is nonsingular.

Separable Systems

On some occasions it is possible to treat an nth-order system as a collection on noninteracting systems of lower order. For example, let the matrices and vectors of Eq. 1 be partitioned in the form

$$x(t) = \text{col } (x_\text{I}(t), x_\text{II}(t)) = \text{col } (x_1(t), \ldots, x_k(t), x_{k+1}(t), \ldots, x_n(t)),$$

$$A(t) = \begin{bmatrix} A_{11}(t) & A_{12}(t) \\ \hline A_{21}(t) & A_{22}(t) \end{bmatrix}, \quad t \in \tau,$$

$$B(t) = \begin{bmatrix} B_k(t) \\ \hline B_{n-k}(t) \end{bmatrix}, \quad t \in \tau,$$

where A_{11} and A_{22} are square matrices of dimension k and $n - k$, respectively, whereas B_k is a $k \times m$ rectangular matrix. In terms of these quantities, Eq. 1 may be written

$$\dot{x}_\text{I}(t) = A_{11}(t)x_\text{I}(t) + A_{12}(t)x_\text{II}(t) + B_k(t)u(t), \quad t \in \tau,$$

$$\dot{x}_\text{II}(t) = A_{21}(t)x_\text{I}(t) + A_{22}(t)x_\text{II}(t) + B_{n-k}(t)u(t), \quad t \in \tau.$$

(11)

Now, if $A_{21} \equiv 0$, the second system can be analyzed separately. If $B_{n-k} \equiv 0$, the second system is unforced. If, in addition, $A_{12} \equiv 0$, the first system is independent of the second and the total system is decomposed into two noninteracting parts.

DEFINITION E. *A linear dynamic system that is equivalent to the system of Eq. 11 with matrices A_{21} or A_{12} (or both) identically zero on τ is called a* *separable system. If A_{21} (respectively A_{12}) is zero and B_{n-k} (respectively B_k) is also zero, the system is called homogeneously separable.*

In other words, if a change of variables $x(t) = K(t)\hat{x}(t)$ can be found to satisfy Definition B, which reduces a linear dynamic system to the form of Eq. 11 with $A_{21} \equiv 0$ or $A_{12} \equiv 0$, the system is called separable. If, in addition, one of the subsystems is unforced, the system is called homogeneously separable. Thus in a homogeneously separable system the forced response is determined by a dynamic system of lower degree. Furthermore, the forced response takes place in a proper subspace of R^n. This is clear from Eq. 11 in which, if $A_{21} \equiv 0$ and $B_{n-k} \equiv 0$, the forced response is determined completely by

$$\dot{x}_I(t) = A_{11}(t)x_I(t) + A_{12}(t)x_{II}(t) + B_k(t)u(t), \qquad t \in \tau,$$

and thus lies entirely in the component subspace $L(e_1, \dots, e_k)$ of R^n; that is, only the first k coefficients of x are influenced by u.

It has been pointed out that if the t_αth sample of the forced response of a linear dynamic system does not define a proper transformation the forcing function effects only a subset $\{\phi_1, \dots, \phi_k\}$ of the columns of $\Phi(t,t_0)$. Thus it would seem that if T_α has a rank less than n the system might be homogeneous separable.

THEOREM B.   *Let T_α denote the t_αth sample of the forced response of the linear dynamic system of Eq. 10. If T_α has rank $k < n$, the system is homogeneously separable over the interval $[t_0, t_\alpha]$.*

To prove this theorem it is necessary only to exhibit an appropriate change of variables which separate the system. There are several changes of variables that might be given. The first to be considered uses the fundamental matrix $K(t) = \Phi(t,t_0)$. Since $\Phi(t,t_0)$ is nonsingular and satisfies the conditions of Definition A for all finite times, it is clear that it can be used in the change of variables

$$x(t) = \Phi(t,t_0)\hat{x}(t), \qquad t \in \tau.$$

According to Eq. 8, the vector $\hat{x}(t)$ obeys a linear differential system with matrices $\hat{A}(t)$ and $\hat{B}(t)$, defined by

$$\hat{B}(t) = [\Phi(t,t_0)]^{-1}B(t),$$

$$\hat{A}(t) = [\Phi(t,t_0)]^{-1}A(t)\Phi(t,t_0) - [\dot{\Phi}(t,t_0)]^{-1}\Phi(t,t_0), \qquad t \in \tau.$$

Since $\Phi(t,t_0)$ satisfies the homogeneous differential system, it follows that

$$\hat{A}(t) \equiv 0.$$

In view of the hypothesis of Theorem B, it is clear that $\hat{B}$ has the form (see the paragraph preceding Remark 2)

$$\hat{B}(t) = \begin{bmatrix} Z(t) \\ 0_{n-k} \end{bmatrix}, \qquad t \in \tau,$$

in which $Z(t)$ is a nonzero block of dimensions $k \times n$. Let $z_i, i = 1, \ldots, k$ denote the ith row of $Z(t)$. The transformed differential system becomes

$$\dot{x}_i(t) = \begin{cases} [z_i(t), u(t)], & i = 1, \ldots, k, \qquad t \in \tau, \\ 0, & i = k+1, \ldots, n, \qquad t \in \tau, \end{cases}$$

which is obviously homogeneously separated, and the theorem is proved.

The use of the fundamental matrix $\Phi(t, t_0)$ as a change of variables provides an easy proof of Theorem B. The procedure also suggests that any basis that decomposes R^n at time $t \in \tau$ into the manifold $L(\phi_1(t), \ldots, \phi_k(t))$ and its complement will produce the same result. This is indeed true. For example, a change of variables can be defined to make use of the general position condition. To keep matters reasonably simple attention is restricted to the single variate system.

THEOREM C. *The system of Eq. 1 is homogeneously separable if and only if the vector b is not in general position.*

For single variate systems the vector b is in general position with respect to A if the vectors $b_1(t) = b(t)$, $b_j(t) = -A(t)b_{j-1}(t) + \dot{b}_{j-1}(t)$ $(j = 2, \ldots, n)$ are linearly independent for every $t \in \tau$. Assume that b is not in general position and, to be precise, assume that $b_1(t), \ldots, b_k(t)$ are linearly independent and that $b_{k+1}(t), \ldots, b_n(t)$ are linear combinations of $b_1(t), \ldots, b_k(t)$ for every $t \in \tau$. Before proceeding with the proof of the theorem, we state a corollary that is proved simultaneously with the theorem.

COROLLARY. *A matrix K, which separates the system, is given by using the tuplets $b_1, \ldots, b_k, \beta_1, \ldots, \beta_{n-k}$ as the columns of K. The tuplets $\beta_1, \ldots, \beta_{n-k}$ may be arbitrarily chosen to make K nonsingular on τ.*

PROOF. The proof of the theorem and corollary is by direct verification. As in the corollary, we set

$$K = \begin{bmatrix} \uparrow & & \uparrow & \uparrow & & \uparrow \\ b_1, & \ldots, & b_k, & \beta_1, & \ldots, & \beta_{n-k} \\ \downarrow & & \downarrow & \downarrow & & \downarrow \end{bmatrix}.$$

By use of the dual notation, K^{-1} may be written

$$\begin{bmatrix} \leftarrow & b_1^+ & \rightarrow \\ & \vdots & \\ \leftarrow & \beta_{n-k}^+ & \rightarrow \end{bmatrix}.$$

Since $b_j = -Ab_{j-1} + \dot{b}_{j-1}$ or $\dot{b}_{j-1} = b_j + Ab_{j-1}$, we see that

$$\dot{K} = \begin{bmatrix} \uparrow & & \uparrow & \uparrow & & \uparrow \\ \dot{b}_1, & \ldots, & \dot{b}_k, & \dot{\beta}_1, & \ldots, & \dot{\beta}_{n-k} \\ \downarrow & & \downarrow & \downarrow & & \downarrow \end{bmatrix}$$

$$= \begin{bmatrix} \uparrow & & \uparrow & & \uparrow & \uparrow & & \uparrow \\ (b_2 + Ab_1), & (b_3 + Ab_2), & \ldots, & (b_k + Ab_{k-1}), & b_k, & \dot{\beta}_1, & \ldots, & \dot{\beta}_{n-k} \\ \downarrow & \downarrow & & \downarrow & \downarrow & \downarrow & & \downarrow \end{bmatrix}$$

and

$$AK = \begin{bmatrix} \uparrow & & \uparrow & & \uparrow \\ Ab_1, & \ldots, & Ab_k, & \ldots, & A\beta_{n-k} \\ \downarrow & & \downarrow & & \downarrow \end{bmatrix}.$$

Hence

$$AK - \dot{K} = \begin{bmatrix} \uparrow & & \uparrow & \uparrow & \uparrow & & \uparrow \\ -b_2, & \ldots, & -b_k, & (Ab_k - \dot{b}_k), & (A\beta_1 - \dot{\beta}_1), & \ldots, & (A\beta_{n-k} - \dot{\beta}_{n-k}) \\ \downarrow & & \downarrow & \downarrow & \downarrow & & \downarrow \end{bmatrix}.$$

Now, if we make the change of variables $x = K^{-1}(t)\hat{x}$, the transformed system has the form

$$\dot{\hat{x}}(t) = [K^{-1}(t)A(t)K(t) - K^{-1}(t)\dot{K}(t)]\hat{x}(t) + K^{-1}(t)bu(t).$$

From the foregoing we find that $K^{-1}AK - K^{-1}\dot{K}$ has the form

$$K^{-1}AK - K^{-1}\dot{K} = \left.\begin{bmatrix} 0 & \cdots & 0 & \alpha_1 & \\ -1 & 0 & \cdots & 0 & \\ 0 & & & \vdots & \vdots & L \\ \vdots & & & & & \\ 0 & & -1 & \alpha_k & \\ \hline & 0 & & & N \end{bmatrix}\right\} k\text{-rows,}$$

$$\underbrace{}_{k\text{-columns}}$$

in which $\alpha_j = [b_j^+, (Ab_k - \dot{b}_k)]$ $(j = 1, \ldots, k)$, the elements of L, are given by $l_{ij} = [b_i^+, (A\beta_j - \dot{\beta}_j)]$ $i = 1, \ldots, k$; $j = 1, \ldots, n - k$ and the elements of N are given by $n_{ij} = [\beta_j^+, (A\beta_j - \dot{\beta}_j)]$. Furthermore, because $b_1 = b$, we see that

$$K^{-1}b = \text{col}(1, 0, \ldots, 0).$$

Hence we see that if $x_k = \text{col}(x_1, \ldots, x_k)$, $x_2 = (x_{k+1}, \ldots, x_n)$ we have

$$\dot{x}_2(t) = N(t)x_2(t),$$

$$\dot{x}_1(t) = M(t)x_1(t) + L(t)x_2(t) + e_1 u(t), \qquad t \in \tau.$$

Thus the theorem is proved. (M, of course, is the $k \times k$ matrix in the northwest corner of $K^{-1}AK - K^{-1}\dot{K}$.)

Example 1.[1]   Consider first the second-order system

$$\dot{y}(t) = \begin{bmatrix} -3 & -1 \\ 2 & 0 \end{bmatrix} y(t) + \begin{bmatrix} 1 \\ -1 \end{bmatrix} u(t).$$

First we find

$$b_1 = \begin{bmatrix} 1 \\ -1 \end{bmatrix},$$

$$b_2 = \begin{bmatrix} -3 & -1 \\ 2 & 0 \end{bmatrix} \cdot \begin{bmatrix} 1 \\ 1 \end{bmatrix} = \begin{bmatrix} -2 \\ 2 \end{bmatrix};$$

hence $b_2 = 2b$, and the system is separable. Letting $\beta_1 = \text{col}(1,0)$, we form K

$$K = \begin{bmatrix} 1 & 1 \\ -1 & 0 \end{bmatrix}.$$

It is easy to find

$$K^{-1} = \begin{bmatrix} 0 & -1 \\ 1 & 1 \end{bmatrix};$$

similarly,

$$K^{-1}AK = \begin{bmatrix} 0 & -1 \\ 1 & 1 \end{bmatrix} \cdot \begin{bmatrix} -3 & -1 \\ 2 & 0 \end{bmatrix} \cdot \begin{bmatrix} 1 & 1 \\ -1 & 0 \end{bmatrix} = \begin{bmatrix} -2 & -2 \\ 0 & -1 \end{bmatrix},$$

$$K^{-1} = \begin{bmatrix} 0 & -1 \\ 1 & 1 \end{bmatrix} \cdot \begin{bmatrix} 1 \\ -1 \end{bmatrix} = \begin{bmatrix} 1 \\ 0 \end{bmatrix}.$$

If $x = Ky$, we have

$$\begin{bmatrix} \dot{x}_1 \\ \dot{x}_2 \end{bmatrix} = \begin{bmatrix} -2 & -2 \\ 0 & -1 \end{bmatrix} \cdot \begin{bmatrix} x_1 \\ x_2 \end{bmatrix} + \begin{bmatrix} 1 \\ 0 \end{bmatrix} u(t),$$

[1]Examples 1 and 2 are reprinted with permission from A. R. Stubberud, *Analysis and*

which is in the separable form $\dot{x}_2 = -x_2$, $x_2 = x_2(0)e^{t^-}$, and $\dot{x}_1 = -2x_1 + [x_2(0)e^{-t} + u(t)]$, which is easily solvable.

Example 2[1]

$$\begin{bmatrix} \dot{y}_1(t) \\ \dot{y}_2(t) \\ \dot{y}_3(t) \end{bmatrix} = \begin{bmatrix} -(1 + e^{-t}) & -1 & 0 \\ (1 + 3e^{-t}) & 0 & -1 \\ -3e^{-t} & 0 & 0 \end{bmatrix} \cdot \begin{bmatrix} y_1(t) \\ y_2(t) \\ y_3(t) \end{bmatrix} + \begin{bmatrix} 0 \\ -1 \\ e^{-t} \end{bmatrix} u(t).$$

As before, $b_1 = \text{col}(0, -1, e^{-t})$,

$$b_2 = - \begin{bmatrix} -(1 + e^{-t}) & -1 & 0 \\ (1 + 3e^{-t}) & 0 & -1 \\ -3e^{-t} & 0 & 0 \end{bmatrix} \cdot \begin{bmatrix} 0 \\ -1 \\ e^{-t} \end{bmatrix} + \begin{bmatrix} 0 \\ 0 \\ -e^{-t} \end{bmatrix} = \begin{bmatrix} -1 \\ e^{-t} \\ -e^{-t} \end{bmatrix},$$

$$b_3 = - \begin{bmatrix} +(1 + e^{-t}) & +1 & 0 \\ -(1 + 3e^{-t}) & 0 & +1 \\ +3e^{-t} & 0 & 0 \end{bmatrix} \cdot \begin{bmatrix} -1 \\ e^{-t} \\ -e^{-t} \end{bmatrix} + \begin{bmatrix} 0 \\ -e^{-t} \\ e^{-t} \end{bmatrix} = \begin{bmatrix} -1 \\ 1 + e^{-t} \\ -2e^{-t} \end{bmatrix}.$$

Since $b_3 = b_2 - b_1$, we conclude that the system is separable. We pick β_1 to be $\beta_1 = \text{col}(0,0,1)$; hence

$$K(t) = \begin{bmatrix} 0 & -1 & 0 \\ -1 & -e^{-t} & 0 \\ -e^{-t} & -e^{-t} & 1 \end{bmatrix},$$

$$\dot{K} = \begin{bmatrix} 0 & 0 & 0 \\ 0 & -e^{-t} & 0 \\ -e^{-t} & e^{-t} & 0 \end{bmatrix},$$

$$K^{-1}(t) = \begin{bmatrix} -e^{-t} & -1 & 0 \\ -1 & 0 & 0 \\ e^{-2t} - e^{-t} & e^{-t} & 1 \end{bmatrix}.$$

For $H(t) = K^{-1}(t)A(t)K(t) - K^{-1}(t)\dot{K}(t)$ the reader can verify that

$$H(t) = \begin{bmatrix} 0 & 1 & 1 \\ -1 & -1 & 0 \\ 0 & 0 & e^{-t} \end{bmatrix}$$

Synthesis of Linear Time-Variable Systems, University of California Press, Berkeley, 1964, Ch. 6.

and that

$$K^{-1}\begin{bmatrix} 0 \\ -1 \\ e^{-t} \end{bmatrix} = \begin{bmatrix} 1 \\ 0 \\ 0 \end{bmatrix}.$$

Hence

$$\begin{bmatrix} \dot{x}_1 \\ \dot{x}_2 \\ \dot{x}_3 \end{bmatrix} = \begin{bmatrix} 0 & 1 & 1 \\ -1 & -1 & 0 \\ 0 & 0 & e^{-t} \end{bmatrix} \cdot \begin{bmatrix} x_1(t) \\ x_2(t) \\ x_3(t) \end{bmatrix} + \begin{bmatrix} 1 \\ 0 \\ 0 \end{bmatrix} u(t),$$

which separates into the two systems

$$\dot{x}_3(t) = e^{-t}x_3(t)$$

$$\begin{bmatrix} \dot{x}_1(t) \\ \dot{x}_2(t) \end{bmatrix} = \begin{bmatrix} 0 & 0 \\ -1 & -1 \end{bmatrix} + \begin{bmatrix} 1 \\ 0 \end{bmatrix} \cdot [u(t) + x_3(t)].$$

Stationary Case

As a summary for this section, let us consider a time-invariant system with a simple system matrix A. To be precise, assume that the first k vectors

$$\begin{aligned} b_1 &= b \\ b_2 &= -Ab_1 \\ &\vdots \\ b_k &= (-1)Ab_{k-1} = (-1)^{k-1}A^{k-1}b \end{aligned}$$

are linearly independent but that all other vectors in this sequence are dependent on $\{b_1, \ldots, b_k\}$.

Since A is to be a simple matrix with eigenvalues $\{\lambda_i\}$ and eigenvectors $\{u_i\}$, $i = 1, \ldots, n$, it follows that A has the spectral decomposition $A' = \sum_{i=1}^{n} e_i \rangle \lambda_i \langle e_i^+$. We know that, because $k < n$, $b_1, \ldots, b_k$ lie in some k-dimensional invariant subspace of A. All invariant subspaces of A, however, are spanned by some combination of the eigenvectors. For convenience we assume that the eigenvectors have been numbered so that the set $\{e_1, \ldots, e_k\}$ spans the subspace that contains $\{b_1, \ldots, b_k\}$. In other words, the manifolds $L(e_1, \ldots, e_k)$ and $L(b_1, \ldots, b_k)$ are identical.

In forming the matrix K, we take $\{b_1, \ldots, b_k\}$ as before as the first K columns. In choosing the remaining columns, however, we are a little more selective than previously and pick the eigenvectors $e_{k+1}, \ldots, e_n$. It is clear that

$$K = \begin{bmatrix} \uparrow & & \uparrow & \uparrow & & \uparrow \\ b_1, & \ldots, & b_k, & e_{k+1}, & \ldots, & e_n \\ \downarrow & & \downarrow & \downarrow & & \downarrow \end{bmatrix}$$

is a nonsingular matrix.

In the time stationary case the variable change $y = Kx$ yields the differential system

$$\dot{y}(t) = K^{-1}AKy(t) + K^{-1}bu(t),$$

and from the foregoing we see that

$$AK = \begin{bmatrix} \uparrow & & \uparrow & \uparrow & & \uparrow & & \uparrow \\ -b_2, & \ldots, & -b_k, & -b_{k+1}, & \lambda_{k+1}e_{k+1}, & \ldots, & \lambda_n e_n \\ \downarrow & & \downarrow & \downarrow & & \downarrow & & \downarrow \end{bmatrix}.$$

Hence, by direct multiplication,

$$K^{-1}AK = \left[\begin{array}{ccccc|cccc} 0 & & & 0 & -[b_1^+, b_{k+1}] & & & & \\ 1 & \nwarrow & & & & & & & \\ 0 & & \ddots & 0 & -[b_2^+, b_{k+1}] & & & 0 & \\ 0 & & & 0 & -[b_3^+, b_{k+1}] & & & & \\ \vdots & & & \ddots & \vdots & & & & \\ 0 & & 0 & \searrow 1 & -[b_k^+, b_{k+1}] & & & & \\ \hline & & & & & \lambda_{k+1} & 0 & \cdots & 0 \\ & & & & & 0 & \nwarrow & \ddots & \vdots \\ & & 0 & & & \vdots & & \ddots & 0 \\ & & & & & 0 & & 0 \searrow & \lambda_n \end{array} \right],$$

and, as before, $K^{-1}b = \mathrm{col}\,(1, 0, \ldots, 0)$; hence the system has been decomposed into a very simple form. It is important to note that this decomposition has been performed with knowledge only of the eigenvectors $e_1, \ldots, e_n$ of the matrix A.

Exercises

1. Let C be an $n \times n$ matrix. Is it possible for the transformation T_α of Remark 2 to be proper if the transformation T_α' is not? Can T_α

be proper if T'_α is not? Can the rank of the transformation T_α (respectively T'_α) decrease as the interval $[t_0, t_\alpha]$ is increased? Give a simple example for each answer. If C is an $m \times n$ matrix, do any of these answers change?

2. Show that the system

$$\dot{q}(t) = -A^*(t)q(t) - C^*(t)v(t), \qquad t \in \tau,$$

$$\lambda(t) = B^*(t)q(t) + D^*(t)v(t), \qquad t \in \tau, \tag{*}$$

is a formal adjoint of the system of Eqs. 1 and 2. What are the residual boundary conditions on u and v? HINT: See Exercises 4 and 5, Section 3.3. Develop the controllability and observability analogies that exist between a linear system and its formal adjoint.

3. Derive for a stationary, discrete, dynamic system the analog to Theorem A.

4. Let $x = Tu$ denote a system with two inputs, $u = (u_1, u_2)$. Clearly, transformations T_1 and T_2 exist such that

$$Tu = T_1 u_1 + T_2 u_2, \qquad \text{all } u.$$

If either T_1 or T_2 is proper, is T necessarily so? If T_1 and T_2 are both improper, is T necessarily so? What minimum condition on T_1 and T_2 will guarantee that T is proper?

5. If two subsystems are coupled in the fashion of the composite system of Figure 2.16, Section 2.5, what is the interdependence between subsystem and coupled-system observability and controllability?

6. Rederive the separability condition for stationary systems from the mode decomposition of Eqs. 8 and 9, Section 3.5. What can be said about observability for the stationary case?

7. Show that if $A(t)$, $t \in \tau$, is any square matrix satisfying the existence conditions of Theorem A, Section 2.4, and H is any stationary matrix of equal dimensions, the two systems

$$\dot{x}(t) = A(t)x(t), \qquad \dot{y}(t) = Hy(t), \qquad t \in \tau,$$

are equivalent for any *finite* τ. HINT: Use the change of variables $K(t) = \Phi(t, t_0) \exp[H(t - t_0)]$, $t \in \tau$, and the fact that $f(A)$ and A commute.

8. Show that if A is a periodic matrix [i.e., $A(t + \omega) = A(t)$, $t \in \tau$] with period ω the matrix $\Phi(t + \omega)$ is a fundamental matrix for Eq. 3 whenever $\Phi(t)$ is also. Show that $\Phi(t, t_0)$ may be written $\Phi(t, t_0) = M(t) \exp[B(t - t_0)] M(t_0)^{-1}$, in which $M(t)$ is periodic and nonsingular. HINT: Use Exercise 7. Show that if B is in Jordan form then M is unique.

9. Suppose that a design study has dictated the synthesis of the system $L_n(D,t)x(t) = M_q(D,t)u(t)$. The size of n,q however, suggests that a best approximation $\tilde{L}_m(D,t)x(t) = u(t)$, with $m = n - q$, be found. Develop a suitable approximation procedure. HINT: Bring the system equations to 1st-order form and perturb the forcing vector to decouple q of the system modes; then change variables to separate the system.

10. In the exercises of Section 3.4 the volume $V_n = 2\prod_{i=1}^{n}\mu_i$ associated with the polar form was introduced as a descriptor of sensitivity. If the T is not proper, then $\mu_i = 0$, some i, hence $V_n = 0$. Discuss the use of the artificial volume $V_n = 2\prod_{i=1}^{n}(\alpha + \mu_i)$ (here $0 < \alpha$, but small) as a measure of controllability of a system.

11. Let S denote the stationary $n \times n$ matrix

$$S = \begin{bmatrix} -a_{n-1} & 1 & 0 & 0 \\ \cdot & 0 & & \\ \cdot & & & 0 \\ \cdot & & & 1 \\ -a_0 & 0 & & 0 \end{bmatrix}.$$

Show that scalars $\beta = (\beta_0, \ldots, \beta_{n-1})$ can always be found so that the matrix $S' = S - [(0, \ldots, 0, 1)\rangle\langle\beta]$ has an arbitrarily determined spectrum $\sigma(A) = \{\lambda_1, \ldots, \lambda_n\}$ of complex values occurring in conjugate pairs. HINT: Use the change of variables T of Appendix 4 and the result of Exercise 11, Section 3.5. We may show that $\beta = T^{-1}\alpha$, where α is determined by this earlier exercise.

12. Prove that if the vector b is in general position with respect to the arbitrary matrix A then a feedback law $\mu(t) = \theta(t) - [\alpha,x(t)]$, with $\alpha = (\alpha_0, \ldots, \alpha_{n-1})$, exists such that the matrix $A = A - [b\rangle\langle\alpha]$ may be forced to take on any suitable spectral values $\sigma(A') = \{\lambda_1, \ldots, \lambda_n\}$. HINT: First use the matrix K of this section to bring A to the form of the final matrix of the section. Introduce a change of variables to bring this result to the form of S and then use the results of Exercise 11.

13. Reconsider Exercises 14, 15, and 16 of Section 3.2. Show that even when $\mathscr{F}(t_f,t)$ becomes singular on some subinterval $[t,t_f] \subset \tau$ the feedback law can be mechanized. HINT: Use Eq. 12 of Section 3.2 to show that the vector $[x(t_f) - \Phi(t_f,t)x(t)]$ is always in the range of $\mathscr{F}(t_f,t)$; hence a suitable left inverse can be used in place of $\mathscr{F}^{-1}(t_f,t)$.

3.7 REFERENCES FOR CHAPTER 3

As general references for Sections 3.1, 3.2, 3.3, and 3.4, Akhiezer and Glazman [A2], Dieudonné [A21], Dunford and Schwartz [A22], Halmos

[A36], Liusternik and Sobolev [A56], Lorch [A57], Riesz and Sz-Nagy [A72], Nirenberg [A65], and Taylor [A83] are recommended. A supplement to Section 3.3 may also be found in Appendix 5 of this book.

The dyad notation is used by Friedman [A30], Goertzel and Tralli [A32], and Zadeh and Desoer [A95]. The last reference also discusses the material of Section 3.5 and portions of Section 3.6. For information on the Jordan canonical form the reader should consider Halmos [A35], Hoffman and Kunze [A42], Nering [A64], and Stoll [A81]. The articles by Hochstadt [B48] and Frame [B36] are also recommended.

The topics of Section 3.6 are available in part in Tou [A86] and Zadeh and Desoer [A95] and in articles by Kalman [B50, B51], Kreindler and Sarachik [B64], Markus and Lee [B77], and Stubberud [B113]. The minimum energy problem is treated as well by Kalman [B53], Balakrishnan [B9], Kuo [B69], Porter [B99], and Tou [A86].

4 GEOMETRIC METHODS IN PROBLEMS OF OPTIMAL CONTROL

The class of engineering and mathematical problems that may be found under the title "problems of optimal control"[1] is both extensive and diverse. This diversity is reflected in the variety of techniques that exist for the solution of one or more of the problems in this class. Attention in this chapter is focused on a particular kind of optimal control problem and an associated technique of solution. The importance of this problem class stems from its impact on linear control theory and its close relationship with signal estimation and filtering problems. Because this chapter is theoretical in nature, it is important to make clear the relationship of the development to the physical problems that motivate the study. With this in mind, and before proceeding with technical matters, we shall discuss an important area of applications for the later results.

The control and guidance of an aerospace vehicle present a fruitful area for the application of modern control theory. Their success requires the interaction of several diverse phenomena, and the design of a system to accomplish the usual mission objectives is a complex task. In this discussion our interest is not in the guidance problem in the "large" but rather in the perturbation or vernier behavior of the system (see Figure 4.1). The working hypothesis is that, in the vicinity of the nominal guidance law and trajectory, small changes in the sensors, controls, and vehicle motions all interact according to a linearized version of the actual dynamic equation.

[1]This chapter is based on reference [B97], and I should like to take this opportunity to acknowledge with thanks the valued collaboration of James P. Williams in this earlier work and for his constructive remarks on the present chapter as well.

269

To be more explicit, consider the dynamic system that for any $t \geq t_0$ satisfies the equations

$$\dot{x}(t) = f(x(t), u(t), t), \qquad x(t_0) = x^0, \tag{1}$$

in which the tuplet $x = \mathrm{col}(x_1, \ldots, x_n)$ includes sufficient variables to describe the physical system behavior and the tuplet $u = \mathrm{col}(u_1, \ldots, u_m)$ denotes the set of system inputs. The function $f(x(t), u(t), t)$ denotes a vector-valued

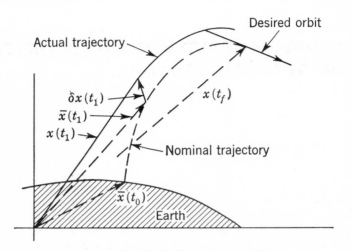

Figure 4.1   A missile guidance profile.

function of $x(t)$ and $u(t)$ with components $\{f_i(x(t), u(t), t)\}_1^n$. The tuplet $(\bar{u}, \bar{x})$ is used to represent a prescribed input and the corresponding solution to Eq. 1. In many cases the tuplet $(\bar{u}, \bar{x})$ will itself be a solution to a system optimization problem. However, in the present discussion only the fact that $(\bar{u}, \bar{x})$ is prescribed is used.

The statement that $(\bar{u}, \bar{x})$ is a nominal control-trajectory pair does not imply that the actual system when supplied with the input $\bar{u}$ will produce the response $\bar{x}$. Instead, $(\bar{u}, \bar{x})$ is a mathematical ideal. Inaccuracies in $\bar{u}$, environmental disturbances, uncertainties in the knowledge of $f(x, u, t)$, and miscellaneous system noise combine to cause the inevitable deviation from this nominal tuplet. Let $(\delta u, \delta x)$ denote the deviation of an actual tuplet (u, x) from the nominal value $(\bar{u}, \bar{x})$; that is, $(\delta u, \delta x) = (u, x) - (\bar{u}, \bar{x})$. Then, assuming that $(\delta u, \delta x)$ is small and that $f(\bar{x}(t), \bar{u}(t), t)$ is sufficiently smooth with respect to $(\bar{u}, \bar{x})$, a standard application of Taylor's expansion of $f(x, u, t)$ about the point $(\bar{u}, \bar{x})$ shows that $(\delta u, \delta x)$ satisfies, to a first-order approximation, the equation

$$\delta \dot{x}(t) = A(t)\delta x(t) + B(t)\delta u(t), \qquad \delta x(t_0) = \delta x^0, \tag{2}$$

where the (i,j) elements of the matrices $A(t)$ and $B(t)$ are the partials $\partial f_i/\partial x_j$ and $\partial f_i/\partial u_j$, respectively, evaluated along $(\bar{u},\bar{x})$. Thus any study dealing with the performance of guidance systems in the vicinity of a nominal trajectory leads naturally to the study of classes of continuous and/or discrete, linear, dynamic systems.

As a practical matter, the perturbation δu is to be selected to produce a desired effect in δx (e.g., drive δx to zero). More often than not it is desirable to accomplish this objective in some optimum manner. For instance, although the criterion for defining $(\bar{u},\bar{x})$ may have been quite complex, the finite supply of onboard fuel may dictate a perturbation control strategy that minimizes a functional J on δu.

For example, if $\delta u_j(t)$, $t \in [t_0,t_f]$, represents the instantaneous fuel flow rate for the jth system actuator, then

$$J_1(\delta u) = \int_{t_0}^{t_f} \sum_{j=1}^{m} |\delta u_j(t)| dt$$

represents the total fuel associated with the control δu. In other cases the energy

$$J_2(\delta u) = \left[\int_{t_0}^{t_f} \sum_{j=1}^{m} |\delta u_j(t)|^2 dt \right]^{1/2},$$

rather than the fuel associated with δu, may be the important quantity. Physical actuators frequently exhibit saturation, which imposes peak limitations on outputs. The maximum amplitude

$$J_3(\delta u) = \max_{1 \le j \le m} \left\{ \sup_{t_0 \le t \le t_f} |\delta u_j(t)| \right\},$$

taken on by all controls $\{\delta u_j\}$, may therefore appear in the analysis. Finally, if the rocket engine is total-thrust-limited (as it is in "solar-sail" or "ion" engines) and the functions $\{\delta u_j\}$ represent thrust direction cosines, the peak instantaneous total thrust

$$J_4(\delta u) = \sup_{t_1 \le t \le t_f} \left[\sum_{j=1}^{m} |\delta u_j(t)|^2 \right]^{1/2}$$

is a natural criterion for optimizing the choice of δu.

In each of these four cases the functional in question can be identified as the norm on B, an appropriate Banach space. Furthermore, Eq. 2 defines a linear transformation defined on B. Thus, without distinguishing between discrete, composite, or continuous systems (which have provided the vehicle for our example, we now formulate an optimization problem.

Problem 1. Let B and D be Banach spaces and T, a bounded linear transformation defined on B with values in D. For each ξ in the range of T

find an element $u \in B$ that satisfies

$$\xi = Tu$$

while minimizing the performance index

$$J(u) = \|u\|.$$

Problem 1 is an obvious generalization from a Hilbert space to a Banach space setting of the minimum energy problem of Section 3.2. For each ξ in the range of T consider the set $T^{-1}(\xi)$ of all preimages of ξ. As in the earlier analysis, these questions are of evident interest. Does this set contain an element of minimum norm? If so, is this element unique? Finally, if both answers are yes and if we write $T^{\dagger}\xi$ for the unique minimum preimage of a vector ξ in the range of T, what is the nature of the function $T^{\dagger}$ so defined and, more specifically, how can we compute its values?

The difficulties to be faced in carrying out this generalization are not to be taken lightly. Consider, for instance, the single variate system which sends the Hilbert space H into R and is defined by

$$\xi = \langle f, u \rangle, \qquad u \in H.$$

If $\xi \in R$ is fixed, the preimage of ξ with minimum norm is unique and may be explicitly determined. In contrast, if B is an arbitrary Banach space and $f \in B^{*}$, then for $\xi \in R$ it is *not* true that a minimum norm preimage under f of ξ need exist and, even if it does, it is not necessarily unique. Two examples exhibit these characteristics in turn.

Example 1. Let C denote the set of all real- or complex-valued continuous functions on the interval $0 \le t \le 1$ which vanishes at $t = 0$. It is easy to see that C is a closed subspace of the usual Banach space of continuous functions on $[0,1]$ and therefore is a Banach space. If T is the transformation (linear functional) defined for $u \in C$ by

$$Tu = \int_{0}^{1} u(t)dt,$$

then

$$|Tu| \le \sup_{0 \le t \le 1} |u(t)| = \|u\|,$$

so that $\|T\| \le 1$. It follows that if $u \in C$ satisfies $Tu = 1$ then $1 = |Tu| \le \|u\|$. On the other hand, it can be verified that

$$\inf\{\|u\| : Tu = 1\} = 1$$

and that this infimum is not attained. Indeed, for any $u \in C$ of norm 1 there is a $\delta > 0$ such that $|u(t)| < \frac{1}{2}$ if $0 \le t \le \delta$ and it follows that

$$|Tu| = |\int_0^\delta u(t)dt + \int_\delta^1 u(t)dt| \le \frac{1}{2} \cdot \delta + (1-\delta) \cdot 1 = 1 - \frac{\delta}{2} < 1.$$

We conclude that the vector (number) 1 has no minimum preimage under T.

Example 2. Let B denote the plane equipped with the norm

$$\|x\| = |x_1| + |x_2| \quad \text{if} \quad x = (x_1, x_2).$$

On B we define the linear transformation T by

$$Tx = x_1 + x_2.$$

It is obvious that $\|T\| = 1$ and hence that any $x \in B$ satisfying $Tx = 1$ has norm ≥ 1. It also follows that *both* vectors $(0,1)$ and $(1,0)$ are minimum preimages of 1 under T.

In short, the minimum effort function $T^\dagger$ associated with T can fail to exist by virtue of a lack or an overabundance of minimum preimages. Because these difficulties exist for such simple transformations as the functionals of Examples 1 and 2, it is apparent that their sources must be determined. Therefore it is necessary to learn a little more about the geometric properties of Banach spaces. This we accomplish (along with the study of $T^\dagger$ when T is of rank 1) in Sections 4.1 and 4.2.

Once these preliminaries are disposed of, the chapter then proceeds to the general study of Problem 1. Extensions of the basic problem are given in Section 4.4 and Appendix 8. Applications of the basic theory take the form of examples and exercises throughout the chapter and in Appendices 8 and 9. A summary of related literature is part of Section 4.5.

4.1 SOME GEOMETRIC NOTIONS

In dealing with optimal control problems, several concepts of a geometric nature are necessary. The reader will find that in most cases the abstract definitions are apparent generalizations of statements about sets in R^2 and R^3. We emphasize this intuitive connection by using planar or three-dimensional diagrams wherever it seems fruitful to do so.

The first few concepts are meaningful in any linear space X with the associated (real or complex) scalars K. Let Q and S denote subsets of B. The vector sum of Q and S is defined by

$$Q + S = \{x : x = q + s, s \in S, q \in Q\}.$$

In particular, if $x_0 \in X$, the set

$$x_0 + Q = \{x : x = x_0 + q, q \in Q\}$$

is called a *translation* of Q along x_0. The scalar multiple αS of a set S with scalar $\alpha \in K$ is defined by

$$\alpha S = \{x : x = \alpha s, s \in S\},$$

and, more generally, if K' is a subset of K, the set $K'S$ is defined by

$$K'S = \{x : x = \alpha s, \alpha \in K', s \in S\}.$$

DEFINITION A. *Let S be a subset of X and $E = \{\alpha : |\alpha| \leq 1, \alpha \in K\}$. Then*
  (1) *S is called* symmetric *if $S = (-1)\,S$,*
  (2) *S is called* circled *if $ES \subset S$,*
  (3) *S is called* absorbing *if for each $x \subset X$ an $\varepsilon > 0$ exists such that $\alpha x \in S$ if $0 < |\alpha| \leq \varepsilon$.*

Since $\alpha = -1$ is in the set E, all circled sets are symmetric and contain 0. An equivalent formulation for (3) is the following: S is absorbing if for each $x \in X$ a $\beta > 0$ exists, such that $x \in \alpha S$ if $|\alpha| \geq \beta$. Note also that by definition each absorbing set must contain 0. Figure 4.2(a) represents in the

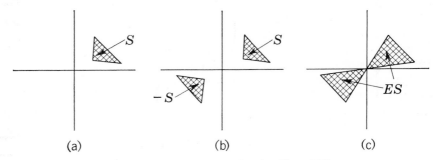

(a)   (b)   (c)

Figure 4.2 The sets S, $S \cup (-S)$, and ES.

space R^2 a set S that is neither symmetric nor circled. In Figure 4.2(b) the set $S \cup (-S)$ is shown. Notice that the set $S \cup (-S)$ is a symmetric but not a circled set. Figure 4.2(c) represents the set ES.

It is obvious that the intersection of circled sets is a circled set. The *circled hull* of S is the intersection of all circled sets containing S, and it is not difficult to show that the circled hull of any set S is precisely ES.

The *line segment* joining any two points x, $y \in X$ is the set of all points of the form $\lambda x + (1 - \lambda)y$ with $0 \leq \lambda \leq 1$. This set is denoted by $[x{:}y]$. The open-ended line segment $(x{:}y)$ denotes the same set minus the end points x, y (i.e., $0 < \lambda < 1$). The sets $(x{:}y]$ and $[x{:}y)$ are defined in the obvious manner. An alternative definition for an absorbing set is: *a set S is absorbing if S contains a line segment in every direction;* that is, for every $z \in X$, $y \neq 0$ such that $[0{:}y] \subset [0{:}z] \cap S$.

DEFINITION B.   *A set S in the space X is said to be convex if whenever x, y ∈ S then [x:y] ⊂ S.*

Clearly, any subspace is convex. By a simple computation it follows that any translate of a convex set is convex. Similarly, any intersection of convex sets is convex. The union of convex sets, however, may not be convex. Since X is convex, the family of all convex sets containing a given set $S \subset X$ is not void. The intersection of all members of this family is called the *convex hull* of S and denoted by S_c. Evidently S_c is the smallest convex set

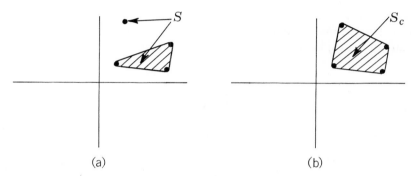

$$(a) \qquad\qquad (b)$$

Figure 4.3   A set and its convex hull.

containing S. Figure 4.3 describes a set S and its convex hull S_c. The following theorem summarizes some additional properties of convex sets.

THEOREM A.   *Let X denote a linear space. Then*
   (1)   *for any subset $S \subset X$, the convex hull of S is given by*

$$S_c = \left\{ x : x = \sum_i \alpha_i x_i, \, x_i \in S, \, \alpha_i \geq 0, \, \sum_i \alpha_i = 1 \right\};$$

   (2)   *if S is convex and α, β positive, $\alpha S + \beta S = (\alpha + \beta)S$;*
   (3)   *if S and Q are nonvoid subsets and λ and γ are scalars, $(\lambda S + \gamma Q)_c = \lambda S_c + \gamma Q_c$;*
   (4)   *if S and Q are nonvoid subsets, $(S \cup Q)_c = \bigcup \{[x:y] : x \in S_c, y \in Q_c\}$.*

The proof of Theorem A is left for the exercises. In Theorem B we examine some elementary properties of convex sets in a Banach space.

THEOREM B.   *Let S be a subset of the Banach space B. Then*
   (1)   *if S is convex, its closure $\bar{S}$ and its interior int (S) are convex sets;*
   (2)   *if S is open, S_c is open.*

P R O O F.   Recall that the operations of addition and scalar multiplication are continuous; that is, if $x_n \to x$ and $y_n \to y$, then $x_n + y_n \to x + y$ and

$\alpha x_n \to \alpha x$. This observation shows that for any subsets S, T of B

$$\bar{S} + \bar{T} \subset \overline{(S + T)},$$

$$\alpha \bar{S} \subset \overline{(\alpha S)}.$$

A set S is convex if and only if $\alpha S + (1 - \alpha)S \subset S$ whenever $0 < \alpha < 1$; hence, if S is convex,

$$\alpha \bar{S} + (1 - \alpha)\bar{S} \subset \overline{(\alpha S + (1 - \alpha)S)} \subset \bar{S};$$

that is, $\bar{S}$ is also convex.

To determine that the interior of a convex set S *is* convex take $x, y \in \text{int}(S)$. We can find two spherical neighborhoods (Figure 4.4) in which

$$\{z \in B: \|z - x\| < \varepsilon\} \subset S,$$

$$\{z \in B: \|z - y\| < \varepsilon\} \subset S.$$

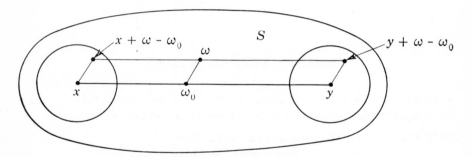

Figure 4.4   The interior of S is convex.

If w_0 is a point of the open segment $(x:y)$, for some $0 < \alpha < 1$, we have $w_0 = \alpha x + (1 - \alpha)y$. It suffices to show that if $\|w - w_0\| < \varepsilon$ then $w \in S$. This, however, follows from the identity

$$w = (1 - \alpha)(y + w - w_0) + \alpha(x + w - w_0)$$

and the fact that $y + w - w_0$ and $x + w - w_0$ belong to S.

Finally, (2) follows from (1). Indeed, if S is open, then $S \subset S_c$ implies $\text{int}(S) = S \subset \text{int}(S_c)$. By (1), however, $\text{int}(S_c)$ is convex, and since S_c is the smallest convex set containing S this means that $S_c \subset \text{int}(S_c)$; hence S_c is open.

DEFINITION C.   *Let X denote a linear space and S an absorbing convex set. The function p whose value at $x \in X$ is given by*

$$p(x) = \inf \{\lambda > 0: x \in \lambda S\}$$

is called the Minkowski functional of the set S.

We may interpret this definition as follows: if x is any point of X, the one-dimensional subspace $L(x)$ intersects the boundary ∂S of S at a point y (Figure 4.5). Then $x = p(x)y$. In other words, $p(x)$ is the amount of expansion (or shrinkage) of the set S necessary to bring x to the boundary ∂S.

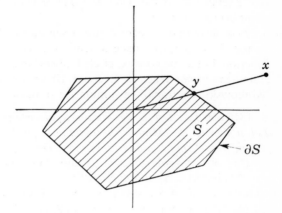

Figure 4.5 A set and its Minkowski functional.

It follows from the fact that S is absorbing that $p(x)$ is defined and finite for each $x \in X$. Note also that the equation $p(x) = 0$ expresses the fact that the entire ray $\{\alpha x: a > 0\}$ belongs to S. In particular, if X is a normed space and S is a *bounded set* (i.e., if the numbers $\|z\|$ for $z \in S$ form a bounded subset of the real axis), then $p(x) = 0$ can hold only for $x = 0$.

THEOREM C.   *Let S be a convex absorbing set in the linear space X. Then*
    (1) $p(0) = 0$, $p(\lambda x) = \lambda p(x)$,   *if $\lambda > 0$;*
    (2) $p(x + y) \leq p(x) + p(y)$; *and, if the set S is circled,*
    (3) $p(\lambda x) = |\lambda| p(x)$ *holds for any scalar λ.*

P R O O F .   Since $0 \in S$, $p(0) = 0$ is self-evident. To prove the second part of (1) take $x \in X$ and a fixed scalar $\lambda > 0$. Then

$$p(\lambda x) = \inf \{\alpha > 0: \lambda x \in \alpha S\} = \inf \{\beta \lambda > 0: \lambda x \in \beta \lambda S\}$$

$$= \lambda \inf \{\beta > 0: x \in \beta S\} = \lambda p(x).$$

To prove (2) fix $x, y \in X$ and suppose $x \in \alpha S$. Then $x + y \in \alpha S + \beta S = (\alpha + \beta)S$, so that $p(x + y) \leq \alpha + \beta$. Hence $p(x + y) \leq \inf\{\alpha + \beta: x \in \alpha S\} = p(x) + \beta$ and, finally, $p(x + y) \leq p(x) + p(y)$.

If S is circled, then $(\lambda/|\lambda|)x \in \beta S$ if and only if $x \in \beta S$. Hence

$$p(\lambda x) = \inf \{\alpha > 0: \lambda x \in \alpha S\} = \inf \left\{|\lambda|\beta > 0: \frac{\lambda}{|\lambda|} |\lambda| x \in \beta |\lambda| S\right\}$$

$$= |\lambda| \inf \left\{\beta > 0: \frac{\lambda}{|\lambda|} x \in \beta S\right\} = |\lambda| p(x)$$

which completes the proof.

A non-negative function p which satisfies (2) and (3) is called a *seminorm*. Theorem C asserts that if S is a convex-circled and absorbing set in X its Minkowski functional is a seminorm. The converse is also true: each seminorm is the Minkowski functional of some convex-circled absorbing set (see Exercise 4). If f is a linear functional on X, the $p(x) = |f(x)|$ defines a seminorm p on X.

It is clear that a norm is just a seminorm that vanishes only at the zero vector. In a Banach space a seminorm is a norm if it is the Minkowski functional of some convex, circled, absorbing, and *bounded* set. The converse statement is *not* true, as Exercise 10 shows. In our final theorem on the Minkowski functional we summarize some additional properties.

THEOREM D. *Let S be a convex absorbing set in the Banach space B. Let p denote the Minkowski functional of S and define the subsets $S_1 = \{x : p(x) < 1\}$ and $S_2 = \{x : p(x) \le 1\}$. Then*

   (1) $p(x) \le 1$ whenever $x \in \bar{S}$ and $p(x) < 1 \Rightarrow x \in S$;
   (2) $\text{int}(S) \subset S_1 \subset S \subset S_2 \subset \bar{S}$;
   (3) $S = S_1$ if S is open, $S = S_2$ if S is closed;
   (4)   if p is continuous, $S_1 = \text{int}(S)$ and $S_2 = \bar{S}$;
   (5) p is continuous if and only if $0 \in \text{int}(S)$.

A convex set $V \subset X$ is called a *cone* with vertex at the origin if, for every $x \in V$, $\alpha x \in V$ for all $\alpha > 0$; that is, the cone V contains the entire half ray $\{\alpha x : \alpha > 0\}$ which passes through each of its points. V_0 is a cone with vertex at the point $y \in X$ if $-y + V_0$ is a cone at the origin. If V is a cone at the origin, x, $y \in V$ must imply that $\alpha x + \beta y \in V$ for all α, $\beta > 0$, as the reader can easily show. Furthermore, if S is any convex set, $V = \bigcup_{\alpha > 0}(\alpha S)$ is the smallest cone at the origin containing S.

Consideration of convex sets in the plane shows that the "corners" are important points. Indeed a triangle is completely determined by three points and a rectangle by four. If we analyze this situation in more detail, we see that the "corners" determine these sets in the sense that the sets are precisely the convex hull of these points. Moreover, the corners can be identified as the only points of the set not contained in any line segment that is itself wholly contained in the set. As a generalization of this notion, we have Definition D.

DEFINITION D. *A point x in a convex set S is an extreme point of S if there is no open segment $(y : z)$ in S that contains x.*

In other words, $x \in S$ is an extreme point of S if the relations

$$x = \alpha y + (1 - \alpha)z, \qquad 0 < \alpha < 1$$

imply $x = y = z$. In the plane a triangle, rectangle, and disk share the property of being the convex hull of their corresponding sets of extreme points. (The extreme points of a disk are the points on the perimeter.) On the other hand, the closed upper half plane, although certainly convex, has no extreme points, hence lacks this property.

THEOREM E (Krein-Milman).   *If S is a convex compact[1] set in B, then S has extreme points. Moreover, S is the closure of the convex hull of the set of its extreme points.*

Thus, if $x \in S$, we can approximate x arbitrarily well by points of the form $\sum_i \alpha_i x_i$, where $\sum_i \alpha_i = 1$, $\alpha_i \geq 0$, and the x_i are extreme points of S.

The Krein-Milman theorem evidently can be applied to the problem of finding a "small" subset of a compact convex set which determines it completely. It also has another significant application. A theorem due to Alaoglu[2] asserts that the unit ball U^* in the dual B^* of the Banach space B is compact in a certain topology. Since U^* evidently is convex, it follows from the Krein-Milman theorem that U^* is the closure (in the appropriate topology) of the set of its extreme points. We thus unexpectedly obtain the following bonus: if E is a Banach space whose unit ball has no extreme points, then E is not the dual of *any* Banach space. For example, the spaces c_0 and $L_1(\tau)$ are not the duals of any Banach space and hence are not reflexive.

Example.   The extreme points of the unit ball U in l_∞ are the points $x = (\alpha_1 \alpha_2, \dots)$ for which $|\alpha_i| = 1$, $i = 1, 2, \dots$.

P R O O F.   Observe first that an extreme point of a unit ball in any Banach space must have norm 1. Indeed, if $\|x\| < 1$, there exists a scalar $\alpha > 1$ such that αx still has norm < 1 and

$$x = \left\{ 1 - \frac{1}{\alpha} \right\} 0 + \frac{1}{\alpha} (\alpha x),$$

so that x is contained in the segment $(0; \alpha x) = U$.

Thus in l_∞ an extreme point has the form $x = (\alpha_1, \alpha_2, \dots)$ with $\sup |\alpha_i| = 1$. We are to show that x is extreme if and only if no $|\alpha_i| < 1$. Necessity is easy, for example, if $|\alpha_1| < 1$, then α_1 is not an extreme point of the unit disk in the complex plane and therefore there are complex numbers $\beta_1 \neq \gamma_1$ of modulus ≤ 1 and a number $0 < \lambda < 1$ with

$$\alpha_1 = \lambda \beta_1 + (1 - \lambda) \gamma_1.$$

---

[1]See Appendix 1.

[2]Although "topologies" are not discussed in this book, we shall on occasion state results that are relevant but inaccessible without this background. The availability of several lucid treatments (see [A54], [A58], [A77], [A83] and [B104]) does much to alleviate this hardship and may perhaps be fruitfully consulted during the second reading. Alaoglu's theorem as a case in point may be found in [A22, Sec. V.4.1].

By putting

$$y = (\beta_1, \alpha_2, \alpha_3, \dots),$$

$$z = (\gamma_1, \alpha_2, \alpha_3, \dots),$$

we have $x = \lambda y + (1 - \lambda)z$ and $y \neq z \in U$.

Conversely, suppose that $|\alpha_i| = 1$ for all i and let $x = \lambda y + (1 - \lambda)z$ for some $0 < \lambda < 1$ with $y, z \in U$, say, $y = (\eta_1, \eta_2, \dots)$ and $z = (\zeta_1, \zeta_2, \dots)$. Then $\alpha_1 = \lambda \eta_1 + (1 - \lambda)\zeta_1$ and, since α_1 is an extreme point of the unit disk in the complex plane, this relation implies $\eta_1 = \zeta_1$. Similarly, $\eta_i = \zeta_i$, $i = 2, 3, \dots$, and it follows that $y = z$. Hence x must be an extreme point of U.

Separation Properties

Let X denote a linear space and L a proper subspace of X. The translate $M = x_0 + L$ of the subspace L along x_0 is called a *linear flat*. We first observe that the specification of a linear flat is by no means unique. Indeed, if $M = x_0 + L$, and $z \in M$, then for each $l \in L$, $z + l = x_0 + l + (2 - x_0)$; and since $z - x_0 \in L$, it is clear that M may equally well be written as the translate $M = z + L$. In R^2 a linear flat is either a point or a straight line (not necessarily through the origin). In R^3 the linear flats are planes, lines, or points.

A subspace L of X is said to have *codimension* k if there are k linearly independent elements $x_1, \dots, x_k$ of X that are disjoint from L and the set $\{x_1, \dots, x_k, L\}$ spans X. If L has codimension 1, then L is said to be a *maximal subspace*. In other words, L is maximal if there is no proper subspace L' of X such that $L \nsubseteq L'$. In R^2 the maximal subspaces are lines through the origin; in R^2 the planes through the origin are maximal subspaces. In any Hilbert space H with $x \in H$ the orthogonal complement of the linear subspace spanned by x is a maximal subspace.

THEOREM F. *The null space of every nonzero linear functional on X is a maximal subspace. Conversely every maximal subspace of X is the null space of a linear functional on X.*

PROOF. Let $L \subset X$ be a subspace of codimension 1. Then $y \in X$ exists such that $y \notin L$ and $\{y, L\}$ spans X. Every $x \in X$ has a unique representation $x = \alpha y + l$ for some scalar α and $l \in L$. (Uniqueness follows from the fact that X is the direct sum of L and the manifold spanned by y.) We can now define a linear functional f on X by the condition

$$f(x) = \alpha \quad \text{if} \quad x = \alpha y + l.$$

Clearly, f is linear, $f(l) = 0$ if and only if $l \in L$ and $f(y) = 1$; thus the second part of Theorem D is proved. Now let $f \neq 0$ be an arbitrary linear functional on X. The null space of f is a linear subspace and it remains to show only that it has codimension 1. Let $y' \in X$ be such that $f(y') \neq 0$; then $y = y'/f(y')$ has the property $f(y) = 1$. It follows that $\{y, N_f\}$ spans X, for if $x \in X$ and $\alpha = f(x)$ then

$$x - \alpha y \in N_f$$

and

$$x = (x - \alpha y) + \alpha y.$$

COROLLARY 1. *If L is a linear subspace of codimension k, there are k linearly independent functionals $f_1, \ldots, f_k$ on X such that*

$$L = \bigcap_{i=1}^{k} N_{f_i}.$$

The proof is left as an exercise.

A translation of a maximal subspace is called a *hyperplane*. For efficient notation maximal subspaces are also called hyperplanes (through the origin). In dealing with hyperplanes, we find the following corollary of Theorem C useful.

COROLLARY 2. *If f is a nonzero functional on X and α an arbitrary scalar, the set $\{x : f(x) = \alpha\}$ is a hyperplane. Conversely, each hyperplane M not containing 0 can be written $M = \{x : f(x) = 1\}$ for a unique functional $f \neq 0$.*

PROOF. The theorem shows that the hyperplanes in X are translates of null spaces of linear functionals on X, hence of the form $\{x : f(x) = \alpha\}$. The uniqueness assertion follows from the fact that if f and g are linear functionals with $\{x : f(x) = 1\} = \{x : g(x) = 1\} = M$, then f and g are identically equal.

REMARK 1. If M is a hyperplane through the origin of the Banach space B, then, because $M \subset \bar{M} \subset B$, it is clear that either $M = \bar{M}$ or $\bar{M} = B$. It can be shown that M is closed if and only if the functional f associated with M is bounded. Thus a hyperplane comes equipped with a functional that is bounded whenever the hyperplane is closed and conversely.

It is helpful to consider a specific example in the real space $X = R^2$. If u is any vector in R^2, M_0 defined by

$$M_0 = \{x : f(x) = \langle x, u \rangle = 0\}$$

is the line through the origin whose normal is u (Figure 4.6). Consequently, if $x_1 \notin M_0$, the hyperplane

$$M = \{x_1 + z : z \in M_0\} = x_1 + M_0$$

is a line parallel to M_0. M obviously divides E^2 into two open half spaces

S_1 and S_2. It is clear from the figure that if $x \in S_1$ then x can be written

$$x = m + ku, \qquad m \in M, \qquad k > 0.$$

Similarly, if $y \in S_2$, then y may be expressed

$$y = m + ku, \qquad m \in M, \qquad k < 0.$$

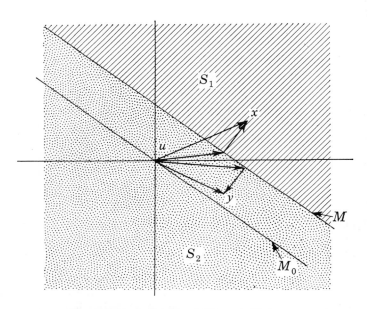

Figure 4.6   A division of R^2 into half spaces.

Thus the half spaces S_1 and S_2 may be defined by

$$S_1 = \{x : f(x) > \alpha\}, \qquad S_2 = \{x : f(x) < \alpha\},$$

where f is the linear functional $f(x) = \langle x, u \rangle$.

This two-dimensional result carries over to the more general setting. If $M = \{x : f(x) = \alpha\}$ is a hyperplane in the real linear space X, each of the sets

$$\{x : f(x) < \alpha\}, \qquad \{x : f(x) > \alpha\}, \qquad \{x : f(x) \le \alpha\}, \qquad \{x : f(x) \ge \alpha\}$$

is convex and is called a *half space* determined by M. If $X = B$ is a Banach space and f is continuous, then M is closed, and the first two of these half spaces are open and the last two are closed.

We shall say that a set S lies on one side of the hyperplane M if S lies entirely in one of the four half spaces determined by M. If S lies on one side of M and $S \cap M = \varnothing$, we say that S lies *strictly* on one side of M. Two sets

S, Q of *X* are said to be *separated* by a hyperplane *M* if they lie in opposite half spaces defined by the hyperplane. Thus *M* separates *S* and *Q* whenever $f(x) \leq \alpha$ for $x \in S$ and $f(x) \geq \alpha$ for $x \in Q$.

In Section 3.2 the Hahn-Banach theorem (Theorem C) was given in its analytic form. In that context this theorem deals with the extension of linear functionals defined on a subspace to the whole space while preserving or satisfying certain properties. The Hahn-Banach theorem also has two geometric forms that reveal more fully the important role played by this theorem in analysis. For completeness we now state the three equivalent forms of this theorem.

THEOREM G (HB Analytic Form). *Let X be a linear space, L a subspace of X, and p a seminorm on X. If f is a linear functional on L such that*

$$|f(x)| \leq p(x), \qquad x \in L,$$

then f has a linear extension $\tilde{f}$ onto X such that $|\tilde{f}(x)| \leq p(x)$ for all $x \in X$.

THEOREM H (HB Geometric Form). *Let S be an open convex set of the (real or complex) Banach space B, and let N be a linear flat that is disjoint from S. Then a closed hyperplane M exists which contains N and is disjoint from S.*

THEOREM I (HB Separation Form). *Let S, Q be convex sets in the real Banach space B. If int (S) $\neq \varnothing$ and int (S) $\cap$ Q $= \varnothing$, then a closed hyperplane M exists which separates S and Q.*

Although we shall not go into details here regarding the proof of the equivalence of the three theorems (see Exercise 8), some remarks should be made. First, in the geometric version it is essential that *S* be open. For example, in R^2, if *S* is the union of the open upper half plane and the point (1,0) and *Q* is the origin, no hyperplane of separation can exist.

COROLLARY. *Each closed convex set Q is the intersection of all the closed half spaces which contain Q.*

P R O O F.   It suffices to show that if $x \notin Q$ there is a half space *H* containing *Q* with $x \notin H$. This, however, follows from the separation theorem, for by hypothesis there is an open ball *S* about *x* that does not meet *Q*.

Let *A* be a convex set and *M*, a hyperplane; then *M* is called a support plane for *A* (more properly a *hyperplane of support* for *A*) if either $A \subset \{x: f(x) \geq \alpha\}$ or $A \subset \{x: f(x) \leq \alpha\}$ and $A \cap M \neq \varnothing$. In nontechnical terms *M* is a support plane for *A* if their intersection is nonvoid and *A* lies on one side of *M*. A closed convex set with a nonvacuous interior is called a *convex body*. Taking $Q = x_0 \in \partial A$ and $S = \text{int}(S)$, we find that the separation theorem implies the important result that every boundary point of a convex body has a closed hyperplane of support passing through it.

Figure 4.7 depicts a convex body in R^2. It is sometimes helpful to visualize the functional f associated with a hyperplane of support as an outward normal to the convex body at the point of support. Indeed, it is sometimes convenient to call f a *support normal*. In general, a point of support may have several distinct hyperplanes of support. In Figure 4.7 the point x_1 has a cone of support normals. Furthermore, distinct boundary points can have the same

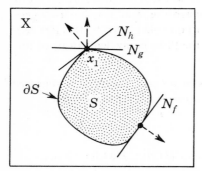
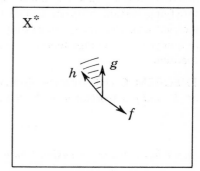

Figure 4.7   A set and its support hyperplanes.

hyperplane of support. It is made clear in the figure that if two distinct boundary points share a hyperplane of support then, by the convexity of the set, the entire line segment between the two points must of necessity lie in the hyperplane in question.

*Complex Spaces

Given a complex linear space X, we can always construct an associated *real* linear space X_0 by taking the vectors of X_0 as the vectors of X but allowing multiplication by real scalars only. Some concepts (e.g., the notion of a convex set) are the same in X as in X_0, whereas others are not. For example, any subspace of X is a subspace of X_0 but the converse is false. For a subspace M of X_0 to be a subspace of X it is necessary and sufficient that $iM \subset M$. Similarly, a circled subset of X_0 need not be a circled subset of X.

Other concepts are also affected by the passage from X to X_0. If X is n-dimensional, then X_0 is $2n$-dimensional. Thus, if $\{e_1, e_2, \ldots, e_n\}$ is a maximal set of independent vectors in X, the vectors $\{e_1, e_2, \ldots, e_n, ie_1, ie_2, \ldots, ie_n\}$ will form a maximal independent subset of X. This is familiar in the case of the plane that is a one-dimensional complex space X (spanned by multiples of 1) or a two-dimensional real space X_0 (spanned by 1 and i).

Any linear functional on X is a linear functional on X_0, but, again, a linear functional f on X_0 need not be linear when it is regarded as acting on X. Because the vectors in X and X_0 are the same, additivity of f is preserved, but homogeneity acquires a stronger meaning in passing from X_0 to X.

*Starred sections may be bypassed on first reading.

It is worthwhile to consider this point in some detail. Let f be a linear functional on X. Then, for each $x \in X$, $f(x)$ is a complex number, and we may separate its real and imaginary parts in the usual way to obtain a pair of real-valued functions such that

$$f(x) = f_0(x) + ig_0(x), \qquad x \in X.$$

Thus f_0 and g_0 are defined for each $x \in X_0$ and are real-valued. We assert also that they are both linear functionals on X_0. For $x, y \in X_0$ we have

$$f(x + y) = f_0(x + y) + ig_0(x + y),$$

$$f(x) + f(y) = [f_0(x) + f_0(y)] + i[g_0(x) + g_0(y)],$$

by definition of f_0, g_0, and, since f is additive, the real and imaginary parts of these expressions agree. Thus f_0 and g_0 are additive.   Next for any real scalar α

$$f(\alpha x) = f_0(\alpha x) + ig_0(\alpha x),$$

$$\alpha f(x) = [\alpha f_0(x)] + i[\alpha g_0(x)],$$

hence

$$f_0(\alpha x) = \operatorname{Re} f(\alpha x) = \operatorname{Re} \alpha f(x) = \alpha f_0(x),$$

$$g_0(\alpha x) = \operatorname{Im} f(\alpha x) = \operatorname{Im} \alpha f(x) = \alpha g_0(x),$$

and so f_0, g_0 are also homogeneous functions on X_0. Finally, note the relationship between f_0 and g_0:

$$-g_0(x) = if_0(x) = if(x) = f(ix) = f_0(ix) + ig_0(ix)$$

implies

$$g_0(x) = -f_0(ix), \qquad f_0(x) = g_0(ix),$$

and we really get only one linear functional on X_0, from f.

The preceding paragraph also tells us how to pass from a linear functional f_0 on X_0 to a linear functional f on X. Indeed, the formula

$$f(x) = f_0(x) - if_0(ix)$$

defines a complex-valued functional on X, and we leave it to the reader to prove that f is additive and homogeneous with respect to complex scalars.

THEOREM J.   *Let X be a complex linear space and X_0 the associated real linear space. There is then a one-to-one correspondence $f \leftrightarrow f_0$ between linear functionals on X and linear functionals on X_0. This correspondence is given by*

$$f(x) = f_0(x) - if_0(ix).$$

If $X = B$ is a Banach space, then B_0 becomes a normed space simply by defining the norm of a vector x in B_0 as the norm of x regarded as an element of B. B_0 is clearly complete. Moreover, if $x_n \to 0$ in B_0 then, since $\|ix_n\| = \|x_n\|$, it follows that $ix_n \to 0$ in B_0. Thus $g_0(x) = -if_0(ix)$ is continuous whenever f_0 is continuous. This, together with the fact that a complex function is continuous if and only if its real and imaginary parts are continuous, shows that $f \in B^*$ if and only if $f_0 \in B_0^*$.

Finally, although the proper setting of the separation theorem is a *real* Banach space, it can be stated for complex spaces B by using the simple device of replacing B with its associated real space B_0 and then performing the desired separation in B_0. The result is a real linear functional f_0, which separates the given sets, or, equivalently, a complex linear functional f whose real part does so.

THEOREM K (HB Complex Separation Form). *Let S, Q be convex sets in the complex Banach space B and suppose that S has a nonempty interior. If Q does not meet* int (S), *there is an $f \in B^*$ such that*

$$\sup_{x \in S} \operatorname{Re} f(x) \leq \inf_{x \in Q} \operatorname{Re} f(x).$$

Exercises

1. Show that (a) the intersection of circled sets is circled; (b) the intersection of convex sets is convex; (c) that any translate of a convex set is convex; (d) that the circled hull of S equals ES. Give an example of two convex sets whose union is not convex.

2. If S and Q are subsets of the Banach space B, show that $S + Q$ is open whenever S is open.

3. Prove Theorem A.

4. Let p be a seminorm on the linear space X. If $S = \{x : p(x) \leq 1\}$, show that S is convex, absorbing, and circled. Show that p is the Minkowski functional of S.

5. Prove that the unit ball of any Banach space is convex, circled, and absorbing.

6. Characterize the extreme points of the unit ball of $L_\infty(a,b)$. Show that the unit ball in c_0 has no extreme points. Show that the extreme points of the unit ball in $C(0,1)$ are the functions of constant modulus 1. What are the extreme points of the unit ball of $L(0,1)$?

7. Prove Corollary 1 of Theorem F.

8. Prove that Theorem I implies Theorem H. HINT: Let Q be the linear flat N. Translate the sets so that $0 \in N$. By Theorem I an $f \in B^*$

exists such that $f(S) \leq c$ and $f(N) \geq c$. From the fact that $0 \in N$ deduce that the null space of f satisfies Theorem H.

9. Let S be a convex set and M a hyperplane. Show that $S \cap M = \varnothing$ implies that S lies strictly on one side of M. HINT: Let $M = \{x : f(x) = \alpha\}$ and assume that $x_1, x_2 \in S$ such that $f(x_1) < \alpha < f(x_2)$. Examine the values of f on the line segment $[x_1 : x_2] \subset S$.

10. (a) Let p be a seminorm on the Banach space B. Show that $\{x : p(x) \leq 1\}$ is a bounded set if and only if for some constant $c > 0$ we have

$$p(x) \geq c\|x\|$$

for all $x \in B$.

(b) It follows from (a) that if $\{x : p(x) \leq 1\}$ is a bounded set then p is actually a *norm* on B. Show that the converse is false. HINT: Let A be a bounded operator on a Hilbert space, which is one-to-one with dense range but which is not invertible, and consider $p(x) = \|Ax\|$.

4.2 THE SOLUTION OF PROBLEM 1 FOR TRANSFORMATIONS OF RANK 1

As the section title indicates, we are concerned here with the solution of Problem 1 under the simplifying assumption that the transformation T has a one-dimensional range. In Section 4.3, however, we find that the tools uncovered in the present section are almost sufficient to solve Problem 1 in its most general form. Hence we shall be rather thorough in our study of this special case.

To define the problem explicitly we use (without loss of generality) the real Banach space B, its conjugate B^*, and the real scalars R. The transformation T is linear; it has range R and is constructed via the bilinear form $\langle \ , \ \rangle$ associated with B and B^*. Two cases are now possible: first, the system inputs lie in the space B; hence T may be identified by the rule

$$Tu = \langle u, f \rangle, \qquad u \in B, \tag{1}$$

where $f \in B^*$ is a fixed functional determined by (and conversely determining) T. On the other hand, if the system inputs are identified with the space B^*, T is to be identified by the rule

$$Tf = \langle u, f \rangle, \qquad f \in B^*, \tag{2}$$

where $u \in B$ is a fixed element determined by and determining for T.

The second case actually contains the first. Indeed, recall that for every $u \in B$ there is a $u^{**} \in B^{**}$ such that

$$\langle u, f \rangle = \langle f, u^{**} \rangle \tag{3}$$

holds for every $f \in B^*$. Using u^{**} in place of u and substituting B^* for B and B^{**} for B^*, we have the first situation. Furthermore, if B is reflexive, the first case contains the second, for then every $u^{**} \in B^{**}$ has associated $u \in B$ such that Eq. 3 holds (i.e., $B = B^{**}$ when B is reflexive). This same substitution identifies the two forms of the problem.

The Existence of a Minimum Element

Consider first the transformation of Eq. 2. Without loss of generality (see Exercise 1), we assume that $\|u\| = 1$ and inquire into the existence of elements of B^* that satisfy $Tf = 1$ while minimizing $\|f\|$. Since for every $f \in B^*$

$$|\langle u, f \rangle| \leq \|f\|, \tag{4}$$

it is clear that every preimage of $1 \in R$ must have $\|f\| \geq 1$. However, a corollary (see Theorem D, Section 3.2) of the Hahn-Banach theorem states that for every $u \in B$ with $\|u\| = 1$ an $f \in B^*$ exists with $\|f\| = 1$ and satisfying

$$\langle u, f \rangle = 1.$$

Therefore with $T : B^* \to R$ we may state unequivocally that a minimum norm solution to Problem 1 exists. (We leave as an exercise the almost trivial verification that the assumptions $\|u\| = 1$ and $\xi = 1$ may be dispensed with.)

In the case in which $T : B \to R$, according to Eq. 1, the results are not so conclusive. In an adaptation of our reasoning (assuming $\|f\| = 1$) we arrive at the implication $Tu = 1 \Rightarrow \|u\| \geq 1$. This inequality, in conjunction with the inequality

$$Tu = \langle u, f \rangle \leq \sup_{\|u\| = 1} |\langle u, f \rangle| = \|f\| = 1, \tag{5}$$

shows that the question of the existence of a preimage of $1 \in R$ with minimum norm is equivalent to the question whether the functional f takes on its supremum on the unit ball of B.

If B is an arbitrary Banach space, functionals on B may or may not attain their supremums on the unit ball. We shall see several examples of this phenomenon later in the section. If B is reflexive, however, every $f \in B^*$ attains its supremum on the unit ball; that is, a $u \in B$ of norm 1 exists in which $f(u) = \|f\|$ (see Exercise 2), and for reflexive spaces the simplified form of Problem 1 always has at least one solution.[1]

---

[1] Those readers who have studied the references on topology suggested earlier will notice that we may obtain this result in another way. If B is reflexive, its unit ball is weakly compact. Hence in this case the mapping $u \to \langle u, f \rangle$ is a real continuous function on a compact set and consequently attains its maximum.

A much deeper result is the converse: if each bounded linear functional on B attains its supremum on the unit ball of B, then B is reflexive. This has been established by R. C. James [B49]. To summarize, we have Theorem A.

THEOREM A.   *Problem 1 has a solution for each transformation on B of rank 1 if and only if B is reflexive.*

Let us make one final observation before leaving the existence question. Transformation T maps the unit ball of B into a set that contains 0; it is convex and contains $-\xi$ whenever it contains ξ. Now, a well-known result states that the convex subsets of the real numbers are intervals; hence the image of the unit ball under T is necessarily one of the intervals $(-\|T\| : \|T\|)$, $[-\|T\| : \|T\|]$. Finally, we have already observed that we can solve Problem 1 for T if and only if T attains its supremum. Putting the pieces together, we have the following criterion: if T is a transformation on B of rank 1, Problem 1 has a solution for T if and only if the image of the unit ball under T is *closed*.

The Uniqueness of a Minimum Element

The question of uniqueness of solutions to Problem 1 is slightly more complicated than the question of existence. Let us standardize the notation $U = \{x \in B : \|x\| \leq 1\}$ to denote the *closed unit ball* in B. The boundary ∂U of U is clearly the unit sphere $\partial U = \{x \in B : \|x\| = 1\}$. The interior of U, namely $\text{int}\,(U) = \{x \in B : \|x\| < 1\}$, is called the open unit ball. Most of the important properties of a Banach space are related to some characteristic of its unit ball. For example, we have already seen that the shape of the unit ball is relevant to the question whether the space can be the dual of some other Banach space. Recall also (see Exercise 5, Section 4.1) that U is a convex absorbing and circled set and that the norm is the Minkowski functional of the unit ball.

Before proceeding with the more general aspects of the section, we consider the shape of U in a simple setting. For this we take B as the real linear space R^2 equipped with the norm

$$\|x\|_p = (|\alpha_1|^p + |\alpha_2|^p)^{1/p}, \qquad x = (\alpha_1, \alpha_2) \in R^2,$$

as p varies over the range $1 \leq p \leq \infty$. In Figure 4.8 the set U is drawn for $p = 1, 2, \infty$. For $p = 1$, U is the square with vertices $(1,0)$, $(0,1)$, $(-1,0)$ and $(0,-1)$. As p increases from 1 to ∞, the corresponding U swells from this square to the square with vertices $(1,1)$, $(-1,1)$, $(-1,-1)$, and $(1,-1)$, and passes through the spherical case for $p = 2$. (The dashed line indicates the case $p = \frac{1}{2}$. Since this set is not convex, it follows that the triangular law cannot hold, hence the function $\|\ \|_{1/2}$ is not a norm.)

Even in this simple example we observe that the unit ball can have both flat spots and corners. It turns out that a Banach space whose unit ball has no flat spots has certain useful properties and accordingly we single out these spaces with Definition A.

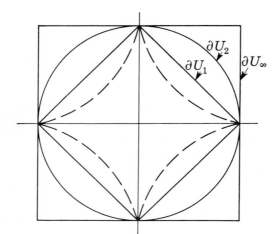

Figure 4.8   The set U for $X = l_p(2)$, $p = 1, 2, \infty$.

DEFINITION A.   *B is called rotund (or strictly convex) if ∂U contains no line segments.*

In other words, B is rotund if each open segment $(x:y)$, joining a pair of distinct points of ∂U, contains only points of norm less than 1. Theorem B lists some equivalent formulations of the concept of rotundity.

THEOREM B.   *The following are equivalent properties of a Banach space B:*
  (1)   *B is rotund;*
  (2)   *$\|x_1 + x_2\| = \|x_1\| + \|x_2\|$ implies $x_1 = \lambda x_2$ or $x_2 = \lambda x_1$ for some $\lambda \geq 0$;*
  (3)   *every point in ∂U is an extreme point of U;*
  (4)   *for each nonzero $f \in B^*$ there is at most one $x \in U$ with $f(x) = \|f\|$;*
  (5)   *each hyperplane of support of U meets U in at most one (and therefore exactly one) point;*
  (6)   *each convex set K in B has at most one minimum element (i.e., there is at most one vector $x \in K$ satisfying $\|x\| \leq \|z\|$ for all $z \in K$).*

P R O O F.   Suppose that B is rotund and let x_1, x_2 satisfy

$$\|x_1 + x_2\| = \|x_1\| + \|x_2\|.$$

We may suppose that $x_1 \neq 0$, $x_2 \neq 0$. Now to prove $(1) \Rightarrow (2)$ it suffices to show that if $0 < \alpha < 1$ then

$$\left\| \alpha \frac{x_1}{\|x_1\|} + (1 - \alpha) \frac{x_2}{\|x_2\|} \right\| = 1,$$

since this is true only if $x_1/\|x_1\| = x_2/\|x_2\|$. This verification is straight-forward (see Exercise 4).

(2) $\Rightarrow$ (3).   Let $x \in \partial U$ be given and suppose that $x = \alpha y + (1 - \alpha)z$ with $y, z \in U$ and $0 < \alpha < 1$. Then, by the triangle inequality, y and z have norm 1, but

$$\|\alpha y + (1 - \alpha)z\| = 1 = \|\alpha y\| + \|(1 - \alpha)z\|$$

and therefore by (2) we must have either

$$\alpha y = \lambda(1 - \alpha)z \quad \text{or} \quad (1 - \alpha)z = \lambda\alpha y$$

for some $\lambda > 0$. If the first holds,

$$0 < \alpha = \|\alpha y\| = \|\lambda(1 - \alpha)z\| = \lambda(1 - \alpha)$$

and therefore $y = z$. Similarly, the second also implies that $y = z$ and there-fore x is an extreme point of U.

(3) $\Rightarrow$ (4).   Suppose that $0 \neq f \in B^*$ and $x_1 \neq x_2$ belongs to U and satisfy $f(x_1) = \|f\| = f(x_2)$. Put $x = \frac{1}{2}(x_1 + x_2)$. Then $x \in U$ and $f(x) = \frac{1}{2}(f(x_1) + f(x_2)) = \|f\|$, from which it follows that

$$\|f\| \cdot \|x\| \geq f(x) = \|f\|, \qquad \|x\| \geq 1.$$

Thus $x \in \partial U$ and x belongs to the segment $(x_1 : x_2) \subset U$; hence x is not an extreme point of U contradicting (3).

(4) $\Rightarrow$ (5).   If H is a hyperplane of support of U, then H has the form $H = \{x : f(x) = 1\}$ for some $f \in B^*$, and we may suppose that

$$\text{Re } f(x) \leq 1, \qquad x \in U.$$

Letting f operate on the unit vector $\overline{(f(x)/|f(x)|)}x$, we obtain $\|f\| \leq 1$; we must have equality here because H meets U at some point x. If $y \in H \cap U$, then $f(y) = 1 = \|f\|$ and $y \in U$; hence, by (4), $y = x$.

(5) $\Rightarrow$ (6).   Let K be a convex set in B. Obviously if $0 \in K$, 0 is a min element so we may suppose that

$$1 = \inf \{\|z\| : z \in K\}.$$

If U is the unit ball in B, clearly int $(U) \neq \varnothing$, int $(U) \cap K = \varnothing$, and therefore by the separation theorem a hyperplane H separates U and K. The collec-tion of minimum elements of K is precisely $U \cap K$ and this is contained in $U \cap H$ which by hypothesis contains at most one vector.

(6) $\Rightarrow$ (1).   If $x_1, x_2 \in U$ and $[x_1 : x_2] \subset \partial U$, the convex set $K = [x_1 : x_2]$ contains more than one element unless $x_1 = x_2$.

R E M A R K   1.   Observe that in (4) we do not assert that each functional f on B attains its supremum on the unit ball, only that if it does then it does so at exactly one point. Similarly, concerning (6), rotundity does not guarantee that K has a minimum element, but merely that it cannot have two such elements. Rotundity is essentially a uniqueness concept.

Now that we have isolated those Banach spaces with no flat spots on the unit ball we focus attention on the existence of corners. Because a corner is a point with several supporting hyperplanes, our definition takes the form given in Definition B.

DEFINITION B.   *A Banach space B is called smooth if at each point of ∂U there is exactly one supporting hyperplane of U.*

Theorem C characterizes smoothness.

THEOREM C.   *The following are equivalent properties of the Banach space B:*

(1)   *B is smooth;*

(2)   *for every $0 \neq x \in B$ there exists at most one $f \in B^*$, $\|f\| = 1$ such that $f(x) = \|x\|$;*

(3)   *at each point $x \in \partial U$ the limit*

$$G(x,z) = \lim_{\varepsilon \to 0} \frac{\|x + \varepsilon z\| - \|x\|}{\varepsilon}$$

exists for every $z \in B$. Moreover, whenever $G(x,z)$ is defined, it is a real linear norm 1 function of z.

PROOF.   By definition, H is a supporting hyperplane of U at a point $x \in \partial U$ if H supports U and contains x. Using our earlier characterization of a hyperplane, this amounts to saying that there is an $f \in B^*$ such that

(a) $\operatorname{Re} f(z) \leq 1$,   all $z \in U$,

(b) $f(x) = 1$.

Now (a) is equivalent to $\|f\| \leq 1$; consequently there is a one-to-one correspondence between hyperplanes H which support U at x and vectors $f \in U^*$ which satisfy $f(x) = \|x\|$. It is therefore clear that (1) and (2) are equivalent. The equivalence of (2) and (3) is proved in Appendix 6.

Using (2) of Theorem C and (4) of Theorem B, we now show that rotundity and smoothness are almost dual properties. Let U^* denote the unit ball in B^*. Theorem B asserts that every $G \in B^{**}$ has at most one $f \in U^*$ such that $G(f) = \|G\|$ if and only if B^* is rotund. Because B may be identified as a subspace of B^{**}, it follows that if B^* is rotund then for each $x \in B$ there is at most one $f \in U^*$ for which $f(x) = \|x\|$. In other words, smoothness of B is, in general, a weaker requirement than rotundity of B^* and an equivalent requirement when B is reflexive. To summarize, if $B^{**} = B$, each functional on B (on B^*) attains its supremum on U (on U^*) in at most one point if and only if B is rotund (B is smooth). Briefly, if B is reflexive, then B is smooth (rotund) if and only if B^* is rotund (smooth).

It is convenient to introduce at this point the following terminology. If $0 \neq f \in B^*$, we call a vector $x \in U$ an *extremal* of f if x satisfies $f(x) = \|f\|$. Clearly, each extremal of f has norm 1. Theorem B then asserts that each $f \in B^*$ has at most one extremal if and only if B is rotund. Similarly, if $0 \neq x \in B$, an element $f \in U^*$ is called an *extremal* of x if f satisfies $f(x) = \|x\|$. Theorem C says that each $x \in B$ has at most one extremal in B^* if and only if B is smooth.

REMARK 2.   If $x \in B$, the Hahn-Banach theorem guarantees the existence of at least one extremal f in B^*. Accordingly, if B is reflexive, every $0 \neq f \in B^*$ $(0 \neq x \in B)$ has a unique extremal in B (in B^*) if and only if B is rotund (B^* is smooth). Finally, if B is reflexive, rotund and smooth, and we denote by $\bar{x}$ (by $\bar{f}$) the unique extremal of x (of f) in B^* (in B), then the following operational properties of the extremal function hold:

(a) $\bar{\bar{x}} = \dfrac{x}{\|x\|}$,   all $0 \neq x \in B$,

(b) $\bar{\bar{\phi}} = \dfrac{\phi}{\|\phi\|}$,   all $0 \neq \phi \in B^*$,

(c) $\overline{(\lambda x)} = \dfrac{|\lambda|}{\lambda}\,\bar{x}$,   any complex scalar λ.

We have already seen that for any Banach space each $x \neq 0$ has at least one extremal $f \in U^*$, and our best information about f is that it must have norm 1. We can improve this somewhat.

THEOREM D.   *Let $x \neq 0$ be given in B. At least one extremal of x is an extreme point of U^*.*

PROOF.   Once more our proof leans heavily on topological properties; namely, the set $C^* = \{f \in U^* : f(x) = \|x\|\}$ is a nonempty convex and (weak star) closed subset of U^* and therefore (weak star) compact. It follows from the Krein-Milman theorem that C^* has an extreme point f_0. It is easy to see that f_0 is actually an extreme point of U^*. Indeed, if $f_0 = \alpha f + (1 - \alpha)g$ with $0 < \alpha < 1$ and $f, g \in U^*$, then

$$\|x\| = f_0(x) = \alpha f(x) + (1 - \alpha)g(x)$$

$$\leq \alpha|f(x)| + (1 - \alpha)|g(x)| \leq \alpha\|x\| + (1 - \alpha)\|x\|$$

implies $f(x) = |f(x)| = \|x\|$, $g(x) = \|x\|$. In other words, f_0 belongs to $(f:g) \subset C^*$ and therefore $f = g$.

Note also that the theorem asserts that if B is reflexive each $\phi \in B^*$ attains its supremum on U at an extreme point of U (and therefore has content only when not every vector in ∂U is an extreme point of U, i.e. when B is not rotund).

Extremals in Some Specific Banach Spaces

In Section 4.3 we shall see that taking extremals is one of the principal steps in the solution of the basic optimization problem. The remainder of this Section catalogs for reference purposes the form that this operation takes in several spaces that are important in the applications. However, since the abstract solution to Problem 1 can be obtained without this concrete information, some readers may prefer to skip ahead to Section 4.3 in the first reading.

Among the common Banach spaces that we have met in earlier sections c_0, l_1, and l_∞ and the corresponding function spaces $C(\tau)$, $L_1(\tau)$, and $L_\infty(\tau)$ are neither rotund nor smooth. On the other side of the ledger we have the fact that L_p, l_p for $1 < p < \infty$, and any Hilbert space are simultaneously rotund and smooth. Because these spaces have nicer geometric properties, we select them as our first example.

Example 1: $L_p(a,b)$ and l_p for $1 < p < \infty$. If X is any one of these spaces, then, for $x \in X$ with $\|x\| = 1$, the relationship $|\langle x,\phi \rangle| \leq \|\phi\|$ for $\phi \in X^*$ is precisely Hölder's inequality. In Section 1.4 it was noted that equality in this relation can hold if and only if x has a specific and unique relationship to ϕ (i.e., x is the extremal of ϕ). Indeed, if $\phi = (\phi_1, \phi_2, \dots) \in l_q$ is a continuous linear functional on l_p, with $1/p + 1/q = 1$, then $\bar{\phi} = (\bar{\phi}_1, \bar{\phi}_2, \dots) \in l_p$, where

$$\bar{\phi}_k = \begin{cases} 0, & \text{if } \phi_k = 0, \\ \dfrac{\tilde{\phi}_k}{|\phi_k|}\left(\dfrac{|\phi_k|}{\|\phi\|}\right)^{q-1}, & \text{if } \phi_k \neq 0. \end{cases}$$

Here $\tilde{\phi}_k$ denotes the complex conjugate of ϕ_k. When real spaces are involved, this expression simplifies to

$$\bar{\phi}_k = \|\phi\|^{(1-q)} \, \text{sign}\,[\phi_k] \cdot |\phi_k|^{q-1},$$

where sign $[\phi_k]$ takes on the values $+1$ or -1 when $\phi_k > 0$ or $\phi_k < 0$, and sign $[\phi_k] = 0$ when $\phi_k = 0$.

Similarly, if $\phi \in L_q(a,b)$ is a functional on $L_p(a,b)$ with $1/p + 1/q = 1$, then $\bar{\phi}$, the extremal of ϕ, has values at $t \in [a,b]$, determined by

$$\bar{\phi}(t) = \begin{cases} 0, & \text{if } \phi(t) = 0, \\ \dfrac{\tilde{\phi}(t)}{|\phi(t)|}\left(\dfrac{|\phi(t)|}{\|\phi\|}\right)^{(q-1)}, & \text{if } \phi(t) \neq 0. \end{cases}$$

As in the sequence case in which ϕ is real, we may reduce this expression to the form

$$\bar{\phi}(t) = \|\phi\|^{(1-q)} \operatorname{sign} [\phi(t)] \cdot |\phi(t)|^{q-1}, \qquad t \in [a,b].$$

It is an easy matter to check that the functions so defined satisfy the necessary conditions. For example, we have

$$\|\bar{\phi}\| = \left[\int_a^b |\bar{\phi}(t)|^p dt \right]^{1/p} = \|\phi\|^{(1-q)} \left[\int_a^b |\phi(t)|^{p(q-1)} dt \right]^{1/p}.$$

However, $1/p + 1/q = 1 \Leftrightarrow p(q-1) = q \Leftrightarrow 1/p = (1/q)(q/p) = (1/q)(q-1)$, and by using these two equivalent forms we have the immediate result $\|\bar{\phi}\| = 1$. Furthermore,

$$\langle \bar{\phi}, \phi \rangle = \|\phi\|^{(1-q)} \int_a^b |\phi(t)|^{p(q-1)} dt = \|\phi\|^{(1-q)} \cdot \|\phi\|^q = \|\phi\|;$$

hence the element $\bar{\phi}$ so defined is an extremal of ϕ.

Example 2: $[l_p(n) \text{ for } p = 1, \infty]$. The spaces $l_1(n)$ and $l_\infty(n)$ are examples of nonrotund spaces. Recall that $l_1(n)$ is reflexive and that $[l_1(n)]^* = l_\infty(n)$. If $\phi = (\phi_1, \dots, \phi_n) \in l_\infty(n)$,

$$\|\phi\| = \max\{|\phi_1|, \dots, |\phi_n|\},$$

and for $x = (x_1, \dots, x_n) \in l_1(n)$,

$$\|x\| = \sum_{i=1}^n |x_i|.$$

It is not difficult to locate the necessary conditions for an extremal in these two cases. Indeed, if $\phi \in l_\infty(n)$, the components of any extremal $\bar{\phi} = (\bar{\phi}_1, \dots, \bar{\phi}_n) \in l_1(n)$ must satisfy

$$\bar{\phi}_k = \alpha_k \operatorname{sign} [\phi_k]$$

where

$$\alpha_k \geq 0, \qquad k = 1, \dots, n,$$

$$\alpha_k = 0, \qquad \text{if } |\phi_k| \neq \|\phi\|,$$

$$\sum_{k=1}^n \alpha_k = 1.$$

In other words, if we select from the set $\{\pm e_i : i = 1, \dots, n\}$, where e_i is the ith coordinate vector, the subset $\{e_i'\}$ such that

$$\langle e_i', \phi \rangle = \|\phi\|,$$

any extremal $\bar{\phi}$ must be a convex combination of $\{e_i'\}$ (i.e., $\bar{\phi}$ is any unit vector in the convex hull of $\{e_i'\}$).

The converse situation is also interesting if $x = (x_1, \ldots, x_n) \in l_1(n)$ and if $\phi = (\phi_1, \ldots, \phi_n)$ is an extremal of x. Then

$$\phi_k = \begin{cases} \text{sign } [x_k], & x_k \neq 0, \\ -1 \leq \phi_k \leq 1, & x_k = 0. \end{cases}$$

It is easy to check the sufficiency of these conditions. Indeed, since $|\phi_k| \leq 1$ in all cases and $|\phi_k| < 1$ for all k if and only if $x = 0$, we have $\|\bar{x}\| = 1$. On the other hand,

$$\langle x, \bar{x} \rangle = \sum x_i \phi_i = \sum |x_i| = \|x\|$$

and the check is complete.

In Figure 4.9 the extremal conditions for $l_1(2)$ and $l_\infty(2)$ are described. Notice that the subset $S_1 = \{x : x_1 = 1, -1 < x_2 < 1\}$ of the unit ball of $l_\infty(2)$ is a flat spot. The functional $(1,0) \in l_1(2)$ defines the common hyperplane of support for S_1 and is the unique extremal for all points in S_1. The

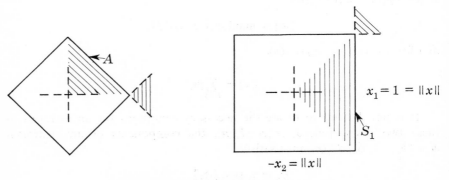

$$x_1 = 1 = \|x\|$$

$$-x_2 = \|x\|$$

Figure 4.9   The unit ball of $l_1(2)$ and $l_\infty(2)$.

corners $x = (1,1)$ and $x = (1,-1)$, however, have an entire cone of support functionals, namely, the set $A = \{\phi : \phi = \alpha(1,0) + (1-\alpha)(0,1), 0 < \alpha < 1\}$. Conversely, any element of S_1 is an extremal of $(1,0) \in l_1(2)$ and defines a support hyperplane at this point. Furthermore, the element $(1,1) \in l_\infty(2)$ is the unique extremal for any point of A. Note also that U_1 has only the four extreme points $(1,0)$, $(0,1)$, $(-1,0)$, and $(0,-1)$. This we may verify on sight. Hence, to find an extremal of $\phi \in l_\infty(2)$ we need only examine its value at these four points.

Example 3: $L_p(a,b)$ for $p = 1, \infty$.   The spaces $L_1(a,b)$ and $L_\infty(a,b)$ may be viewed as limiting cases of $L_p(a,b)$, $1 < p < \infty$. Recall that $L_\infty(a,b)$ is the set of all (Lebesgue measurable) functions such that

$$\|x\|_\infty = \text{ess sup } |x(t)| < \infty.$$

The conjugate of $L_1(a,b)$ can be identified with $L_\infty(a,b)$; hence we may inquire into the characterization of the extremal relationship from $L_1(a,b)$ into $L_\infty(a,b)$. If $x \in L_1(a,b)$, it is not difficult to see that every extremal $\bar{x} \in L_\infty(a,b)$ of x must have values $\bar{x}(t)$, $t \in [a,b]$ which satisfy

$$\bar{x}(t) = \begin{cases} \text{sign}[x(t)], & \text{if } x(t) \neq 0, \\ |\bar{x}(t)| \leq 1, & \text{if } x(t) = 0. \end{cases}$$

Indeed, we immediately have $\|\bar{x}\| = 1$ and

$$\langle x,\bar{x} \rangle = \int_a^b x(t) \text{ sign } [x(t)]\, dt = \int_a^b |x(t)|\, dt = \|x\|.$$

Although every $x \in L_1(a,b)$ has at least one $\bar{x} \in L_\infty(a,b)$, the converse of this statement is not true. As examples we consider the two functions $f_1, f_2 \in L_\infty(a,b)$ of Figure 4.10. The function f_2 has an extremal $\bar{f}_2$, namely the function

$$\bar{f}_2(t) = \begin{cases} 1/(t_2 - t_1), & t_1 \leq t \leq t_2, \\ 0, & \text{otherwise,} \end{cases}$$

whereas the function f_1 has not. In general, if the set $\tau = \{t \in [a,b]: f(t) = \|f\|\}$ has nonzero measure $m(\tau)$ the function

$$\bar{f}(t) = \begin{cases} 1/m(\tau), & t \in \tau, \\ 0, & \text{otherwise,} \end{cases}$$

is an extremal for f.

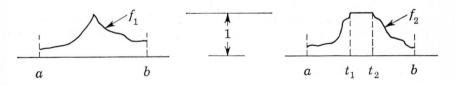

Figure 4.10   Two functions in $L_\infty(a,b)$.

Example 4.   The space $C(\tau)$ is another important example of a nonreflexive nonrotund Banach space. If τ is the closed interval $[a,b]$, then

$$\|x\| = \sup_{t \in [a,b]} |x(t)| = \max_{t \in [a,b]} |x(t)|, \quad x \in C[a,b],$$

and the unit ball of $C[a,b]$ evidently consists of all continuous functions x

with values satisfying $-1 \leq x(t) \leq 1$, $t \in \tau$ (Figure 4.11). Notice that the unit ball of $C[a,b]$ has exactly two extreme points; namely, the constant functions $x(t) = 1$, $t \in \tau$, and $x(t) = -1$, $t \in \tau$.

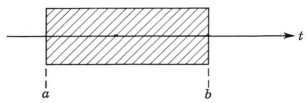

Figure 4.11   The set U in $C[a,b]$.

To examine the extremals in $C^*[a,b]$ of $x \in (a,b)$ we consider the set $S = \{t \in [a,b]: x(t) = \|x\|\}$. Since every continuous function attains its supremum on every closed bounded interval, it follows that S is not empty. If $t_k \in S$ and g denotes the unit step function

$$g_k(t) = \begin{cases} 0, & a \leq t < t_k, \\ \text{sign } [x(t_k)], & t_k \leq t \leq b, \end{cases}$$

then $\text{var}_{[a,b]} (g_k) = \|g_k\| = 1$ and furthermore

$$\langle x, g_k \rangle = \int_a^b x(t) dg_k(t) = |x(t_k)| = \|x\|;$$

that is, the extremal of x is identified with a unit delta function at t_k.

If the set S has more than a single point, multiple extremals exist. For example, if $S = \{t_1, \ldots, t_n\}$ and $\{g_1, \ldots, g_n\}$ are step functions defined by the foregoing equality as k runs from 1 to n, then not only are the g_k extremals of x but all convex combinations are as well. Finally, if S has positive measure, extremals may be constructed by integrating $L_1(a,b)$ functions. For instance, with x as the function f_2 of Figure 4.9, any $L_1(a,b)$ function with $\|g\| = 1$ and satisfying

$$g(t) \geq 0, \qquad t \in [t_1, t_2],$$

$$g(t) = 0, \qquad t \in [a,b] \sim [t_1, t_2],$$

is an extremal of x.

Since the space $C[a,b]$ is not reflexive, it follows that these are functionals in $C[a,b]^*$ which do not attain their supremums on the unit ball of $C[a,b]$. As an example, we have the functional defined by

$$f(x) = \int_0^{1/2} x(t) dt - \int_{1/2}^1 x(t) dt, \qquad x \in C[a,b].$$

It is easily shown that $\|f\| = 1$, yet the conditions $\sup |x(t)| \leq 1$ and $f(x) = 1$ imply that

$$x(t) = 1, \qquad 0 \leq t \leq \tfrac{1}{2},$$

$$x(t) = -1, \qquad \tfrac{1}{2} \leq t \leq 1,$$

which is clearly not in $C(a,b)$. On the other hand, the functional

$$f(x) = \int_0^1 x(t) \, dt$$

does attain its supremum uniquely at the function $x(t =) 1$.

Extremal Problems in Product Spaces

In the first *four* examples attention is restricted to those elementary function spaces that occur most often in the study of single variate systems. In dealing with multivariate systems, however, it is not these elementary spaces that are of interest but rather finite or infinite Cartesian products of such spaces. As an example, consider the composite system of Figure 2.16 (Section 2.5). We have seen that this system may be represented as a linear transformation $T: B \to D$ between Banach spaces B and D, in which B, for instance, may be taken as any of the product spaces

$$B = l_{p_1}(\sigma) \times \cdots \times l_{p_s}(\sigma) \times L_{p_{s+1}}(\tau) \times \cdots \times L_{p_m}(\tau).$$

If all p_j's satisfy $1 < p_j < \infty$, then B is a Cartesian product of rotund, reflexive spaces. It is natural to inquire about the types of norm that may be imposed on this Cartesian product in which these desirable properties are carried over to B itself.

With multivariate system applications as the motivation, we now consider the space $B = \prod_{i=1}^n B_i$, which is a finite product of Banach spaces B_i, $i = 1, \ldots, n$. We assume that the norm on B preserves convergence properties in the sense that, if $\{x^k\}$ is a sequence, $x^k = (x_1^k, \ldots, x_n^k) \in B$ such that $x^k \to x^0$; then $x_i^k \to x_i^0$, $i = 1, 2, \ldots, n$. An alternative condition is that the projections of B into the subspaces B_i, $i = 1, \ldots, n$ are continuous. If this criterion is met, then for $x = (x_1, \ldots, x_n) \in B$ the tuplet $f = (f_1, \ldots, f_n)$ with $f_i \in B_i^*, i = 1, \ldots, n$ defines, by means of the formula

$$\langle x, f \rangle = \sum_{i=1}^n \langle x_i, f_i \rangle,$$

a bounded linear functional f on B. Conversely, every $f \in B^*$ can be shown to have a representation of this form; hence $B^* = \prod_{i=1}^n B_i^*$. Such norms are said to maintain the product topology.

Suppose now that $B = \prod_{i=1}^n B_i$ is a finite product of Banach spaces equipped with a norm that maintains the product topology. Then B is reflexive if and only if each subspace B_i is reflexive. On the other hand, it does not follow that B can inherit rotundity from the spaces B_i for such a broad class of norms on the product. (Indeed, the real line is rotund, but the plane, considered as the product of the real line with itself, has many non-rotund norms; for example, $l_1(2)$ and $l_\infty(2)$ are nonrotund versions of R^2.)

Even though rotundity is more difficult to preserve than reflexiveness, the next two theorems list several product norms that are rotund.

THEOREM E.   *Let $B_1, \ldots, B_n$ be normed linear spaces. For $x = (x_1, \ldots, x_n)$ $\in \prod_{i=1}^n B_i = B$ define the norm* $|\ |$ *of x by*

$$|x| = \left(\sum_{i=1}^n \|x_i\|^p \right)^{1/p}, \qquad 1 < p < \infty,$$

where $\|x_i\|$ is the norm of x_i in B_i. Then

(1) $|\ |$ *is a rotund norm on B if and only if each of the factors B_i, $i = 1$, $\ldots, n$ (with its given norm) is rotund;*

(2)   *if $\phi \in B^*$, then $\phi = (\phi_1, \ldots, \phi_n)$ with $\phi_i \in B_i^*$, $i = 1, \ldots, n$ and*

$$|\phi| = \left(\sum_{i=1}^n \|\phi_i\|^q \right)^{1/q}, \qquad 1/p + 1/q = 1;$$

(3)   *with B rotund, $\phi = (\phi_1, \ldots, \phi_n) \in B^*$ and $\bar{\phi}_i$ the extremal of $\phi_i \in B_i$, $i = 1, \ldots, n$ the extremal $\bar{\phi} \in B$ of ϕ is given by*

$$\bar{\phi} = (\alpha_1 \bar{\phi}_1, \alpha_2 \bar{\phi}_2, \ldots, \alpha_n \bar{\phi}_n),$$

where

$$\alpha_i = \left(\frac{\|\phi_i\|}{|\phi|} \right)^{(q-1)};$$

(4)   *if each B_i is reflexive and smooth, then B is also, and the extremal $\bar{x} \in B^*$ of each $x = (x_1, \ldots, x_n) \in B$ is given by*

$$\bar{x} = (\beta_1 \bar{x}_1, \beta_2 \bar{x}_2, \ldots, \beta_n \bar{x}_n),$$

where $\beta_i = (\|x_i\|/|x|)^{(p-1)}$ and $\bar{x}_i \in B_i^*$ is the extremal of $x_i \in B_i$, $i = 1, \ldots, n$.

The proof of this theorem is given in Appendix 6. It should be noted that (4) is a dualization of (3). Any conceptual difficulties with this theorem probably arise from its length rather than the sophistication of its statement. Hence it may prove helpful to consider a concrete example.

Example 5.   As the motivation for this example, we consider once again the composite system of Section 2.5. To be specific (without much loss of generality, however) we assume that this system has two discrete and two continuous inputs, that is,

$$u = (u_1, u_2) \in l_{p_1}(\sigma) \times l_{p_2}(\sigma) = B_1 \times B_2,$$

$$v = (v_1, v_2) \in L_{p_3}(\tau) \times L_{p_4}(\tau) = B_3 \times B_4.$$

Assuming that we are dealing with real spaces and that $1 < p_i < \infty$ and $1/p_i + 1/q_i = 1$ for $i = 1, 2, 3, 4$, all component spaces are rotund and smooth. Furthermore, the results of Example 1 apply.

If the space $B = \prod_{i=1}^{4} B_i$ is equipped with the norm of Theorem E for some $1 < p < \infty$, that is,

$$|(u_1, u_2, v_1, v_2)| = [\|u_1\|^p + \|u_2\|^p + \|v_1\|^p + \|v_2\|^p]^{1/p}$$

$$= \left[\left(\sum_\sigma |u_1(t_k)|^{p_1} \right)^{p/p_1} + \left(\sum_\sigma |u_2(t_k)|^{p_2} \right)^{p/p_2} \right.$$

$$\left. + \left(\int_\tau |v_1(t)|^{p_3} dt \right)^{p/p_3} + \left(\int_\tau |v_2(t)|^{p_4} dt \right)^{p/p_4} \right]^{1/p},$$

the norm of any $\phi = (\phi_1, \phi_2, \phi_3, \phi_4) \in B^*$, $\phi_i \in B_i^*$ has the value

$$|\phi| = [\|\phi_1\|^q + \|\phi_2\|^q + \|\phi_3\|^q + \|\phi_4\|^q]^{1/q}$$

$$= \left[\left(\sum_\sigma |\phi_1(t_k)|^{q_1} \right)^{q/q_1} + \left(\sum_\sigma |\phi_2(t_k)|^{q_2} \right)^{q/q_2} \right.$$

$$\left. + \left(\int_\tau |\phi_3(t)|^{q_3} dt \right)^{q/q_3} + \left(\int_\tau |\phi_4(t)|^{q_4} dt \right)^{q/q_4} \right]^{1/q}.$$

Furthermore, by using (3) of Theorem E, we know exactly how to compute the unique extremal $\bar{\phi} \in B$ for every $\phi \in B^*$. The first step is to compute the number $|\phi|$ by the preceding formula. The scalars $\alpha_i = (\|\phi_i\| / |\phi|)^{(q-1)}$ are then immediate. The component extremals must satisfy

$$\bar{\phi}_i(t) = \|\phi_i\|^{(1-q_i)} \text{ sign } [\phi_i(t)] \cdot |\phi_i(t)|^{q_i - 1}, \qquad i = 1, 2, 3, 4,$$

as t runs through σ or τ; hence the tuplet

$$\bar{\phi}(t, s) = [\alpha_1 \bar{\phi}_1(s), \alpha_2 \bar{\phi}_2(s), \alpha_3 \bar{\phi}_3(t), \alpha_4 \bar{\phi}_4(t)], \qquad (t, s) \in \tau \times \sigma,$$

is completely defined.

The second norm on a finite product that we shall specifically mention is a slight variation on the first.

THEOREM F. *Let B denote the Cartesian product of the normed linear spaces B_i, $i = 1, \ldots, n$. Let $[a_{ij}]$ be a positive definite symmetric $n \times n$ matrix* *each of whose elements is non-negative. Then the function*

$$x \rightarrow |||x||| = \left(\sum_{i,j=1}^{n} a_{ij}\|x_i\| \cdot \|x_j\| \right)^{1/2}$$

for $x = (x_1, \ldots, x_n) \in B$ *is a norm on* B. *Furthermore,*

   (1)   *B is rotund (reflexive) if and only if each of the factors B_i, $i = 1, \ldots, n$ is rotund (reflexive).*

   (2)   *If $\phi = (\phi_1, \ldots, \phi_n) \in B^*$, then the norm $|||\phi|||$ of ϕ is given by*

$$|||\phi||| = \left(\sum_{i,j=1}^{n} b_{ij}\|\phi_i\| \cdot \|\phi_j\| \right)^{1/2},$$

      where $[b_{ij}]$ is the inverse of the matrix $[a_{ij}]$.

   (3)   *If $\bar{\phi}_i \in B_i$ is the extremal of $\phi_i \in B_i^*$, $i = 1, \ldots, n$, then $\bar{\phi} \in B$, the extremal of $\phi \in B^*$, is given by*

$$\bar{\phi} = (\alpha_1\bar{\phi}_1, \alpha_2\bar{\phi}_2, \ldots, \alpha_n\bar{\phi}_n),$$

      where $\alpha_i = (|||\phi|||)^{-1}(\sum_{i=1}^{n} b_{ij}\|\phi_j\|)$; the number $|||\phi|||$ is computed by (2).

   (4)   *If each B_i is smooth and reflexive, then $\bar{x} \in B^*$, the extremal of $x \in B$, is given by*

$$\bar{x} = (\delta_1\bar{x}_1, \delta_2\bar{x}_2, \ldots, \delta_n\bar{x}_n),$$

      where $\delta_i = (|||x|||)^{-1}(\sum_{i=1}^{n} a_{ij}\|x_j\|)$ and $|||x|||$ is computed as in (1.)

R E M A R K 3.   It is clear that any diagonal matrix with positive entries on the diagonal satisfies the hypothesis of Theorem F, hence may be used to define a rotund product norm. Nondiagonal positive definite matrices with non-negative entries also exist in abundance. For example, if D is any $n \times n$ matrix with non-negative entries, then $A = D^*D$ will have non-negative entries and will be non-negative definite ($A \geq 0$). (A may be made positive definite by the addition of εI, where $\varepsilon > 0$.)

The theorem, however, is *not* valid for *any* positive definite matrix. To illustrate, consider the matrix

$$A = \begin{pmatrix} 3/2 & -1 \\ -1 & 3/2 \end{pmatrix}.$$

The reader can show that the spectrum of A consists of the points $\frac{1}{2}$, $\frac{5}{2}$, and consequently A is a positive matrix. In the product $B \times B$, let $x = (z, -z)$ and $y = (z,z)$, where $z \in B$ is of norm 1. Then

$$|||x|||^2 = \tfrac{3}{2}\|x\|^2 - \|z\|^2 - \|z\|^2 + \tfrac{3}{2}\|z\|^2 = \|z\|^2 = 1,$$

$$|||y|||^2 = \tfrac{3}{2}\|z\|^2 - \|z\|^2 - \|z\|^2 + \tfrac{3}{2}\|z\|^2 = 1.$$

However,

$$\||x + y\||^2 = \||(2z,0)\||^2 = \tfrac{3}{2}\|2z\|^2 = \tfrac{3}{2}4\|z\|^2 = 6,$$

so that

$$\||x + y\|| = \sqrt{6} > 2 = \||x\|| + \||y\||.$$

Therefore the matrix A does *not* define a norm on $B \times B$.

Extremals in Vector-Valued Function Spaces

In dealing with systems of a single type (i.e., all variables are time sequences or all variables are time functions), it is possible to view the product space problem from a different point of view. For instance, consider the real continuous time system with inputs $u = (u_1, \ldots, u_m)$ defined on an interval τ and normed by the function

$$\|u\| = \left[\sum_{i=1}^{m} \int_{\tau} |u_i(t)|^p dt \right]^{1/p}.$$

From the earlier discussion we observe that u may be considered as an element of the product $\prod_{i=1}^{m} L_p(\tau)$ equipped with the norm of Theorem E. We may, however, rearrange (without changing its value) the norm function to read

$$\|u\| = \left[\int_{\tau} \left| \left(\sum_{i=1}^{m} |u_i(t)|^p \right)^{1/p} \right|^p dt \right]^{1/p}.$$

This expression suggests that the relationship $t \to u(t)$, $t \in \tau$, be viewed as a mapping from τ into $l_p(m)$; that is, u is a vector-valued function with values $u(t) \in R^n$ and with norm given by

$$|u(t)|_p = \left[\sum_{i=1}^{m} |u_i(t)|^p \right]^{1/p}, \qquad t \in \tau.$$

The scalar-valued function $t \to |u(t)|$ is then an element of $L_p(\tau)$, with norm

$$\|u\| = \left[\int_{\tau} |u(t)|_p^p dt \right]^{1/p},$$

which agrees with the first computation.

A considerable volume of mathematical literature is available on vector-valued functions (see, for example, [A41, ch. 3]). Most of the familiar operations on scalar-valued functions, such as differentiation, integration, and summation, can be extended in a natural way to vector-valued functions. In Chapter 2, in an analysis of finite families of first-order differential and difference equations, we developed a rudimentary extension of this type. This is not to say that in a more general setting the extension does not involve some complexities. We are content, however, to summarize those results that are of greatest utility for our purposes.

Let X denote a Banach space and τ an interval of the real line. The notation $x(\cdot)$ is used to denote a function $\tau \to X$ which associates with every $t \in \tau$ a unique vector $x(t) \in X$. We also have the notation $| \; |$ to denote the norm on X; thus $|x(t)|$ is a scalar and $|x(\cdot)|$ is a function from τ to the real scalars.

DEFINITION C. *The space* $\mathbf{L}_p(X;\tau)$ *consists of those functions*[1] $x(\cdot)$ *from* τ *to* X *such that* $[\int_\tau |x(t)|^p dt]^{1/p} < \infty.$

The space $\mathbf{L}_p(X;\tau)$ becomes a Banach space when equipped with the norm

$$\|x(\cdot)\|_p = \left[\int_\tau |x(t)|^p dt \right]^{1/p}, \qquad 1 \leq p < \infty,$$

or

$$\|x(\cdot)\|_\infty = \text{ess sup } |x(t)|, \qquad p = \infty.$$

It can be shown that when $1 < p < \infty$ and X is reflexive, $\mathbf{L}_p(X;\tau)$ is reflexive Furthermore, the adjoint space $\mathbf{L}_p^*(X;\tau)$ may be identified as the space $\mathbf{L}_q(X^*;\tau)$, where $1/p + 1/q = 1$.

The norm $\| \; \|_p$, $1 \leq p \leq \infty$ can be viewed as the composition of the norm in X followed by the norm in $L_p(\tau)$. The form taken by the functionals of $\mathbf{L}_p(X;\tau)$ is also of interest. Let us use the notation $\langle x, f \rangle$ to indicate the usual bilinear relationship between X and X^*. The bilinear relationship between elements $x(\cdot) \in \mathbf{L}_p(X;\tau)$ and $f(\cdot) \in \mathbf{L}_q(X^*;\tau)$ is denoted by $\langle\!\langle x(\cdot), f(\cdot) \rangle\!\rangle$ and computed according to the rule

$$\langle\!\langle x(\cdot), f(\cdot) \rangle\!\rangle = \int_\tau \langle x(t), f(t) \rangle dt.$$

In the present context three distinct extremal functions are also of interest. First, we have the extremal (unique if X is smooth) $\bar{x} \in X^*$ for every $x \in X$. Second is the extremal (unique if $1 < p < \infty$) $\tilde{\alpha} \in L_q(\tau)$ for every $\alpha \in L_p(\tau)$ $(1/p + 1/q = 1)$. If we assume that it is known how these two extremals are computed, our next theorem tells us how to construct the third extremal, namely, $\hat{x}(\cdot) \in \mathbf{L}_q(X^*;\tau)$ of elements $x(\cdot) \in \mathbf{L}_p(X;\tau)$.

---

[1]As in the scalar-valued L_p spaces, a generalized form of integration is necessary to define the functions in $\mathbf{L}_p(X;\tau)$ rigorously. If X is separable, each $x(\cdot)$ must in conjunction with every $f \in X^*$ produce a scalar function $\langle x(\cdot), f \rangle$ which satisfies the measurability requirements of the scalar L_p spaces. As with scalar functions, $\mathbf{L}_p(X;\tau)$ consists of equivalence classes rather than functions, although in the applications it is safe to overlook this difference.

THEOREM G.   *Let* $x(\cdot) \in \mathbf{L}_p(X;\tau)$ *be arbitrary; then any extremal* $\hat{x}(\cdot)$
$\in \mathbf{L}_q(X^*;\tau)$ *must have the form*

$$\hat{x}(t) = \widetilde{|x(\cdot)|}(t)\bar{x}(t), \qquad t \in \tau,$$

where $1 \le p < \infty$ *and* $1/p + 1/q = 1$.

For clarity we emphasize that $\bar{x}(t)$ denotes the extremal in X^* of the element $x(t) \in X$. The function $|x(\cdot)|$ is an element of $L_p(\tau)$ and $\widetilde{|x(\cdot)|} \in L_q(\tau)$ is the extremal of this function. The number $(\widetilde{|x(\cdot)|})(t)$ is the value of $\widetilde{|x(\cdot)|}$ at time $t \in \tau$. By an abuse of notation we shall write

$$\hat{x}(t) = \widetilde{|x(t)|} \cdot \bar{x}(t), \qquad t \in \tau,$$

in place of the more proper notation of the theorem.

As for the proof of Theorem G, we note first that the inequalities

$$\lang\!\langle x(\cdot), f(\cdot) \rangle\!\rangle = \int_\tau \langle x(t), f(t) \rangle dt \le \int_\tau |x(t)| \cdot |f(t)| dt \le \|x(\cdot)\|_p \cdot \|f(\cdot)\|_q$$

hold for any $x(\cdot) \in \mathbf{L}_p(X;\tau)$ and $f(\cdot) \in \mathbf{L}_q(X^*;\tau)$. Fixing $x(\cdot)$, we observe that the last inequality on the right holds if and only if $|f(\cdot)| \in L_q(\tau)$ is a scalar multiple of the extremal of $|x(\cdot)| \in L_p(\tau)$. The first inequality holds if and only if $f(t) \in X^*$ is proportional to an extremal of $x(t) \in X$ for every $t \in \tau$ (neglecting as usual sets of measure zero). Hence, if $\|f(\cdot)\|_q = 1$ and

$$\lang\!\langle x(\cdot), f(\cdot) \rangle\!\rangle = \|x(\cdot)\|_p,$$

then $f(\cdot)$ must have the form given by the theorem.

COROLLARY.   *The space* $\mathbf{L}_p(X;\tau)$ *is rotund (smooth) whenever* X *is rotund (smooth) and* $1 < p < \infty$.

PROOF.   Since both extremals $\bar{x}(t)$ and $|x(\cdot)|$ are unique when X is smooth, it follows that $\hat{x}(t)$ is unique, hence $\mathbf{L}_p(X;\tau)$ is smooth. When X is rotund, X^* is smooth, which implies $\mathbf{L}_p(X^*;\tau)$ is smooth, hence $\mathbf{L}_p(X;\tau)$ is rotund.

The notation of the preceding development is rather elaborate and it is therefore useful to consider these concepts in a less abstract setting.

Example 6.   Throughout this example the pairs (r,s) and (p,q) denote conjugate indices (i.e., $1/r + 1/s = 1$, $1/p + 1/q = 1$) and X is the real n-dimensional space $l_r(n)$ equipped with the usual norm $|\ |_r$ (see Examples 1, 2) for $1 \le r \le \infty$. We shall use $B_{p,r}$ in lieu of the more cumbersome notation $\mathbf{L}_p(l_r(n),\tau)$ to denote the space of all finite vector-valued functions $\tau \to l_r(n)$

equipped with the norm

$$\|x\|_p = \left[\int_\tau |x(t)|_r^p dt \right]^{1/p}, \qquad x \in B_{p,r}, \qquad 1 \le p < \infty, 1 \le r \le \infty.$$

We have observed earlier that $B_{p,r}^*$ may be identified with $B_{q,s}$ for $1 < r$, $p < \infty$. It is instructive to delineate the computation of the extremal function from $B_{p,r}$ into its conjugate. From Example 2 for $1 < r < \infty$ the unique extremal of $\xi \in l_2(n)$ is the element $\bar\xi \in l_s(n)$, $1/r + 1/s = 1$, defined by

$$\bar\xi = |\xi|_r^{(1-r)}(\bar\xi_1, \dots, \bar\xi_n), \qquad \bar\xi_i = \text{sign}[\xi_i]|\xi_i|^{r-1}.$$

To use Theorem G we recall from Example 1 that for $z \in L_p(\tau)$ the extremal is the element $\tilde z \in L_q(\tau)$, $1/p + 1/q = 1$, computed by the formula

$$\tilde z(t) = \|z\|_p^{(1-p)} \text{sign}[z(t)]|z(t)|^{p-1}, \qquad t \in \tau.$$

With these formulas at our disposal, we may compute the extremal $\hat x \in B_{q,s}$ of an element $x \in B_{p,r}$. Using these results, we obtain

$$\bar x(t) = |x(t)|_r^{(1-r)}[\bar x_1(t), \dots, \bar x_n(t)], \qquad \bar x_i(t) = \text{sign}[x_i(t)]|x_i(t)|^{r-1}, \qquad t \in \tau,$$

$$\widetilde{|x(t)|_r} = \left[\left(\int_\tau |x(t)|_r^p dt \right)^{1/p} \right]^{(1-p)} |x(t)|_r^{p-1},$$

and finally

$$\hat x(t) = (\widetilde{|x(t)|_r})\bar x(t), \qquad t \in \tau.$$

Since the expressions involved are complicated, it is instructive to check this result. First notice that

$$\langle\!\langle x,x \rangle\!\rangle = \int_\tau \langle x(t),\hat x(t) \rangle dt = \int_\tau \widetilde{|x(t)|_r}\langle x(t),\bar x(t) \rangle dt,$$

where

$$\langle x(t),\bar x(t) \rangle = |x(t)|_r^{(1-r)} \sum_{i=1}^n |x_i(t)|^r = |x(t)|_r.$$

Substitution of the second expression into the first yields

$$\langle\!\langle x,\hat x \rangle\!\rangle = \int_\tau \widetilde{|x(t)|_r} \cdot |x(t)|_r dt = \int_\tau \|x\|_p^{(1-p)} \cdot |x(t)|_r^p dt = \|x\|_p.$$

Knowing that $\langle\!\langle x,\hat x \rangle\!\rangle = \|x\|$, it remains only to show that $\|\hat x\| = 1$. To check this we verify first that $|\hat{x}(t)|_s = \widetilde{|x(t)|}_r$, which follows from the equality chain

$$|\hat{x}(t)|_s = |(\widetilde{|x(t)|}_r)| \cdot |\bar{x}(t)|_s = \widetilde{|x(t)|}_r \cdot |x(t)|_s^{(1-s)} \cdot \left(\sum_{i=1}^{n} |\bar{x}_i(t)|^s\right)^{1/s}$$

$$= \widetilde{|x(t)|}_r \cdot |x(t)|_r^{(1-r)} \cdot \left(\sum_{i=1}^{n} |x_i(t)|^r\right)^{1/s}$$

$$= \widetilde{|x(t)|}_r \cdot |x(t)|_r^{(1-r)} \cdot |x(t)|_r^{(r-1)} = \widetilde{|x(t)|}_r.$$

Now we have

$$\|\hat{x}\| = \left[\int_\tau |\hat{x}(t)|_s^q dt\right]^{1/q} = \left[\int_\tau (\widetilde{|x(t)|}_r)^q dt\right]^{1/q}$$

$$= \left[\left(\int_\tau |x(t)|_r^p dt\right)^{1/p}\right]^{(1-p)} \left[\int_\tau |x(t)|_r^{q(p-1)} dt\right]^{1/q},$$

and since $q(p-1) = p$ and $1/q = (p-1)/p$ it is immediately seen that $\|\hat{x}\| = 1$.

Example 7.   The limiting cases $p, r = 1$ of Example 6 are also of interest in the applications. Let us agree to the interpretation of $B_{\infty, r}$ as the space of all n-tuples $x(t) = [x_1(t), \ldots, x_n(t)]$, $t \in \tau$, equipped with the norm

$$\|x\|_\infty = \sup_{t \in \tau} \{|x(t)|_r\}, \qquad x \in B_{\infty, r}.$$

Then it can be shown, as when $n = 1$, that the identifications $B_{1,r}^* = B_{\infty, s}$, $B_{1,1}^* = B_{\infty, \infty}$, and $B_{p,1}^* = B_{q, \infty}$ are valid. The spaces $B_{1,r}$ and $B_{p,1}$, $1 \leq p$, $r < \infty$, are not smooth; hence the extremal relationship into the respective conjugates is not unique. Grimmell [B43] has studied these spaces and determined the conditions that an extremal must satisfy.

The element $\hat{x} \in B_{\infty, s}$, defined by

$$\hat{x}(t) = (\hat{x}_1(t), \ldots, \hat{x}_n(t)), \qquad t \in \tau,$$

is an extremal of the element $x \in B_{1,r}$

$$x(t) = (x_1(t), \ldots, x_n(t)), \qquad t \in \tau,$$

if it satisfies the following conditions:
  (1) When $s = 1$, then

$$\hat{x}_i(t) = k_i(t) \operatorname{sign} [x_i(t)], \qquad t \in \tau, i = 1, \ldots, n,$$

where $k_i(t) \geq 0$, $t \in \tau$, $i = 1, \ldots, n$ with $\sum_{i=1}^{n} k_i(t) = 1$, $t \in \tau$, and $k_i(t) = 0$ wherever $|x_i(t)| < \max_j\{|x_j(t)|\}$.

(2) When $1 < s < \infty$, $1/s + 1/r = 1$, then

$$\hat{x}_i(t) = M(t)|x_i(t)|^{r/s} \operatorname{sign}\,[x_i(t)], \qquad t \in \tau, \qquad i = 1, 2, \ldots, n,$$

where $M(t) = \left[\sum_{i=1}^{n}|x_i(t)|^r\right]^{-1/s}$, $t \in \tau$.

(3) When $s = \infty$, then

$$\hat{x}_i(t) = \operatorname{sign}\,[x_i(t)], \qquad \text{if} \quad x_i(t) \neq 0,$$

$$|x_i(t)| \leq 1, \qquad \text{if} \quad x_i(t) = 0.$$

Exercises

1. Let u_ξ denote a minimum element of $T^{-1}(\xi)$ and show that λu_ξ is a minimum element of $T^{-1}(\lambda\xi)$.

2. Use the Hahn-Banach theorem to show that if B is reflexive then for every $f \in B^*$, $u \in B$, $\|u\| = 1$ exists such that $f(u) = \|f\|$.

3. Show that every Hilbert space H is rotund and smooth. Prove that the extremal of $x \in H$ is $\bar{x} = x/\|x\|$.

4. Complete the proof of Theorem B by showing $(1) \Rightarrow (2)$. HINT: Regroup terms in the expression $\|[\alpha\|x_2\|x_1 + (1 - \alpha)\|x_1\|x_2]\|$ and use the triangle inequality.

5. Let C be a convex set in the Banach space B and $\xi \in \partial C$. Show that the set of all outward normals to C at ξ form a cone. Show that the set of all extremals of $x \in B$ form a cone.

6. Show that $L_2(X;\tau)$ is a Hilbert space whenever X is. Illustrate for the case $X = l_2$.

7. Consider the three Banach spaces $B = L_p(a,c)$, $B_1 = L_p(a,b)$, and $B_2 = L_p(b,c)$, where $a \leq b \leq c$, $1 < p < \infty$. Verify that the space B may be treated as a product of B_1 and B_2 if $x = (x_1,x_2)$ is interpreted to mean the function

$$x(t) = \begin{cases} x_1(t), & t \in [a,b), \\ x_2(t), & t \in [b,c]; \end{cases}$$

where the product $B_1 \times B_2$ is equipped with the norm of Theorem D. Deduce from this result that if $\bar{x} \in L_q(\tau)$ is the extremal of $x \in L_p(\tau)$ the extremal of any "segment" of x is the corresponding "segment" of $\bar{x}$.

8. Consider the system with input u and output x defined by the equation

$$x(t) = \int_0^t W(t,s)u(s)ds, \qquad t \geq 0.$$

The system operates in a two-stage manner for which the criterion of performance is the index

$$J(u) = \left[\int_0^{t_1} |u(s)|^{3/2} ds \right]^{2p/3} + \left[\int_{t_1}^{t_2} \mu(s)|u(s)|^2 ds \right]^{p/2},$$

where $\mu(t) > 0$ all $t \geq 0$ and $1 < p < \infty$. Find the unique control that satisfies $x(t_2) = \xi$ which minimizes J. HINT: Use Exercise 7.

9. Let B denote the Banach space $B_1 \times B_2$ equipped with the norm

$$\||(u_1, u_2)\|| = |(\|u_1\|, \|u_2\|)|,$$

where the double bars denote norms on B_1 and B_2, and $|\ |$ denotes a norm on R^2. Let U, U_1, and U_2 denote the unit balls of these spaces. Show that

$$U \supset \{(u_1, u_2): u_1 \in \alpha U_1, u_2 \in (1 - \alpha)U_2, 0 \leq \alpha \leq 1\}.$$

In other words, $U \supset \alpha[U_1 \times \{0\}] + (1 - \alpha)[\{0\} \times U_2]$. Show that if $\||(u_1, u_2)\|| = \|u_1\| + \|u_2\|$ the reverse inclusion is true. Give an example for which the reverse inclusion does not hold.

10. Let B denote the space $\mathbf{L}_1(l_2(n);\tau)$ of Examples 6 and 7; that is,

$$\|x\| = \int_\tau \left[\sum_{j=1}^n |x_j(t)|^2 \right]^{1/2} dt, \qquad x = (x_1, \ldots, x_n) \in B.$$

Show that $B^* = \mathbf{L}_\infty(l_2(n):\tau)$ and that

$$\|f\| = \sup_{t \in \tau} \left[\sum_{j=1}^n |f_j(t)|^2 \right]^{1/2}, \qquad f = (f_1, \ldots, f_n) \in B^*.$$

Show that the extremal $\hat{x} \in B^*$ of $x \in B$ is defined by

$$\hat{x}(t) = \begin{cases} \dfrac{x(t)}{|x(t)|}, & x(t) \neq 0, \\ |x(t)| \leq 1, & x(t) = 0, \end{cases}$$

for $t \in \tau$ where $|x(t)| = \left[\sum_{j=1}^n \|x_j(t)\|^2 \right]^{1/2}$.

4.3 THE SOLUTION OF PROBLEM 1

With the background developed in Sections 4.1 and 4.2, we are now in a position to solve Problem 1. Throughout this section B and D denote Banach spaces and T a bounded linear transformation from B *onto* D. Let U and ∂U denote the unit ball and unit sphere of B, respectively, and $C = T(U)$ the image of U in D under T. The boundary of C is denoted by ∂C. The elementary properties of the set C are summarized by Lemma A.

LEMMA A. (a) *The set C is a convex circled neighborhood of 0 in D.*
(b) $C \cap \partial C \subset T(\partial U)$.
(c) *C is closed if and only if $\partial C \subset T(\partial U)$.*

P R O O F. That C is convex and circled follows easily from the linearity of T and the definition of C. Since T is onto, it follows from the open mapping theorem (see Appendix 7) that $T(U)$ contains a multiple of the unit ball in D and hence that C is a neighborhood of 0 in D. To prove (b) we suppose that $\xi \in C \cap \partial C$. Then $\xi = Tu$ for some $u \in U$. Moreover, if $\lambda > 1$, then $\lambda \xi \notin C$ and therefore $\lambda u \notin U$. This means that $\|u\| > 1/\lambda$ and, since λ is arbitrary, $\|u\| \geq 1$. Hence $\xi \in T(\partial U)$.[1] Finally, if C is closed, $\partial C = C \cap \partial C$ and by (b) $\partial C \subset T(\partial U)$. Conversely, the condition $\partial C \subset T(\partial U)$ gives $\partial C \subset T(U) = C$ so that C is closed.

R E M A R K 1. It is easy to construct examples to show that the reverse inclusion to (c) it not valid in general. For example, let B be a three-dimensional Euclidean space and let T be the linear transformation from B onto the two-dimensional Euclidean space given by

$$T(x_1, x_2, x_3) = (x_1, x_2).$$

Then

$$U = [(x_1, x_2, x_3): |x_1|^2 + |x_2|^2 + |x_2|^2 \leq 1]$$

and

$$T(U) = C = [(x_1, x_2): |x_1|^2 + |x_2|^2 \leq 1].$$

The vector $(0,0,1)$ belongs to ∂U, whereas its image $(0,0)$ is certainly not a boundary point of C.

LEMMA B. *If $\xi \in \partial C$, every preimage of ξ has norm at least 1.*

P R O O F. From Lemma A the closure of C is a convex body. Hence, if $\xi \in \partial C$, there exists a $\phi \in D^*$ such that

$$\mathrm{Re}\langle \xi, \phi \rangle \geq \mathrm{Re}\langle \eta, \phi \rangle, \qquad \text{all } \eta \in C.$$

Since $C = T(U)$ is circled, this implies that

$$\mathrm{Re}\langle \xi, \phi \rangle \geq |\langle Tu, \phi \rangle| = |\langle u, T^*\phi \rangle|, \qquad \text{all } u \in U.$$

Taking the supremum of the right side over U, we obtain

$$\mathrm{Re}\langle \xi, \phi \rangle \geq \|T^*\phi\|.$$

It now follows that if $u \in B$ maps into ξ, then

$$\|u\| \cdot \|T^*\phi\| \geq \mathrm{Re}\langle u, T^*\phi \rangle = \mathrm{Re}\langle \xi, \phi \rangle \geq \|T^*\phi\|;$$

that is, $\|u\| \geq 1$.

---

[1] Part (b) may also be proved by noting that since T maps open sets into open sets it follows that T [int (U)] is an open subset of C; hence int $(C) \subset T$ [int (U)]. This implies $C \cap \partial C \subset T(\partial U)$.

Let us use the set inverse notation $T^{-1}(\xi)$ to denote the set of all pre-images of the vector $\xi \in D$. Our next theorem indicates when $T^{-1}(\xi)$ has a minimum element.

THEOREM A.   *Let $\xi \in \partial C$. Then $T^{-1}(\xi)$ has a minimum element if and only if $\xi \in C$.*

PROOF.   If $\xi \in C \cap \partial C$, then $T^{-1}(\xi)$ contains an element of U and because $\xi \in \partial C$ it follows from Lemma B that this element has the minimum norm. Conversely, suppose that u_ξ is a minimum element of $T^{-1}(\xi)$. It is clear from the homogeneity of T that αu_ξ is a minimum element of $T^{-1}(\alpha \xi)$ for any scalar $\alpha > 0$. Now, if $\alpha < 1$, then $\alpha \xi \in C$ and therefore $\alpha \xi$ has a pre-image of norm ≤ 1. Consequently, $\|\alpha u_\xi\| \leq 1$. Since α is arbitrary, it follows that $\|u_\xi\| \leq 1$. Thus $u_\xi \in \partial U$ and $\xi = T u_\xi \in C$.

COROLLARY 1.   *$T^{-1}(\xi)$ contains a minimum element for each $\xi \in D$ if and only if C is closed.*

PROOF.   If $T^{-1}(\xi)$ has a minimum element for each $\xi \in D$, any $\xi \in \partial C$ belongs to C by Theorem A. Conversely, suppose C is closed and p is the Minkowski functional of C. If $\xi \neq 0$ belongs to D, we have $p(\xi)^{-1}\xi \in \partial C \cap C$; hence by Theorem A the element $[p(\xi)]^{-1}\xi$ has a minimum preimage, which implies that ξ has a minimum preimage.

In Theorem A and its corollary we have isolated the key ingredients in the existence question for Problem 1. The preceding case, in which T has rank 1, is clearly visible within these results. The characterization following Theorem A of Section 4.2 has a striking resemblance to the solution of Problem 1 in its present form.

Our first example shows that even for very simple physical systems the set C can be quite interesting.

Example 1.   Figure 4.12 is a simplified three-integrator system with switching. Let us assume that the system inputs are continuous functions

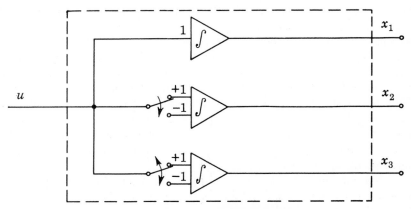

Figure 4.12   A simple linear system.

and that we are interested in the values of the outputs $\{x_1, x_2, x_3\}$ at time $t = 1$. If we assume zero integrator initial conditions, it is clear that the system may be viewed as a linear transformation $T: C(0,1) \to R^3$. To define T it remains only to specify the switching behavior of the system. The middle switch changes polarity once at time $t = \frac{1}{2}$ from plus to minus. The other switch reverses polarity three times, being initially plus and switching at times $\{\frac{1}{4}, \frac{1}{2}, \frac{3}{4}\}$.

With $\chi(a,b)$ denoting the characteristic function of the interval $(a,b]$, the three functions defined by $f_1 = \chi(0,1)$, $f_2 = \chi(0,\frac{1}{2}) - \chi(\frac{1}{2},1)$, and $f_3 = \chi(0,\frac{1}{4}) - \chi(\frac{1}{4},\frac{1}{2}) + \chi(\frac{1}{2},\frac{3}{4}) - \chi(\frac{3}{4},1)$ are of bounded variation and may be used to define the following functionals on $C(0,1)$:

$$f_1(u) = \langle u, f_1 \rangle = \int_0^1 u(s)ds, \qquad\qquad\qquad u \in C(0,1),$$

$$f_2(u) = \langle u, f_2 \rangle = \int_0^{1/2} u(s)ds - \int_{1/2}^1 u(s)ds, \qquad\qquad u \in C(0,1),$$

$$f_3(u) = \langle u, f_3 \rangle = \int_0^{1/4} u(s)ds - \int_{1/4}^{1/2} u(s)ds + \int_{1/2}^{3/4} u(s)ds$$

$$- \int_{3/4}^1 u(s)ds, \qquad\qquad u \in C(0,1).$$

With these definitions the system transformation can be written

$$T = \sum_{i=1}^{3} e_i \gt \lt f_i,$$

where $\{e_1, e_2, e_3\}$ is the coordinate basis for R^3.

The closure of the set $C = T(U)$ for this system turns out to be the convex closure of the points $\{(1,0,0), (0,1,0), (0,0,1), (\frac{1}{2},\frac{1}{2},\frac{1}{2}), (\frac{1}{2},-\frac{1}{2},\frac{1}{2}), (\frac{1}{2},\frac{1}{2},-\frac{1}{2}), (\frac{1}{2},-\frac{1}{2},-\frac{1}{2})\}$ and their negatives. Thus in each octant of R^3 the set $\bar{C}$ has the same shape, resembling, when viewed from the exterior of C, an equilateral triangle (Figure 4.13). The sets C and $\bar{C}$ can differ only in the matter of boundary points. It can be shown that the set C has one configuration in four of the eight octants of R^3 and a second configuration in the others.

The four octants with the first configuration are those containing the points $\{(\frac{1}{2},\frac{1}{2},\frac{1}{2}), (\frac{1}{2},-\frac{1}{2},-\frac{1}{2}), (-\frac{1}{2},\frac{1}{2},\frac{1}{2})$, and $(-\frac{1}{2},-\frac{1}{2},-\frac{1}{2})\}$, respectively. Figure 4.13(a) depicts the set C in one of these octants. In this octant *only* the boundary points $(0,0,1)$ and $(\frac{1}{2},\frac{1}{2},\frac{1}{2})$, the line segment between them, and the isolated point $(0,1,0)$ are *not* in C.

In the remaining octants the set C has quite a bit of missing boundary. Figure 4.13(b) describes the octant containing $(\frac{1}{2},\frac{1}{2},-\frac{1}{2})$. It is not difficult to show that the face of ∂C consisting of the convex closure of $\{(0,1,0),$

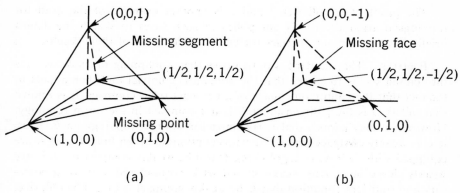

Figure 4.13   Two views of the set *C*.

$(0,0,-1)$, $(\frac{1}{2},\frac{1}{2},-\frac{1}{2})\}$ is *not* contained in *C*; *C* does contain the remainder of ∂C in this quadrant.

Two cases when C is closed. The situation in which Problem 1 has solutions for every $\xi \in D$ is of special interest and we now consider two specific cases in which this occurs. In both cases *B* is the conjugate of another space; that is, another Banach space *X* exists such that $B = X^*$. The first case occurs when *B* is reflexive [here *X* may be taken as B^*; i.e., $B^{**} = (B^*)^* = B$]. Then if *T* is any bounded linear transformation *C* is closed. In other words we can solve Problem 1 for *any* transformation *T* on *B* regardless of the nature of its range *D*, provided that *B* is reflexive (and *T* is onto). Conversely, if Problem 1 has a solution for every transformation (in particular, those of rank 1), James's result, cited earlier, shows that *B* must be reflexive. This gives us the following corollary to Theorem A.

COROLLARY 2.   *Problem 1 has a solution for every bounded linear (onto) transformation defined on B if and only if B is reflexive.*

In the second case that we shall describe explicitly we replace the condition "*B* is reflexive" by conditions on *T* and *D*. In this case a Banach space *Y* must exist such that $D = Y^*$, and we denote by $S: Y \to X$ a bounded linear transformation which sends *Y* into *X*. Then S^* is a bounded linear transformation between the right spaces (i.e., $B \to D$) for Problem 1. (The reader may find it helpful to sketch a set operator diagram of case two.) Now, if *S*, defined on all of *Y*, is one-to-one and maps onto a *closed* subspace of *X*, the set $C = S^*(U) \subset D = Y^*$ is closed. Thus we have the following corollary.

COROLLARY 3.   *Let S be a one-to-one and bounded linear transformation from Y onto a closed subspace of X. Problem 1 can then always be solved for the transformation $T = S^*$; that is, for every $\xi \in D = Y^*$ there is a preimage $u_\xi \in B = X^*$ of ξ under $T = S^*$ with minimum norm.*

The proof of Corollaries 2 and 3 is another example of the need for topological arguments. It is our policy in such cases to sketch the details briefly, thus saving our energies for enjoying the fruits of these results.

P R O O F. The standard way to prove that a mapping takes closed sets into closed sets is to ensure that the domain is compact and then appeal to the fact that the continuous image of a compact set is compact. It is known that unless B is finite-dimensional U is not compact in the norm topology. However, it may happen that U is compact in another topology on B. Thus, if U is weakly compact (since T remains continuous when both B and D are equipped with their weak topologies), C will be weakly compact in D, hence weakly closed in D. Any weakly closed set is norm-closed. Finally, a necessary and sufficient condition that U be weakly compact is that B be reflexive, and Corollary 2 is proved.

Earlier we had occasion to mention that the unit ball in the dual of any Banach space is weak-star compact (Alaoglu's theorem). This yields Corollary 3. More precisely, we make use of the following facts: if S is a bounded linear transformation from a Banach space Y into a Banach space X, its conjugate S^* maps X^* into Y^*. The mapping of S^* is continuous when both X^* and Y^* are equipped with their weak-star topologies; hence, if U denotes the unit ball in X^*, then $S^*(U^*)$ is weak-star compact in Y^* and therefore is norm-closed in Y^*. If S is one-to-one and maps open sets of Y into open sets of X [in particular, if S is one-to-one and has closed range (see Theorem B, Appendix 7)], $S^*(U^*)$ will contain a multiple of the unit ball in Y^*.

Finally, we note that an immediate consequence of Corollary 2 is that if B is finite-dimensional Problem 1 will always have a solution. Similarly, if D is finite-dimensional and S is one-to-one, Corollary 3 guarantees that the problem is solvable for every $\xi \in Y^*$.

The Form of the Optimal Control

Now that we have established the necessary and sufficient conditions for existence of solutions to Problem 1 our interest turns toward obtaining a more explicit characterization of the set $\partial C \cap C$ and the form of the solutions to Problem 1. As in Section 4.2, the notation $\bar{f} \in B$ ($\bar{x} \in B^*$) denotes the extremal or the set of all extremals of the element $f \in B^*$ ($x \in B$).

THEOREM B. *Let $\phi \in D^*$ and suppose that the set $\overline{T^*\phi}$ is nonempty. Then the set containment $T(\overline{T^*\phi}) \subset C \cap \partial C$ holds. Conversely each $\xi \in C \cap \partial C$ can be written as $T(\overline{T^*\phi})$ for some $\phi \in D^*$ for which the set $\overline{T^*\phi}$ is nonempty.*

P R O O F. Suppose that $\phi \in D^*$ is given and that $T^*\phi$ has an extremal u_ϕ in B. Put $\xi_\phi = Tu_\phi$. Clearly $\xi_\phi \in C$ so that it suffices to prove that $\xi_\phi \in \partial C$. To this end note that each vector $\eta \in C$ has the form $\eta = Tu$ for some $u \in U$, and consequently

$$\text{Re}\langle \eta, \phi \rangle = \text{Re}\langle u, T^*\phi \rangle \leq \|T^*\phi\| = \langle u_\phi, T^*\phi \rangle$$
$$= \langle \xi_\phi, \phi \rangle.$$

In other words, the functional ϕ assumes its maximum value on C at the vector ξ_ϕ, which, together with the fact that any linear functional maps open sets into open sets, shows that ξ_ϕ cannot belong to the interior of C. This shows that $\{T(\overline{T^*\phi}) : \phi \in D^*\} \subset C \cap \partial C$.

To complete the proof we show that if $\xi \in C \cap \partial C$ then the minimum preimages of ξ guaranteed by Theorem A each have the form $\overline{T^*\phi}$ for some $\phi \in D^*$. Now, since $\xi \in \partial C$ and C has an interior (hence a convex body), we may choose a vector $\phi \in D)^*$ with

$$\text{Re}\langle \xi, \phi \rangle \geq \|T^*\phi\|.$$

On the other hand, ξ belongs to C, hence $\xi = Tu$ for some $u \in U$, so that

$$\|T^*\phi\| \geq \text{Re}\langle u, T^*\phi \rangle = \text{Re}\langle \xi, \phi \rangle.$$

These two inequalities prove that $\langle \xi, \phi \rangle$ is real and that

$$\langle u, T^*\phi \rangle = \langle \xi, \phi \rangle = \|T^*\phi\|.$$

Since $u \in U$, this implies u is an extremal of $T^*\phi$ and therefore $\xi = Tu \in \{T(\overline{T^*\phi}) : \phi \in D^*\}$.

The relation between ξ and ϕ is made clear by Corollary 1.

COROLLARY 1.   *If $\xi \in C \cap \partial C$, then $\xi = T(\overline{T^*\phi})$ for some $\phi \in D^*$ if and only if this ϕ defines a hyperplane of support of C at ξ.*

P R O O F.   In proving the theorem we showed that if ϕ defines a hyperplane of support of C at ξ then $T(\overline{T^*\phi}) = \xi$. Conversely, if the vector $\phi \in D^*$ satisfies $T(\overline{T^*\phi}) = \xi$, it follows that for each $u \in U$

$$\text{Re}\langle Tu, \phi \rangle = \text{Re}\langle u, T^*\phi \rangle \leq \|T^*\phi\| = \langle \overline{T^*\phi}, T^*\phi \rangle$$
$$= \langle \xi, \phi \rangle$$

and consequently the hyperplane

$$\{\eta : \langle \eta, \phi \rangle = \langle \xi, \phi \rangle\}$$

supports C at ξ.

COROLLARY 2.   *Let $\xi \in \partial C \cap C$ and let ϕ support C at ξ. Then $T^*\phi$ attains its supremum on U. Conversely, if for some $\phi \in D^*$ the functional $T^*\phi$ attains its supremum on U, then $T^{-1}(\xi_\phi)$ will have a minimum element for each $\xi_\phi \in T(\overline{T^*\phi})$.*

P R O O F.   If ϕ supports C at ξ, the proof of Theorem B will show that $T^*\phi$ has an extremal. Conversely, if $\overline{T^*\phi}$ is nonempty for some $\phi \in D^*$, then, by Theorem B, $T(\overline{T^*\phi}) \subset C \cap \partial C$. Hence by Theorem A each $\xi_\phi \in T(\overline{T^*\phi})$ has a minimum preimage.

R E M A R K   2.   If B is reflexive or the conditions of Corollary 3, Theorem A, hold, then by combining Theorems A and B we see that $T^{-1}(\xi)$ has minimum elements for every $\xi \in D$. Each minimum element must have the form $u_\xi = p(\xi)\overline{T^*\phi}$ for some outward normal ϕ to C at $[p(\xi)]^{-1}\xi$ and some extremal of $T^*\phi$. If, in the latter case, Y is reflexive, we may identify ϕ as an element of Y rather than as an element of $D^* = (Y^*)^*$. Similarly, we may replace T^* by its restriction to Y, namely S. By taking extremals from X into $B = X^*$ instead of X^{**} into X^*, this characterization becomes $u_\xi = p(\xi)(\overline{S\phi})$.

In Theorem B and its corollaries we have reduced the optimal control problem to one of constructing hyperplanes of support for convex sets and computing extremals in Banach spaces. To illustrate these steps in a concrete setting, our next example deals with a physical system for which the set C is closed.

Example 2 (Grimmell [B43]).   We have seen that a variety of simple dynamic systems is described in whole or in part by differential equations of the second order. Figure 4.14 shows the analog simulation of one system whose governing equations are given by

$$\begin{bmatrix} \dot{x}_1(t) \\ \dot{x}_2(t) \end{bmatrix} = \begin{bmatrix} a & b \\ c & d \end{bmatrix} \cdot \begin{bmatrix} x_1(t) \\ x_2(t) \end{bmatrix} + \begin{bmatrix} e & g \\ f & h \end{bmatrix} \cdot \begin{bmatrix} u_1(t) \\ u_2(t) \end{bmatrix}, \qquad t \geq t_0. \qquad (1)$$

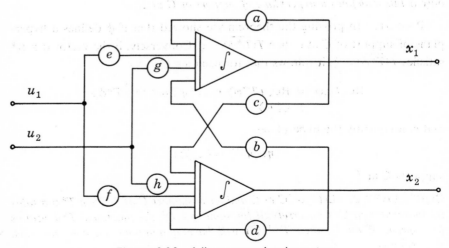

Figure 4.14   A linear second-order system.

To be absolutely explicit in this example we shall use the numerical values $a = \frac{1}{2}$, $b = -\frac{1}{2}$, $c = \frac{1}{2}$, $d = -\frac{1}{2}$, $e = 1$, $f = 1$, $g = 1$, and $h = -1$. It then follows that Eq. 1 can be written in equivalent form:

$$\begin{bmatrix} x_1(t) \\ x_2(t) \end{bmatrix} = \begin{bmatrix} 1 + \frac{1}{2}(t - t_0) & -\frac{1}{2}(t - t_0) \\ \frac{1}{2}(t - t_0) & 1 - \frac{1}{2}(t - t_0) \end{bmatrix} \cdot \begin{bmatrix} x_1(t_0) \\ x_2(t_0) \end{bmatrix}$$

$$+ \int_{t_0}^{t} \begin{bmatrix} 1 + \frac{1}{2}(t - s) & -\frac{1}{2}(t - s) \\ \frac{1}{2}(t - s) & 1 - \frac{1}{2}(t - s) \end{bmatrix} \cdot \begin{bmatrix} 1 & 1 \\ 1 & -1 \end{bmatrix} \cdot \begin{bmatrix} u_1(s) \\ u_2(s) \end{bmatrix} ds, \quad t \geq t_0. \quad (2)$$

To investigate problems of an optimal transfer $[x_1(t_0), x_2(t_0)] \to [x_1(t_f), x_2(t_f)]$ it is sufficient to study the problem $\xi = Tu$ in which $u(t) = [u_1(t), u_2(t)]$, $t \in [t_0, t_f]$ and $\xi = (\xi_1, \xi_2,)$ with

$$\begin{bmatrix} \xi_1 \\ \xi_2 \end{bmatrix} = \begin{bmatrix} \frac{1}{2} & \frac{1}{2} \\ \frac{1}{2} & -\frac{1}{2} \end{bmatrix} \cdot \left(\begin{bmatrix} 1 - \frac{1}{2}(t - t_0) & \frac{1}{2}(t - t_0) \\ -\frac{1}{2}(t - t_0) & 1 + \frac{1}{2}(t - t_0) \end{bmatrix} \begin{bmatrix} x_1(t_f) \\ x_2(t_f) \end{bmatrix} - \begin{bmatrix} x_1(t_0) \\ x_2(t_0) \end{bmatrix} \right)$$

and with T being the linear transformation sending u into R^2 according to the rule

$$T(u) = \int_{t_0}^{t_f} \begin{bmatrix} 1 & -(s - t_0) \\ 0 & 1 \end{bmatrix} \cdot \begin{bmatrix} u_1(s) \\ u_2(s) \end{bmatrix} ds. \quad (3)$$

The criterion of optimality to be studied here is motivated by the engineering considerations mentioned earlier. Suppose that our system is mechanical and that the functions u_1, u_2 represent fuel flow rates. Now fuel sources are frequently flow rate limited by orifice (valve opening) or fuel-line diameter restrictions; that is, the supply systems saturate as functions of $|u_1(t)|$ and $|u_2(t)|$. Such saturation must be taken into account in the controller design. Even in this simple example saturation can take a variety of forms.

C A S E 1.   Consider first the circumstances in which u_1 and u_2 represent flow rates from independent fuel supplies for which saturation sets in at the same value[1] for each supply. If the fuel supply itself is unlimited, it is natural to choose as an optimality criterion the function

$$J(u) = \sup_{t \in [t_0, t_f]} \max \{|u_1(t)|, |u_2(t)|\}.$$

Without loss of engineering significance, we require that u_1, u_2 be measurable. $J(u)$ then coincides with the norm of the tuplet (u_1, u_2) as an element of the space $B_{\infty, \infty}$ (see Example 7, Section 4.2, with $n = 2$). Hence the optimal control problem is a minimum norm problem for a mapping $T : B_{\infty, \infty} \to R^2$.

To apply the techniques of this section we first inquire into the circumstances of our transformation and its domain. $B_{\infty, \infty}$ is not reflexive, but we

---

[1] A judiciously chosen change of variables will often reduce more complicated saturation profiles to this form.

have seen that it is the conjugate of the Banach space $B_{1,1}$, and, if S is the linear transformation $R^2 \to B_{1,1}$ given by

$$(S\phi)(t) = \begin{bmatrix} 1 & 0 \\ -(t - t_0) & 1 \end{bmatrix} \cdot \begin{bmatrix} \phi_1 \\ \phi_2 \end{bmatrix}, \qquad t \in [t_0, t_f], \tag{4}$$

for arbitrary $\phi = (\phi_1, \phi_2) \in R^2$, it can be shown that $T = S^*$. Furthermore, S is onto a closed subspace, namely, the manifold spanned by the columns of the S matrix.

From these remarks it follows by Corollary 3 of Theorem A that the set $C = T(U)$ will be closed. Using the rules for computing extremals given in Example 7, Section 4.2, and the specific form of S given by Eq. 4, we find that the tuplet (u_1, u_2) is an extremal of $S\phi$ if

$$u_1(t) = \begin{cases} \text{sign}[\phi_1], & \phi_1 \neq 0, \\ |u_1(t)| \leq 1, & \phi_1 = 0, \, t \in [t_0, t_f], \end{cases} \tag{5}$$

$$u_2(t) = \text{sign}[(t_0 - t)\phi_1 + \phi_2], \qquad t \in [t_0, t_f].$$

C A S E 2.   Now suppose that u_1 and u_2 are fuel flows which emanate from a common source and that the limiting factor in the system performance is the total instantaneous flow. It is natural to choose as an optimality criterion the function

$$J(u) = \sup_{t \in \tau} (|u_1(t)| + |u_2(t)|).$$

This function coincides with the norm of the tuplet (u_1, u_2) as an element of the space $B_{\infty,1}$. Hence the optimal control problem is a minimum norm problem for a mapping $T : B_{\infty,1} \to R^2$.

We have seen that $B_{\infty,1}$ is the conjugate of the Banach space $B_{1,\infty}$. Also S, as previously defined, may be considered as a linear transformation from $R^2 \to B_{1,\infty}$, and again $T = S^*$. By applying Corollary 2, Theorem A, we see that the image of the unit ball of $B_{\infty,1}$ is closed. Using the form of S and the results of Example 7, Section 4.2, we see that the tuplet (u_1, u_2) is an extremal of $S\phi$ if

$$u_1(t) = \begin{cases} \text{sign}[\phi_1], & t \in E, \\ 0, & t \in [t_0, t_f] \sim E, \end{cases} \tag{6}$$

$$u_2(t) = \begin{cases} \text{sign}[\phi_2 + (t_0 - t)\phi_1], & t \in [t_0, t_f] \sim E, \\ 0, & t \in E, \end{cases}$$

where

$$E = \{t \in [t_0, t_f] : |\phi_1| > |\phi_2 + (t_0 - t)\phi_1|\}.$$

Since the set C is closed, ∂C may be traced out by computing the points $\{T(\overline{S\phi}): \phi \in R^2\}$. In the present example this computation is not difficult, and Figure 4.15 shows the set C for Cases 1 and 2 (here $t_0 = 0$, $t_f = 1$).

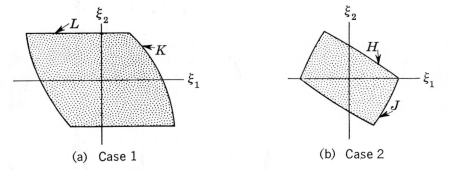

(a) Case 1   (b) Case 2

$K = \{(\xi_1,\xi_2):\xi_1 - 1.5 = -.25(\xi_2 + 1)^2\}$, $H = \{(\xi_1,\xi_2):\xi_1 - 1.5 = -.5(\xi_2 + 1)^2\}$,

$L = \{(\xi_1,\xi_2):\xi_2 = 1.0\}$, $J = \{(\xi_1,\xi_2):\xi_1 - 1 = -.5\xi_2^2\}$.

Figure 4.15 Two range sets.

It is instructive to trace the steps that are necessary to find a minimum norm control. As a concrete example, we consider the range element $\xi = (23, -8)$. Since the form of ∂C is explicitly known, we may readily determine where the ray from the origin through ξ intersects ∂C. To three-place accuracy, this point of intersection is $\xi'' = (0.946, -0.329)$ in Case 2 and $\xi' = (1.450, -0.500)$ in Case 1.

For Case 2 an outward normal to C at ξ'' is $\phi = (1, -0.329)$. Using Eq. 4, we find that

$$(S\phi)(t) = \begin{bmatrix} 1 \\ -t - 0.329 \end{bmatrix}, \qquad t \in [0,1].$$

Now, taking the extremal of $S\phi$, we can find the minimum norm preimage of ξ''. Since $\xi = 24.9\xi''$, we then multiply this extremal by 24.9 to find the minimum norm preimage of ξ. The resultant tuplet (u_1,u_2) is given by the conditions

$$u_1(t) = 24.9, \qquad u_2(t) = 0, \qquad \text{for } 0 \le t < 0.671,$$
$$u_1(t) = 0, \qquad u_2(t) = -24.9, \qquad \text{for } 0.671 \le t \le 1.$$

For Case 1 an outward normal to C at ξ' is $\phi = (4,1)$. It follows that

$$(S\phi)(t) = \begin{bmatrix} 1 \\ -4t + 1 \end{bmatrix}, \qquad t \in [0,1],$$

and since $\xi = 16\xi'$ the optimal control (u_1, u_2) for the first case is given by

$$u_1(t) = 16 \qquad \text{for} \qquad 0 \le t \le 1,$$

$$u_2(t) = \begin{cases} 16 & \text{for} \qquad 0 \le t < 0.25, \\ -16 & \text{for} \qquad 0.25 \le t \le 1, \end{cases}$$

which completes the solution to the optimal control problem.

Example 2 exhibits several important features of Problem 1. From Figure 4.15 it is clear that the set C can have both flat spots and corners. The flat spot L of Case 1 stems from the fact that the normal $\phi = (0,1)$ is carried by S into a functional with a nonunique extremal (see Eq. 5). The transformation T maps the set $\{\overline{S(0,1)}\}$ onto the line segment L; however, for each point on L it is easy to show that the minimum preimage is not unique. At the corner of the sets K and L there is a cone of outward normals to C. For each $\phi = (\phi_1, \phi_2)$ in this cone with $\phi_1 \ne 0$, however, the relation $\phi_2 + (t_0 - t_f)\phi_1 > 0$ holds; hence Eq. 5 shows that the optimal control is unique.

These ambiguities are not peculiar to the system of Example 2. Exercise 1 gives a second system for which the outward normal at some points of ∂C is not unique, although the optimal control is; at other points of ∂C the outward normal is unique but the optimal control is not. The system of Exercise 2 exhibits both situations and has in addition points in ∂C for which neither the outward normal nor the optimum control is unique.

At first it is annoying to find that in many cases the optimal control is not unique. However, from an engineering viewpoint this ambiguity provides a bonus of flexibility in the choice of the control function, a degree of freedom which perhaps can be used to achieve some other operational objective such as decreasing the system excursion into specified regions of the state space. The ambiguity may also be resolved by minimizing a secondary cost function determined by such factors as simplicity of the control function generation equipment, the bandwidth required by the signal, or system sensitivity to predictable disturbances. The system designer may also find this flexibility helpful in minimizing the inherent differences between the mathematical model used in the optimization and the actual behavior of the physical system.

Example 3.   Consider a system whose inputs are of the form $u = (u_1, u_2, u_3)$ where the u_i are real valued measurable functions defined on the interval $\tau = [t_0, t_f]$. Suppose the system operation can be represented by a linear transformation $T : B_{2,2}[t_0, t_f] \to R^n$ which is continuous and onto, and assume the following restrictions are placed on u: for all $t \in \tau$, $|u_1(t)| \le 1$, $|u_2(t)| \le 1$, and

$$\int_{t_0}^{t_f} (|u_1^2(t)|^2 + |u_2(t)|^2 + |u_3(t)|^2) dt \le 1.$$

To determine whether the system can accomplish a given state transfer, interest naturally focuses on the optimal control problem with the optimality criterion given by

$$J(u) = \max \{a(u), b(u)\},$$

$$a(u) = \sup_{t \in \tau} [\max \{|u_1(t)|, |u_2(t)|\}],$$

$$b(u) = \left(\int_{t_0}^{t_f} \sum_{i=1}^{3} |u_i(t)|^2 dt\right)^{1/2}.$$

It can be shown (see Grimmell [B43]) that for this problem, every state transfer can be accomplished in an optimal manner.

The reader may verify as an exercise that extremals of $T^*\phi$ have the form

$$u_1(t) = \begin{cases} c(T^*\phi)_1(t) & t \in ([t_0, t_f] \sim E_1) \\ \text{sign}[(T^*\phi)_1(t)] & t \in E_1 \end{cases}$$

$$u_2(t) = \begin{cases} c(T^*\phi)_2(t) & t \in ([t_0, t_f]) \sim E_2) \\ \text{sign}[(T^*\phi)_2(t)] & t \in E_2 \end{cases}$$

$$u_3(t) = c(T^*\phi)_2(t) \qquad t \in [t_0, t_f],$$

where $(T^*\phi)_i$ denotes the ith component of $T^*\phi$ and

$$E_1 = \{t \in \tau : c|(T^*\phi)_1(t)| \geq 1\},$$

$$E_2 = \{t \in \tau : c|(T^*\phi)_2(t)| \geq 1\},$$

while c is determined by the condition

$$\int_{t_0}^{t_f} \sum_{i=1}^{3} |u_i(t)|^2 dt = 1.$$

To aid in this regard consider

$$f = (f_1, f_2, f_3)$$

where

$$f_1(t) = \begin{cases} (T^*\phi)_1(t) & t \in [t_0, t_f] \sim E_1 \\ \dfrac{1}{c} \text{sign} [(T^*\phi)_1(t)] & t \in E_1 \end{cases}$$

$$f_2(t) = \begin{cases} (T^*\phi)_2(t) & t \in [t_0, t_f] \sim E_2 \\ \dfrac{1}{c} \text{sign} [(T^*\phi)_2(t)] & t \in E_2 \end{cases}$$

$$f_3(t) = (T^*\phi)_3(t).$$

If $\alpha_1(u)$, $\alpha_2(u)$ are defined by

$$\alpha_1(u) = \sum_{i=1}^{3} \int_{t_0}^{t_f} f_i(t)u_i(t)dt,$$

$$\alpha_2(u) = \int_{E_1} u_1(t)[(T^*\phi)_1(t) - f_1(t)]dt + \int_{E_2} u_2(t)[(T^*\phi)_2(t) - f_2(t)]dt,$$

respectively, then $\langle u, T^*\phi \rangle = \alpha_1(u) + \alpha_2(u)$. Now show that over the set of all u such that $J(u) = \sup_{t \in \tau}[\max\{u_1(t), u_2(t)\}]$, the u specified above maximizes $\alpha_2(u)$, and that over the set of all u such that $\int_{t_0}^{t_f} \sum_{i=1}^{3}|u_i(t)|^2 dt = 1$, the u specified above maximizes $\alpha_2(u)$.

Uniqueness Considerations in Problem 1

In Hilbert spaces Problem 1 is particularly well behaved; the set C has a unique unit outward normal at every boundary point and the set $T^{-1}(\xi)$ has a unique minimum element for every $\xi \in D$. A natural question to ask is whether some Banach spaces and/or some transformations also exhibit these nice properties.

Before proceeding, let us list once again the types of nonuniqueness that can occur in Theorem B: first, each $\xi \in C \cap \partial C$ may have more than one associated outward normal; second, for each outward normal ϕ at ξ the element $T^*\phi$ may have several extremals (conversely, $\overline{T^*\phi_1} = \overline{T^*\phi_2}$ may hold even though $\phi_1 \neq \phi_2$). Finally, two distinct extremals of a $T^*\phi$ may or may not map into the same element of $C \cap \partial C$ under T. What we shall now show is that these ambiguities may be systematically eliminated by restrictions on the domain B.

Observe that the set $T^{-1}(\xi)$ of preimages of ξ is closed and convex. Therefore, if B is rotund, this set will have *at most* one minimum element (see Theorem B, Section 4.2), which leads to the following theorem: *suppose B is rotund and let $\xi \in C \cap \partial C$. The* unique *minimum element of $T^{-1}(\xi)$ is given by $\overline{T^*\phi}$ for some $\phi \in D^*$; that is, if distinct outward normals ϕ_1, ϕ_2 to C at $\xi \in C \cap \partial C$ exist, then either $\overline{T^*\phi_1} = \overline{T^*\phi_2}$ or $T(\overline{T^*\phi_1}) \neq T(\overline{T^*\phi_2})$.* (Exercise 6 actually eliminates this latter possibility.)

It is worth noting that the hypothesis that B be rotund is also necessary in a sense. More precisely, if for *every* transformation T defined on B (with closed range) we require that the set $T^{-1}(\xi)$ have at most one minimum element for each ξ, then B is rotund. Indeed, the condition implies that each linear functional on B attains its supremum over U in at most one point, and this is equivalent to rotundity of B.

With this preliminary result at our disposal, we can readily prove Theorem C.[1]

---

[1] By analogy with the Hilbert space problem (i.e., minimum energy) the conditions of Theorem C are referred to on occasion as the *minimum effort problem.*

THEOREM C. *Let B be reflexive, rotund, and smooth. Let D, T, and C be as before and p be the Minkowski functional of C. For every $\xi \in D$ a unique unit $\phi_\xi \in D^*$ exists for which*

$$u_\xi = T^\dagger \xi = p(\xi)\overline{T^*\phi_\xi}$$

defines the unique preimage of ξ with minimum norm. The functional ϕ_ξ is uniquely determined by $\|\phi_\xi\| = 1$, and either of the conditions

(1) $\langle \eta, \phi_\xi \rangle \leq [p(\xi)]^{-1} \langle \xi, \phi_\xi \rangle$, all $\eta \in C$,
(2) $\|T^*\phi_\xi\| = [p(\xi)]^{-1} \langle \xi, \phi_\xi \rangle$.

(If *B* is complex (1) reads $\mathrm{Re}\langle \eta, \phi_\xi \rangle \leq [p(\xi)]^{-1} \mathrm{Re}\langle \xi, \phi_\xi \rangle$.)

  PROOF. If ϕ_1, ϕ_2 are two outward normals to *C* at $\xi \in \partial C \cap C$ we have from the rotundity of *B*

$$\overline{T^*\phi_1} = u_\xi = \overline{T^*\phi_2}.$$

Since *B* is also smooth we may take extremals on both sides of this equality with the result

$$\overline{T^*\phi_1} = \overline{T^*\phi_2} \Rightarrow \frac{T^*\phi_1}{\|T^*\phi_1\|} = \frac{T^*\phi_2}{\|T^*\phi_2\|}.$$

The theorem now follows from the condition $\|\phi\| = 1$ and the fact that T^* is one-to-one.

  Figure 4.16 is a two-dimensional version of Theorem C. For artistic convenience the range space *D* is depicted as a Hilbert space. Thus ϕ_ξ, the

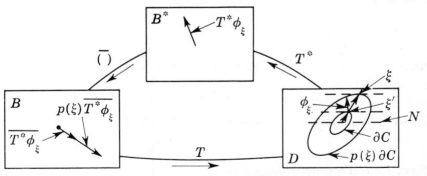

Figure 4.16 The elements of Theorem C.

unit outward normal to *C* at $\xi' = [p(\xi)]^{-1}\xi$, is drawn in *D* rather than as an element of D^*. Except perhaps for the set *N*, which is the null space of ϕ_ξ, the entries of Figure 4.16 are self-explanatory.

  Although the function $T^\dagger$ is well defined in Theorem C, it is done so in an implicit manner involving ϕ_ξ. To establish an explicit form of Theorem

C, we shall investigate the mapping $\xi \to \phi_\xi$ by making use of the conjugate-like function $K: B^* \to B$, which is defined in terms of the extremal operation by

$$K(f) = \|f\|\bar{f}, \qquad f \in B^*;$$

that is, the function K takes extremals and then restores the norm. From the properties of the extremal it is apparent that $K(\lambda f) = \bar{\lambda} K(f)$ for all λ and that $\langle f, Kf \rangle = \|f\|^2$.

Consider now the function $J: D^* \to D$ defined by $J = TKT^*$; that is,

$$J(\phi) = \|T^*\phi\| T(\overline{T^*\phi}), \qquad \phi \in D^*. \tag{7}$$

LEMMA C. *The function J is conjugate homogeneous, one-to-one, onto, and bounded.*

PROOF. The conjugate homogeneity of J [i.e, $J(\lambda x) = \bar{\lambda} J(x)$] is inherited from the homogeneity of T, T^* and the conjugate homogeneity of K. Since T and T^* are bounded, so is J. Because $\xi = \|T^*\phi_\xi\|^{-1}J(\phi_\xi)$ is the mapping of $\phi_\xi \to \xi$ between a unit outward normal and its support point $\xi \in \partial C$, it follows that J is onto. In Exercise 3 we note that J is one-to-one and in fact a *monotonic function*,

$$0 \leq \langle \phi_1 - \phi_2, J\phi_1 - J\phi_2 \rangle, \qquad \text{all } \phi_1, \phi_2 \in D^*.$$

Since J is bounded one-to-one and onto, the inverse J^{-1} exists. This inverse mapping is useful in our next characterization of $T^\dagger$.

COROLLARY 1. *If the conditions of Theorem C hold and $J: D^* \to D$ is defined by Eq. 7, the pseudoinverse function $T^\dagger$ may be written*

$$T^\dagger = KT^*J^{-1}.$$

PROOF. Let $\xi \in D$ be arbitrary. From Theorem C we have the existence of a unique element ϕ_ξ with norm 1 which satisfies

$$\xi = p(\xi)T(\overline{T^*\phi_\xi}).$$

By using the definition of J we can rewrite this equality as

$$\xi = p(\xi)\|T^*\phi_\xi\|^{-1}J(\phi_\xi).$$

Since J is real homogeneous, we have

$$\xi = J(p(\xi)\|T^*\phi_\xi\|^{-1}\phi_\xi);$$

that is, the ϕ_ξ' which satisfies the equation $\xi = J(\phi_\xi')$ is a multiple of ϕ_ξ. The proof is completed by noting that if $J^{-1}\xi = \phi_\xi'$ then

$$\xi = J(J^{-1}\xi) = TKT^*J^{-1} = Tu_\xi;$$

hence in a trivial way it follows that

$$u_\xi = KT^*J^{-1}\xi = T^\dagger\xi.$$

The difference between Theorem C and its corollary is primarily one of emphasis. In Theorem C attention is focused on the computation of the number $p(\xi)$ and the support hyperplane at point $[p(\xi)]^{-1}\xi \in \partial C$. In the corollary the computational problem is the inversion of the operator J. In a nonrigorous sense Theorem C is a pointwise specification of $T^\dagger$, whereas the corollary is a global specification of this function.

Example 4.   Most of our examples have dealt with systems of the continuous time variety. Let us take this opportunity to emphasize that the results of the chapter apply equally well to discrete time and composite systems. Consider once again the composite system of Figure 2.16, Section 2.5. For simplicity we consider a fixed point $t' \in \sigma \cap \tau$ and focus attention on the transformation $T: B \to R^n$; the value of T at $(u,v) \in B$ is given by

$$(x,y) = T(u,v),$$

where

$$x = \sum_{j=0}^{[t']-1} W_1(t',t_j)u(t_j),$$

$$y = \sum_{j=0}^{[t']-1} W_3(t',t_j)u(t_j) + \int_{t_0}^{t'} W_2(t',\beta)v(\beta)d\beta.$$

The matrices W_1, W_2, and W_3 are defined by Eq. 18, Section 2.5.
  The linear space B consists of the vectors

$$B = l_{p_1}(\sigma) \times \cdots \times l_{p_l}(\sigma) \times L_{p_{l+1}}(\tau) \times \cdots \times L_{p_m}(\tau),$$

with the usual rules for addition and scalar multiplication. Assume that $1 < p_j < \infty$, $j = 1, \ldots, m$ and that B is equipped with the norm of Theorem E, Section 4.2. B is then reflexive and rotund. The space D (and consequently D^*) is E^n. The conjugate transformation T^* of T sends E^n into B^* and is computed by multiplication with the matrix W^* whose value at (s,t) is given by

$$W^*(t',r) = \left[\begin{array}{c|c} W_1^*(t',s) & W_3^*(t',t) \\ \hline 0 & W_2^*(t',s) \end{array}\right], \qquad r = (s,t) \in \sigma \times \tau,$$

where $s,t \le t'$.
  To be even more explicit consider the case treated in Example 5, Section 4.2 ($m = 4$, $l = 2$). For every $\phi = (\phi_1,\phi_2,\phi_3,\phi_4) \in E^n$

$$(T^*\phi)(s,t) = W^*(t';s,t)\phi, \qquad (s,t) \in \sigma \times \tau,$$

and the norm and extremal of this vector (i.e., $T^*\phi$) can be computed by the direct methods described in Example 5, Section 4.2. Because the transformation T is well defined, the transformation J is also. Indeed, except for the obvious difficulties of inverting J (or, alternatively, of finding ϕ_ξ), the solution to the minimum norm problem is pleasantly straightforward.

R E M A R K 3. In Theorem C the conditions on the domain B are sufficient to ensure that both ϕ_ξ and u_ξ will be unique for *every* ξ and *every* (onto) transformation T. For a particular T it can happen that either ϕ_ξ or u_ξ (or both) will be unique for every ξ, although B is neither rotund nor smooth. For instance, let us assume that every functional in the range of T^* (or the range of S, as the case may be) has a unique extremal. Then, clearly, the function J of Eq. 7 is well defined and $\overline{T^*\phi_1}$ and $\overline{T^*\phi_2}$ are preimages of $\xi \in \partial C$ if and only if $J\phi_1 = J\phi_2$. Exercise 3 shows that $\|\overline{T^*\phi_1}\| = \langle T^*\phi_1, \overline{T^*\phi_2} \rangle$, which implies that $\overline{T^*\phi_2}$ is an extremal of $T^*\phi_1$ and, since there is only one such element, we have $\overline{T^*\phi_1} = \overline{T^*\phi_2}$. Exercise 4 provides examples that illustrate uniqueness without rotundity or smoothness of the domain.

Some Closing Remarks

The following observations may prove helpful in the assimilation of the results of this section.

R E M A R K 4. It is easy to obtain the Hilbert space solution for Problem 1 from the corollary to Theorem C. Since in a Hilbert space the extremal of x takes the form $\bar{x} = x/\|x\|$, it follows that the function K becomes the identity, J reduces to the operator TT^*, and consequently

$$T^\dagger = KT^*J^{-1} = T^*(TT^*)^{-1},$$

which agrees with our earlier results.

R E M A R K 5. Observe also that it follows from the development that $\|T^\dagger(\xi)\| = p(\xi)$. Since the latter is a continuous function of ξ, we see that the minimum effort associated with each state $\xi \in D$ is a continuous function of ξ: if two vectors ξ_1, ξ_2 in R are close and u_1 and u_2 are their minimum preimages under T, the norms of u_1 and u_2 are correspondingly close.

R E M A R K 6. In the solution to Problem 1 the concept of controllability has not been explicitly mentioned. It is easy, however, to recognize the role that this concept plays in the present class of problems. To be specific we shall say that a system $T: B \to D$ is *norm controllable* if and only if every $\xi \in D$ has a preimage $u \in B$ under T. From Lemma Á (or, more correctly, the open mapping theorem) it is apparent that a system is norm-controllable if and only if T is onto. An interesting consequence is that when T is compact the system is norm-controllable if and only if D is finite-dimensional. This conclusion is a direct result of the observation that the set C is compact when T is compact and only finite-dimensional spaces can have compact neighborhoods of the origin. In other words, being compact and onto are incompatible conditions for transformations of infinite rank. This result has a direct role in Appendix 9.

REMARK 7. The solution given for Problem 1 has been obtained in an open-loop form. Indeed, to use these results an appropriate $\xi \in D$ is first determined. Theorem B or C then specifies the optimal control and, finally, this control is applied to drive the system in the optimum manner. Once $\xi \in D$ is determined, no further information from or observation of the system is necessary. As control system engineers, however, we recognize the merits of using feedback whenever possible to control our systems. In short, we would like a rule which, at every time t, determines $u(t)$, the instantaneous system input, from $x(t)$, the instantaneous system output. Moreover, this rule should produce the same optimal control as our open loop results.

Such a rule, if it can be found, is called an optimal feedback law, and the synthesis or implementation of this law is called an optimum feedback controller. In theory, optimal feedback laws almost always exist. Their existence is derived in part from the causal nature of systems (see Exercise 4, Section 2.5). In some cases, such as the classical "bang-bang" second-order servo problem (see [B98]), these laws take very simple forms. In most non-trivial settings, however, the explicit determination of the optimal control law is a difficult task.

In Exercises 14 and 15, Section 3.2, we found that an optimal feedback controller could be synthesized for the minimum-energy problem. Moreover, the linearity of $T^\dagger$ in Hilbert spaces was inherited by this controller. In Exercise 9 of this section an analogous result is obtained for the minimum-effort problem. Since $T^\dagger$ is not linear for Banach spaces, it is not surprising that this optimal controller involves a nonlinear function. Apart from the general result, however, the determination of the optimal control law seems best handled on a specific case-by-case basis.

Exercises

1. (Waltz [B116].) For the system variables described in Figure 4.17 show that the system transition matrix is given by

$$\Phi\,(t,t_0) = \begin{bmatrix} 1 & (t - t_0) \\ 0 & 1 \end{bmatrix}, \qquad t,t_0 \in \tau$$

If $\tau = [0,2]$ and all $b_{ij}(t) = 0$ except for the values $b_{11}(t) = 1 - t$

for $t \in [0,1]$, $b_{12}(t) = -(t-1)(2-t)$ for $t \in [1,2]$, $b_{22}(t) = t-1$ for $t \in [1,2]$, show that

$$x_1(2) = \int_0^1 (1-t)u_1(t)dt,$$

$$(*)$$

$$x_2(2) = \int_1^2 (t-1)u_2(t)dt.$$

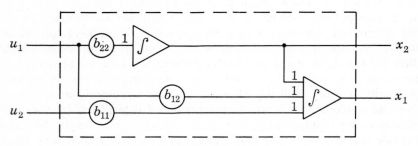

Figure 4.17

Let the equations $(*)$ define a mapping T from $B = \mathbf{L}_\infty(l_2(2); [0,2])$; that is, $B_{\infty,2}$ with $n = 2$ into $D = R^2$. Show that T is onto and that $C = T(U)$ is the square

$$C = \{x = (x_1, x_2) \in R^2 : |x_i| \le \tfrac{1}{2}, i = 1,2\},$$

which is closed. HINT: See Exercise 10, Section 4.2. Find an optimal control for each of the elements $\xi_1 = (0.8, 0.6)$ and $\xi_2 = (0.5, 0.5)$. Does more than one exist?

2. (Waltz [B116].) Consider the system defined by the equations $\dot{x} = Ax + Bu$, $x(0) = 0$, where $x(t) = [x_1(t), x_2(t), x_3(t)]$ and $u(t) = [u_1(t), u_2(t), u_3(t)]$, and A, B are the matrices

$$A = \begin{bmatrix} 0 & 1 & 0 \\ 0 & 0 & 1 \\ 0 & 0 & 0 \end{bmatrix}, \quad B(t) = \begin{bmatrix} b_{11}(t) & b_{12}(t) & b_{13}(t) \\ 0 & b_{22}(t) & b_{23}(t) \\ 0 & 0 & b_{33}(t) \end{bmatrix},$$

for $t \in [0,3]$. Let the coefficients be identically zero except for the values $b_{11}(t) = 1 - t$ for $t \in [0,1]$, $b_{12}(t) = -3(t-1)(2-t)(3-t)$, and $b_{22}(t) = 3(t-1)(2-t)$ for $t \in [1,2]$, $b_{12}(t) = \tfrac{1}{2}(t-2)(3-t)^2$, $b_{23}(t) = -(t-2)(3-t)$, and $b_{33}(t) = (t-2)$ for $t \in [2,3]$. Show that

$$x_1(3) = \int_0^1 (1-s)u_1(s)ds,$$

$$x_2(3) = \int_1^2 3(s-1)(2-s)u_2(s)ds,$$

$$x_3(3) = \int_2^3 (s-2)u_3(s)ds,$$

represents the system as a linear transformation onto R^2. If $B = L_\infty(l_2(3); [0,3])$, show that $C = T(U)$ is the closed square

$$C = \{(x_1,x_2,x_3) \in R^2 : |x_i| \leq \tfrac{1}{2}, \, i = 1, 2, 3\};$$

show also that (a) for ξ on the face of the cube C the optimal control u_ξ is not unique; (b) for ξ at a corner of C, although the outward normal to C at ξ is not unique, all such normals specify the same optimal control; (c) for ξ on an edge of C neither the outward normal nor the optimal control is unique. [Notice in (c) that the ambiguity in u_ξ always occurs on the same intervals.]

3. Prove that the function J of Eq. 5 is one-to-one. HINT: Since $J\phi_1 = J\phi_2$ implies that $\langle \phi_1 - \phi_2, J\phi_1 - J\phi_2 \rangle = 0$, it suffices to show that this equality may be expanded to the form

$$(\|T^*\phi_1\| - \|T^*\phi_2\|)^2 + \|T^*\phi_1\|(\|T^*\phi_2\| - \langle T^*\phi_2, \overline{T^*\phi_1} \rangle)$$
$$+ \|T^*\phi_2\|(\|T^*\phi_1\| - \langle T^*\phi_1, \overline{T^*\phi_2} \rangle) = 0,$$

Use the rotundity and smoothness of B to show that this implies $\phi_1 = \phi_2$.

4. (Waltz [B116].) Let T be the linear transformation from $L_\infty(0,1)$ onto R^2 defined by

$$Tu = \int_0^1 \begin{bmatrix} 1-s \\ 1 \end{bmatrix} u(s)ds, \qquad u \in L_\infty(0,1);$$

show that the set $C = T(U)$ has corners at the points $\{\pm(\tfrac{1}{2},1)\}$ but has no flat spots. If A denotes the linear transformation from $B = L_\infty(l_2(2);[0,1))$ onto R^2 defined by

$$Au = \int_0^1 \begin{bmatrix} 1-s & 0 \\ 0 & 1 \end{bmatrix} \begin{bmatrix} u_1(s) \\ u_2(s) \end{bmatrix} ds, \qquad u \in B,$$

show that the set $C = A(U)$ has neither corners not flat spots. Show that in both systems the optimal control is *unique*.

5. Let B, D, T, C, and p be as in Theorem B. Show that the functional p is a norm on D equivalent to the given norm. HINT: For $0 \neq \xi \in D$ and $\lambda \geq p(\xi)$ we have $\xi \in \lambda T(U) \Rightarrow \|\xi\| \leq \lambda\|T\| \Rightarrow p(\xi) \geq (\|T\|)^{-1}\|\xi\|$. Use also the fact that C is a bounded set.

6. Let D_1 be the space D equipped with the norm $|\xi| = p(\xi)$ discussed in Exercise 5. Show that D_1 is rotund (and smooth) whenever B is. HINT: Note that $|\xi| = \|T^\dagger\xi\|$ for each $\xi \in D_1$ and that $T^\dagger\xi_1 + T^\dagger\xi_2 \in T^{-1}(\xi_1 + \xi_2)$; hence

$$\|T^\dagger(\xi_1 + \xi_2)\| \leq \|T^\dagger\xi_1 + T^\dagger\xi_2\| \leq \|T^\dagger\xi_1\| + \|T^\dagger\xi_2\|.$$

Thus

$$|\xi_1 + \xi_2| = |\xi_1| + |\xi_2| \Rightarrow \|T^\dagger\xi_1 + T^\dagger\xi_2\| = \|T^\dagger\xi_1\| + \|T^\dagger\xi_2\|,$$

and hence the rotundity of $B \Rightarrow T^\dagger\xi_1 = \lambda T^\dagger\xi_2$ for some $\lambda > 0$. This in turn imples $\xi_1 = \lambda\xi_2 \Rightarrow D_1$ is rotund. To prove that D_1 is rotund and smooth when B_1 is rotund and smooth use the fact that the map $\xi \to \phi_\xi$ is one-to-one.

7. Let D_1 be the rotund, smooth space of Exercise 4 and $\xi \in \partial C$. Show that the extremal $\xi' \in D_1^*$ of ξ is ϕ_ξ. HINT: Use the defining conditions

(a) $\langle \xi, \xi' \rangle = |\xi| = p(\xi) = 1$,
(b) $|\xi'| = \sup_{\eta \in C}\langle \eta, \xi' \rangle = \sup_{u \in U}\langle u, T^*\xi' \rangle = \|T^*\xi'\| = 1$.

Note that this result provides the alternative formulation

$$T^\dagger\xi = |\xi|\overline{(T^*\xi')}$$

for the pseudoinverse of T.

8. Let $\{x_1, \ldots, x_n\}$ denote a linearly independent subset of the Banach space B. From the subset $Q = \{f \in B^*: f(x_i) = a_i, i = 1, 2, \ldots, n\}$, where $a_1, \ldots, a_n$ are fixed scalars, find the element with minimum norm. This problem is an elementary version of "the problem of moments" (see [B1]). HINT: Let $\{e_1, \ldots, e_n\}$ denote the coordinate basis for R^n and define $S: R^n \to B$ by

$$S = \sum_{i=1}^{n} x_i \rangle \langle e_i.$$

Show that $f \in Q \Leftrightarrow S^*f = \xi$, where $\xi = (a_1, \ldots, a_n)$ and then apply Theorem A or B.

9. Consider the linear operator $u \to x$ defined by $x = Tu = \int_{t_0}^{t_f}\Phi(t_f, s) B(s)u(s)ds$, where $u \in B$ is a rotund, smooth reflexive Banach space and T is onto R^n. For some $t \in [t_0, t_f]$ define also the operators $F_t u = \int_{t_0}^{t} \Phi(t_f, s)B(s)u(s)ds$ and $G_t u = \int_{t}^{t_f}\Phi(t_f, s)B(s)u(s)ds$ from B into R^n. If $B_t^- = \{x \in B: x(s) = \alpha, s \in [t_0, t]\}$ and $B_t^+ = \{x \in B: x(s) = 0, s \in [t_0, t]\}$, then B_t^- and B_t^+ are rotund, smooth reflexive spaces (see Exercise 7 of Section 4.2), and we may identify $B = B_t^- \times B_t^+$ in a natural way. Show that we may write uniquely

(a) $Tu = F_t u_1 + G_t u_2,$ $u_1 \in B_t^-, u_2 \in B_t^+, u \in B,$
(b) $T^*\phi = (F_t^*\phi, G_t^*\phi),$ $\phi \in R^n.$

Using Exercise 7, Section 4.2, show that

(c) $\overline{T^*\phi} = (\alpha_1 \overline{F_t^*\phi}, \alpha_2 \overline{G_t^*\phi}),$ $\phi \in R^n, \alpha_1, \alpha_2$ scalars,
(d) $J\phi = \beta_1 J_1 \phi + \beta_2 J_2 \phi,$ $\phi \in R^n, \beta_1, \beta_2$ scalars,

where

$$J\phi = \|T^*\phi\| T(\overline{T^*\phi}),$$

$$J_1\phi = \|F_t^*\phi\| F_t (\overline{F_t^*\phi}),$$

$$J_2\phi = \|G_t^*\phi\| G_t^*(\overline{G_t^*\phi}),$$

and

$$\beta_1 = \alpha_1 \|T^*\phi\|/\|F_t^*\phi\|, \qquad \beta_2 = \alpha \|T^*\phi\|/\|G_t^*\phi\|.$$

Using the properties of linear dynamic systems, show that if

$$x(t_f) = \Phi(t_f, t_0)x(t_0) = J(\phi),$$

then

(e) $x(t_f) - \Phi(t_f, t_1)x(t_1) = \beta_2 J_2(\phi),$
(f) $x(t_1) - \Phi(t_1, t_0)x(t_0) = \beta_1 J_1(\phi),$

hence that

(g) $G_t^\dagger [x(t_f) - \Phi(t_f, t)x(t)] = T^\dagger [x(t_f) - \Phi(t_f, t_0)x(t_0)]$

holds over the interval $(t, t_f]$. In other words, the nonlinear function

$$u(t) = G_t^\dagger [x(t_f) - \Phi(t_f, t)x(t)]$$

is the instantaneous feedback mechanism for synthesizing the minimum-effort, closed-loop controller.

10. (Grimmell [B43].) In designing a system for the purpose of causing a plant to perform a particular task, one may be faced with the problem of choosing a design which minimizes a functional dependent on both a peak fuel flow value and the total fuel consumption. As an example consider a plant which acts as a double integrator, that is, a plant whose operation is described by the transformation $u \to \xi$ computed by

$$\begin{bmatrix} \xi_1 \\ \xi_2 \end{bmatrix} = \int_{t_0}^{t_f} \begin{bmatrix} -t \\ 1 \end{bmatrix} u(t)dt.$$

Let the optimality criterion be

$$J(u) = \sup_{t \in \tau} |u(t)| + \int_{t_0}^{t_f} |u(t)| dt$$

where $\tau = [t_0, t_f]$. It can be shown that $J(\cdot)$ defines a norm on $L_\infty(\tau)$ which is *equivalent* to the usual norm on this space (i.e., $\|u\| = \sup_{t \in \tau} |u(t)|$).

From this it follows that the plant can perform every transfer in an optimal manner. (Optimal controls exist for every ξ.) Show that the optimal controls, corresponding to extremals of $T^*\phi$, for $\phi_1 = (0.8,1)$, $\phi_2 = (0.4,1)$ and $\phi_3 = (0.1,1)$ are, respectively,

$$u_1(t) = \begin{cases} 0.384 & 0.0 \le t \le 0.552 \\ 0 & 0.552 < t < 1.948 \\ -0.384 & 1.948 \le t \le 3 \end{cases}$$

$$u_2(t) = \begin{cases} 0.408 & 0 \le t < 1.45 \\ 0 & 1.45 \le t \le 3 \end{cases}$$

$$u_3(t) = 0.25 \qquad 0 \le t \le 3$$

HINT: Let $G(u) = \int_{t_0}^{t_f} (T^*\phi)(t) u(t) dt$. Then extremals can be found by noting that for a given scalar $\bar{u} = \sup_{t \in \tau} |u(t)|$, $G(u)$ is maximized by letting $|u(t)| = \bar{u}$ for the values of t where $|T^*\phi(t)|$ is greatest, $u(t) = 0$ otherwise, and letting $u(t)$ be nonzero on a set of measure $(1 - \bar{u})/\bar{u}$. Expressions for $G(u)$ in terms of $\bar{u}$ can then be found and maximized.

11. (Grimmell [B43].) Write out the linear transformation associated with the operation over the interval $\tau = [t_0, t_f]$ of the system described by the differential equation

$$\begin{bmatrix} \dot{x}_1(t) \\ \dot{x}_2(t) \\ \dot{x}_3(t) \\ \dot{x}_4(t) \end{bmatrix} = \begin{bmatrix} 0 & 1 & 0 & 0 \\ 0 & 0 & 0 & 0 \\ 0 & 0 & 0 & 1 \\ 0 & 0 & 0 & 0 \end{bmatrix} \cdot \begin{bmatrix} x_1(t) \\ x_2(t) \\ x_3(t) \\ x_4(t) \end{bmatrix} + \begin{bmatrix} 0 & 0 & 0 \\ 1 & 0 & \frac{1}{2} \\ 0 & 0 & 0 \\ 0 & 1 & \frac{1}{2} \end{bmatrix} \cdot \begin{bmatrix} u_1(t) \\ u_2(t) \\ u_3(t) \end{bmatrix}$$

Let the optimality criterion for the system operation be given by

$$J(u) = ([\sup_{t \in \tau} (\max\{|u_1(t)|, |u_2(t)|\})]^2 + \int_{t_0}^{t_f} |u_3(t)|^2 dt)^{1/2}.$$

It can be shown that the above optimality criterion corresponds to the norm of a Banach space which satisfies the hypothesis of Corollary 3 of Theorem A.

Show that optimal controls for this problem have the form

$$u_1(t) = \left[\frac{c_1}{(c_1^2 + c_2^2)^{1/2}}\right]\text{sign}[\phi_1(t_0 - t) + \phi_2]$$

$$u_2(t) = \left[\frac{c_1}{(c_1^2 + c_2^2)^{1/2}}\right]\text{sign}[\phi_3(t_0 - t) + \phi_4]$$

$$u_3(t) = \left[\frac{1}{(c_1^2 + c_2^2)^{1/2}}\right]\left[(t_0 - t)\frac{(\phi_1 + \phi_2)}{2} + \frac{(\phi_2 + \phi_4)}{2}\right]$$

where

$$c_1 = \int_{t_0}^{t_f}(|\phi_1(t_0 - t) + \phi_2| + |\phi_3(t_0 - t) + \phi_4|)dt,$$

$$c_2 = \left(\int_0^{t_f}\left[(t_0 - t)\frac{(\phi_1 + \phi_3)}{2} + \frac{(\phi_2 + \phi_1)}{2}\right]^2 dt\right)^{1/2},$$

and

$$(\phi_1, \phi_2, \phi_3, \phi_4) \in R^n.$$

HINT: Write out $\langle u_1 T^*\phi\rangle = \sum_{i=1}^{3}\int_{t_0}^{t_f}(T^*\phi_i)(t)u(t)dt$. Apply appropriate inequalities to the three integrals, and then Schwartz's inequality to the resulting sum.

4.4 GENERALIZED MINIMUM–EFFORT PROBLEMS

Now that the statement and solution of Problem 1 have been thoroughly resolved we turn our attention to some of the variations on this problem which occur frequently in the applications. To illustrate, let us consider again the space-vehicle guidance system discussed in the introduction to this chapter. In the notation of that discussion the tuplets $(\bar{x},\bar{u})$, (x,u), and $(\delta x,\delta u)$ $= (x,u) - (\bar{x},\bar{u})$ represent the nominal, the actual, and the perturbed control-trajectory pairs, respectively.

It is well known that mission profiles are influenced to varying degrees by heating, maneuver rates, g-loadings, wind velocities, and abort considerations. These factors specify constraints (Figure 4.18) which presumably have been taken into account in determining the nominal variables $(\bar{u},\bar{x})$. Since violation of these constraints can be fatal to the mission, the criterion of optimality for the choice of δu should be sensitive not only to the size of δu but to these other factors as well. Since the severity of a constraint violation is commensurate with the size of δx, a natural problem (which we shall generalize later as Problem 2) is to require that the control δu satisfy

$\delta x(t_f) = \xi$ while minimizing a function of the form

$$ J(u) = \left[\int_{t_0}^{t_f} \left(\sum_{j=1}^{n} |\delta x_j(t)|^p \right) dt \right]^{1/p} + \left[\int_{t_0}^{t_f} \left(\sum_{j=1}^{m} |\delta u_j(t)|^p dt \right) \right]^{1/p}, \qquad 1 \le p < \infty. $$

(When $p = 2$, this functional may be interpreted as the equal weighting of r.m.s. deviation δx from $\bar{x}$ and r.m.s. vernier control energy.)

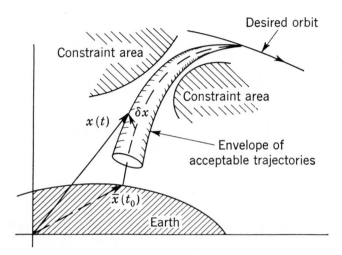

Figure 4.18   A guidance profile with constraints.

With these remarks as motivation, we pose in this section a number of optimization problems which seem more complex than Problem 1. In each, however, a judicious choice of function spaces and/or linear operators makes it possible to reduce the advanced problem precisely to Problem 1. Since the main interest here is the identification of Problem 1 in its disguised forms, technical matters are simplified by restricting attention to the minimum-effort setting. We also make use of the fact that $T^\dagger$ is most efficiently determined in the Hilbert spaces to illustrate the solutions of these new problems in this setting. Most of the results, however, can be brought to the full generality of Section 4.3 by the techniques of that section.

In the following B, B_1, and B_2 are used to denote rotund, reflexive, and Banach spaces and D is a Banach space. Our first two extensions are relatively minor.

Problem 1(a).   Let $B, D, T,$ and ξ be as in Problem 1 and let $\hat{u}$ be a given vector in B. Find a u in B satisfying $Tu = \xi$ which minimizes

$$ J(u) = \|u - \hat{u}\|. $$

THEOREM A. *Problem 1(a) has exactly one solution, namely, the vector*

$$u_\xi = T^\dagger(\xi - T\hat{u}) + \hat{u}.$$

PROOF. It is clear that $\hat{u}_\xi$ maps into ξ under T. If u is any preimage of ξ under T, then $T(u - \hat{u}) = \xi - T\hat{u}$ implies, by definition of $T^\dagger$, that

$$\|u - \hat{u}\| \geq \|T^\dagger(\xi - T\hat{u})\| = \|u_\xi - \hat{u}\|.$$

It follows that u_ξ is a solution of (1a) and, since this last inequality is strict unless $u - \hat{u} = T^\dagger(\xi - T\hat{u})$, we see that u_ξ is the *only* solution.

A second variation on Problem 1 is what we shall call 1(b) and consists in minimizing the functional $\|Fu\|$ subject to the constraint $Tu = \xi$. Here F is assumed to be a bounded linear transformation from B into B_1. However, we shall need additional restrictions on F. From our earlier results we know that a unique solution u_ξ will exist for every $\xi \in D$ if (1) $|u| = \|Fu\|$ is a norm on B, (2) B is reflexive, and (3) B is rotund in this new norm.

The first condition holds if and only if F is one-to-one. Since we have

$$|u| \leq \|F\| \cdot \|u\|,$$

the two norms are comparable. If $\{B, | \ |\}$ is a Banach space, a corollary of the closed graph theorem (cited in Appendix 7) shows that the two norms must be equivalent (i.e., $\alpha\|u\| \leq |u|$ for some $\alpha > 0$), which, however, implies that the space $\{B, | \ |\}$ is reflexive whenever the space $\{B, \| \ \|\}$ is. Therefore, to satisfy (1) and (2) it is necessary (and evidently sufficient) that F be bounded below:

$$\|Fu\| \geq \alpha\|u\|, \qquad \text{all } u \in B.$$

Finally, it is easy to see that for any F the space B is smooth with respect to $|u| = \|Fu\|$ (provided, of course, that B is originally smooth); if F is one-to-one, this new norm also preserves rotundity. Thus the condition that F be bounded below is necessary and sufficient to assume that B remain rotund, smooth, and reflexive. This, in turn, means that F is a bounded linear invertible transformation from B onto the Banach space $B_1 = F(B)$. The proper statement of 1(b) is then the following.

Problem 1(b). Let F be a one-to-one and bounded linear transformation from B onto B_1. For each $\xi \in D$ find the unique vector $u_\xi \in B$ satisfying $Tu = \xi$ which minimizes $J(u) = \|Fu\|$.

THEOREM B. *The unique solution u_ξ of Problem 1(b) is given by*

$$u_\xi = p_F(\xi)F^{-1}(\overline{F^{*-1}(T^*\eta)}),$$

where $p_F(\xi)$ is the Minkowski functional with respect to the set C_F,

$$C_F = \{Tu: \|Fu\| \leq 1\},$$

and η is the unique vector in D^* of norm 1 that satisfies

$$\langle \xi, \eta \rangle = \| F^{*-1} T^* \eta \|.$$

P R O O F.   Since F is one-to-one and onto, the inverse F^{-1} exists as a bounded linear transformation from B_1 into B. It follows (see Theorem C, Section 3.3) that F^* has a bounded inverse and that $(F^*)^{-1} = (F^{-1})^*$. Notice now that the relations

$$J(u) = \| Fu \| = |v|,$$

$$Tu = (TF^{-1})(Fu) = (TF^{-1})v,$$

where $v = Fu$, hold for every $u \in B$. Hence it is obvious that Problem 1(b) is exactly Problem 1 in which TF^{-1} has been replaced by T as the transformation in question. Theorem B is in fact no more than Theorem C of Section 4.3 with this substitution.

Our next extension is the principal problem of this section. We distinguish it with the number 2.

Problem 2.   Let F and T denote bounded linear transformations defined on B with values in B_1 and D, respectively. For an arbitrary $\xi \in D$ determine the element that minimizes the functional

$$J(u) = \| Fu \|^2 + \| u \|^2$$

over the set $T^{-1}(\xi) \subset B$ of all preimages of ξ under T.

In the statement of Problem 2 the assumption that the minimizing element exists and is unique anticipates later developments, which show that the assumed properties on B, B_1, and D are sufficient to guarantee this result. In our analysis of Problem 2 we shall need to recall the definition of the graph of a transformation. If F is a mapping from B into B_1, the set

$$B(F) = \{ (u,v) \colon v = Fu, u \in B \}$$

is called the graph of F; that is, the graph of a transformation is the subset of the product space $B \times B_1$ for which the ordinate v is related to the abscissa by $v = Fu$. The basic properties, pertinent to the present discussion, are summarized by Lemma A.

LEMMA A.   *Define addition and scalar multiplication in $B \times B_1$ in the usual way:*

$$(u_1, v_1) + (u_2, v_2) = (u_1 + u_2, v_1 + v_2)$$

$$\alpha(u,v) = (\alpha u, \alpha v).$$

Then

    (a) $B \times B_1$ *is a rotund reflexive Banach space when endowed with the norm*

$$\|(u,v)\|^2 = \|u\|^2 + \|v\|^2;$$

    (b) $B(F)$ *is a closed subspace of* $B \times B_1$, *hence is also a rotund reflexive Banach space;*

    (c)   *if* $G: B(F) \to D$ *is the transformation defined by*

$$G(u,Fu) = Tu, \qquad u \in B,$$

    then G *is linear and bounded from* $B(F)$ *into* D.

    P R O O F.   Assertion (a) follows from Theorem E of Section 4.2 and the fact that a finite product of reflexive spaces is reflexive. To prove (b) note that $B(F)$ inherits rotundity from $B \times B_1$ and because a closed subspace of a reflexive space is also reflexive (see Problem 9, Section 3.3) we need prove only that $B(F)$ is closed in $B \times B_1$. This, however, follows from the obvious fact that $(u_n,Fu_n) \to (u,v)$, if and only if

$$u_n \to u, \qquad Fu_n \to v,$$

and the fact that F is continuous. Finally, (c) follows from the observation that $\|G(u,Fu)\| = \|Tu\|$ and the computation

$$\|Tu\| \le \|T\| \cdot \|u\| \le \|T\|(\|u\|^2 + \|Fu\|^2)^{1/2} = \|T\| \cdot \|(u,Fu)\|.$$

    The relevance of Lemma A stems from the observation that Problem 2 asks for a vector (u,Fu) in $B(F)$ such that $G(u,Fu) = \xi$ and that

$$J(u) = \|u\|^2 + \|Fu\|^2 = \|(u,Fu)\|^2$$

is a minimum. In other words, Problem 2 is the same as Problem 1, but $G: B(F) \to D$ replaces $T: B \to D$ as the operator of prime interest. As a result of this discovery we have Theorem C.

THEOREM C.   *Problem 2 has a unique solution* u_ξ *for each* $\xi \in D$, *namely, the abscissa of the vector* $G^\dagger(\xi)$ *in* $B(F)$.

    It is important to recognize that Theorem C does not explicitly solve Problem 2 but rather reduces the problem to a computation of the function $G^\dagger$. In spite of the complexities that may be involved in computing $G^\dagger$, Theorem C is indeed a big step toward the solution of Problem 2, for it focuses attention on such concrete matters as constructing appropriate hyperplanes and extremals.

    R E M A R K 1.   We can view the reduction of Problem 2 to Problem 1 in a slightly different though useful manner. Let us introduce a new norm $|\ |$

on B by writing

$$|u| = (\|u\|^2 + \|Fu\|^2)^{1/2}$$

and let $\tilde{B}$ denote B equipped with the norm $|\ |$. Then $\tilde{B}$ inherits rotundity, reflexiveness and smoothness from B and B_1. Problem 2 may now be identified with finding the $u \in \tilde{B}$ for which $Tu = \xi$ and $|u|$ is a minimum and is thus recognized as Problem 1.

REMARK 2.   The   foregoing   viewpoint   suggests   immediately   that Problem 2 can be phrased in its most general form by equipping $B \times B_1$ with any norm for which it is reflexive and rotund (see Theorems E and F, Section 4.2). If $J(u)$ consists of a norm on $B(F)$ induced by any eligible norm on $B \times B_1$ the result is equivalent to Problem 1. For example, the minimum-effort problem in which $J(u)$ given by

$$J(u) = \|u\|^p + \|Fu\|^p, \qquad 1 < p < \infty,$$

or

$$J(u) = a_{11}\|u\|^2 + a_{12}\|u\| \cdot \|Fu\| + a_{21}\|u\| \cdot \|Fu\| + a_{22}\|Fu\|^2$$

is equivalent to Problem 1. Finally, it is clear that Problem 1 also contains the case in which $J(u)$ has the form

$$J(u) = \sum_{i=0}^{n} \|F_i u\|^p, \qquad F_0 = I,$$

where $F_i : B \to B_i$ are given transformations.

The Function $G^\dagger$

The computation of $G^\dagger$ is a nontrivial problem. Let us consider first the case in which B, B_1 are the Hilbert spaces H and H_1. It is easily verified that

$$\langle (u_1,v_1), (u_2,v_2) \rangle = \langle u_1,u_2 \rangle + \langle v_1,v_2 \rangle$$

defines an inner product on $H \times H_1$. By Lemma A, $H \times H_1$ is complete with respect to the norm induced by this inner product. Thus it follows that $H \times H_1$, and therefore $H(F)$, the graph of F in $H \times H_1$, is also a Hilbert space.

The Hilbert space solution of Problem 1 was given by restricting the transformation T to the orthogonal complement of its null space. This restriction was nonsingular, and its inverse maps any ξ in the range of T back into its preimage with minimum norm. This process will work as well for the present situation, and we shall locate the orthogonal complement of the null space of G.

Observe first that the null space of G, denoted by N_G, is given by the set

$$N_G = \{(u,Fu) : u \in N_T\},$$

and, since for any $u \in H$ we have $G(u,Fu) = Tu$, it follows that $u \in N_T$ if and only if $(u,Fu) \in N_G$.

LEMMA B.   *Let Q and M denote the orthogonal complements of the null spaces of the transformations G and T, respectively. Then Q is given by*

$$Q = \{(u,Fu): (I + F^*F)u \in M\}.$$

P R O O F.   The proof of Lemma 2 is given by the following chain of set equalities:

$$Q = \{(u,Fu) : (u,Fu) \perp (v,Fv), \text{ all } v \in N_T\}$$
$$= \{(u,Fu) : \langle u,v \rangle + \langle Fu,Fv \rangle = 0, \, v \in N_T\}$$
$$= \{(u,Fu) : \langle u,v \rangle + \langle F^*Fu,v \rangle = 0, \, v \in N_T\}$$
$$= \{(u,Fu) : \langle (I + F^*F)u,v \rangle = 0, \, v \in N_T\}$$
$$= \{(u,Fu) : (I + F^*F)u \in M\}.$$

R E M A R K   3.   It is sometimes convenient to deal with the set of abscissas of elements in Q. This set is denoted by S. It is clear from Lemma 2 that S may be specified in any of the equivalent ways:

$$S = \{u : (u,Fu) \in Q\} = \{u : (I + F^*F)u \in M\}$$
$$= \{u : u = (I + F^*F)^{-1}v, \, v \in M\} = (I + F^*F)^{-1}M.$$

Here the fact that $(I + F^*F)$ is invertible has been used. This follows from the observation that F^*F is positive; hence the spectrum of $I + F^*F$ does not contain 0 (see Appendix 5).

The determination of $G^{\dagger}$ in Hilbert spaces can now be concisely formulated.

THEOREM D.   *The unique solution u_ξ of Problem 2 for Hilbert spaces is given by*

$$u_\xi = (I + F^*F)^{-1} T^{\dagger}\phi,$$

where ϕ is the unique vector in D^* satisfying

$$\xi = T(I + F^*F)^{-1}T^{\dagger}\phi.$$

P R O O F.   Using the notation just introduced and appealing to the solution of Problem 1, we see that (u_ξ, Fu_ξ) is characterized by
  (1) $(u_\xi,Fu_\xi) \in Q$,
  (2) $G(u_\xi,Fu_\xi) = \xi$.
Now by Lemma B $(u_\xi,Fu_\xi) \in Q$ if and only if $u_\xi = (I + F^*F)^{-1}v$ for some

$v \in M$, and it is clear that v is uniquely determined by u_ξ. Since $T^\dagger$ is a one-to-one mapping from D^* onto M, $v = T^\dagger \phi$ for a unique vector $\phi \in D^*$. The theorem now follows from the definition $G(u_\xi, Fu_\xi) = Tu_\xi$.

Theorem D reaffirms the earlier observation that the major distinction between the solutions to Problem 1 and to Problem 2 is computational. For example, in Problem 1 with $D = R^n$ the vectors $\{f_i\}$ occurring in the polar canonical form of T provided a ready basis for M. In Problem 2 with $D = R^n$ a basis for S must be computed. For example, the set $\{g_i = (I + F^*F)^{-1}f_i\}$ is a basis for S. Unfortunately, the inverse of $(I + F^*F)$ is not in general solvable in closed form and the elements $\{g_i\}$ must be obtained as solutions to the equation $f_i = (I + F^*F)g_i$, $i = 1, \ldots, n$. This, however, is a computational difficulty which is readily handled in several ways by computer techniques, some of which are mentioned later.

Example 1.   Let $Q(t)$ and $R(t)$ denote square matrices of dimension n and m, respectively, which are bounded and positive definite for every $t \in \tau = [t_0, t_f]$. The Hilbert space $H_Q(\tau)$ is defined as the class of functions $L_2^n(\tau)$ equipped with the inner product

$$\langle x, y \rangle_Q = \int_{t_0}^{t_f} [x(s), Q(s)y(s)]ds, \qquad x, y \in H_Q(\tau).$$

Similarly, the Hilbert space $H_R(\tau)$ is defined as the set of functions $L_2^m(\tau)$ equipped with the inner product

$$\langle u, v \rangle_R = \int_{t_0}^{t_f} [u(s), R(s)v(s)]ds, \qquad u, v \in H_R(\tau).$$

That $H_Q(\tau)$ and $H_R(\tau)$ so defined are actually Hilbert spaces was proved in Exercise 6, Section 3.4.

Now consider the linear dynamic system with response x to input u determined by

$$x(t) = \int_{t_0}^{t} \Phi(t,s)B(s)u(s)ds, \qquad t \in \tau. \tag{1}$$

A frequent problem in optimal control is to find the input u that takes the system conditions (t_0, x_0) to (t_f, x_f) while minimizing the performance index

$$J(u) = \int_{t_0}^{t_f} [u(s), R(s)u(s)]ds + \int_{t_0}^{t_f} [x(s), Q(s)x(s)]ds.$$

If F denotes the linear transformation defined in Eq. 1 and $x_0 = 0$, $x_f = \xi$, the problem is evidently equivalent to minimizing

$$J(u) = \|Fu\|_Q^2 + \|u\|_R^2,$$

while satisfying

$$\xi = Tu,$$

where T is determined from Eq. 1 by fixing $t = t_f$. Since this is the exact form of Problem 2, the solution is given by Theorem C.

The transformation T has been dealt with earlier. As an exercise, the reader is asked to verify that the adjoint F^* of F takes [for the spaces $H_Q(\tau)$ and $H_R(\tau)$] the form

$$(F^*y)(t) = \int_t^{t_f} R^{-1}(t)B^*(t)\Phi^*(s,t)Q(s)y(s)ds. \tag{2}$$

It is shown in the next example that Eqs. 1 and 2 are sufficient to specify $(I + F^*F)^{-1}T^\dagger$, and this example is completed at that time.

Computing $G^\dagger$ for Banach Spaces

Let us now examine the Banach space solution of Problem 2 in more detail. Let $\tilde{B}$ denote the space B equipped with the new norm

$$|u| = (\|u\|^2 + \|Fu\|^2)^{1/2},$$

which is evidently equivalent to the given norm on B, so that $\tilde{B}$ and B have the same bounded linear functionals. Of course, the norm $|f|$ of an $f \in \tilde{B}^*$ will not necessarily agree with the norm $\|f\|$ of f regarded as an element of B^*. In Lemma A it is shown that $\tilde{B}$ is rotund, smooth, and reflexive wherever B and B_1 are. In Exercise 1 we show that the extremal x' of an x in $\tilde{B}$ is given by

$$x' = \frac{M(x)}{|x|}, \tag{3}$$

where

$$M(x) = \|x\|\bar{x} + \|Fx\|F^*(\overline{Fx}) \tag{4}$$

and $\bar{x}$, $\overline{Fx}$ denote the usual extremal operations in B and B_1, respectively. Moreover, M is one-to-one, onto, and preserves norms, and $M(\lambda x) = \bar{\lambda}M(x)$ (Exercise 2).

In this new notation Problem 2 asks for the unique vector $u = u_\xi$ in $\tilde{B}$ for which $Tu = \xi$ and $|u|$ is a minimum. According to the solution of Problem 1, there exists a unique vector η in D^* of norm 1 for which

$$u_\xi = p_G(\xi)(T^*\eta)', \tag{5}$$

where $p_G(\xi)$ is the Minkowski functional of the set C_G:

$$C_G = \{\xi = Tu : |u| \le 1\};$$

η is determined by the condition $\|\eta\| = 1$ and

$$\langle \xi, \eta \rangle = |T^*\eta|. \tag{6}$$

We let $K: B^* \to B$ denote the function defined on $\tilde{B}^*$ by

$$K(f) = |f|f',$$

where f' denotes the extremal of $f \in \tilde{B}^*$ with respect to the $|\ |$ norm on $\tilde{B}$. Next, we introduce the function $J: D^* \to D$, which is defined by the formula

$$J(\eta) = |T^*\eta|T(T^*\eta)', \qquad \eta \in G^*. \tag{7}$$

It is clear that $J = TKT^*$ and that J sends the element $\eta \in D^*$ into a scalar multiple of the point $\xi \in \partial C_G$, for which η defines the hyperplane of support. From Eq. 5 it follows that

$$\xi = Tu_\xi = p_G(\xi)T(T^*\eta)' = p_G(\xi)|T^*\eta|^{-1}J\eta;$$

hence we have

$$\eta = |T^*\eta|[p_G(\xi)]^{-1}J^{-1}\xi, \qquad \xi \in D, \tag{8}$$

which in conjunction with Eq. 5 yields

$$G^\dagger\xi = KT^*J^{-1}\xi, \qquad \xi \in D \tag{9}$$

as an explicit characterization of $G^\dagger$.

Observe that if $F = 0$ then $|T^*\eta| = \|T^*\eta\|$, so that the vector η, determined by Eq. 6 and $\|\eta\| = 1$, is the previously encountered outward normal ϕ to $C = C_G$ at ξ. Also, in this case the extremal from $\tilde{B}^*$ to $\tilde{B}$ reverts to its original form and thus Eq. 5 and the functions J and K reduce to their earlier forms.

Aside from the expected difficulties of finding the set C_G, the introduction of the transformation F into Problem 1 does bring about two added complications. The most critical is the computation of the function K. We note that K and M take extremals in opposite directions while preserving norms. Since B is rotund and smooth, this implies that K is the inverse of M.

It is interesting to speculate on the possibility of computing the function K explicitly. The simplest nontrivial case probably occurs when B, B_1 are the Hilbert spaces H, H_1, respectively. Extremals are then computed by the rule $\bar{x} = x/\|x\|$ and the function M then becomes

$$M(x) = \|x\|\bar{x} + \|Fx\|F^*(\overline{Fx}) = (I + F^*F)x.$$

Since $(I + F^*F)^{-1}$ can be explicitly written only in series form, it appears that we should not be hopeful of computing K by other than an expansion technique.

Let us now show that the Hilbert space version of Problem 1 follows from the present results. By rewriting Eq. 5 in the form

$$u_\xi = p_G(\xi)|T_G\eta|^{-1}K(T^*\eta)$$

we have immediately that

$$u_\xi = (I + F^*F)^{-1}[p_G(\xi)|T^*\eta|^{-1}T^*\eta].$$

Comparing this result with Theorem D and using the relation $T^\dagger = T^*(TT^*)^{-1}$, we have only to show that we may write

$$(TT^*)\phi = p_G(\xi)|T^*\eta|^{-1}\eta$$

for some $\phi \in D$. Since (TT^*) is one-to-one and invertible on D, this is also immediate.

It is therefore clear that the Banach space solution to Problem 2, as given by Eqs. 3–6, includes both the Hilbert space version of Problem 2 and the general version of Problem 1, as it should. Moreover, the fact that M, even in the relatively simple Hilbert space situation, cannot be inverted without the use of a computer technique indicates that at best we can only hope for an iterative technique for computing M^{-1}. We shall not pursue this problem at present.

Finally, let us consider the problem of computing the number $|T^*\eta|$ as a function of η. The definition

$$|T^*\eta| = \sup_{|u|=1} |\langle u, T^*\eta\rangle| = \sup_{u \in B} \frac{|\langle u, T^*\eta\rangle|}{(\|u\|^2 + \|Fu\|^2)^{1/2}}$$

gives one technique. Two others are given by Lemma C.

LEMMA C.   *For each η in R^* we have*

(a) $|T^*\eta|^2 = \inf\limits_{f_2 \in B_2{}^*} \|T^*\eta - F^*f_2\|^2 + \|f_2\|^2,$

(b) $|T^*\eta|^2 = \langle K(T^*\eta), T^*\eta\rangle.$

The second assertion follows from the fact that

$$K(T^*\eta) = \frac{|T^*\eta|}{p_G(\xi)}u_\xi = |T^*\eta|(T^*\eta)'.$$

The proof of assertion (a) is given in Exercise 3.

We conclude this discussion of Problem 2 by summarizing our results in a final Theorem.

THEOREM E.   *The unique solution u_ξ of Problem 2 is given by*

$$u_\xi = KT^*\left(\frac{p_G(\xi)}{|T^*\eta|}\eta\right) = KT^*J^{-1}\xi,$$

where η is the unique vector of D^* with $\|\eta\| = 1$ and satisfying either of the two equivalent conditions

(1) $p_G(\xi)|T^*\eta|^{-1}\eta = J^{-1}\xi,$

(2) $\langle \xi, \eta \rangle = |T^*\eta|,$

and $K^{-1} = M$ is the mapping from B onto B^* defined by Eq. 4. The numbers $p_G(\xi)$ and $|T^*\eta|$ may be computed from either of the following:

$$p_G(\xi) = (\|u_\xi\|^2 + \|Fu_\xi\|^2)^{1/2},$$

$$p_G(\xi) = \inf\{\lambda > 0 : \xi \in \lambda C_G\},$$

$$|T^*\eta| = \sup_{u \in B_1} \frac{|\langle u, T^*\eta \rangle|}{(\|u\|^2 + \|Fu\|^2)^{1/2}},$$

$$|T^*\eta|^2 = \langle K(T^*\eta), T^*\eta \rangle,$$

$$|T^*\eta|^2 = \sup_{f_2 \in B_2^*} \|T^*\eta - F^*f_2\|^2 + \|f_2\|^2.$$

The set $C_G = \{Tu: \|u\|^2 + \|Fu\|^2 \leq 1\}$ is a convex, circled, weakly compact neighborhood of 0 in D and has exactly one hyperplane of support through each of its boundary points.

Variations on Problem 2

It is apparent that problems of the 1(a), 1(b), and 2 variety may be taken in combination to increase the utility of the basic results. We shall consider two typical problems of this sort. The first is analogous to Problem 1(b).

Problem 2(b).   Let $B, B_1,$ and B_2 be given Banach spaces and $F_0: B \to B_2,$ $F: B \to B_1$ bounded linear transformations, with F_0 assumed one-to-one and onto. Find the unique vector u_ξ in B satisfying $Tu = \xi$ that minimizes

$$J(u) = \|F_0 u\|^2 + \|Fu\|^2.$$

Using the same reasoning that precedes the statement of Problem 1(b), we find that the conditions required of the transformation F_0 are both necessary and sufficient for the space B to remain reflexive, rotund, and smooth when equipped with the norm $|u| = J^{1/2}(u)$. Therefore, Problem 2(b) has a unique solution u_ξ for every $\xi \in D$, namely,

$$u_\xi = p_{F_0}(\xi)(T^*\eta)',$$

where p_{F_0} is the Minkowski functional with respect to the set C_{F_0}:

$$C_{F_0} = \{Tu: \|F_0 u\|^2 + \|Fu\|^2 \leq 1\}$$

and $\eta \in D^*$ is the element of norm 1 satisfying

$$\langle \xi, \eta \rangle = \sup_{u \in B_1} \frac{|\langle u, T^*\eta \rangle|}{(\|F_0 u\|^2 + \|Fu\|^2)^{1/2}} = |T^*\eta|.$$

Here $(T^*\eta)'$ is the vector u_0 in B_1 satisfying the conditions

(a) $\|F_0 u_0\|^2 + \|Fu_0\|^2 = 1$,
(b) $\langle u_0, T^*\eta \rangle = |T^*\eta|$.

We may also obtain the solution u_ξ by reducing Problem 2(b) to Problem 2. The substitution $v = F_0 u$ produces the equalities

$$J(u) = \|v\|^2 + \|FF_0^{-1}v\|^2,$$

$$Tu = (TF_0^{-1})v;$$

hence the identification with Problem 2. We omit the details and assert only that Theorem E remains the same with the obvious changes. The function $M(x)$ becomes

$$M(x) = \|F_0 x\| F_0^*(\overline{F_0 x}) + \|Fx\| F^*(\overline{Fx}).$$

The analog of the last formula for $|T^*\eta|^2$ is expressed by

$$\sup_{n \in B_1} \frac{|\langle u, T^*\eta \rangle|}{(\|F_0 u\|^2 + \|Fu\|^2)^{1/2}} = \inf_{f_2 \in B_2^*} (\|T^*\eta - F_0^{*-1}Ff_2\|^2 + \|f_2\|^2)^{1/2}.$$

The present line of development is brought to its climax in Problem 2(a).

Problem 2(a).   Let F be a bounded linear transformation from B into B_1, let T be a bounded linear transformation from B onto D, and let $\hat{u}$, $\hat{y}$, and ξ be given vectors in B, B_1, and D, respectively. Find a u in B satisfying $Tu = \xi$ that minimizes

$$J(u) = \|u - \hat{u}\|^2 + \|Fu - \hat{y}\|^2.$$

To study Problem 2(a) we use the graph $B(F)$ of F in the product space $B \times B_1$ and the transformation $G: B(F) \to D$ already defined. Let $\hat{w} = (\hat{u}, \hat{y})$. With this change in notation Problem 2(a) asks for a $w = (u, Fu)$ in $B(F)$ satisfying $G(w) = \xi$ and product $\|w - \hat{w}\|^2$ is a minimum. Now, if $\hat{w} \in B(F)$, we recognize the foregoing as precisely Problem 1(a) [with $B(F)$, G, and w replacing B, T, and $\hat{u}$, respectively], hence by using the solution of that problem we see that

$$(u_\xi, Fu_\xi) = G^\dagger(\xi - G\hat{w}) + (\hat{u}, F\hat{u})$$

defines the unique solution of Problem 2(a).

If $\hat{w}$ does not belong to $B(F)$ (i.e., if $\hat{y} \neq F\hat{u}$), we cannot appeal to Problem 1(a), but it is easy to see that Problem 2(a) still has a unique solution. Let M_ξ be the subset of $B \times B_1$ defined by

$$M_\xi = \{(u,Fu) - (\hat{u},\hat{y}): G(u,Fu) = \xi\};$$

that is, M_ξ is the translate $G^{-1}(\xi) - (\hat{u},\hat{y})$ of the closed linear flat $G^{-1}(\xi)$. Evidently M_ξ is closed and convex, and since $B \times B_1$ is rotund and reflexive M_ξ has a unique element $(u_0,Fu_0) - (\hat{u},\hat{y})$ of minimum norm. In other words, a unique vector u_0 is in B with $Tu_0 = \xi$ and

$$\begin{aligned} J(u_0) &= \|(u_0,Fu)_0 - (\hat{u},\hat{y})\|^2 \\ &= \min \{\|(u,Fu) - (\hat{u},\hat{y})\|^2: G(u,Fu) = \xi\} \\ &= \min \{J(u): Tu = \xi\}. \end{aligned}$$

We have proved part of Theorem F.

THEOREM F. *Problem 2(a) always has a unique solution u_ξ. If $\hat{y} = F\hat{u}$, this solution is determined by*

$$(u_\xi,Fu_\xi) = G^\dagger(\xi - T\hat{v}) + (\hat{u},\hat{y}).$$

If $B = H$ and $B_1 = H_1$ are Hilbert spaces and $(\hat{u},\hat{y})$ is arbitrary, then u_ξ satisfies

$$(u_\xi,Fu_\xi) = G^\dagger(\xi - T\tilde{u}) + (\tilde{u},F\tilde{u}),$$

where $(\tilde{u},F\tilde{u})$ is the orthogonal projection of $(\hat{u},\hat{y})$ on $H(F)$.

PROOF. It remains only to prove the assertion concerning Hilbert spaces. First note that $w_0 = G^\dagger(\xi - T\tilde{u}) + (\tilde{u},F\tilde{u}) - (\hat{u},\hat{y})$ is an element of M_ξ. Furthermore, $(\hat{u},F\hat{u}) - (\hat{u},\hat{y})$ is orthogonal to $G^\dagger(\xi - T\tilde{u}) \in H(F)$; hence

$$\begin{aligned} \|w_0\|^2 &= \|G^\dagger(\xi - T\tilde{u}) + (\tilde{u},F\tilde{u}) - (\hat{u},\hat{y})\|^2 \\ &= \|G^\dagger(\xi - T\tilde{u})\|^2 + \|(\tilde{u},F\tilde{u}) - (\hat{u},\hat{y})\|^2. \end{aligned} \tag{10}$$

Also, if $u \in H$ satisfies $G(u,Fu) - \xi$, the vector $(u,Fu) - (\tilde{u},F\tilde{u})$ maps into $\xi - T\tilde{u}$ under G and therefore

$$\|(u,Fu) - (\tilde{u},F\tilde{u})\| \geq \|G^\dagger(\xi - T\tilde{u})\|.$$

Hence $G(u,Fu) = \xi$ implies

$$\begin{aligned} \|(u,Fu) - (\hat{u},\hat{y})\|^2 &= \|(u,Fu) - (\tilde{u},F\tilde{u}) + (\tilde{u},F\tilde{u}) - (\hat{u},\hat{y})\|^2 \\ &= \|(u,Fu) - (\tilde{u},F\tilde{u})\|^2 + \|(\tilde{u},F\tilde{u}) - (\hat{u},\hat{y})\|^2 \\ &\geq \|G^\dagger(\xi - T\tilde{u})\|^2 + \|(\tilde{u},F\tilde{u}) - (\hat{u},\hat{y})\|^2. \end{aligned} \tag{11}$$

It follows from Eqs. 10 and 11 that w_0 is the smallest element in M_ξ and this completes the proof.

The Projection on *H(F)*

Let the operator V on the Hilbert space $H \times H_1$ be defined by the relation

$$V(u,v) = (-v,u), \qquad (u,v) \in H \times H_1.$$

Evidently V is a linear isometry from $H \times H_1$ onto $H_1 \times H$.

LEMMA D.   *The orthogonal complement of $H(F)$ in $H \times H_1$ is given by*

$$H(F)^\perp = VH(F^*).$$

PROOF.   Let (x,y) be an arbitrary element of $H(F)^\perp$. Then for every $u \in H$

$$0 = \langle (x,y),(u,Fu) \rangle = \langle x,u \rangle + \langle y,Fu \rangle = \langle x + F^*y,u \rangle,$$

which implies $x = -F^*y$ or that (x,y) is of the form

$$(x,y) = (-F^*y,y) = V(y,F^*y).$$

Thus $(x,y) \in VH(F^*)$, hence $H(F)^\perp \subset VH(F^*)$. Conversely, if $(x,y) \in VH(F^*)$ then

$$(x,y) = V(v,F^*v) = (-F^*v,v), \qquad v \in H_2.$$

For any (u,Fu), however, $(u,Fu) \perp (-F^*v,v)$, hence $(-F^*v,v) \in H(F)^\perp$, which implies $VH(F^*) \subset H(F)^\perp$ and the lemma is proved.

A consequence of this lemma is that an orthogonal decomposition of $H \times H_1$ is given explicitly by the formula

$$H \times H_1 = H(F) \oplus VH(F^*). \tag{12}$$

This formula will prove useful in defining the orthogonal projection P of $H \times H_1$ on $H(F)$. To compute this function let $(\hat{u},\hat{y}) \in H \times H_1$ denote an arbitrary vector. Then, in view of Eq. 12, a unique decomposition exists in the form of

$$(\hat{u},\hat{y}) = (\tilde{u},F\tilde{u}) + V(u_1,F^*u_1)$$

$$= (\tilde{u},F\tilde{u}) + (-F^*u_1,u_1)$$

$$= (\tilde{u} - F^*u_1, F\tilde{u} + y_1).$$

This equality implies the two equalities

$$\hat{u} = \tilde{u} - F^*u_1, \qquad \hat{y} = F\tilde{u} + u_1.$$

Operating on the second equation with F^* and using the result to eliminate F^*u_1 in the first equation, we obtain

$$\tilde{u} = (I + F^*F)^{-1}[\hat{u} + F^*\hat{y}]. \tag{13}$$

Similarly, it is easily shown that u_1 satisfies

$$u_1 = (I + FF^*)^{-1}[\hat{y} - F\hat{u}].$$

Since the tuplet $(\tilde{u}, F\tilde{u})$ is determined completely by $\tilde{u}$, Eq. 13 is sufficient to define the projection P of $H \times H_1$ on $H(F)$. An easy check on these results may be obtained by verifying that

$$(\tilde{u}, F\tilde{u}) \perp [(\hat{u}, \hat{y}) - (\tilde{u}, F\tilde{u})] \quad \text{for all} \quad (\hat{y}, \hat{u}) \in H \times H_1.$$

The preceding discussion together with the characterization of $G^\dagger$ obtained from Theorem D yields Theorem G.

THEOREM G. *The unique solution u_ξ of the Hilbert space version of Problem 2(a) is given by*

$$u_\xi = (I + F^*F)^{-1}(T^\dagger\eta + \hat{u} + F^*\hat{y}),$$

where η is the unique vector in D satisfying

$$\xi = T(I + F^*F)^{-1}(T^\dagger\eta + \hat{u} + F^*\hat{y}).$$

R E M A R K 4. It is clear that Problem 2(a) contains Problems 2 ($\hat{u} = \hat{y} = 0$), 1(a) ($\hat{y} = 0$, $F = 0$), and 1 ($\hat{u} = \hat{y} = 0$, $F = 0$) as special cases. This is reflected in the fact that Theorem G reduces to Theorems D, A, and C (Section 4.3) in these cases, respectively. Thus, if $\hat{u} = \hat{y} = 0$, u_ξ is determined by

$$u_\xi = (I + F^*F)^{-1}T^\dagger\eta,$$

$$\xi = T(I + F^*F)^{-1}(T^\dagger\eta).$$

If $\hat{y} = 0$ and $F = 0$, u_ξ is determined by

$$u_\xi = T^\dagger\eta + \hat{u}$$

$$\xi = T(T^\dagger\eta + \hat{u}) = \eta + T\hat{u};$$

that is,

$$u_\xi = T^\dagger(\xi - T\hat{u}) + \hat{u}.$$

If $\hat{u} = 0$, $\hat{y} = 0$, and $F = 0$, then u_ξ is determined by

$$u_\xi = T^\dagger\eta$$

$$\xi = T(T^\dagger\eta) = \eta.$$

Example 2. Let us now consider a variation of the problem posed in Example 1. We adopt the notation of that example but add the symbol $x = Fu$ to denote the forced response of the system and the symbol z to denote the total response. The problem of interest here is one of transferring the initial tuplet (t_0, z_0) to the final tuplet (t_f, z_f) while minimizing the functional

$$J(u) = \int_{t_0}^{t_f} [z(s) - \hat{v}(s), Q(s)(z(s) - \hat{v}(s))]$$

$$+ [u(s) - \hat{u}(s), R(s)(u(s) - \hat{u}(s))]ds,$$

where $\hat{u} \in H_R(\tau)$ and $\hat{v} \in H_Q(\tau)$ are arbitrary but fixed elements. Since the elements z and x are related by

$$z(t) = \Phi(t,t_0)z_0 + x(t), \qquad t \in [t_0, t_f],$$

it is apparent that $\xi = z(t_f) - \Phi(t_f,t_0)z_0$ is the desired range element. Introducing the variable $\hat{y}$, defined by

$$\hat{y}(t) = \hat{v}(t) - \Phi(t,t_0)z_0, \qquad t \in [t_0, t_f]$$

and the Hilbert spaces $H_R(\tau)$ and $H_Q(\tau)$, we write the functional $J(u)$ more simply as

$$J(u) = \|x - \hat{y}\|^2 + \|u - \hat{u}\|^2 = \|(u, Fu) - (\hat{u}, \hat{y})\|^2.$$

From this juncture the solution of the example problem involves a sequence of straightforward operations. If $\hat{p}$ denotes the element $\hat{u} + F^*\hat{y}$, then (see Eq. 2 of Example 1) in the present case $\hat{p}$ may be explicitly computed by the rule

$$\hat{p}(t) = \hat{u}(t) + \int_t^{t_f} R^{-1}(t)B^*(t)\Phi^*(s,t)Q(s)\hat{y}(s)ds, \qquad t \in [t_0, t_f].$$

From Theorem G it is clear that the solution to this example problem hinges on inverting the operator $(IF + {}^*F)$. Indeed, if $\tilde{u}$ is the unique solution to $(I + F^*F)\tilde{u} = \tilde{p}$, then from Theorem G and the linearity of the transformations we see that η is the unique element satisfying

$$\xi = T(I + F^*F)^{-1}T^\dagger \eta + T\tilde{u}.$$

Since T and $T^\dagger$ are well defined, the problem again reduces to inversion of $(I + F^*F)$ on the range of $T^\dagger$. According to Lemma 2, we may concentrate on solving

$$(I + F^*F)u = v \tag{14}$$

for arbitrary $v \in M$ as a means of computing $(I + F^*F)^{-1}$ on the range of $T^\dagger$.

Clearly the change in inner product introduced in the definition of $H_R(\tau)$ and $H_Q(\tau)$ does not disturb the set N_T. The set $M = N_T^\perp$, however, is a function of the inner product. It is easily verified that for the space H_R the set M is given by

$$M = \{v : v(s) = R^{-1}(s)\, B^*(s)\, \Phi^*(t_0, s)\, c,\ c \in R^n,\ s \in [t_0, t_f]\}.$$

If $q = Fu$, Eq. 14 becomes

$$u = v - F^*q, \qquad v \in M.$$

Using Eq. 14 and the identification of F^* given in Example 1, we have the problem of solving the equations

$$u(t) = R^{-1}(t)B^*(t)\Phi^*(t_0,t)c - R^{-1}(t)B^*(t)\Phi^*(t_0,t)\int_t^{t_f} \Phi^*(s,t_0)Q(s)q(s)ds$$

$$q(t) = \int_{t_0}^t \Phi(t,\tau)B(\tau)u(\tau)ds \tag{15}$$

for every c. Letting $\alpha(t)$ denote the tuplet

$$\alpha(t) = c - \int_{t_0}^{t_f}\Phi(s,t_0)Q(s)q(s)ds = \alpha(t_0) + \int_{t_0}^t \Phi(s,t_0)Q(s)q(s)ds$$

we may write $u(t)$ more simply as

$$u(t) = R^{-1}(t)\, B^*(t)\, \Phi^*(t_0,t)\alpha(t). \tag{16}$$

Consider the vector $\lambda(t) = \Phi^*(t_0,t)\alpha(t)$; by using the property $\Phi^*(t_0,t) = \Psi(t,t_0)$, where $\Psi(t,t_0)$ is the transition matrix for the adjoint system, we have

$$\dot\Psi(t,t_0) = -A^*(t)\Psi(t,t_0), \qquad \Psi(t_0,t_0) = I.$$

It then becomes apparent from Eq. 15 that

$$\lambda(t) = \Phi^*(t_0,t)\lambda(t_0) + \Phi^*(t_0,t)\int_{t_f}^t \Phi^*(s,t_0)Q(s)q(s)ds$$

$$= \Psi(t,t_0)\lambda(t_0) + \Psi(t,t_0)\int_{t_f}^t \Psi(t_0,s)Q(s)q(s)ds,$$

which implies immediately that $\lambda(t)$ is the solution to the differential system

$$\dot\lambda(t) = -A^*(t)\lambda(t) + Q(t)q(t), \qquad \lambda(t_0) = \lambda_0.$$

Similarly, from Eqs. 15 and 16 it is apparent that $q(t)$ satisfies

$$\dot q(t) = A(t)q(t) + B(t)u(t)$$

$$= A(t)q(t) + B(t)R^{-1}(t)B^*(t)\lambda(t), \qquad q(t_0) = 0.$$

Thus, in all, we have the $2n$ linear differential equations

$$\dot{q}(t) = A(t)q(t) + B(t)R^{-1}(t)B^*(t)\lambda(t), \qquad q(t_0) = 0,$$

$$\dot{\lambda}(t) = Q(t)q(t) - A^*(t)\lambda(t), \qquad\qquad \lambda(t_0) = \lambda_0,$$

(17)

the solution of which determines $\lambda(t)$, which in turn determines $u(t)$ by the expression $u(t) = R^{-1}(t)B^*(t)\lambda(t)$.

An important point that must not be overlooked is that $\lambda_0 \in R^n$ is still an arbitrary tuplet. Indeed, a review of the development shows that the original arbitrary nature of c has been passed along to λ_0, hence to u. This arbitrariness, of course, is removed by invoking the boundary condition $\xi = Tu$. In the present example the result is particularly simple, for $\xi = Tu = (Fu)(t_f =)q(t_f)$, and consequently λ_0 is precisely the initial condition on λ such that the system of Eq. 17 satisfies $q(t_f) = \xi$.

We return now to the original problem of the optimal transfer of (t_0,z_0) to (t_f,z_f); it follows that $\xi = z(t_f) - \Phi(t_f,t_0)z_0$. The function $\tilde{u}$ is taken as $\hat{u}$ when $(\hat{u},\hat{y}) \in H(F)$ and is computed by $(I + F^*F)\tilde{u} = \hat{p}$ otherwise. The computation $\tilde{y}(t_f) = T\tilde{u}$ is immediately $\tilde{y}(t_f) = \hat{y}(t_f)$, when $(\hat{u},\hat{y}) \in H(F)$, and the optimal control u_0 is defined by

$$u_0(t) = R^{-1}(t)B^*(t)\lambda(t) + \tilde{u}(t),$$

where $\lambda(t)$ satisfies Eq. 17 with

$$q(t_f) = z(t_f) - \Phi(t_f,t_0)z_0 - \tilde{y}(t_f),$$

$$q(t_0) = 0.$$

This completes the example.

Exercises

1. Prove (without peeking at Appendix 6) that Eq. 3 defines the extremal from B^* into B. HINT: Verify and use the inequality

$$|[\|x\|\langle y,\bar{x}\rangle + \|Fx\|\langle Fy,\overline{Fx}\rangle]| \le (\|x\|^2 + \|Fx\|^2)^{1/2}(\|y\|^2 + \|Fy\|^2)^{1/2}$$

and use this result to show that the functional $x' = M(x)/|x|$ has value $|x|$ at x and is of norm 1 in B^*.

2. Verify that the function M of Exercise 1 preserves norms, that it is one-to-one and onto, and that $M(\lambda x) = \bar{\lambda}M(x)$.

3. In this exercise we sketch the proof of part (a) of Lemma C. The annihilator $L^0 \subset B^*$ of a subspace $L \subset B$ is defined by $L = \{f: \langle x,f\rangle = 0, \text{ all } x \in L\}$. In Hilbert spaces obviously $L^0 = L^\perp$. Show that L^0 is a closed linear subspace of B^*. Show that the

annihilator of the graph $B(F) \subset B \times B_1$ is the set

$$B(F)^0 = \{(-F^*f,f): f \in B_1^*\}.$$

Since $B(F)$ is a Banach space in its own right, it also has a dual. Show that $B(F)^*$ may be identified with the (quotient space; see [A83] or [A22]) set of vectors (cosets) of the form

$$\widehat{(f_1,f_2)} = (f_1,f_2) + B(F)^0 = \{(f_1 - F^*f_2', f_2 + f_2'): f_2' \in B_2^*\},$$

with the norm

$$\|\widehat{(f_1,f_2)}\| = \inf_{f_2' \in B_2^*} (\|f_1 - F^*f_2'\|^2 + \|f_2 + f_2'\|^2)^{1/2}.$$

Hence the computation

$$\langle G(u,Fu),\eta \rangle = \langle (u,Fu), (T^*\eta - F^*f_2',f_2') \rangle, \qquad f_2' \in B_2^*$$

shows that $G^*\eta$ is the coset $(T^*\eta, 0)$.

4. Let H, H_1 be Hilbert spaces, D a Banach space, and T, F bounded linear transformations with domain H and values in D and H_1, respectively. Assuming that T is onto, find the element of $T^{-1}(\xi)$ for arbitrary $\xi \in D$ which minimizes the functionals

   (a) $J_1(u) = \|u\|^2 - \langle u,v_0 \rangle$
   (b) $J_2(u) = \|Fu\|^2 - \langle Fu,z_0 \rangle + \|u\|^2 - \langle u,v_0 \rangle,$

where $v_0 \in H$, $z_0 \in H_1$ are fixed elements. If $H_1 = H$ are real spaces and if $(F + F^*) > mI$, $m > 0$ (see Appendix 5), find the element of $T^{-1}(\xi)$ that minimizes

   (c) $J_3(u) = \|Fu\|^2 + \langle u,Fu \rangle.$

HINT: $J_1(u) = \|u - \tfrac{1}{2}v_0\|^2 - \|\tfrac{1}{2}v_0\|^2$. If $F = VR$ is the polar form of F (see Appendix 5), then $J_2(u) = \|Ru - \tfrac{1}{2}V^*z\|^2 + \|u - \tfrac{1}{2}v_0\|^2 - \tfrac{1}{4}[\|v_0\|^2 + \|V^*z\|^2]$. $J_3(u) = \|FG^{-1}v\|^2 + \|v\|^2$, where $G = [(F + F^*)/2]^{1/2}$ and $u = Gv$.

5. If T is the linear transformation $B \to R^n$ defined by

$$Tu = \int_{t_0}^{t_f} \Phi(t_f,s)B(s)u(s)ds,$$

detail the concrete conditions that the element of $T^{-1}(\xi)$, $\xi \in R^n$, which minimizes

$$J(u) = \left[\int_{t_0}^{t_f} \sum_{i=1}^{m} |u_i(t)|^{p_1}dt\right]^{2/p_1} + \left[\int_{t_0}^{t_f} \sum_{i=1}^{m} |u_i(t)|^{p_2}dt\right]^{2/p_2}$$

must satisfy. HINT: Consider the graph of the identity.

6. In Exercises 14 and 15 of Section 3.2, the solution of the minimum energy problem is synthesized in closed loop feedback form. Can this realization be carried out for Problem 2(a) of this section? What are the additional computational difficulties? Draw a functional diagram of the synthesized system.

4.5 DISCUSSION

A detailed summary of the present chapter can be obtained in a review of the theorems. In these closing remarks we shall highlight those aspects of the chapter that seem most significant and mention briefly the related literature.

The key section of the chapter is Section 4.3, in which the basic optimization problem is formulated and solved. The tools used in solving Problem 1 are based on the Hahn-Banach theorem, the open mapping theorem, and assorted geometric properties of Banach spaces. As general references on these topics the texts by Simmons [A77], Robertson and Robertson [B104], Taylor [A83], Nirenberg [A65], and Hille and Phillips [A41] are recommended. Of equal importance are the books by Bourbaki [A12], Day [A20], Kelley, Namioka, et al. [A48], Clarkson [B27], Klee et al. [B58], Eggleston [A24], and Dunford and Schwartz [A22].

On the whole the results of the chapter are pleasantly concise and explicit, and it is not difficult to pin down the reason why this is so. Competitive techniques, for example, the maximum principle (see [A69]), the calculus of variations (see [A31], [A26], [B53], and [B13]), programming methods (see [B96], [A97]), and others (see [A25], [A56, ch. 6], [A91], [B2], [B18], [B19], [B83]), generally approach problems of a particular dynamic character, such as differential equations, treating linear and nonlinear forms (at least in theory) on an equal footing. In contrast, the present development assumes linearity and a specialization in the performance index (i.e., a norm) in exchange for greater breadth in admissible system types. This adjustment in analytic framework allows the use of the powerful but specialized tools cited. In short, this chapter cuts across a different swath of problems than those amenable to the more conventional techniques (see also [A98], [A14], [A67], [A74], [A86] for other applications).

Emphasis is on linear systems of all types, including composite families of difference and differential equations, which can and should be thought of as concrete members of an abstract family. To amplify this hypothesis Appendix 9 shows that the results of the chapter can be used as well to solve optimization problems for distributive systems. These and other extensions seem to require ingenuity in formulating appropriate Banach spaces and computing extremals.

The development of the chapter is an outgrowth of Reference [B100] (see also [B101] and [B102]). Several other papers are of interest, however, and we mention several of them briefly. Krein [B1] presents a problem similar to that posed in Exercise 7, Section 4.3. His results were used to study specific optimization problems, first by Krasovskii [B61,B62], and later by Kulikowski [B65,B66,B67,B68]. Similar studies were carried out by Neustadt [B90,B93], Reid [B103], and Antosiewicz [B3]. Beginning with Bushaw [B20] and continuing with Bellman, Glicksberg, and Gross [B12], Gamkrelidze [B38], LaSalle [B71], Halkin [B44], Sonneborn and Van Vleck [B112] and Falb [B34], time-optimal bang-bang control problems have been studied (see also [B77], [B57], [B73], [B74], and [B91]).

Engineering applications related to the general theory have been considered by several authors. The texts [A14], [A67], [A74], [A86], [A88], [A96], [A97], [A98] are of an applied nature. Articles by Flugge-Lotz and Marbach [B35], Cadzow [B26], Ladd and Friedland [B70], Stubberud [B113], Wonham and Johnson [B121], Kranc and Sarachik [B60], Athans [B4], [B5], Athans, Falb, and Lacoss [B6,B7], Waltz [B116], Meditch [B81,B82], Balakrishnan [B9], Porter [B99], Nahi [B88], Kuo [B69], Grimmell [B43], and many others represent a cross section of the engineering literature.

In the majority of applications one or more "construction" problems must be solved. In Problem 1 the unit outward normal ϕ_ξ and the number $p(\xi)$ must be computed. (In the minimum effort case, alternatively, we may compute J^{-1}, which simplifies to $(TT^*)^{-1}$ in Hilbert spaces.) In Problem 2 the operator K (or $I + F^*F$ in Hilbert spaces) must be inverted. Several computational algorithms perform these tasks, but much work remains to be done. As general references the texts [B46], [B114], [B55], [A97], and [A74] will prove useful. We recommend also Ho [B47], Neustadt [B89], Eaton [B29], Harvey [B45], Babunashvili [B8], Gilbert [B39], Fadden [B33], Barr [B10], Balakrishnan [B9], Bass and Webber [B11], Friedland [B37], Graham [B42], Waltz [B116], Bryson and Denham [B18,B19], Knudsen [B59], Kulikowski [B66,B67], Lee [B72], Meditch [B80], and Paiewonskiy [B94,B95].

Some of these references deal with minimum-time problems (see Appendix 7) or the feedback synthesis problem (see Remark 7, Section 4.3). In most articles the titles are explicit enough to pinpoint their contents for the reader.

In Hilbert spaces the pseudoinverse function is linear and its computation involves the inversion of a linear, strictly positive operator (namely TT^* or $(I + F^*F)$ in Problems 1 and 2, respectively). Several methods are described by Altman [B2], and Kantorovich [B55] (see also Balakrishnan [B9]). The derivation of the Ricardi equations in Section 4.4 is due to Kuo [B69], and may be derived by variational techniques (see Kalman [B53]).

1 A SUPPLEMENT ON METRIC SPACES

Appendix 1 is a brief résumé of the concepts of countable (denumerable) sets, separable spaces, and compact spaces. The first topic is included for purposes of completeness; the other two have important roles in Appendix 2, Appendix 5, and in the applications of Chapters 3 and 4.

COUNTABLE SETS

Suppose that the sets A and B contain a finite number of elements and that we wish to determine if these respective numbers are the same. An obvious solution is to count the elements in each set. That is, we place each of the elements in correspondence with one of the integers 1, 2, 3, ... The largest integer used is called the (cardinal) number of elements in the set. The use of the integers is not necessary, however, because our question can be answered without actually counting the elements of the sets. For instance, let A be a set of Latin letters,

$$A = \{a,b,c,d,e\},$$

and B a set of Greek letters,

$$B = \{\alpha,\beta,\gamma,\delta,\varepsilon\}.$$

If we arrange these sets as

A:	a	b	c	d	e
B:	α	β	γ	δ	ε

we can see without any counting that A and B have the same number of elements. What is characteristic of this method of comparing sets? For each element of a set one and only one corresponds to an element in the other set, and conversely.

The power of this seemingly trivial second method of comparison lies in the fact that it can be applied when the sets are infinite. For instance, if N is the set of all positive integers and M is the set of all numbers of the form $1/n$, the second method of comparison shows at once that the number of elements (in some sense) is the same in both the sets N and M. To convince ourselves of this, it is sufficient to arrange our sets as follows:

$$N: \quad 1 \quad 2 \quad 3 \quad 4 \quad \cdots$$

$$M: \quad 1 \quad 1/2 \quad 1/3 \quad 1/4 \quad \cdots$$

and pair off the numbers n and $1/n$. Thus we have determined the numerical equivalence of the two sets without dealing with the question of the absolute number of elements in each set.

Any two sets A and B are said to be *numerically equivalent* if and only if there exists a rule which defines a one-to-one correspondence between their elements; that is, each $a \in A$ has exactly one $b \in B$ related to it and vice versa. The reader should verify that the following simple propositions hold:

(1)   Every set is numerically equivalent to itself.
(2)   For any sets A and B, if A is equivalent to B, then B is equivalent to A.
(3)   For any sets A, B, and C, if A is equivalent to B and B is equivalent to C, then A is equivalent to C.

DEFINITION A.   *A set is infinite if and only if it can be placed in one-to-one correspondence with a proper subset of itself. A set that is not infinite is called finite.*

To illustrate the underlying principle of this definition we consider the set $N = \{1, 2, 3, \ldots\}$ of all positive integers. N seems obviously "larger" than the set $\{2, 4, 6, \ldots\}$ of all even positive integers, for it contains this set as a proper subset. When dealing with infinite sets, however, we must remember that our criterion in these matters is whether a one-to-one correspondence between the two sets exists (not whether one set is or is not a proper subset of the other). Actually the pairing

$$1, 2, 3, \ldots, n, \ldots$$

$$2, 4, 6, \ldots, 2n, \ldots$$

is a suitable one-to-one correspondence between these sets. Each positive integer in the upper row is matched with the even positive integer (its double) directly below it. These two sets must therefore be regarded as numerically equivalent.

As a second example, we can show that there are just as many perfect squares (1, 4, 9, 16, 25, ...) as there are positive integers. The pairing scheme

$$1, \ 2, \ 3, \ 4, \ ...$$

$$1^2, 2^2, 3^2, 4^2, \ ...$$

makes this statement obvious. To allay any uneasy feeling that the preceding examples have to do with some quirk in the set of integers we consider Figure A1.1.

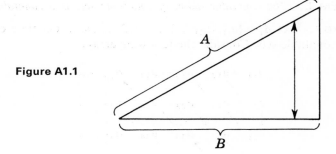

Figure A1.1

Let A be the set of points constituting the hypotenuse and B the set of points constituting the lower leg of the triangle. Despite the fact that the set B is a shorter line segment than the set A, a one-to-one correspondence between the two sets can be set up by projecting A on B. Hence, as in the preceding examples, we have encountered a set that is equivalent to a proper subset of itself. It is clear that a finite set cannot contain proper subsets equivalent to itself. It is thus the infiniteness of the set A that produces this curious phenomenon.

DEFINITION B. *A set is said to be countably infinite if it is equivalent to the set of positive integers. If a set is finite or countably infinite, it is called countable.*

It follows therefore from this definition that a set is countably infinite if its elements can be arranged in an infinite sequence. There are many interesting and useful theorems about countably infinite sets. For the sake of brevity we ration ourselves to the following group.

THEOREM A. *Every set has a countable subset. Any subset of a countable set is countable.*

P R O O F .   Since the finite case is trivial, assume that A is an infinite set. A countable subset of A can be generated by choosing elements sequentially from the set A and labeling them a_i, $i = 1, \ldots, n, \ldots$. The resulting subset is in obvious correspondence with the integers. If A is countable and $B \subset A$, the elements of B may be associated with the integers by arranging them according to their arrangement in A.

THEOREM B.   *The union of a finite number of countable sets is countable.*

P R O O F .   Let $A = \{a_1, a_2, \ldots\}$ and $B = \{b_1, b_2, \ldots\}$ be countable infinite sets. Then $A \cup B$ is countably infinite because the elements can be arranged in the sequence $a_1, b_1, a_2, b_2, \ldots, a_n, b_n, \ldots$. To prove that the union of n countably infinite sets, in which n is any positive integer greater than 1, is countably infinite we need only apply mathemetical induction by using the result for $n = 2$.

THEOREM C.   *The countable union of countable sets is a countable set.*

P R O O F .   Let $A_i = \{a_{i1}, a_{i2}, \ldots\}$, $i = 1, 2, \ldots, n, \ldots$ denote a countable class of countable sets. Consider the following array:

$$
\begin{array}{cccccc}
a_{11} \to a_{12} & a_{13} \to a_{14} & a_{15} \to \cdots \\
a_{21} & a_{22} & a_{23} & a_{24} & a_{25} & \cdots \\
a_{31} & a_{32} & a_{33} & a_{34} & a_{35} & \cdots \\
a_{41} & a_{42} & a_{43} & a_{44} & a_{45} & \cdots \\
a_{51} & a_{52} & a_{53} & a_{54} & a_{55} & \cdots \\
\vdots & \vdots & \vdots & \vdots & \vdots & \vdots
\end{array}
$$

The elements can be arranged in a sequence as indicated by the arrows and clearly every element of every set is included. Thus the elements of the set $\bigcup_i A_i$ are put in sequence by this procedure. If the A_i are disjoint (i.e., $A_i \cap A_j = \varnothing$, $i \neq j$), the set $\bigcup_i A_i$ has been put in one-to-one correspondence with the integers. If the sets $\{A_i\}$ are not disjoint, we need only agree to throw out any element in the chain that has already occurred.

THEOREM D.   *The set of rational numbers is countably infinite.*

P R O O F .   Each rational number can be put in the form p/q, in which p is an integer and q is a positive integer. Consider that each rational number is in its lowest form. Assign to each rational number an index $|p| + q$. We now place the rationals in a sequence according to their indices. Numbers with greater indices succeed numbers with smaller indices. Numbers with the same index are ordered according to absolute value with the negative number first. The sequence begins

$$0, \frac{-1}{1}, \frac{1}{1}, \frac{-1}{2}, \frac{1}{2}, \frac{-2}{1}, \frac{2}{1}, \frac{-1}{3}, \frac{1}{3}, \frac{-3}{1}, \frac{3}{1}, \frac{-1}{4}, \frac{1}{4}, \frac{-2}{3}, \frac{2}{3}, \frac{-3}{2}, \frac{3}{2}, \frac{-4}{1}, \frac{4}{1}, \ldots,$$

which completes the proof.

At this point the reader may have reached the unwarranted conclusion that all infinite sets are countable. We shall now settle this point with the following example of an uncountable set.

THEOREM E. *The set of real numbers* $\{x : x \in R \text{ and } 0 \le x \le 1\} = [0,1]$ *is uncountable.*

P R O O F . Assume that a one-to-one correspondence exists between the set of positive integers and the set of real numbers between zero and one. These real numbers may be represented by their binary expansions. According to our assumption, we can arrange all the reals between zero and one in a sequence. Taken in a random order the following correspondence then results:

$$1 \leftrightarrow .0\,0\,0\,0\,0\,0 \ldots$$
$$2 \leftrightarrow .0\,1\,1\,0\,0\,1 \ldots$$
$$3 \leftrightarrow .0\,0\,1\,1\,0\,1 \ldots$$
$$\vdots$$
$$n \leftrightarrow .1\,0\,1\,1\,1\,0\,0 \ldots$$
$$\vdots$$

If the assumption that $[0,1]$ is countable is true, every number in this interval must appear in this table.

Let us define a real number $x \in [0,1]$ as follows. Consider the main diagonal of the array. Let the nth decimal place of $\hat{x}$ contain a zero or one, according to whether the element in the nth place on the main diagonal is a one or a zero. The constructed number then differs in the nth place from the nth number on the main diagonal, hence is not in the sequence. It follows that our original assumption is incorrect and that the set is uncountable.

THEOREM F. *The set* P'_∞ *of algebraic polynomials with rational coefficients is countable.*

The proof is left as an exercise with the hint that the sets P'_n of polynomials with rational coefficients and degree $\le n$ are countable and that P'_∞ may be expressed as the countable union $P'_\infty = \bigcup_{n=1}^\infty P'_n$.

SEPARABLE SPACES

In the set R of all real numbers the subset E of all rational numbers has the important property that every element of R can be expressed as a limit of a sequence of elements of E; that is, the closure $\bar{E} = R$. This property is called the density of the set of rational numbers in R. Let us now transfer the notion of density into the metric space setting.

DEFINITION C.   *A set S of points of the metric space X is called everywhere dense (or dense in X) if $\bar{S} = X$.*

According to Definition J, Section 1.2, the equality $\bar{S} = X$ means that every $x \in S$ can be expressed in the form $x = \lim x_n$, where $x_n \in S$, or for every $x \in X$ and any $\varepsilon > 0$ an $x' \in S$ can be found such that $\rho(x,x') < \varepsilon$. The definition does not preclude the case where X is a subset of a larger metric space.

DEFINITION D.   *A metric space is called separable if it contains a countable, everywhere-dense subset.*

The majority of spaces considered as examples in Chapter 1 are separable.

In R^n every vector can be expressed as a limit of a vector sequence with rational components. Tuplets with rational components constitute a denumerable set by the corollary to Theorem C. Consequently, R^n is separable. The separability of l_2 may be established as follows: First if $x = (\xi_1, \xi_2, \dots)$ is an element of l_2, then the series $\sum_{k=1}^{\infty} |\xi_k|^2$ is convergent so that by choosing n large enough, we can make $\sum_{k=n+1}^{\infty} |\xi_k|^2$ as small as we please. In other words, we can approximate the given vector x arbitrarily closely by a vector of the form

$$x_n = (\xi_1, \xi_2, \dots, \xi_n, 0, \dots).$$

For the real space l_2 each ξ_i is real and therefore may be approximated by a rational ξ_i. This leads to an approximation of the given vector x by a vector in l_2 which has only finitely many nonzero components each of which is rational. This latter subset of l_2 is countable and so we conclude that l_2 is separable. For the complex l_2 space the argument is similar.

By an analogous argument the reader may show that the set $P'_{\infty}(a,b)$ of all polynomials on the interval (a,b) with rational coefficients is dense in the metric space $P_{\infty}(a,b)$ of all polynomials on (a, b) (with the usual supremum metric). A theorem of Weierstrass states that every function $x \in C(a,b)$ may be represented as the uniform limit of a sequence of polynomials. If we substitute an approximating element from the set $P'_{\infty}(a,b)$, it follows that the set $P_{\infty}(a,b)$ is everywhere dense in $C(a,b)$.

To conclude our discussion of separability we consider two general theorems.

THEOREM G.   *Every subset X^1 of the separable metric space X is a separable space.*

PROOF.   For every $x_n \in S$ we pick a $y_n^k \in X^1$ (if one exists) such that $\rho(x_n, y_n^k) < 1/k$. The set $\{y_n^k\}$ of all such points we denote by S_k and note that S_k is countable and that $S_k \subset X^1$. Similarly, $S^1 = \bigcup_k S_k$ is a countable subset of X^1.

To show that S^1 is dense in X^1 we choose, for arbitrary $\varepsilon > 0$, a k such that $1/k < \varepsilon/2$. Since S is dense in X an $x_n \in S$ exists such that $\rho(x_n, x) < 1/k$ holds for arbitrary $x \in X^1$. This implies, however, the existence of a $y_n^k \in S^1$ such that $\rho(y_n^k, x_n) < 1/k$. By the triangular law,

$$\rho(y_n^k, x) \leq \rho(y_n^k, x_n) + \rho(x_n, x) < 2/k < \varepsilon,$$

the density of S^1 in E^1, hence the separability of E^1, is thus established.

THEOREM H. *If an everywhere-dense subset X^1 of the metric space X is a separable space, then X is also separable.*

P R O O F . Let A be a countable everywhere-dense subset of X^1. For any $x \in X$ and $\varepsilon > 0$ (since X^1 is everywhere dense in X) there exists $x' \in X'$ such that $\rho(x, x') < \varepsilon/2$. Since A is everywhere dense in X', there exists $x'' \in A$ such that $\rho(x', x'') < \varepsilon/2$. Hence it follows that $\rho(x, x'') < \varepsilon$, and from the arbitrariness of ε we conclude that A is everywhere dense in X.

COMPACT SPACES

An important theorem is the Bolzano-Weierstrass theorem: *Every infinite bounded sequence of real numbers contains a convergent subsequence.* If A is an arbitrary bounded subset of R, then from the Bolzano-Weierstrass theorem we conclude that any sequence formed from the elements of A has a convergent subsequence. On the other hand, if A is unbounded, a sequence approaching infinity can be selected, none of whose subsequences is bounded. Thus the space R has the property that boundedness of a set is equivalent to the property that every sequence of elements from the set has a convergent subsequence.

As is true with many properties of the real line, some difficulties are involved in carrying over the Bolzano-Weierstrass property to arbitrary metric spaces. The concept of a compact space, as delineated in our first definition, isolates those spaces that have the Bolzano-Weierstrass property.

DEFINITION E. *The subset A of the metric space X is called compact if every infinite sequence of points from A contains a convergent subsequence with limit in A. If X possesses this property, then X is called a compact space.*

It is clear that every set with a finite number of points is compact, for every infinite sequence must repeat one of the points an infinite number of times to provide automatically an infinite convergent subsequence.

THEOREM I. *Every compact set is bounded.*

P R O O F . Let A denote an unbounded set. For any $r > 0$ we pick an $x_1 \in A$ and note that A, being unbounded, is not contained in the sphere $S_r(x_1)$ of radius r about x_1. Thus an $x_3 \in A$ exists such that $p(x_2, x_1) > r$. The unboundedness of A implies that an $x_3 \in A$ lies outside the spheres $S_r(x_1)$ and $S_r(x_2)$. If we repeat the process, an infinite sequence of points from A is generated, none of whose subsequences can be convergent. This means that A cannot be compact and the theorem is proved.

Contrary to the situation in R, the converse of Theorem I does not hold in general; that is, it is not true that every bounded closed subset of an arbitrary metric space is compact. To settle this question once and for all we consider Example 1.

Example 1. The unit sphere $S = \{x : \|x\| = 1\}$ of l_2 is an example of a closed bounded but *not* compact set. Indeed, the points

$$e_1 = (1, 0, 0, \ldots)$$

$$e_2 = (0, 1, 0, \ldots)$$

constitute an infinite subset of S such that $\rho(e_i, e_j) = \sqrt{2}$ for $i \neq j$. Hence this sequence $\{e_i\}$ can contain no convergent subsequences. The space l_2, however, does contain compact sets, one of which is the collection Q of points $x = (x_1, x_2, \ldots, x_n, \ldots) \in l_2$, satisfying

$$|x_1| \leq \tfrac{1}{2}, \qquad |x_2| \leq (\tfrac{1}{2})^2, \ldots, \qquad |x_n| \leq (\tfrac{1}{2})^n, \ldots.$$

THEOREM J. *Every closed bounded subset of a finite-dimensional normed linear space is compact.*

PROOF. Let n be the dimension of the space X and S a closed bounded subset of X. By introducing a basis $\{x_1, \ldots, x_n\}$ for X every element of the set S is associated with a tuplet $(\alpha_1, \ldots, \alpha_n) \in R^n$ by the expansion

$$x = \sum_{i=1}^{n} \alpha_i x_i$$

along this basis. Let A_i, $i = 1, \ldots, n$ denote the set of all values taken on by the ith coefficient in this expansion as x ranges over S. Since S is bounded, one can show (using Theorem B, Section 1.4) that each A_i is bounded. Furthermore, each infinite sequence $\{x^k\}$ in S generates an infinite sequence $\{\alpha_i^k\}$ in each A_i, $i = 1, \ldots, n$. A convergent subsequence of the x^k is chosen as follows: from A_1 pick any convergent subsequence $\{\alpha_i^{k'}\}$. The associated sequence $\{x^{k'}\}$ in S generates an infinite sequence $\{\alpha_2^k\}$ in A_2. Choose a convergent subsequence $(\alpha_2^{k''})$ in A_2. The associated sequence $\{x^{k''}\}$ in S is still infinite and has convergent coefficient sequences in A_1 and A_2. Repetition of the selection process n times produces a subsequence of the original sequence which inherits convergence from the convergence in the coordinate spaces.

DEFINITION F. *Let A be a subset of a metric space X and let $\varepsilon > 0$. A set $B \subset A$ is called an ε-net for A if there exists a $b \in B$ for every $a \in A$ such that $\rho(b, a) < \varepsilon$.*

In other words B is an ε-net for A if there are enough points in B so that by locating a spherical neighborhood of diameter ε at each point of B the set A is covered. Every set is an ε-net for itself. If a set A has a *finite* ε-net for each $\varepsilon > 0$, then A is said to be *totally bounded*. Clearly, every totally bounded set is bounded.

THEOREM K. *In a complete metric space it is necessary and sufficient that a compact set be closed and totally bounded.*

PROOF. The necessity, which we prove first, does not require that the space be complete. Assume for some $\varepsilon > 0$ that the compact set A does not possess an ε-net. Then, for $x_1 \in A$, a point $x_2 \in A$ such that $p(x_1, x_2) > \varepsilon$ may be found. Likewise, a set $\{x_1, \ldots, x_n\} \subset A$ may be found such that $\rho(x_i, x_j) > \varepsilon$ for $i \neq j$, for otherwise this set would be a finite ε-net for A. Continuing the process by induction on the subscript n, we arrive at an infinite sequence $\{x_i\}$, such that $\rho(x_i, x_j) > \varepsilon$, $i \neq j$, and which as a consequence has no convergent subsequence. A cannot be compact, and therefore total boundedness is certainly necessary.

Assume now that A has an ε-net for some $\varepsilon > 0$. For convenience let $\varepsilon_1 = 1$; a finite number of spherical neighborhoods of radius 1 will cover the set A. Let $\{x_n\}$ be an infinite sequence of the points in A. One of these neighborhoods, call it S_1, contains an infinity of points from $\{x_n\}$. Select a subsequence $\{x_n^1\}$ by deleting the members of $\{x_n\}$ outside S_1. The points x_n in S_1 form a subsequence, and we renumber them again for convenience as $x_1^{(1)}, x_2^{(1)}, \ldots,$ $x^{(1)}, \ldots$.

Now we take $\varepsilon_2 = \frac{1}{2}$. Proceeding from the derived sequence $\{x_n^{(1)}\}$ and reasoning in a similar way, it is clear that some sphere S_2 of radius $\frac{1}{2}$ contains an infinite subsequence $x_1^{(2)}, x_2^{(2)}, \ldots, x_n^{(2)}, \ldots$, chosen from the first subsequence. The process is repeated indefinitely by choosing in turn a subsequence contained in a sphere S_n of radius $\varepsilon_n = 1/n$ for $n = 1, 2, \ldots$.

The subsequences so chosen may be written in the following form:

$$x_1^{(1)}, x_2^{(1)}, x_3^{(1)}, \ldots, x_n^{(1)}, \ldots$$

$$x_1^{(2)}, x_2^{(2)}, x_3^{(2)}, \ldots, x_n^{(2)}, \ldots$$

$$x_1^{(3)}, x_2^{(3)}, x_3^{(3)}, \ldots, x_n^{(3)}, \ldots$$

$$\vdots \qquad \vdots \qquad \vdots \qquad \quad \vdots$$

$$x_1^{(n)}, x_2^{(n)}, x_3^{(n)}, \ldots, x_n^{(n)}, \ldots$$

$$\vdots \qquad \vdots \qquad \vdots \qquad \quad \vdots$$

Here every row represents a subsequence chosen from the preceding row. In addition, the nth row has the property that all its elements are contained in a sphere of radius $1/n$.

Let us now apply the "diagonal method," which is a classic of mathematics; namely, we form the sequence of all points on the diagonal of the table

$$x_1^{(1)}, x_2^{(2)}, \ldots, x_n^{(n)}, \ldots.$$

This is a subsequence of the original sequence and for any $m, p \geq n$ we have

$$\rho(x_m^{(m)}, a) < \frac{1}{n}, \qquad \rho(x_p^{(p)}, a) < \frac{1}{n},$$

where a is the center of the sphere S_n. Therefore

$$\rho(x_m^{(m)}, x_p^{(p)}) \leq \rho(x_m^{(m)}, a) + \rho(a, x_p^{(p)}) < \frac{2}{n}.$$

Thus the subsequence is Cauchy and so convergent by the completeness of X and the theorem is proved.

To illustrate this theorem let us use the fact that every closed bounded subset of an n-dimensional Banach space can be enclosed in a sufficiently large cube (i.e., a set of points with coordinates along any basis satisfying magnitude constraints). If such a cube is divided into subcubicles with diagonals of length $e/\sqrt{n}$, the vertices of these cubicles form an ε-net for the set; hence the set is compact.

An ε-net for the set Q of Example 1 can be specified by choosing the number n such that $(\frac{1}{2})^n < e/2$. Associate with each $x = (x_1, x_2, \ldots) \in Q$ the point $x' = (x_1, x_2, \ldots, x_n, 0, 0, \ldots)$; then

$$\rho(x, x') = \left(\sum_{n+1}^{\infty} |x_k|^2 \right)^{1/2} \leq \left(\sum_{n+1}^{\infty} \left(\frac{1}{2} \right)^{2k} \right)^{1/2} < \frac{\varepsilon}{2}.$$

The set Q' of all such points x' lies in a finite-dimensional subspace. By the triangular inequality any $\varepsilon/2$ net for Q' will be an ε-net for Q.

This example suggests the following corollary to Theorem G.

COROLLARY. *A necessary and sufficient condition that a subset M of a complete metric space X be compact is that for every $\varepsilon > 0$ a compact ε-net for M exist.*

In dealing with specific applications, the conditions for compactness are not always simple. The space $C(a,b)$, which is fundamental to the study of linear dynamic systems, provides a useful illustration of the special tools that are sometimes necessary to determine compactness. To state the basic theorem, we need two special concepts. A set of functions $M = \{x(t)\}$ is *uniformly bounded* if there exists a constant $\alpha > 0$ such that $|x(t)| < \alpha$ for all t and all $x \in M$. The set M is said to be *equicontinuous* if for every $\varepsilon > 0$ a δ can be found such that $|x(t_1) - x(t_2)| < \varepsilon$ for every $|t_1 - t_2| < \delta$ and for all $x \in M$. The criterion for compactness in $C(a,b)$ is due to Arzela.

THEOREM L. *A necessary and sufficient condition for a subset M of $C(a,b)$ to be compact is that M be uniformly bounded and equicontinuous.*

REFERENCES

In compiling this appendix the author has leaned heavily on Chapter 1 of [A63] and on Sections 3.6–3.8 of [A93]. The reader is referred also to [A4], [A6], [A77, chs. II–IV], [A21, ch. III], [A50, chs. I, II], [A56, ch. I], and [A83, ch. II].

2 FOURIER EXPANSIONS

In this appendix we consider a topic that no doubt is familiar to the reader. Indeed, Fourier expansions play a prominent role in mechanics, field theory, thermodynamics, distributive control systems and, in fact, wherever systems that satisfy ordinary or partial differential equations are under investigation. In the present treatment an abstract formulation of the Fourier expansion is given. This treatment is free from the clutter of specific computations and shows the underlying elegance of the concept. In addition, this appendix is designed to provide the reader with the opportunity for additional mental exercise on abstract reasoning.

THEOREM A. *Let* $S = \{e_1, e_2, \ldots, e_n\}$ *be a finite orthonormal set in a Hilbert space* H. *If* x *is any vector in* H, *then the following relations hold:*

$$(1) \quad \sum_{i=1}^{n} |\langle x, e_i \rangle|^2 \leq \|x\|^2,$$

$$(2) \quad \left(x - \sum_{i=1}^{n} \langle x, e_i \rangle e_i\right) \perp e_j, \quad \text{any } j.$$

PROOF. The inequality of the theorem can be proved by a computation that is similar to that used in proving Schwarz's inequality:

$$0 \le \| x - \sum_{i=1}^{n} \langle x, e_i \rangle e_i \|^2$$

$$= \langle x - \sum_{i=1}^{n} \langle x, e_i \rangle e_i,\ x - \sum_{j=1}^{n} \langle x, e_j \rangle e_j \rangle$$

$$= \langle x, x \rangle - \sum_{i=1}^{n} \langle x, e_i \rangle \overline{\langle x, e_i \rangle} - \sum_{j=1}^{n} \langle x, e_j \rangle \overline{\langle x, e_j \rangle}$$

$$+ \sum_{i=1}^{n} \sum_{j=1}^{n} \langle x, e_i \rangle \overline{\langle x, e_j \rangle} \langle e_i, e_j \rangle.$$

Using the orthonormality of S, we have

$$0 \le \| x \|^2 - \sum_{i=1}^{n} |\langle x, e_i \rangle|^2.$$

To prove the second assertion we observe that

$$\langle [x - \sum_{i=1}^{n} \langle x, e_i \rangle e_i], e_j \rangle = \langle x, e_j \rangle - \sum_{i=1}^{n} \langle x, e_i \rangle \langle e_i, e_j \rangle$$

$$= \langle x, e_j \rangle - \langle x, e_j \rangle = 0.$$

Evidently inequality (1) can be geometrically interpreted as saying that the sum of the squares of the components of a vector in various perpendicular directions does not exceed the square of the length of the vector itself. This initial theorem, although restricted in form, sets the pattern for everything that is to be said about Fourier expansions. What we shall do in the sequel is to extend the range of applicability of this result.

THEOREM B.   *Let L be the closed linear subspace spanned by the orthonormal set $S = \{e_1, \ldots, e_n, \ldots\}$. Then for any $x \in L$*

(1) $$x = \lim_{n \to \infty} \sum_{i=1}^{n} \langle x, e_i \rangle e_i,$$

(2) $$\| x \|^2 = \lim_{n \to \infty} \sum_{i=1}^{n} |\langle x, e_i \rangle|^2.$$

PROOF.   By the proof of Lemma B, Section 1.5, we know that each $x \in L$ can be written as the limit of a sequence $\{x_n\}$, where each x_n is a (finite) linear combination of the $\{e_j\}$. Hence for each $\varepsilon > 0$ there exists a linear combination $\sum_{i=1}^{n} \alpha_i e_i$ such that

$$\| x - \sum_{i=1}^{n} \alpha_i e_i \| < \varepsilon.$$

Moreover, by definition of the norm we have

$$\left\| x - \sum_i \alpha_i e_i \right\|^2 = \left\langle x - \sum_i \alpha_i e_i, x - \sum_j \alpha_j e_j \right\rangle$$

$$= \langle x,x \rangle + \sum_{i,j} \alpha_i \bar{\alpha}_j \langle e_i,e_j \rangle - \sum_i \alpha_i \langle e_i,x \rangle - \sum_i \bar{\alpha}_i \langle x,e_i \rangle$$

$$= \|x\|^2 - \sum_i \bar{\alpha}_i c_i - \sum_i \alpha_i \bar{c}_i + \sum_i |\alpha_i|^2,$$

where $c_i = \langle x,e_i \rangle$ and we have used the fact that $\langle e_i,e_j \rangle = \delta_{ij}$. We may rewrite this expression as

$$\left\| x - \sum_i \alpha_i e_i \right\|^2 = \|x\|^2 + \sum_i (c_i \bar{c}_i - \bar{\alpha}_i c_i - \alpha_i \bar{c}_i + \alpha_i \bar{\alpha}_i) - \sum_i c_i \bar{c}_i$$

$$= \|x\|^2 - \sum_i |c_i|^2 + \sum_i |\alpha_i - c_i|^2.$$

Observe now that the right-hand side of this equation assumes its least value precisely when $\alpha_i = c_i$; hence

$$0 \le \|x\|^2 - \sum_{i=1}^n |c_i|^2 = \left\| x - \sum_{i=1}^n c_i e_i \right\|^2 \le \left\| x - \sum_{i=1}^n \alpha_i e_i \right\|^2 < \varepsilon^2.$$

Since ε is arbitrary, this means that

$$x = \lim_{n \to \infty} \sum_{i=1}^n c_i e_i = \lim_{n \to \infty} \sum_{i=1}^n \langle x,e_i \rangle e_i.$$

In addition, the inequality implies that

$$\lim_{n \to \infty} \sum_{i=1}^n |\langle x,e_i \rangle|^2 = \|x\|^2$$

and the proof is complete.

COROLLARY (Bessel's Inequality). *If $S = \{e_i\}$ is any countable ortho-normal set in a Hilbert space H, then*

$$\sum_i |\langle x,e_i \rangle|^2 \le \|x\|^2$$

for every vector x in H.

PROOF. If S is finite, this corollary is equivalent to Theorem A. If S is infinite, consider the closed linear subspace $L(e_1, e_2, \ldots, e_n, \ldots)$. By the projection theorem each $x \in H$ has a unique representation

$$x = y + z, \qquad y \in L, z \in L^\perp.$$

By Theorem B

$$\|y\|^2 = \lim_{n \to \infty} \sum_{i=1}^n |\langle y,e_i \rangle|^2.$$

Since $\langle z, e_i \rangle = 0$ for all i, this may be written

$$\|y\|^2 = \lim_{n \to \infty} \sum_{i=1}^{n} |\langle x, e_i \rangle|^2.$$

The corollary now follows from the fact that

$$\|x\|^2 = \|y\|^2 + \|z\|^2.$$

REMARKS. The scalars $\langle x, e_i \rangle$ are called the Fourier coefficients of x with respect to the set $\{e_1, e_2, \ldots, e_n, \ldots\}$. Henceforth we shall use the notation $\sum_{i=1}^{\infty}$ to denote the operation $\lim_{n \to \infty} \sum_{i=1}^{n}$.

Note that in proving the Bessel inequality we actually found that the vector x belongs to $\overline{L}$ if and only if $\|x\|^2 = \sum_{i=1}^{\infty} |\langle x, e_i \rangle|^2$.

Observe that the Schwarz inequality $|\langle x, y \rangle| \le \|x\| \cdot \|y\|$ may be obtained from the Bessel inequality by considering the orthonormal set consisting of the single vector $y/\|y\|$.

COMPLETENESS OF ORTHONORMAL SETS

A collection S of orthonormal vectors in H is said to be *complete* if S is not contained in any larger orthonormal set.[1] This is clearly the same as requiring that 0 be the only vector in H orthogonal to the vectors of S. If H is the Euclidean space E^n, any set of n orthonormal vectors will be complete. In an infinite-dimensional Hilbert space a complete orthonormal set is necessarily infinite. It is obvious that there are many infinite collections of orthonormal vectors which are not complete. The following theorem, which we shall not prove, shows that our definition is meaningful.

THEOREM C. *Every Hilbert space contains a complete orthonormal set.*

The usual proof of this theorem actually shows a little more; namely, that if S is *any* collection of orthonormal vectors in H there is a *complete* orthonormal set S' containing S, which we abbreviate by saying that any orthonormal set may be extended to a complete orthonormal set.

We emphasize that the theorem does not assert that a complete orthonormal set is countable. It can be shown, however, that any two complete orthonormal sets in H are numerically equivalent. This, with Theorem C, shows that with each Hilbert space H there is associated in a natural way a cardinal number α. It is natural to speak of α as the (Hilbert space) *dimension* of H. Because we have already introduced a notion of vector space dimension, let us point out that if the dimension of H in either sense is finite the values coincide. The two notions do not agree in general. In fact, it can be shown that

---

[1] Observe that this notion of completeness is distinct from that introduced in Section 1.2. The precise meaning of the term "complete" will be clear from the context and should cause no confusion.

a Hilbert space *never* has a countable vector space dimension, whereas a wide class of Hilbert spaces has *countable* complete orthonormal sets. In order to avoid ambiguity, let us agree to understand by "dimension" the previously introduced (vector space) concept. We have little need for the other concept and will refer to it as the "Hilbert space dimension" if necessary.

We shall study complete orthonormal sets only in the special case in which they are countable. Formally, we have the following Definition.[1]

DEFINITION A. *A Hilbert space H is separable if it contains a complete orthonormal sequence.*

The foregoing discussion allows us to conclude that in a separable Hilbert space every orthonormal set is either finite or countably infinite. It is easy to show that l_2 is separable. We shall meet other examples in the sequel.

THEOREM D. *Let H be a separable Hilbert space, amd let $S = \{e_i\}$ be an orthonormal set in H. The following conditions are equivalent:*

(1)   *S is complete.*
(2) $x \perp S$ *implies* $x = 0$.
(3)   *For each x in H, $x = \sum_i \langle x, e_i \rangle e_i$.*
(4)   *For each x in H, $\|x\|^2 = \sum_i |\langle x, e_i \rangle|^2$.*
(5)   *H is the closure of the linear manifold $L(S)$ spanned by the e_i.*

P R O O F.   To prove the theorem it is enough to show that each condition implies the one following and that (5) implies (1).

(1) $\Rightarrow$ (2). If $x \perp S$ and $x \neq 0$, then $x \notin S$ and so S is a proper subset of the orthonormal sequence $\{x\} \cup S$. This contradicts the assumption (1) that S is complete.

(2) $\Rightarrow$ (3). Let $x \in H$ be given. Then

$$\langle x - \sum_i \langle x, e_i \rangle e_i, e_j \rangle = \lim_{n \to \infty} \langle x - \sum_{i=1}^{n} \langle x, e_i \rangle e_i, e_j \rangle = 0$$

for $j = 1, 2, \ldots$; hence, by (2), $x - \sum_i \langle x, e_i \rangle e_i = 0$. (Note that we have used the continuity of the linear product; see Exercise 14 of Section 2.1.)

(3) $\Rightarrow$ (4) $\Rightarrow$ (5). See Theorem B, its corollary, and the second Remark on page 368.

(5) $\Rightarrow$ (1). If (1) does not hold, there is a vector $x \neq 0$ in H which is orthogonal to S, hence orthogonal to $\overline{L(S)}$. This means that $\overline{L(S)}$ is a proper subspace of H, which contradicts (5).

In view of (3) it is natural to refer to a complete orthonormal sequence $\{e_i\}$ in a separable Hilbert space H as a (Hilbert space) *basis* for H. (The reader is cautioned to avoid confusing this basis with the notion of vector space basis. The latter means that each $x \in H$ has a representation as a *finite* linear combination of the e_i.) The equation in (3) is called the *Fourier expansion* of x with respect to the basis $\{e_i\}$. The importance of (4), which is

---

[1]It can be shown that this definition does not conflict with Definition D of Appendix 1.

referred to as the Parseval relation, is suggested by the fact that it trivially implies Bessel's inequality and reduces to the theorem of Pythagoras when H has dimension 2 or 3.

To complete this appendix we offer two examples from the field of mathematical physics. In all cases a rigorous discussion of the function spaces and particularly the completeness of the orthonormal sets mentioned requires an understanding of the modern theory of measure and integration. Because we have tried to avoid assuming this knowledge in the reader and because it is in no way essential to the purpose of these examples, the reader may treat all integrals as ordinary Riemann integrals.

Example 1. Let $L_2[0,2\pi]$ denote the Hilbert space of all square integrable functions on an interval $[0,2\pi]$. Recall that the inner product and norm are given by

$$\langle f,g \rangle = \int_0^{2\pi} f(t)\overline{g(t)}dt,$$

$$\|f\| = (\langle f,f \rangle)^{1/2} = \left[\int_0^{2\pi} |f(t)|^2 dt \right]^{1/2}.$$

The reader may easily verify that the functions e^{int} for

$$n = 0, \pm 1, \pm 2, \dots$$

are mutually orthogonal in L_2:

$$\int_0^{2\pi} e^{int} e^{-imt} dt = \begin{cases} 0, & m \neq n, \\ 2\pi, & m = n. \end{cases}$$

If we define the functions $\{e_n; n = 0, \pm 1, \pm 2, \dots\}$ by $e_n(t) = e^{int}/\sqrt{2\pi}$, the set $S = \{e_i\}$ is an orthonormal set in L_2. For any function f in L_2, the scalars

$$c_n = \langle f,e_n \rangle = \frac{1}{\sqrt{2\pi}} \int_0^{2\pi} f(t)e^{-int} dt$$

are the classical Fourier coefficients of the function. Bessel's inequality takes the following concrete form in this space:

$$\sum_{n=-\infty}^{\infty} |c_n|^2 \leq \int_0^{2\pi} |f(t)|^2 dt.$$

Theorem E states that $\{e_n\}$ is complete.

THEOREM E. *If f is integrable and $\int_0^{2\pi} f(x)e^{-inx} dx = 0, n = 0, \pm 1, \pm 2, \dots,$ then $f = 0$.*

PROOF. Suppose first that f is continuous on $[0,2\pi]$ and that for some x_0 $(0 < x_0 < 2\pi), f(x_0) > 0$. Then there is a closed interval $\Delta = [x_0 - \delta, x_0 + \delta]$

in which $f(x) > \frac{1}{2}f(x_0)$. Now it is easy to check that the functions

$$T_n(x) = [1 + \cos(x - x_0) - \cos \delta]^n$$

have the following properties:

(1) $T_n(x)$ is a linear combination of exponentials.
(2) $T_n(x) \geq 0$ on l.
(3) If $0 < \delta' < \delta$ and $\Delta = [x_0 - \delta', \, x_0 + \delta']$, then $T_n(x) \to \infty$ uniformly in l.
(4) $|T_n(x)| \leq 1$ outside l.

By (1) and the hypothesis we have

$$0 = \int_0^{2\pi} f(x)T_n(x)dx = \int_\Delta f(x)T_n(x)dx + \int_{[0,2\pi] \sim \Delta} f(x)T_n(x)dx.$$

By (4) the second integral on the right does not exceed $2\pi \sup_x |f(x)|$. Hence the first integral must be bounded, but in view of (3) this is a contradiction. A similar argument shows that f cannot be negative at x_0. Hence $f(x) = 0$ if $0 < x < 2\pi$. By continuity this proves that f is identically 0 on $0 \leq x \leq 2\pi$.

Suppose now that f is any integrable function for which $\int_0^{2\pi} f(x)e^{inx}dx = 0$, $n = 0, \pm 1, \pm 2, \ldots$. Let $F(x) = \int_0^x f(t)dt$. An integration by parts shows that

$$\int_0^{2\pi} F(x)e^{inx}dx = 0, \qquad n = \pm 1, \pm 2, \ldots.$$

Thus, if $A_0 = \int_0^{2\pi} F(x)dx$, the function $F(x) - A_0$ is continuous and orthogonal to e^{-inx} for all n. So by the first part of the proof

$$F(x) - A_0 = 0.$$

We have shown that the indefinite integral of f is constant. It is intuitively clear (and capable of being rigorously proved) that this implies that $f = 0$ except on a set of measure 0; that is, considered as an element of $L_2(0,2\pi)$, we have $f = 0$.

COROLLARY. *The trigonometric polynomials are dense in* $L_2(0,2\pi)$.

As a result of this completeness, Bessel's inequality can be strengthened to Parseval's equation:

$$\sum_{n=-\infty}^{\infty} |c_n|^2 = \int_0^{2\pi} |f(t)|^2 dt.$$

In addition, Theorem E tells us that the completeness of $\{e_n\}$ is equivalent to the statement that each f in L_2 has a Fourier expansion:

$$f(t) = \frac{1}{\sqrt{2\pi}} \sum_{n=-\infty}^{\infty} c_n e^{int}.$$

It must be emphasized that this expansion is *not* to be interpreted as saying that the series converges pointwise to the function. On the contrary, Hilbert spaces are complete with respect to the inner product norm and, in this case, if the vectors f_n in L_2 are defined by

$$f_n(t) = \frac{1}{\sqrt{2\pi}} \sum_{k=-n}^{n} c_k e^{int},$$

the convergence of the sequence $\{f_n\}$ to the vector f means convergence in the sense of the L_2 norm:

$$\|f_n - f\| \to 0.$$

This situation is often expressed by saying that f is the limit in the mean of the f_n's.

In order to convey some sense of the generality of our theory, we consider now two cases similar to Example 1.

Example 2.   The three different sets of this example are based on the solution of the second-order differential equation

$$\frac{d}{dt}\left[p(t)\frac{dx}{dt}\right] + q(t)x(t) = -\lambda r(t)x(t), \qquad t \in \tau \qquad (*)$$

with appropriate boundary conditions. Each of the sets is a complete orthonormal basis for the Hilbert space $L_2(\tau;r)$, where $r(t) > 0$, $t \in \tau$, and the inner product is defined by the expression

$$\langle x,y \rangle = \int_{\tau} r(t)x(t)y(t)dt, \qquad x,y \in L_2(\tau;r).$$

The first example consists of the *Hermite* polynomials which are defined by $h_0(t) = 1$, $h_1(t) = 2t$, $h_2(t) = 4t^2 - 2$, ..., with the general term

$$h_n(t) = (-1)^n e^{t^2} \frac{d^n}{dt^n}[e^{-t^2}], \qquad t \in [-\infty, \infty].$$

The function h_n satisfies equation $(*)$ when

$$p(t) = e^{-t^2}, \qquad q(t) = 0, \qquad r(t) = e^{-t^2}$$

and

$$\lambda_n = 2n, \qquad n = 1, 2, \ldots.$$

The normalized polynomials

$$p_n(t) = (2^n n! \sqrt{\pi})^{-1/2} h_n(t), \qquad t \in [-\infty, \infty],$$

constitute a complete orthonormal basis for $L_2(-\infty, \infty; e^{-t^2})$.

Consider now the *Laguerre* polynomials $l_0 = 1, l_1 = -t + 1, \ldots$, with the general term

$$l_n = e^t \frac{d^n}{dt^n} [t^n e^{-t}].$$

These functions satisfy the equation (∗) over the interval $[0, \infty]$ when

$$p(t) = te^{-t}, \qquad q(t) = 0, \qquad r(t) = e^{-t}$$

and

$$\lambda_n = n, \qquad n = 1, 2, \ldots.$$

The normalized Laguerre polynomials $\varphi_n(t) = (1/n!)l_n(t), n = 0, 1, \ldots$, constitute an orthonormal basis for $L_2(0, \infty; e^{-t})$.

The *Legendre* polynomials defined by

$$f_n(t) = \frac{d^n}{dt^n} [t^2 - 1]^n, \qquad n = 0, 1, 2, \ldots,$$

satisfy equation (∗) on the interval $[-1,1]$ when

$$p(t) = t^2 - 1, \qquad q(t) = 0, \qquad r(t) = 1, \qquad t \in [-1,1]$$

and λ takes on the values

$$\lambda_n = n(n + 1), \qquad n = 0, 1, 2, \ldots.$$

When normalized $\phi_n(t) = (2^n n!)^{-1} f_n(t), n = 0, 1, \ldots$, these functions form a complete orthonormal basis for $L_2(-1,1)$.

Example 3.   Consider the rectangle $\Delta = \{(t,s): t \in [a,b], s \in [c,d]\} \subset R^2$ and the set S of all functions f defined (and measurable) on Δ such that

$$\int_c^d \int_a^b |f(t,s)|^2 dt ds < \infty.$$

This set becomes a Hilbert space H when equipped with the inner product

$$\langle f,g \rangle = \int_c^d \int_a^b f(t,s) g(t,s) dt ds.$$

Now a set $\{\phi_n\}$ is orthonormal for $\langle \phi_n, \phi_m \rangle = 0, n = m$, and

$$\|\phi_n\|^2 = \int_c^d \int_a^b |\phi_n(t,s)|^2 dt ds = 1, \qquad n = 1, \ldots.$$

The Fourier expansion of a function $f \in H$ along a complete orthonormal set $\{\phi_i\}$ must take the form

$$f(t,s) = \sum_{i=0}^{\infty} c_i \phi_i(t,s),$$

where $c_i = \langle f, \varphi_i \rangle$.

Without loss of generality, assume $a = c = -\pi$ and $b = d = \pi$. The functions

$$1, \cos mt, \sin mt, \cos ns, \sin ns, \ldots,$$

$$\cos mt \cdot \cos ns, \sin mt \cdot \cos ns, \ldots,$$

$$\cos mt \cdot \sin ns, \sin mt \cdot \sin ns, \ldots, \qquad m,n = 1, 2, \ldots,$$

then form a complete orthogonal basis for H. The pairwise orthogonality of these functions is easily verified. The reader may also verify that

$$\|1\| = 2\pi,$$

$$\|\cos mt\| = \|\sin mt\| = \sqrt{2\pi}$$

$$\|\cos mt \cdot \cos ns\| = \|\sin mt \cdot \cos ns\| = \|\sin mt \cdot \sin ns\| = \pi.$$

The Fourier series for $f \in H$ may be written in the compact form (see [A84], ch. 7)

$$f(t,s) = \sum_{m,n=-\infty}^{\infty} c_{mn} \exp\left[i(mt + ns)\right],$$

where

$$c_{mn} = (\tfrac{1}{4}\pi^2) \int_{-\pi}^{\pi} \int_{-\pi}^{\pi} f(t,s) \exp\left[-1(mt + ns)\right] dt\, ds, \qquad m,n = 0, \pm 1, \pm 2, \ldots.$$

Exercises

1. Let $\{e_i\}$ and $\{f_i\}$ be two orthonormal sequences in $L_2(a,b)$, and suppose that $\sum_{i=1}^{\infty} \|e_i - f_i\|^2 < 1$. Then $\{e_i\}$ is complete if and only if $\{f_i\}$ is complete.

2. Verify the orthonormality of the normalized Hermite, Laguerre, and Legendre polynomials. Show that these functions do satisfy the differential equation $(*)$.

3. Derive the normalized Hermite polynomials by applying the Gram–Schmidt orthogonalization process in $L_2(-\infty, \infty; e^{t^2})$ to the set $\{1, t, t^2, \ldots, t^n, \ldots\}$.

4. Rewrite the Laguerre equation in the form

$$ty''(t) + (1 - t)y'(t) + \lambda y(t) = 0, \qquad t \in [0,\infty].$$

Assume a power series solution in t and examine the "indicial equation" to show that when $\lambda = 1, 2, 3, \ldots, n \ldots$, the solution is a polynomial of degree $1, 2, \ldots, n, \ldots$, respectively.

5. Expand the functions

$$f(t) = |t|, \quad t \in [-1,1],$$

$$g(t) = \begin{cases} 0, & x \in [-1,0], \\ 1, & x \in [0,1], \end{cases}$$

in a Legendre polynomial series.

6. Show that the function $f(t,s) = ts$, $(t,s) \in [-\pi,\pi] \times [-\pi,\pi]$ has the double Fourier expansion

$$f(t,s) = 4 \sum_{m,n=1}^{\infty} (-1)^{m+n} \frac{\sin mt \sin ns}{mn}.$$

REFERENCES

See also [A19], [A44, ch.5], and [A21, ch.VI].

3 COMPUTING THE TRANSITION MATRIX

In Chapter 2 it is made abundantly clear that the transition matrix plays a key role in describing the dynamic behavior of first-order systems of linear differential and/or difference equations. The mathematical properties of this matrix, as developed in Section 2.3, are sufficient for theoretical purposes. In applying the theoretical results to a physical system, however, it is necessary, of course, to come to grips with the problem of the actual numerical computation of the system transition matrix. In this appendix we shall note some of the ways in which an explicit determination can be accomplished.

It is possible to determine a system transition matrix numerically by a direct machine integration of the differential equations it satisfies. In most cases either digital integration or an analog simulation will provide accuracies consistent with the actual knowledge of the values of system parameters. We note that in proving Theorem A, Section 2.3, an actual computational device has been established; that is, the Picard iterative procedure is well defined at each step and can be used to generate a sequence,[1] which, when summed, converges uniformly to the desired transition matrix.

In both cases systems of differential equations are treated without distinguishing between the stationary and nonstationary cases. For theoretical purposes there is no need to make a distinction nor is it desirable to do so. The stationary case, however, has some special computational properties of which

---

[1]Modify Eq. 13, Section 2.3, to read $\Phi_0(t,t_0) = I$, $\Phi_1(t,t_0) = I + \int_{t_0}^{t} A(s)\Phi_0(s,t_0) ds, \ldots, \Phi_n(t,t_0) = I + \int_{t_0}^{t} A(s)\Phi_{n-1}(s,t_0)ds.$

we shall now take note. These special features are all indirectly related to Theorem A.

THEOREM A. *The transition matrix* $\Phi(t,t_0)$ *satisfying*

$$\dot{\Phi}(t,t_0) = A\Phi(t,t_0), \qquad \Phi(t_0,t_0) = I, \qquad t_0, t \in \tau, \tag{1}$$

where A is a constant matrix on τ may be written as

$$\Phi(t,t_0) = \exp\{A(t - t_0)\}, \qquad t, t_0 \in \tau. \tag{2}$$

The function $\exp\{A(t - t_0)\}$ *is defined by the series*

$$\exp\{A(t - t_0)\} = I + A(t - t_0) + \cdots + \frac{A^k(t - t_0)^k}{k!} + \cdots \qquad t, t_0 \in \tau, \tag{3}$$

which converges uniformly for any finite interval.

PROOF. Using the standard norm inequalities on the right-hand side of Eq. 3 shows that

$$\| \exp\{A(t - t_0)\} \| \leq \sum_{i=0}^{n} \frac{\|A\|^k(t - t_0)^k}{k!}$$

$$= \exp\{\|A\|(t - t_0)\}, \qquad t, t_0 \in \tau. \tag{4}$$

Thus the matrix exponent is well defined by Eq. 3, and this series converges absolutely for all finite intervals τ. The absolute convergence of Eq. 3 allows term-by-term differentiation. Thus we have

$$\frac{d}{dt} \exp\{A(t - t_0)\} = A + A^2(t - t_0) + \cdots + \frac{A^{k+1}(t-t_0)^k}{k!} + \cdots$$

$$= A\left\{I + A(t - t_0) + \cdots + \frac{A^k(t - t_0)^k}{k!} \cdots\right\}$$

$$= A \exp\{A(t - t_0)\}.$$

Since $\exp\{0\} = I$, it is clear that the matrix exponent satisfies Eq. 1 and the proof is complete.

Although the summation of Eq. 3 converges uniformly for any finite interval, it is clear from Eq. 4 that the rate of convergence is a function of the product of the scalar $\|A\|$ and the length of the interval τ. The series expansion of Theorem A has the weakness of being a nonclosed form for the transition matrix. In spite of this flaw the main properties of the matrix exponent can be uncovered by using this expansion.

THEOREM B. *Let A, B, and T be three square nonsingular matrices. The* *matrix exponential then has the following properties:*

(1) $e^{TBT^{-1}} = Te^B T^{-1}$.

(2) $e^{A(t+s)} = e^{At} \cdot e^{As}$.

(3) $[e^{At}]^{-1} = e^{-At}$.

(4) $e^{(A+B)t} = e^{At} e^{Bt}$ *if and only if* $AB = BA$.

(5) e^{At} *is defined* $-\infty < t < \infty$.

(6) $\det [e^A] = e^{\text{trace}\,A}$.

PROOF.   Property (3) follows from (2) with $s = -t$. Property (5) is a consequence of the proof of Theorem A. Property (1) may also be verified by substitution in the defining series of the matrix exponent. To prove property (2) we have

$$\exp [At] \cdot \exp [As] = \left(\sum_{k=0}^{\infty} \frac{A^k t^k}{k!} \right) \left(\sum_{j=0}^{\infty} \frac{A^j t^j}{j!} \right)$$

$$= \sum_{k,j=0}^{\infty} \frac{A^{k+j} t^k s^j}{k! j!},$$

which is valid because of the absolute convergence of the series. By reordering the summation with $n = j + k$ we have

$$\exp [At] \cdot \exp [As] = \sum_{n=0}^{\infty} (A^n) \left(\frac{1}{n} \cdot \sum_{j=0}^{n} \frac{n!}{(n-j)! j!} \, t^{n-j} s^j \right)$$

$$= \sum_{n=0}^{\infty} \frac{A^n (t+s)^n}{n!}$$

$$= \exp [A(t+s)].$$

Property (4) can also be verified by an examination of the defining series on both sides of the equality, and property (6) is a corollary to Theorem E, Section 2.3.

REMARK 1.   The matrix exponent is so useful for examining the transition matrix for the stationary case that we are naturally tempted to try to formulate the time-varying transition matrix in a similar form. If $\dot{x}(t) = A(t)x(t)$ is the equation of interest, the natural extension of the stationary case would be to define

$$B(t) = \int_{t_0}^{t} A(s) ds$$

and to determine if $e^{B(t)}$ satisfies the differential equation. It is easy to see that in general this is not so. Indeed, by differentiating the series expansion,

$$e^B = \sum_{k=0}^{\infty} \frac{B^k}{k!}.$$

Term by term, it is immediate that $\exp\{B(t)\} = \exp\left\{\int_{t_0}^{t} A(\tau)d\tau\right\}$ satisfies the differential equation only when $B(t)$ and $(dB/dt)(t)$ commute or alternatively when $A(t)$ and $\int_{t_0}^{t} A(\tau)d\tau$ commute.

The state transition matrix has an expansion, called the Neumann series, in terms of the integrals of $A(t)$, which is given by

$$\Phi(t,t_0) = I + \int_{t_0}^{t} A(\tau)d\tau + \int_{t_0}^{t} A(\tau_1)\left[\int_{t_0}^{\tau_1} A(\tau_2)d\tau_2\right]d\tau_1 + \cdots.$$

Here, again, if A is constant, this expression reduces to Taylor's expansion

$$\Phi(t - t_0) = \exp\{A(t - t_0)\} = \sum_{k=0} \frac{A(t - t_0)^k}{k!}.$$

REMARK 2.   The matrix exponent can be determined in closed form in a number of ways. In Section 3.5, for instance, the invariant subspaces of the matrix A are used to obtain such a representation. It is also possible to use the Laplace transformation on this problem. Setting $t_0 = 0$, we see that the Laplace transformation of Eq. 1 becomes

$$[sI - A]\Phi(s) = I,$$

where $\Phi(s) = \mathscr{L}[\Phi(t,0)]$ denotes the usual Laplace transformation of the matrix $\Phi(t,0)$. Hence it follows (when s is not an eigenvalue of A) that

$$\Phi(s) = [sI - A]^{-1}.$$

The latter matrix has elements that are proper rational functions, and it follows that

$$\exp\{At\} = \mathscr{L}^{-1}\{[sI - A]^{-1}\}.$$

The use of the Laplace transformation to determine the matrix exponent is well documented in Zadeh and Desoer ([A95], Chapter 5) and Tou ([A86], Chapters 2 and 3), and we shall not dwell on such matters here (see also Hochstadt [B48], Bellman [A10], Frame [B36], and Kaplan [A46,A47]).

The matrix exponent is one example in which special information about the system (namely, that A is stationary) allows particular techniques to be developed for computing the system transition matrix. As a second example, we shall use Theorem C of Section 2.3. Let the dependence of the matrix $A(t;\varepsilon)$ on the parameter ε take the form

$$A(t;\varepsilon) = A_1 + \varepsilon A_2(t), \qquad t \in \tau.$$

Since the matrix A depends continuously on ε, Theorem C of Section 2.3 states that the transition matrix $\Phi(t,t_0;\varepsilon)$ is a continuous function of ε. We make the stronger assumption that this matrix has Taylor's expansion of the form

$$\Phi(t,t_0;\varepsilon) = \sum_{j=0}^{\infty} \varepsilon^j \Phi_j(t,t_0), \qquad t, t_0 \in \tau. \tag{5}$$

To determine the matrices $\{\Phi_j(t,t_0): t,t_0 \in \tau, j = 0, 1, ...\}$ we substitute this assumed form into both sides of the equation

$$\dot{\Phi}(t,t_0;\varepsilon) = A(t,\varepsilon)\Phi(t,t_0;\varepsilon), \qquad \Phi(t_0,t_0,\varepsilon) = I. \tag{6}$$

Equating the coefficients of equal powers of ε on both sides of the series equality, we find the following set of differential equations:

$$\begin{aligned}
\dot{\Phi}_0(t,t_0) &= A_1\Phi_0(t,t_0), & \Phi_0(t_0,t_0) &= I, \\
\dot{\Phi}_1(t,t_0) &= A_1\Phi_1(t,t_0) + A_2(t)\Phi_0(t,t_0), & \Phi_1(t_0,t_0) &= 0, \\
&\;\;\vdots \qquad\qquad \vdots \qquad\qquad \vdots & &\;\;\vdots \\
\dot{\Phi}_n(t,t_0) &= A_1\Phi_n(t,t_0) + A_2(t)\Phi_{n-1}(t,t_0), & \Phi_n(t_0,t_0) &= 0, \\
&\;\;\vdots \qquad\qquad \vdots \qquad\qquad \vdots & &\;\;\vdots
\end{aligned} \tag{7}$$

Since A_1 is time-invariant, each equation in this set can be solved in turn; for example,

$$\Phi_1(t,t_0) = \int_{t_0}^{t} \exp\{A_1(t-s)\}A_2(s)\exp\{A_1(s-t_0)\}, \qquad t, t_0 \in \tau.$$

When ε is small, the right-hand side of Eq. 5 can be truncated at the first few terms to yield an accurate approximation for $\Phi(t,t_0;\varepsilon)$.

Exercises

1. Using the Laplace transformation and the matrices

$$A_1 = \begin{bmatrix} 1 & 0 \\ 3 & 1 \end{bmatrix}, \qquad A_2 = \begin{bmatrix} +15 & -12 \\ -24 & -19 \end{bmatrix},$$

show that

$$\exp\{A_1 t\} = \begin{bmatrix} e^t & 0 \\ 3te^t & e^t \end{bmatrix},$$

$$\exp\{A_2 t\} = e^t \begin{bmatrix} 9 & -6 \\ 12 & -8 \end{bmatrix} + e^{3t} \begin{bmatrix} -8 & 6 \\ -12 & 9 \end{bmatrix}.$$

Using a few terms in the expansion of Eq. 3, try to determine the result for $\exp\{A_1 t\}$.

2. In Eq. 4 we have seen that for every matrix A constants M, μ exist such that $\| \exp \{A(t - t_0)\} \| \le M \exp [\mu(t - t_0)]$ for t, $t_0 \in \tau$. Using this property and assuming that $\|A_2(t)\| \in L_1(\tau)$, investigate the convergence of Eq. 5.

3. In Figure A3.1 a second-order position servo and its equivalent block

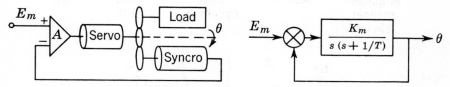

Figure A3.1 A position servo and its block diagram.

diagram are depicted. Verify that the system transfer function is given by

$$\frac{\theta(s)}{E_m(s)} = \frac{AK_m}{(s^2 + s/T + AK_m)}.$$

Using the variables $x_1 = \theta$, $x_2 = \dot{\theta}$, model the system in first-order form: $\dot{x} = Ax$, where $x = (x_1, x_2)$. For the values $AK_m = 2$, $T = \frac{1}{3}$, show that

$$\exp\{At\} = \begin{bmatrix} 2e^{-t} - e^{2t} & e^{-t} - e^{-2t} \\ 2e^{-2t} - 2e^{-t} & 2e^{-t} - e^{-t} \end{bmatrix}, \quad t \ge 0.$$

The system of Figure A3.1 may also be visualized as a satellite attitude control system. In this setting the motor is replaced by a proportional reaction jet actuator. When $1/T = 0$, $AK_m = 4$, show that the transition matrix for this attitude control system is given by

$$e^{At} = \begin{bmatrix} \cos 2t & \frac{1}{2} \sin 2t \\ 2 \sin 2t & \cos 2t \end{bmatrix}.$$

4. Figure A3.2 is an electrohydraulic actuator. Verify that the characteristic equation of this open-loop system is given by

$$(s + \tau)(s^2 + 2\xi\omega_n s + \omega_n^2) = 0,$$

where $\tau = (r_p + R_L)/L$, $\omega_n = K/M$, and $\xi = B/2\sqrt{KM}$. For the values $\tau = 2$, $\omega_n = \sqrt{3}$, and $\xi = 2/\sqrt{3}$ show that the roots of this equation are $\{-1, -2, -3\}$. Using the variables $x_1 = X_v, x_2 = \dot{X}_v$, and $x_2 = D_v$, model the system in the first-order form, $\dot{x} = Ax$, where $x = (x_1, x_2, x_3)$.

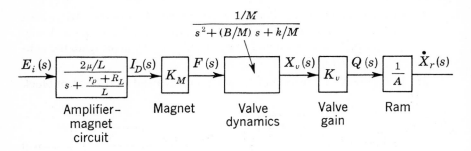

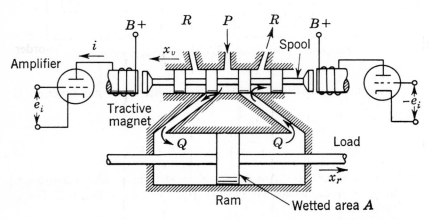

Figure A3.2   Electrohydraulic valve and its block diagram.

Show that the first row of the transition matrix $\exp\{At\}$ is given by

$$[\exp\{At\}]_{11} = 3e^{-t} - 3e^{-2t} + e^{-3t},$$

$$[\exp\{At\}]_{12} = (\tfrac{5}{2}e)^{-t} - 4e^{-2t} + (\tfrac{3}{2})e^{-3t},$$

$$[\exp\{At\}]_{13} = (-\tfrac{1}{2})e^{-t} + e^{-2t} - (\tfrac{1}{2})e^{3t}.$$

Show also that the second row of $\exp\{At\}$ is the time derivative of the first and that the third row is the time derivative of the second; that is, $[\exp\{At\}]_{21} = (d/dt)[\exp\{At\}]_{11}$, etc.[1]

[1]This problem was motivated by Section 4.4 of R. N. Clark, *Introduction to Automatic Control Systems*, Wiley, New York, 1962. Figure A3.2 is used with permission.

4 nth–ORDER EQUATIONS

In this appendix attention is focused on the nth-order differential operator

$$L_n(D,t) = a_n(t)D^n + a_{n-1}(t)D^{n-1} + \cdots + a_0(t), \qquad t \in \tau$$

(where D^j denotes the jth time derivative) and nth-order differential equations of the form

$$L_n(D,t)x(t) = u(t), \qquad t \in \tau. \tag{1}$$

In those cases where the specific order n of the operator $L_n(D,t)$ is unimportant the subscript may be suppressed.

It is assumed throughout that $a_n(t) \neq 0$ on the interval of interest τ. This condition guarantees that the equation behaves as an nth-order differential equation at all times. Since $a_n(t)$ is nonzero on τ, both sides of Eq. 1 may be divided through by $a_n(t)$. In the present treatment the equivalent operation is carried out by assuming that in all cases $a_n(t) \equiv 1$ on τ.

The operator $L(D,t)$ is clearly linear. The domain of $L(D,t)$ is normally taken to be $C_n(\tau)$, where $C_1(\tau) = C(\tau)$ and $C_n(\tau)$ is defined by $C_n(\tau) = \{x : x, Dx, \ldots, D^{n-1}x \text{ exist and are continuous and } D^n x \in L_1(\tau)\}$. Thus $L(D, t) : C_n(\tau) \to L_1(\tau)$. It will be shown that this mapping is onto.

In order to express Eq. 1 in the form of a first-order system, it is necessary only to define a new set of variables. The classical choice is to utilize the derivatives of x; that is,

$$y_1(t) = x(t), \qquad t \in \tau,$$

$$y_2(t) = Dx(t), \qquad t \in \tau,$$

$$\vdots$$

$$y_{n-1}(t) = D^{n-2}x(t), \qquad t \in \tau,$$

$$y_n(t) = D^{n-1}x(t), \qquad t \in \tau. \tag{2}$$

Differentiation of both sides of these equations yields

$$Dy_1(t) = y_2(t), \qquad t \in \tau,$$

$$Dy_2(t) = y_3(t), \qquad t \in \tau,$$

$$\vdots$$

$$Dy_{n-1}(t) = y_n(t), \qquad t \in \tau,$$

$$Dy_n(t) = D^n x(t), \qquad t \in \tau.$$

The last equation is now identified with the nth-order Eq. 1 by solving this equation for $D^n x(t)$. In terms of the new variables, we have

$$D^n x(t) = -a_0(t)x(t) - a_1(t)Dx(t) - \cdots - a_{n-1}(t)D^{n-1}x(t) + u(t),$$

$$= -a_0(t)y_1(t) - a_1(t)y_2(t) - \cdots - a_{n-1}(t)y_n(t) + u(t), \qquad t \in \tau.$$

Replacing the right-hand side of the last equation of the preceding set by this expression, we have

$$Dy_1(t) = y_2(t), \qquad\qquad\qquad\qquad\qquad\qquad\qquad t \in \tau,$$

$$\vdots$$

$$Dy_{n-1}(t) = y_n(t), \qquad\qquad\qquad\qquad\qquad\qquad\qquad t \in \tau,$$

$$Dy_n(t) = -a_0(t)y_1(t) - a_1(t)y_2(t) - \cdots - a_{n-1}(t)y_n(t) + u(t), \qquad t \in \tau.$$

This first-order system is immediately written in the vector matrix form

$$Dy(t) = A(t)y(t) + e_n u(t), \qquad t \in \tau, \tag{3}$$

where $y = \text{col}(y_1, \ldots, y_n)$, $e_n = \text{col}(0, \ldots, 0, 1)$, and A is the $n \times n$ matrix whose value at $t \in \tau$ is given by

$$A(t) = \begin{bmatrix} 0 & 1 & 0 & \cdots & 0 \\ \vdots & & \ddots & & \vdots \\ & & & \cdot & \\ & & & & \\ & & & & \ddots & \vdots \\ \vdots & & & & & 1 \\ -a_0(t) & \cdots & & & -a_{n-1}(t) \end{bmatrix}, \qquad t \in \tau; \tag{4}$$

that is, $A(t)$ has a superdiagonal of ones, the bottom row, $[-a_0(t) - a_1(t) - \cdots - a_{n-1}(t)]$, and zeros elsewhere. Thus the nth-order differential equation (Eq. 1) is identified by the variables of Eq. 2 with the first-order normal system of Eq. 3 with the particular system matrix A given by Eq. 4.

To make effective use of this identification the results of Sections 2.3 and 2.4 will now be re-examined in light of the present context. Let us consider the homogeneous case $u = 0$. For the system of Eq. 3 it has been shown (see Theorems A and B, Section 2.3) that under nonrestrictive conditions on A for every $\|\zeta\| < \infty$ and t, $t_0 \in \tau$ there exists a unique vector $y(t;\zeta,t_0)$ on the interval τ satisfying the system equations and the condition

$$y(t_0;\zeta,t_0) = \zeta = \text{col}\,(\zeta_1, \dots, \zeta_n).$$

In particular, the components of y satisfy at time t_0 the conditions

$$y_1(t_0) = \zeta_1,\, y_2(t_0) = \zeta_2,\, \dots,\, y_n(t_0) = \zeta_n.$$

It is easy to see that if y is a solution to Eq. 4 the top component $y_1 = x$ is a solution to Eq. 1. Indeed, from Eq. 2 it is clear that $Dy_n(t) = D^n x(t)$, and, since the bottom row of Eq. 3 is given by $Dy_n(t) = -a_0(t)y_1(t) - a_1(t)y_2(t) - \cdots -a_{n-1}(t)y_n(t)$, it follows that $D^n x(t) = -a_0(t)x(t) - a_1(t)Dx(t) - \cdots - a_{n-1}(t) D^{n-1}x(t)$; hence Eq. 1 is satisfied. The converse statement is equally obvious, and thus the set of all solutions $\{x_i(t)\}$ to the equation

$$L(D,t)x_i(t) = 0, \qquad t \in \tau \tag{5}$$

and the set of all vectors $\{y(t)\}$ satisfying

$$Dy(t) = A(t)y(t), \qquad t \in \tau, \tag{6}$$

are mapped into each other by Eq. 2. Taking into account the initial conditions induced by Eq. 2, we have Theorem A.

THEOREM A. *Equation set 2 defines an isomorphism between the solutions to Eqs. 5 and 6. The function satisfying Eq. 5 and the initial conditions $x(t_0) = \xi_1$, $Dx(t_0) = \xi_2, \dots, D^{n-1}x(t_0) = \xi_n$ is carried into the vector y satisfying Eq. 6 and the initial condition $y(t_0) = \xi = \text{col}\,(\xi_1, \dots, \xi_n)$.*

This identification of the components of a vector with a function and its higher derivatives has much appeal in the physical applications. If x is a physical quantity, such as the displacement of a mechanism, the velocity Dx and acceleration $D^2 x$ are necessary to describe the condition or state of the mechanism. Notice also that by solving the differential problem in the system form the solution x to nth order equation can be found by simply taking the inner product of y with the tuplet $e_1 = (1, 0, \dots, 0)$. Furthermore, Dx is found by taking the inner product of y with the tuplet $e_2 = (0, 1, 0, \dots, 0)$ and in the same manner $(D^j x)(t) = [e_j, y(t)]$.

The technique used here to transform the nth-order equation to an n-dimensional differential system is by no means unique. In fact, for more complicated situations (to be discussed later) a second technique is more appropriate. In the immediate sequel it is assumed, however, that Eq. 2 is universally used in shuttling from the nth-order equations to first-order systems and back.

COROLLARY.   *The null space of the operator $L_n(D,t)$ is n-dimensional.*

P R O O F.   This corollary is an immediate result of Theorem D, Section 2.3, and Theorem A. To illustrate, let $\phi_1(t), \ldots, \phi_n(t)$ denote n linearly independent solution vectors of Eq. 3. The matrix

$$\Phi(t) = \begin{bmatrix} \phi_{11}(t) & \phi_{21}(t) & \cdots & \phi_{n1}(t) \\ \vdots & \vdots & & \vdots \\ \phi_{n1}(t) & \phi_{n2}(t) & \cdots & \phi_{nn}(t) \end{bmatrix}, \qquad t \in \tau$$

is a fundamental matrix for the system. The top row of $\Phi(t)$, that is, $[\phi_{11}, \ldots, \phi_{n1}]$, is a set of solutions $(x_1, \ldots, x_n)$ to Eq. 5. The other rows of Φ are derivatives of this row. The linear independence of the columns $\{\phi_i\}_1^n$ implies the linear independence of functions $\{x_i\}_1^n$. Thus the null space of $L_n(D,t)$ is at least n. However, if $n + 1$ linearly independent solutions exist, this set can be used to generate a set of $n + 1$ linearly independent solution vectors to Eq. 6, contradicting Theorem D, Section 2.3.

Let $S = \{x_i\}_1^n$ denote a set of linearly independent solutions to Eq. 5. Then S is a basis for the null space of $L_n(D,t)$. Furthermore, the matrix

$$\Phi(t) = \begin{bmatrix} x_1(t) & x_2(t) & \cdots & x_n(t) \\ Dx_1(t) & Dx_2(t) & \cdots & Dx_n(t) \\ \vdots & \vdots & & \vdots \\ D^{n-1}x_1(t) & D^{n-1}x_2(t) & \cdots & D^{n-1}x_n(t) \end{bmatrix}, \qquad t \in \tau,$$

is a fundamental matrix for Eq. 6. From Section 2.3 it is clear that $\det \Phi(t) \neq 0$ for all $t \in \tau$. For the special case under consideration the determinant of this matrix is called the Wronskian of the operator $L_n(D,t)$ with respect to the basis S and is denoted by $W(x_1, \ldots, x_n)$. It is a function of t on τ and for fixed $\{x_1, \ldots, x_n\}$ its value at any time t is denoted by $W[x_1, \ldots, x_n](t)$.

THEOREM B.   *A necessary and sufficient condition that n solutions $x_1, \ldots, x_n$ of $L_n(D,t)x = 0$ on an interval τ be linearly independent is*

$$W(x_1, \ldots, x_n)(t) = 0, \qquad t \in \tau.$$

Furthermore, the Wronskian satisfies the relation

$$W(x_1, \ldots, x_n)(t) = W(x_1, \ldots, x_n)(t_0)\left\{\exp\left[\int_{t_0}^{t} a_1(s)ds\right]\right\}, \qquad t \in \tau.$$

P R O O F. Since $W(x_1, \ldots, x_n)(t) = 0$ is a specialization of $\det \Phi(t) = 0$ for any fundamental matrix, the first part of this theorem is implied by the proof of Theorem D, Section 2.3. The second condition follows from Theorem E of that section and the fact that for the particular matrix of Eq. 6 trace $[A(t)] = -a_1(t)$.

THEOREM C. *Suppose $(\phi_1, \ldots, \phi_n)$ are n functions that possess continuous nth order derivatives on a real interval τ, and $W(\phi_1, \ldots, \phi_n)(t) \neq 0$ on τ. Then there exists a unique homogeneous differential equation of order n (with a_n, the coefficient of $D^n x$ equals 1) for which these functions form a fundamental set, namely*

$$(-1)^n \frac{W(x, \phi_1, \ldots, \phi_n)}{W(\phi_1, \ldots, \phi_n)} = 0. \qquad (7)$$

P R O O F. The Wronskian $W(x, \phi_1, \ldots, \phi_n)$ is the determinant of the matrix in which the first row consists of the elements $x, \phi_1, \ldots, \phi_n$ and the other rows are the derivatives of the first row up to order n for the last row. Clearly, $W(\phi_i, \phi_1, \ldots, \phi_n) = 0$ $(i = 1, \ldots, n)$, for two columns of this determinant are equal. An expansion of the numerator, $W(x, \phi_1, \ldots, \phi_n)$, by the first column shows that Eq. 7 is a differential equation of order n, and the coefficient of $D^n x$ in $W(x, \phi_1, \ldots, \phi_n)$ is just $(-1)^n W(\phi_1, \ldots, \phi_n)$, which proves that the coefficient of $D^n x$ in Eq. 7 is unity. Since $W(\phi_1, \ldots, \phi_n) \neq 0$, it follows that $\phi_1, \ldots, \phi_n$ form a fundamental set for the differential equation. The uniqueness follows from the fact that the corresponding vectors ϕ_i with components $\phi_{11}, \phi_{21}, \ldots, \phi_{n1}$ determine the coefficient matrix of the associated system uniquely. Since there is a one-to-one correspondence between linear equations of order n and linear systems of this type, the proof is complete.

Let $\Phi(t, t_0)$ denote the transition matrix for Eq. 3. The free response of Eq. 3 is given by

$$y(t) = \Phi(t, t_0)\xi, \qquad t \in \tau.$$

Since the top component of the tuplet y is the homogeneous solution to Eq. 2 (with initial conditions satisfying 2 at t_0), it is immediate that

$$x(t) = [e_1, \Phi(t, t_0)\xi] = \sum_{j=1}^{n} \phi_{1j}(t, t_0)\xi_j, \qquad t \in \tau \qquad (8)$$

is the homogeneous solution to Eq. 1. From the discussion of the corollary of Theorem A and Theorem B it is evident that the set $\{\phi_{ij}\}$ is also uniquely defined by

$$\begin{aligned} L_n(D, t)\phi_{ij}(t, t_0) &\equiv 0, \qquad t \in \tau, \\ D^{k-1}\phi_{ij}(t_0, t_0) &= \delta_{jk}, \qquad j, k = 0, 1, \ldots, n-1. \end{aligned} \qquad (9)$$

THE NONHOMOGENEOUS CASE

As in the homogeneous case, the correspondence that has been established between Eqs. 1 and 3 reduces the analysis of Eq. 1 to a specialization of the preceding results for nonhomogeneous differential systems. The principal result is Theorem D.

THEOREM D.   *Let the set $\{\phi_{1,i}(t,t_0)\}_1^n$ be defined as in Eq. 9. The solution of the nonhomogeneous Eq. 1 is given by*

$$x_u(t;\xi,t_0) = \sum_{i=1}^{n} \phi_{1i}(t,t_0)\xi_i + \int_{t_0}^{t} \phi_{1n}(t,s)u(s)ds, \qquad t \in \tau. \tag{10}$$

PROOF.   We deduce this theorem from the solution already derived for the general nonhomogeneous differential system. The general solution to Eq. 3 is given by

$$y_u(t;\zeta,t_0) = \Phi(t,t_0)\zeta + \int_{t_0}^{t} \Phi(t,s)e_n u(s)ds, \qquad t \in \tau.$$

The first component of y_u is the solution x desired. We can extract this component explicitly by taking the inner product

$$x_u(t;\zeta,t_0) = [e_1, y_u(t;\zeta,t_0)], \qquad t \in \tau.$$

This operation, carried out on this equation, produces

$$x(t;\xi,t_0,u) = [e_1,\Phi(t,t_0)\xi] + \int_{t_0}^{t} [e_1,\Phi(t,s)e_n]u(s)ds, \qquad t \in \tau.$$

By a previous remark $[e_1,\Phi(t,t_0)\xi]$ is in the proper form. Moreover, by direct computation the reader can verify that

$$[e_1,\Phi(t,s)e_n] = \phi_{1n}(t,s), \qquad t \in \tau;$$

hence the theorem is proved.

The function $\phi_{n1}(t,s)$ is important enough to merit a special designation and we use $k(t,s)$, which is called the "kernel function," associated with the differential operator $L_n(D,t)$. Its important properties are summarized in Theorem E.

THEOREM E.   *For each fixed $s \in \tau$, $k(t,s)$ has the following properties*:

(1) $\left.\dfrac{\partial^\alpha}{\partial t^\alpha} k(t,s)\right|_{t=s} = 0, \qquad \alpha = 0, 1, \dots, n - 2.$

(2) $\left.\dfrac{\partial^{n-1}}{\partial t^{n-1}} k(t,s)\right|_{t=s} = 1.$

(3) $L(D,t)k(t,s) = 0$ (*for each fixed $s \in \tau$*), $t \in \tau$.

(4) $k(t,s)$ *is unique*, $t, s \in \tau$.

P R O O F.   These statements follow directly from the definition of $\phi_n(t,s)$.

R E M A R K S.   If the set $\{\phi_1, \ldots, \phi_n\}$ is a basis for the solution space to $L(D,t)$ but is not normal, the foregoing procedure differs in that $\det[\Phi(t)\Phi^{-1}(s)]$ must be used where $\Phi(t)$ is the fundamental matrix for Eq. 3 formed from $\{\phi_1, \ldots, \phi_n\}$. However, a nonsingular constant matrix H is such that $\Phi(t) = \Phi(t,t_0)H$. Hence $\Phi^{-1}(s) = H^{-1}\Phi^{-1}(s,t_0)$ and $\Phi(t)\Phi^{-1}(s) = \Phi(t,t_0)H[H^{-1}\Phi^{-1}(s,t_0)] = \Phi(t,s)$ and Theorem E holds in this case also.

The reader will find it interesting to verify that an alternate form for $k(t,s)$ is

$$k(t,s) = \frac{1}{W(\phi_1, \ldots, \phi_n)(s)} \begin{vmatrix} \phi_1(s) & \cdots & \phi_n(s) \\ \vdots & & \vdots \\ \phi_1^{n-2}(s) & \cdots & \phi_n^{n-2}(s) \\ \phi_i(t) & \cdots & \phi_n(t) \end{vmatrix}. \tag{11}$$

Exercises

The exercises in this set deal with the nth-order difference equation

$$\Delta^n x(t_k) + a_{n-1}(t_k)\Delta^{n-1}x(t_k) + \cdots + a_0(t_k)x(t_k) = u(t_k), \qquad t_k \in \sigma,$$
$$\Delta^j x(t_0) = \xi_j, \qquad j = 0, 1, \ldots, n-1, \qquad t_0 \in \sigma. \tag{12}$$

1. Bring Eq. 12 to a standard first-order equivalent form analogous to Eq. 3.

2. What is the dimension of the solution space for the homogeneous form of Eq. 12? Write out the free response of this system in a form analogous to Eq. 8.

3. Write out the total response of Eq. 12 in a form analogous to Eq. 10. What are the properties of the kernel function?

4. Draw a functional analog computor diagram, including initial conditions for Eq. 3. Develop a discrete functional diagram for simulation of the system of Exercise 1.

ALTERNATIVE FIRST–ORDER FORMS

The change of variables defined in Eq. 2 by no means exhausts the possibilities that exist for bringing Eq. 1 to an equivalent first-order form. In dealing with differential equations of the form

$$L_n(D,t)x(t) = M_q(D,t)u(t), \qquad t \in \tau, \tag{13}$$

where

$$L_n(D,t) = \sum_{j=0}^{n} a_j(t)D^j, \qquad a_n(t) = 1,$$

$$M_q(D,t) = \sum_{k=0}^{q} b_k(t)D^k, \qquad q \le n, \tag{14}$$

it is desirable to proceed in an entirely different way.

To gain insight into why this is so, let us note that if the class of admissible inputs of which $u(t)$ is a member includes the requirement that each input must have a sectionally continuous qth derivative [i.e., $v \in C_q(\tau)$], we may simply define a new function f by the formula

$$f(t) = M_q(D,t)u(t), \qquad t \in \tau$$

and, using f as the input function, proceed as before to formulate the first-order system. However, requiring u to be q times differentiable is not only mathematically restrictive but physically unreasonable. Indeed, since $q \le n$, it is clear that the system represented by Eq. 12 is "lowpass" in nature, and any u that is at least sectionally continuous will produce a unique, well-defined response x. Furthermore, it is computationally inconvenient to keep track of $u(t)$ as well as its higher derivatives even if they exist. What is needed is a first-order formulation which has a vectorial forcing function dependent only on u itself.

As an introduction to the general case, let us consider the equation

$$D^3x(t) + a_2 D^2x(t) + a_1 Dx(t) + a_0x(t) = u(t), \qquad t \in \tau. \tag{15}$$

The steps we now follow are identical to the procedure in the general case. First we transpose all but the highest derivative of x to the right-hand side and integrate both sides of the resulting equation n times. This yields the sequence of equations that holds for all $t \in \tau$.

$$D^3x(t) = u(t) - a_2D^2x(t) - a_1Dx(t) - a_0x(t),$$

$$D^2x(t) = -a_2Dx(t) - a_1x(t) + \int^t [-a_0x(\tau) + u(\tau)]dz + k_1,$$

$$Dx(t) = -a_2x(t) + \int^t \left(-a_1x(\alpha) + \int^\alpha [-a_0x(\tau) + u(\tau)]d\tau + k_1\right)d\alpha + k_2,$$

$$x(t) = \int^t \left\{-a_2x(\beta) + \int^\beta [-a_1x(\alpha) + \int^\alpha (-a_0x(\tau) + u(\tau))d\tau + k_1]d\alpha \right.$$

$$\left. + k_2\right\}d\beta + k_3,$$

where k_1, k_2, and k_3 are appropriate constants of integration. Now define three new variables directly from this equation set, namely,

$$x(t) = z_1(t) = \int^t \left(-a_2 x(\beta) + \int^\beta \left\{ -a_1 x(\alpha) + \int^\alpha [-a_0 x(\tau) + u(\tau)] d\tau \right. \right.$$

$$\left. \left. + k_1 \right\} d\alpha + k_2 \right) d\beta + k_3,$$

$$z_2(t) = \int^t \left\{ -a_1 x(\alpha) + \int^\alpha [-a_0 x(\tau) + u(\tau)] d\tau + k_1 \right\} d\alpha + k_2,$$

$$z_3(t) = \int^t [-a_0 x(\tau) + \mu(\tau)] d\tau + k_1.$$

Differentiating each equation once yields

$$\dot{z}_1(t) = -a_2 x(t) + z_2(t), \qquad t \in \tau,$$
$$\dot{z}_2(t) = -a_1 x(t) + z_3(t), \qquad t \in \tau,$$
$$\dot{z}_3(t) = -a_0 x(t) + u(t), \qquad t \in \tau.$$

Since $x = z_1$,

$$\dot{z}_1(t) = -a_2 z_1(t) + z_2(t), \qquad t \in \tau,$$
$$\dot{z}_2(t) = -a_1 z_1(t) + z_3(t), \qquad t \in \tau, \qquad (16)$$
$$\dot{z}_3(t) = -a_0 z_1(t) + u(t), \qquad t \in \tau;$$

if we identify $z = \mathrm{col}(z_1, z_2, z_3)$, $b = \mathrm{col}\,(0,0,1)$, and

$$A' = \begin{bmatrix} -a_2 & 1 & 0 \\ -a_1 & 0 & 1 \\ -a_0 & 0 & 0 \end{bmatrix}, \qquad (17)$$

we have the system $\dot{z}(t) = A'z(t) + bu(t)$. The form of the A' matrix is familiar, but it is not identical to the system matrix when the reduction of Eq. 2 is made. In this case (see Eq. 4) the system matrix A has the form

$$A = \begin{bmatrix} 0 & 1 & 0 \\ 0 & 0 & 1 \\ -a_0 & -a_1 & -a_2 \end{bmatrix}.$$

This difference is important, for although $z_1 = x, z_2$ is given by $z_2 = Dx + a_2 x$

and $z_3 = D^2 x + a_2 Dx + a_1 x$. Thus, if $y = (x, Dx, D^2 x)$, we have the relation $z = Ty$ where the matrix T is given by

$$T = \begin{bmatrix} 1 & 0 & 0 \\ a_2 & 1 & 0 \\ a_1 & a_2 & 1 \end{bmatrix}.$$

It is an easy consequence that

$$T^{-1} = \begin{bmatrix} 1 & 0 & 0 \\ -a_2 & 1 & 0 \\ -a_1 + a_2^2 & -a_2 & 1 \end{bmatrix}$$

and that $A' = TAT^{-1}$; hence the two methods of formulating the differential system are related by the change of variables $z = Ty, y = T^{-1}z$. To pick off the coordinate Dx from the vector z it is immediately apparent that we can use $Dx = [e_2, T^{-1}z] = [(-a_2, 1, 0), z]$; similarly, $D^2 x = [e_3, T^{-1}z] = [(-a_1 + a_2^2, -a_2 1), z]$. These relations will be useful later.

Let us consider the time-invariant, third-order differential equation

$$D^3 x + a_2 D^2 x + a_1 Dx + a_0 x = b_3 D^3 u + b_2 D^2 u + b_1 Du + b_0 u, \quad (18)$$

in which for simplicity the independent variable t is suppressed. By transposing and integrating both sides three times, we obtain the successive relationships

$$D^3 x = -a_2 D^2 x - a_1 Ds - a_0 x + b_3 D^3 u + b_2 D^2 u + b_1 Du + b_0 u,$$

$$D^2 z = -a_2 Dx - a_1 x + b_3 D^2 u + b_2 Du + b_1 u + \int [-a_0 x + b_0 u] + k_1, \quad (19)$$

$$Dx = -a_2 x + b_3 Du + b_2 u + \int [-a_1 x + b_1 u + \int(-a_0 x + b_0 u) + k_1] + k_2,$$

$$x = b_3 u + \int \{-a_2 x + b_2 u + \int [-a_1 x + b_1 u + \int(-a_0 x + b_0 u) + k_1] + k_2 \} + k_3,$$

where the k's are constants of integration. Taking our cue from the form of these equations and the prior derivation, we define the new variables

$$z_3(t) = \int^t [-a_0 x(s) + b_0 u(s)] ds + k_1, \qquad t \in \tau,$$

$$z_2(t) = \int^t [-a_1 x(s) + b_1 u(s) + z_3(s)] ds + k_2, \qquad t \in \tau, \quad (20)$$

$$z_1(t) = \int^t [-a_2 x(s) + b_2 u(s) + z_2(s)] ds + k_3, \qquad t \in \tau.$$

In other words, $x = b_3 u + z_1$, and we have the system

$$\dot{z}_1(t) = -a_2 x(t) + b_2 u(t) + z_2(t), \qquad t \in \tau,$$

$$\dot{z}_2(t) = -a_1 x(t) + b_1 u(t) + z_3(t), \qquad t \in \tau,$$

$$\dot{z}_3(t) = -a_0 x(t) + b_0 u(t), \qquad t \in \tau,$$

which generates the system (by replacing x with $b_3 u + z_1$)

$$\dot{z}_1(t) = -a_2 z_1(t) + z_2(t) + (b_2 - a_2 b_3) u(t), \qquad t \in \tau,$$

$$\dot{z}_2(t) = -a_1 z_1(t) + z_3(t) + (b_1 - a_1 b_3) u(t), \qquad t \in \tau,$$

$$\dot{z}_3(t) = -a_0 z_1(t) + (b_0 - a_0 b_3) u(t), \qquad t \in \tau.$$

Letting $z = \text{col}(z_1, z_2, z_3)$ we have

$$\dot{z}(t) = A' z(t) + b u(t), \qquad t \in \tau,$$

$$\dot{x}(t) = b_3 u(t) + [e_1, z(t)], \qquad t \in \tau,$$

(21)

where A', b are

$$A' = \begin{bmatrix} -a_2 & 1 & 0 \\ -a_1 & 0 & 1 \\ -a_0 & 0 & 0 \end{bmatrix}, \qquad b = \begin{bmatrix} b_2 - b_3 a_2 \\ b_1 - b_3 a_1 \\ b_0 - b_3 a_0 \end{bmatrix}, \qquad (22)$$

respectively. Thus the original operator relation has been reduced to a first-order nonhomogeneous differential system. The variable x is found from this system and the input by a passive "readout" is performed by taking the inner product of the vector e_1 with the solution to the nonhomogeneous system.

The reader should observe that the reduction of Eqs. 15 and 18 to first-order form has resulted in the same system matrix A' (see Eqs. 17 and 22). This should be expected, for the homogeneous equation $L_n(D)x(t) = 0$ is the same in both cases. The extension of this technique to higher-order operators is apparent, and the result is suggested by the forms of A and b for the third-order system.

The reduction process, defined in Eq. 19, uses successive integrations to reduce the order of the remaining derivatives at each step. If the coefficients involved are time-dependent, the reduction process will proceed as before with appropriate adjustments in each integration involved. For example, the term $b_1 Dx$ is reduced to the form

$$\int_{t_0}^{t} b_1(s) \dot{x}(s) ds = b_1(s) x(s) \Big|_{t_0}^{t} - \int_{t_0}^{t} \dot{b}_1(s) u(s) ds.$$

rather than simply to $b_1 x$, as in the stationary case.

As a concrete example, consider the differential equation

$$D^3 x(t) = (t + 2)D^2 x(t) + t^2 Dx(t) + (t + 1)x(t) + t^3 D^3 u(t)$$
$$+ Du(t) + u(t), \qquad t \in \tau. \tag{23}$$

The reader may verify that three successive integrations produce the equation set

$$D^2 x(t) = (t + 2)Dx(t) + (t^2 - 1)x(t) + t^3 D^2 u(t) - 3t^2 Du(t)$$

$$+ 7tu(t) + \int^t [(1 - s)x(s) - 6u(s)]ds + k_1,$$

$$Dx(t) = (t + 2)x(t) + t^3 Du(t) - 6t^2 u(t) + \int^t \left((\beta^2 - 2)x(\beta) + 19\beta u(\beta) \right.$$

$$+ \int^\beta [(1 - s)x(s) - 6u(s)]ds + k_1 \bigg) d\beta + k_2,$$

$$x(t) = t^3 u(t) + \int^t \left((\alpha + 2)x(\alpha) - 9\alpha^2 u(\alpha) + \int^\alpha \left\{ (\beta^2 - 2)x(\beta) \right. \right.$$

$$+ 19\beta u(\beta) + \int^\beta [(1 - s)x(s) - 6u(s)]ds + k_1 \bigg\} d\beta + k_2 \bigg) d\alpha + k_3.$$

Now, as in the preceding example, we define the variables

$$z_3(t) = \int^t [(-s + 1)x(s) - 6u(s)]ds + k_1,$$

$$z_2(t) = \int^t [(s^2 - a)x(s) + 19su(s) + z_1(s)]ds + k_2,$$

$$z_1(t) = \int^t [(s + 2)x(s) - 9s^2 u(s) + z_2(s)]ds + k_3,$$

which produce the relations

$$x(t) = z_1(t) + t^3 u(t)$$

and

$$\dot{z}_3(t) = (-t + 1)x(t) - 6u(t),$$
$$\dot{z}_2(t) = (t^2 - 2)x(t) + 19tu(t) + z_3(t), \tag{24}$$
$$\dot{z}_1(t) = (t + 2)x(t) - 9t^2 u(t) + z_2(t),$$

or, by eliminating the variable x in the second set and writing the result in matrix form, we have

$$\dot{z}(t) = A(t)z(t) + b(t)u(t),$$
$$x(t) = t^3 u(t) + [e_1, z(t)],$$

(25)

where

$$A(t) = \begin{bmatrix} t+2, & 1 & 0 \\ t^2 - 2, & 0 & 1 \\ -t+1, & 0 & 0 \end{bmatrix}, \quad b(t) = \begin{bmatrix} t^4 + 2t^3 - 9t^2 \\ t_5 - 2t^3 + 19t \\ -t^4 + t^3 - 6 \end{bmatrix}.$$

(26)

THE ADJOINT OPERATOR

In this section let L_n denote the differential operator of Eq. 1 and $\mathscr{L}$ the associated differential operator

$$(\mathscr{L}y)(t) = \dot{y}(t) - A(t)y(t), \qquad t \in \tau,$$

(27)

where A is given by Eq. 4. In the exercises of Section 3.3 it is pointed out that the operator $\mathscr{L}^*$, defined by

$$(\mathscr{L}^*z)(t) = \dot{z}(t) + A^*(t)z(t), \qquad t \in \tau,$$

(28)

is a formal adjoint in the sense that

$$\int_{t_0}^t [z(s), (\mathscr{L} y)(s)]ds - \int_{t_0}^t [(\mathscr{L}^*z)(s), y(s)]ds = [y(t), z(t)]_{t_0}^t.$$

(29)

Let the components of z be $z_1, z_2, \ldots, z_n$; then by letting Eq. 28 equal zero, the adjoint system breaks down on a component basis to the set

$$\dot{z}_1(t) = \bar{a}_0 z_n(t)$$

$$\dot{z}_2(t) = \bar{a}_1 z_n(t) - z_1(t)$$

$$\dot{z}_3(t) = \bar{a}_2 z_n(t) - z_2(t)$$

(30)

$$\vdots \qquad \vdots$$

$$\dot{z}_n(t) = \bar{a}_{n-1}(t)z_n(t) - z_{n-1}(t).$$

This first-order system can be reduced to a single nth-order equation. To do so, we operate on the kth equation in the foregoing system by $(-1)^{k-1}D^{k-1}$. Adding the resulting equations, we have

$$(-1)^n D^n z_n(t) + (-1)^{n-1} D^{n-1}[\bar{a}_{n-1}(t)z_n(t)] + \cdots + (-1)D[\bar{a}_1(t)z_n(t)] + \bar{a}_0(t)z_n(t) = 0. \quad (31)$$

According to Eq. 31, the operator $L^*(D,t)$ is defined by

$$L_n^*(D,t) = \sum_{i=0}^{n} (-1)^i D^i a_i(t). \tag{32}$$

It is clear from Eq. 31 that by carrying out the indicated derivatives in this equation and recollecting in terms of the derivatives of $z(t)$, $L_n^*(D,t)$ is an nth-order differential operator. The reader may verify as an exercise that if the coefficients $a_j^*(t)$ are defined by

$$a_j^*(t) = \sum_{k=i}^{n} (-1)^k \binom{k}{k-i} D^{k-i}[a_k(t)] \tag{33}$$

then $L_n^*(D,t)$ may be alternatively written

$$L_n^*(D,t) = \sum_{i=0}^{n} a_i^*(t) D^i. \tag{34}$$

In either form the implicit assumption that the coefficients of $L_n(D,t)$ are of the class $a_j \in C_j(\tau), j = 0, 1, \ldots, n-1$ is made to ensure that the derivatives exist.

It is easy to verify that L_n^* is a formal adjoint to L_n in much the same sense that $\mathscr{L}^*$ is adjoint to $\mathscr{L}$. The reader may verify that if M_k is defined by

$$M_k = a_k D^k$$

then

$$M_k^* = (-1)^k \sum_{\alpha=0}^{k} \binom{k}{\alpha} a_k^{(k-\alpha)} D^\alpha \tag{35}$$

in the sense that

$$\int_{t_0}^{t_1} u(s)(M_k v)(s) ds - \int_{t_0}^{t_1} v(s)(M_k^* u)(s) ds = E_k(u,v) \Big|_{t_0}^{t_1},$$

where $E_k(u,v)\big|_{t_0}^{t_i}$ is a residual boundary condition. Using the fact that

$$L_n = \sum_{k=0}^{n} M_k$$

we find that Eq. 34 follows from Eq. 35.

An alternative derivation may be based on the properties of $\mathscr{L}$ and $\mathscr{L}^*$. Introducing the notations

$$\langle u,v \rangle_1 = \int_{t_0}^{t_1} u(s) v(s) ds,$$

$$\langle x,y \rangle_n = \int_{t_0}^{t_1} [x(s),y(s)] ds = \int_{t_0}^{t_1} \sum_{i=1}^{n} x_i(s) y_i(s) ds,$$

we observe for the present from the form of A that the expression $\langle z, \mathscr{L}x \rangle_n$ reduces on a component basis to

$$\langle z, \mathscr{L}x \rangle_n = \int_{t_0}^{t_1} \{z_1(s)[\dot{x}_1(s) - x_2(s)] + \cdots + z_{n-1}(s)[\dot{x}_{n-1}(s)$$

$$- x_n(s)] + z_n(s)[L_n x_1](s)\} ds.$$

Since $\dot{x}_i = x_{i-1}$, $i = 1, \ldots, n - 1$, it follows that

$$\langle z, \mathscr{L}x \rangle_n = \langle z_n, L_n x_1 \rangle_1.$$

Similarly, it is only slightly more complicated to deduce from the form of A^* that

$$\langle \mathscr{L}^* z, x \rangle = \langle L^*_n z_n, x_1 \rangle_1 + \prod(x_1, z_n) \Big|_{t_0}^{t_1}.$$

Thus Eq. 29 implies that

$$\langle v, L_n u \rangle_1 - \langle L^*_n v, u \rangle = \prod(u, v) \Big|_{t_0}^{t_1}. \tag{36}$$

The boundary condition $\prod(u, v)|_{t_0}^{t_i}$ is called the *Lagrange bilinear concomitant*. It is equivalent to the boundary condition of Eq. 29 and may be evaluated by reducing this expression or by collecting the terms $\sum_{k=1}^{n} E_k(u, v)|_{t_0}^{t_1}$. The reader is left to verify as an exercise that

$$\prod(u, v) = \sum_{k=0}^{n} \sum_{\alpha=0}^{k-1} (-1)^\alpha (D^\alpha[v a_k])(D^{k-1-\alpha} u)$$

$$= [v a_1] u$$

$$+ [v a_2] Du - u D[v a_2]$$

$$+ [v a_3] D^2 u - D[v a_3] Du + D^2[v a_3] u$$

$$\vdots$$

$$+ [v a_0] D^{n-1} u - D[v a_0] D^{n-2} u + \cdots + (-1)^{n-1} D^{n-1}[v a_0] u,$$

which is evaluated to the end points t_0, t_1.

THE GENERAL FORMULATION

The final result of this appendix is Theorem F.

THEOREM F.   *Any differential equation of the form* $L_n(D, t)x = M_q(D, t)u$

can be reduced to the equivalent first-order form

$$x(t) = [e_1, z(t)] + (-1)^n b_n^*(t)u(t),$$

$$\dot{z}(t) = A(t)z(t) + b(t)u(t), \qquad t \in \tau.$$

Here $z(t) = \operatorname{col}(z_1(t), \ldots, z_n(t))$; $b_j^*(t)$ and $a_k^*(t)$ are the coefficients defined in the adjoint operators $L_n^*(D,t)$ and $M_q^*(D,t)$, respectively; the matrix $A(t)$ and the vector $b(t)$ are given by

$$A(t) = \begin{bmatrix} (-1)^n a_{n-1}^*(t) & 1 & \cdots & 0 \\ & 0 & \ddots & 0 \\ \vdots & & & \\ & & & 1 \\ (-1)a_0^*(t) & 0 & \cdots & 0 \end{bmatrix}$$

$$b(t) = \begin{bmatrix} (-1)^{2n}b_n^* a_{n-1}^* + (-1)^{n-1}b_{n-1}^* \\ \vdots \\ (-1)^{n+m}b_n^* a_{m-1}^* + (-1)^{m-1}b_{m-1}^* \\ \vdots \\ (-1)^{n+2}b_n^* a_1^* + (-1)^0 b_0^* \\ (-1)^{n+1}b_n^* a_0^* \end{bmatrix}$$

The proof of this theorem is again relegated to the exercises.

Note that if the order q of the operator $M_q(D,t)$ is less than the order n of the operator $L_n(D,t)$ by at least one then $B_n^*(t) = 0$ and the output has no direct transmission from the input; that is, $x(t)$ is a function of $z(t)$ only.

Example. To illustrate the use of this theorem we can reduce the equation of the last example to the basic form by using the adjoint equation. From $L_3(D,t)x = D^3 y + (-t - 2)D^2 x + (-t^2)Dx + (-L - 1)x$ we find

$$L_3^*(D,t)x(t) = (-1)^3 D^3 x(t) + D^2[(-t-2)x(t)] + D[t^2 x(t)] + (-t-1)x(t),$$

which reduces to

$$L_3^*(D,t)x = -D^3 x(t) - (t+2)D^2 x(t) + (t^2 - 2)Dx(t) + (t-1)x(t).$$

Similarly, we find that

$$M^*(D,t)u(t) = -t^3 D^3 u(t) - 9t^2 D^2 u(t) - 19t Du(t) - 6u(t).$$

An evaluation $A(t)$ and $b(t)$ by means of Theorem F reproduces Eq. 26 derived earlier by direct means.

INITIAL CONDITIONS

A differential equation of the form $L_n(D,t)x = 0$ is usually accompanied by a set of initial conditions on x and its first $n - 1$ derivatives. In order to use the reduced form $\dot{z}(t) = A(t)z(t)$, we must transform the original condition, given by $\zeta = \text{col}\,(x(t_0), \dot{x}(t_0), \ldots, x^{(n-1)}(t_0))$, to a condition on $z(t_0)$. We must solve the equations of the transformation for $z(t_0)$ in terms of ζ. The transformation is given by

$$z_1 = x,$$

$$\dot{z}_1 = (-1)^n a^*_{n-1} z_1 + z_2,$$

$$\vdots$$

$$\dot{z}_m = (-1)^{m-n+1} a^*_{n-m} z_1 + z_{m+1}, \qquad m = 1, \ldots, m-1,$$

$$\vdots$$

$$\dot{z}_n = (-1)^1 a^*_0 z_1.$$

Solving for the z_m, we have

$$z_1 = x$$

$$z_2 = \dot{z}_1 - (-1)^n a^*_{n-1} x,$$

$$\vdots$$

$$z_{m+1} = \dot{z}_m - (-1)^{m-n+1} a^*_{n-m} x, \qquad m = 1, \ldots, m-1,$$

$$\vdots$$

$$z_n = \dot{z}_{n-1} - (-1)^2 a^*_1 x.$$

Now we can solve for the z_m in terms of x and its first $n - 1$ derivatives by substituting each equation into the next. The first few equations are

$$z_1 = x,$$

$$z_2 = \dot{x} - (-1)^n a^*_{n-1} x,$$

$$z_3 = \dot{x} - (-1)^n a^*_{n-1} \dot{x} - (-1)^n \dot{a}^*_{n-1} x - (-1)^{n-1} a^*_{n-2} x.$$

We can write this transformation in the vector form

$$z(t) = Ty(t),$$

where T is the obvious triangular matrix. In particular, at $t = t_0$,

$$z(t_0) = T\zeta.$$

MULTIVARIATE SYSTEMS

It has been assumed in the preceding discussion that the differential-operator equation has only one input. However, since the differential equations under consideration are linear, multiple inputs can be handled by superposition. For multiple inputs the differential equation becomes

$$L_n(D,t)x(t) = \sum_{k=1}^{l} M_{q_k}(D,t)u_k(t), \qquad t \in \tau,$$

where $M_{q_k}(D,t)$ and $u_k(t)$, $k = 1, \ldots, l$ are operators in the form of Eq. 14 and the kth system input, respectively.

To convert this equation to first-order form each input may be treated separately. The result in vectorial differential equations is

$$\dot{z}_k(t) = A(t)z_k(t) + b_k(t)u_k(t), \qquad k = 1, \ldots, l,$$

$$x_k(t) = [d,z_k(t)] + (-1)^n b_{n_k}^*(t)u_k(t), \qquad k = 1, \ldots, l,$$

where x_k is the solution to the differential equation with all except the input u_k equal to zero. By superposition the total response of the differential equation becomes

$$\dot{z}(t) = A(t)z(t) + B(t)u(t), \qquad t \in \tau,$$

$$x(t) = D(t)z(t) + C(t)u(t), \qquad t \in \tau,$$

where

$$z(t) = \sum_{k=1}^{l} z_k(t), \qquad t \in \tau,$$

$$x(t) = \sum_{k=1}^{l} x_k(t), \qquad t \in \tau,$$

and B is the matrix formed from the column vectors $\{b_k\}$:

$$B = \begin{bmatrix} \uparrow & \uparrow & & \uparrow \\ b_1, & b_2 & \ldots, & b_e \\ \downarrow & \downarrow & & \downarrow \end{bmatrix}.$$

Systems of m equations (in the form of Eq. 1 or 13) can also be handled with the same techniques. Since the distinction from other cases is primarily a matter of notation (which is tedious), we are content with one example.

Example. Consider the two-input, three-output system defined by the equations

$$y_1''' - t^2 y_2 + (t + 1)y_3' - y_3 = tx_1'' + x_1 + x_2, \tag{37}$$

$$t^3 y_1'' + y_2'' - y_2' + 2y_3' - y_1 = (t + 2)x_1 + tx_2'', \tag{38}$$

$$ty_1' - y_3' + y_2 = x_1 + x_2. \tag{39}$$

The mth equation can be integrated n_m times; n_m is the order of the highest-order derivative in the mth equation. Utilizing integration by parts, we arrive at

$$y_1 + \int^t \left\{ -\beta x_1 + \int^\beta \left[-\alpha^2 y_2 + (\alpha + 1)y_3 + x_1 + \int^\alpha (2sy_2 - 2y_3 - x_1 - x_2)\,ds \right. \right.$$

$$\left. \left. + k_{11} \right] d\alpha + k_{12} \right\} d\beta + k_{13} = 0, \tag{40}$$

$$y_2 + t^3 y_1 - tx_2 + \int^t \left\{ -6\beta^2 y_1 - y_2 - 2y_3 + 2x_2 + \int^\beta [(6s - 1)y_1 \right.$$

$$\left. - (s + 2)x_1]\,ds + k_{21} \right\} d\beta + k_{22} = 0, \tag{41}$$

$$y_3 - ty_1 + \int^t (y_1 - y_2 + x_1 + x_2)\,d\beta + k_{31}. \tag{42}$$

We write the following definitions:

$$z_1 = \int^t (2\beta y_2 - 2y_3 - x_1 - x_2)\,d\beta + k_{11},$$

$$z_2 = \int^t [-\beta^2 y_2 + (\beta + 1)y_3 + x_1 + z_1]\,d\beta + k_{12},$$

$$z_3 = \int^t (-\beta x_1 + z_2)\,d\beta + k_{13},$$

$$z_4 = \int^t [(6\beta - 1)y_1 - (\beta + 2)x_1]\,d\beta + k_{21}, \tag{43}$$

$$z_5 = \int^t (-6\beta^2 y_1 - y_2 + 2y_3 + 2x_2 + z_4)\,d\beta + k_{22},$$

$$z_6 = \int^t (y_1 - y_2 + x_1 + x_2)\,d\beta + k_{31}.$$

Or, by taking derivatives,

$$z_1' = 2ty_2 - 2y_3 - x_1 - x_2,$$

$$z_2' = -t^2y_2 + (t+1)y_3 + x_1 + z_1,$$

$$z_3' = -tx_1 + z_2,$$

$$z_4' = (6t - 1)y_1 - (t + 2)x_1,$$ \qquad (44)

$$z_5' = -6t^2y_1 - y_2 + 2y_3 + 2x_2 + z_4,$$

$$z_6' = y_1 - y_2 + x_1 + x_2.$$

Equations 40, 41, and 42 can now be written

$$y_1 = -z_3,$$

$$t^3y_1 + y_2 = -z_5 + tx_2,$$ \qquad (45)

$$-ty_1 + y_3 = -z_6.$$

This system of linear equations has a unique solution if and only if the determinant of the coefficients is nonzero in the interval $t_1 < t < t_2$. Since

$$\det \begin{bmatrix} 1 & 0 & 0 \\ t^3 & 1 & 0 \\ -t & 0 & 1 \end{bmatrix} = 1 = 0,$$

we have the unique solution

$$y_1 = -z_3,$$

$$y_2 = t^3z_3 - z_5 + tx_2,$$ \qquad (46)

$$y_3 = -tz_3 - z_6.$$

Substituting Eq. 46 into Eq. 44 and putting the result in matrix form, we have

$$\begin{bmatrix} z_1' \\ z_2' \\ z_3' \\ z_4' \\ z_5' \\ z_6' \end{bmatrix} = \begin{bmatrix} 0 & 0 & 2t(t^3+1) & 0 & -2t & 2 \\ 1 & 0 & -t(t^4+t+1) & 0 & t^2 & -(t+1) \\ 0 & 1 & 0 & 0 & 0 & 0 \\ 0 & 0 & -(6t-1) & 0 & 0 & 0 \\ 0 & 0 & -t(t^2+6t+2) & 1 & 1 & -2 \\ 0 & 0 & -(t^3+1) & 0 & 1 & 0 \end{bmatrix} \cdot \begin{bmatrix} z_1 \\ z_2 \\ z_3 \\ z_4 \\ z_5 \\ z_6 \end{bmatrix}$$

$$+ \begin{bmatrix} -1 & (2t^2-1) \\ 1 & -t^3 \\ -t & 0 \\ -(t+2) & 0 \\ 0 & -(t-2) \\ 0 & -(t-1) \end{bmatrix} \cdot \begin{bmatrix} x_1 \\ x_2 \end{bmatrix}.$$ \qquad (47)

Equation 47 is in the basic form and the transformation Eq. 46 is of the required type. Clearly, such a construction can be carried through if and only if the determinant of the coefficients of the highest-order derivatives in each equation is nonvanishing in the time interval of interest. This requirement is equivalent to $a_n = 1$ in the single equation.

Exercise

Using the technique of equation, express the equations

$$y''' + 6y'' + y' + 6y = 0,$$

$$y(0) = 1, \qquad y'(0) = y''(0) = 0,$$

in first-order form. Show that the solution to this first-order system is given by

col $[(3e^{-t} - 3c^{-2t} + e^{-3t}), (-3e^{-t} + 6e^{-2t} - 3e^{-3t}), (3e^{-t} - 12e^{-2t} + 9e^{-3t})]$.

What is the solution y to the original equation?

5 A SUPPLEMENT ON CANONICAL FORMS

In Section 3.4 attention is focused on structure problems for linear transformations with finite rank. In this appendix some of the concepts of that section are extended to linear transformations of infinite rank. Specifically, we consider questions pertaining to reducing subspaces for normal operators and the polar canonical form for linear transformations.

In order to motivate the discussion of bounded operators on an infinite-dimensional Hilbert space, let us consider in some detail the operator M of "multiplication by x" in $L_2(0,1)$. Here, for $f \in L_2(0,1)$, $Mf = g$ is the function $g(x) = xf(x)$. It is clear that M is bounded with $\|M\| = 1$.

Our first observation is that M has no eigenvalues. Indeed, the equation $Mf = \lambda f$ is equivalent to

$$0 = \|Mf - \lambda f\|^2 = \int_0^1 |x - \lambda|^2 |f(x)|^2 dx$$

and therefore holds only when f vanishes almost everywhere, that is, when f is the 0 element of $L_2(0,1)$.

In particular, $Mf = 0$ holds only for $f = 0$, so that M is one-to-one. Contrary to the situation in finite-dimensional spaces, however, this fact does *not* imply that M is invertible. For any $0 \le \lambda \le 1$ the range of $M - \lambda I$ does not contain the function identically equal to 1; hence $M - \lambda I$ has no inverse [defined on all of $L_2(0,1)$].

We have already seen, and it is trivial to verify, that the adjoint M^* of M is given by

$$(M^*f)(x) = xf(x);$$

that is, M is self-adjoint. Knowing this fact, we can now show that the set of λ's for which $M - \lambda I$ fails to be invertible is precisely the unit interval $0 \le \lambda \le 1$. If the complex number λ does not belong to this interval, then an $\varepsilon > 0$ exists such that

$$|\lambda - x| \ge \varepsilon, \quad \text{all } x \in [0,1],$$

and therefore for all $f \in L_2(0,1)$

$$\|(M - \lambda I)f\|^2 = \int_0^1 |(x - \lambda)f(x)|^2 dx \ge \varepsilon^2 \|f\|^2.$$

Therefore if $\lambda \notin [0,1]$, the operator $M - \lambda I$ is bounded below. Because M is self-adjoint this implies that $M - \lambda I$ has a bounded inverse defined on all of $L_2(0,1)$. (See Exercise 11(a).)

We are therefore led to define the *spectrum* of an operator A as the collection of all complex numbers λ for which $A - \lambda I$ has no *bounded* inverse. In a finite-dimensional space every operator is bounded; hence this definition of $\sigma(A)$ agrees with our earlier one.

We have shown that M is self-adjoint and that $\sigma(M) = [0,1]$. What about a diagonal representation for M? In finite dimensions we had a representation $\sum_i \lambda_i P_i$ which involved two things: the eigenvalues λ_i of the operator and the projections P_i onto certain reducing subspaces of that operator. Since M has no eigenvalues, we cannot hope to obtain the same decomposition of M. Recall, however, that even in the finite-dimensional case the most basic of these two ingredients is the family $\{P_i\}$ of projections; that is, if we can find *any* pairwise orthogonal collection of self-adjoint projections whose sum is the identity and any set $\{\lambda_i\}$ of complex numbers such that $A = \sum \lambda_i P_i$, it will follow that the λ_i are the eigenvalues of A and the P_i are the projections onto the corresponding eigenspaces of A. Thus in the present case we are naturally lead to find such a family of projections for M or, equivalently, to find a decomposition of $L_2(0,1)$ into a direct sum of closed subspaces, each of which reduces M.

It is easy to find such a decomposition of $L_2(0,1)$. Indeed, if $[\alpha,\beta]$ is a proper subinterval of $[0,1]$, the collection $S = S(\alpha,\beta)$ of functions in $L_2(0,1)$, which vanish outside $[\alpha,\beta]$, is a reducing subspace for M. The only thing that needs proof here is the fact that S is closed, which follows from the observation that the operator of multiplication by the characteristic function of $[\alpha,\beta]$ (i.e., the map $f \rightarrow \chi(\alpha,\beta) \cdot f$) defines a self-adjoint projection whose range is precisely $S(\alpha,\beta)$.

It follows immediately that if $0 = \alpha_0 < \alpha_1 < \cdots < \alpha_{n-1} < \alpha_n = 1$ is a subdivision of $[0,1]$ then

$$L_2(0,1) = S(\alpha_0,\alpha_1) \oplus S(\alpha_1,\alpha_2) \oplus \cdots \oplus S(\alpha_{n-1},\alpha_n)$$

is a decomposition of $L_2(0,1)$ into a direct sum of pairwise orthogonal subspaces, each of which reduces M. If P_i denotes the projection of $L_2(0,1)$ onto

$S(\alpha_{i-1},\alpha_i)$, then these form a family of projections of the required sort. The equation $M = \sum \lambda_i P_i$ would mean that M is a constant multiple of the identity operator on each subspace $S(\alpha_{i-1},\alpha_i)$, which it clearly is not. However, this is approximately true in the sense that if λ_i is a fixed point of $[\alpha_{i-1},\alpha_i]$ then for each $f_i \in S(\alpha_{i-1},\alpha_i)$ we have

$$\|(M - \lambda_i I)f_i\|^2 = \int_{\alpha_{i-1}}^{\alpha_i} |x - \lambda_i|^2 \cdot |f_i(x)|^2 dx \le (\alpha_i - \alpha_{i-1})^2 \|f_i\|^2$$

so that

$$\|M - \lambda_i I\| \le \alpha_i - \alpha_{i-1}.$$

It follows that if $f = \sum_i P_i f \in L_2(0,1)$ then

$$\|(M - \sum \lambda_i P_i)f\|^2 = \|M \sum_i p_i f - \sum_i \lambda_i P_i f\|^2$$

$$= \|\sum_i (M - \lambda_i) P_i f\|^2$$

$$= \|\sum_i P_i (M - \lambda_i) f\|^2 = \sum_i \|P_i (M - \lambda_i) f\|^2$$

$$\le \varepsilon^2 \sum_i \|P_i f\|^2 = \varepsilon^2 \|f\|^2,$$

where $\varepsilon = \max_i(\alpha_i - \alpha_{i-1})$.[1] Since f is an arbitrary element of $L_2(0,1)$, we conclude

$$\|M - \sum_i \lambda_i P_i\| \le \varepsilon. \tag{1}$$

In other words, the operator M is a uniform limit of operators of the type already encountered, with the minor exception that the projections P_i no longer have one-dimensional ranges. We have obtained the promised diagonalization of M.

Before discussing the general situation we must cast the preceding results in a more suitable form. To do this we define $E(\lambda)$ for $0 \le \lambda \le 1$ as the projection of $L_2(0,1)$ onto the subspace $S(0,\lambda)$. In the notation just given we have

$$P_i = E(\alpha_i) - E(\alpha_{i-1}).$$

If $\chi(0,\lambda)$ denotes the characteristic function of $[0,\lambda]$, we have

$$E(\lambda)f = \chi(0,\lambda)f, \qquad f \in L_2(0,1), \tag{2}$$

and, in particular,

$$\langle E(\lambda)f,g \rangle = \int_0^\lambda f(x)\overline{g(x)}dx \qquad f,g \in L_2(0,1). \tag{3}$$

---

[1]Note that we are using the fact that P and M commute (see Exercise 1).

We now make the observation that $\langle E(\lambda)f,f \rangle$, as the indefinite integral of the integrable function $|f(x)|^2$, is a real-valued function of bounded variation on the interval $[0,1]$ (in fact, it is absolutely continuous). Consequently, the polarization identity

$$\langle E(\lambda)f,g \rangle = \tfrac{1}{4}\{\langle E(\lambda)(f+g),f+g \rangle - \langle E(\lambda)(f-g),f-g \rangle$$

$$+ i\langle E(\lambda)(f+ig),f+ig \rangle - i\langle E(\lambda)(f-ig),f-ig \rangle\}$$

shows that $\langle E(\lambda)f,g \rangle$ is a complex-valued function of bounded variation on $[0,1]$.

We now look at Eq. 1 in two ways. First of all, expressing the P's in terms of the E's, we have for any choice of points $\lambda_i \in [\alpha_{i-1},\alpha_i]$

$$\| M - \sum \lambda_i [E(\alpha_i) - E(\alpha_{i-1})] \| \leq \varepsilon,$$

provided only that the points of subdivision are chosen with $\max_i(\alpha_i - \alpha_{i-1})$ $= \varepsilon$. We can abbreviate this statement by writing $M = \int_0^1 \lambda dE(\lambda)$, in obvious analogy with the ordinary Stieltjes integral. The definition of the right-hand side of this equation is implicit in the foregoing derivation and reads exactly like the ordinary definition of the function $f(\lambda) = \lambda$ with respect to a function of bounded variation, except that absolute values must be replaced by norms and the integrator $\lambda \to E(\lambda)$ recognized as an operator-valued function. At any rate, for our purposes here, we interpret the equation $M = \int \lambda dE(\lambda)$ as shorthand for the more cumbersome sentence about subdivisions and epsilons.

Another entirely equivalent way of looking at Eq. 1 begins with the observation that this equation implies that

$$|\langle Mf,g \rangle - \sum_i \lambda_i \langle P_i f,g \rangle| \leq \varepsilon \|f\| \cdot \|g\|,$$

where $f, g \in L_2(0,1)$. Again there is a subdivision $0 = \alpha_0 < \alpha_1 < \cdots < \alpha_n = 1$ lurking in the background: $y_i \in [\alpha_{-1},\alpha_i]$ and $\varepsilon = \max(\alpha_i + \alpha_{i-1})$. In terms of the E's we have

$$|\langle Mf,g \rangle - \sum_i \lambda_i \{\langle E(\alpha_i)f,g \rangle - \langle E(\alpha_{i-1})f,g \rangle\}| < \varepsilon \|f\| \cdot \|g\|,$$

which results in a theorem: *The value of the (ordinary) Stieltjes integral $\int_0^1 \lambda d\langle E(\lambda)f, g \rangle$ of the function $f(\lambda) = \lambda$ with respect to the function $\lambda \to \langle E(\lambda)f,g \rangle$ of bounded variation is precisely the complex number $\langle Mf,g \rangle$,*

$$\langle Mf,g \rangle = \int_0^1 \lambda d\langle E(\lambda)f,g \rangle.$$

The advantage to this approach lies in the fact that it involves no new concepts and depends only on classical analysis for its meaning and proof. For the operator M, of course, we can arrive at the last equation very quickly from Eq. 3:

$$\langle Mf,g \rangle = \int_0^1 \lambda f(\lambda)\overline{g(\lambda)}d\lambda = \int_0^1 \lambda d\left(\int_0^\lambda f(\lambda)\overline{g(\lambda)}d\lambda\right),$$

which uses only the definitions of M and $E(\lambda)$ and the classical statement about reducing Stieltjes integrals to ordinary integrals.

In this approach we make use of the fact that

$$\int_0^1 \phi(\lambda)d\langle E(\lambda)f,g \rangle$$

exists for each function $\phi(\lambda)$, which is continuous on $[0,1]$, and, in particular, for polynomials. We leave it for the reader to show that if $\psi(\lambda) = \sum_0^N \alpha_n \lambda^n$ then

$$\langle \psi(M)f,g \rangle = \int_0^1 \psi(\lambda)d\langle E(\lambda)f,g \rangle,$$

and we point out that this formula gives a natural definition of $\phi(M)$ for each continuous function ϕ.

Next observe that

$$\| Mf \|^2 = \langle Mf,Mf \rangle = \int_0^1 \lambda d\langle E(\lambda)f,Mf \rangle = \int_0^1 \lambda^2 d\langle E(\lambda)f,f \rangle$$

because

$$\langle E(\lambda)f,Mf \rangle = \int_0^\lambda f(x)\overline{xf(x)}dx.$$

More generally, if ψ is a polynomial,

$$\| \psi(M)f \|^2 = \int_0^1 |\psi(\lambda)|^2 d\langle E(\lambda)f,f \rangle,$$

and we leave it to the reader to verify that this gives

$$\| \psi(M) \| = \sup_{\lambda \in \sigma(M)} |\psi(\lambda)| = \| \psi \|_\infty,$$

where the norm on the right is the usual norm on the Banach space $C(\sigma(M))$ of functions continuous on $\sigma(M)$.

We now indicate what the solution is for *any* bounded self-adjoint operator A on a Hilbert space H. The spectrum $\sigma(A)$ of A is defined exactly as it was for M. Since A is self-adjoint, $\sigma(A)$ is a closed bounded subset of the real line (Exercise 10(b)). The spectral theorem then asserts that there is a spectral family $\{E(\lambda)\}$ defined for all real λ with the following properties:

(1) $E(\lambda)$ is a projection on H.

(2) $E(\lambda)$ is continuous from the right: $\|E(\lambda + \varepsilon) - E(\lambda)\| \to 0$ as $\varepsilon \to 0^+$.

(3) $E(\lambda) = 0$ for $\lambda < \min \sigma(A)$; $E(\lambda) = I$ for $\lambda \geq \max \sigma(A)$.

(4) $E(\lambda) E(\mu) = E(\lambda)$ for $\lambda \leq \mu$.

Moreover, we have $A = \int_{\sigma(A)} \lambda dE(\lambda)$ or, equivalently, in terms of ordinary Stieltges integrals,

$$\langle Af, g \rangle = \int_{\sigma(A)} \lambda d\langle E(\lambda)f, g \rangle,$$

$$\|Af\|^2 = \int_{\sigma(A)} \lambda^2 d\langle E(\lambda)f, f \rangle.$$

Also, as before, we can express functions of A as the integral of the corresponding numerical function, and this can be done for each $\phi^2 C(\sigma(A))$. We will then have the equality $\|\phi(A)\| = \sup_{\lambda \in \sigma(A)} |\phi(\lambda)|$ for each continuous function ϕ. In particular, the norm of a self-adjoint operator is its spectral radius

$$\|A\| = \max \{|\lambda| : \lambda \in \sigma(A)\}.$$

For a general normal operator A the situation is basically the same, but we now have the technical annoyance that $\sigma(A)$ may be any closed bounded subset of the plane. This is reflected in the fact that the spectral family associated with A is in general a function of two variables, and accordingly we get a decomposition of A as a double integral of $z = x + iy$ over $\sigma(A)$.

However, when A is unitary ($A^*A = I = AA^*$), $\sigma(A)$ is a subset of the unit circle (Exercise 10(d)), and we arrive at a decomposition $A = \int_0^{2\pi} e^{i\theta} dE(\theta)$, in which $E(\theta)$ is a spectral family on the interval $0 \leq \theta \leq 2\pi$.

As a final comment, the spectral family associated with a given operator is uniquely determined by that operator. For example, if we have two families $\{E(\lambda)\}$ and $\{F(\lambda)\}$, both representing a self-adjoint operator A in the foregoing sense, then for any polynomial $\psi(\lambda)$ we have

$$\int \psi(\lambda) d\langle E(\lambda)f, g \rangle = \langle \psi(A)f, g \rangle = \int \psi(\lambda) d\langle F(\lambda)f, g \rangle.$$

This, together with the normalizations imposed on E and F in (2) and (3), implies that $\langle E(\lambda)f, g \rangle = \langle F(\lambda)f, g \rangle$ and, since g and f are arbitrary, that $E(\lambda) = F(\lambda)$.

Exercises

1. Let A be an operator on the Hilbert space H and let M be a subspace of H. Let P be the projection of H onto M. Then M is invariant A if and only if $PAP = P$. Apply this to A^* to prove that M reduces A if and only if P and A commute.

2. Let M be multiplication by x in $L_2(0,1)$ and let R be an invariant subspace of M. Then $R = \chi_E \cdot L_2$ for some measurable subset E of $[0,1]$. HINT: Let $e_n(x) = x^n$ $(n \geq 0)$. The smallest closed subspace of L_2 containing each e_n is $L_2(0,1)$. Let P be the projection of $L_2(0,1)$ onto R.

  (a) R is the (closed) linear subspace spanned by the vectors Pe_n.

  (b) Use the fact that P commutes with M to show that if $\phi = Pe_0$ then $Pe_n = e_n \cdot \phi$ [i.e., $(Pe_n)(x) = x^n \phi(x)$]. Conclude that if $p = \sum_0^N \alpha_n e_n$ then $Pp = p \cdot \phi$.

  (c) Choose a sequence of polynomials, $\{p_n\}$ converging to ϕ in L_2. Then $Pp_n \to P\phi = \phi$. Show that $(p_n - \phi) \cdot \phi \to 0$ and therefore that $\phi^2 = \phi$.

  (d) Let $E = \{x \in [0,1] : \phi(x) = 1\}$. Show that $Pe_n \in \chi_E \cdot L_2 (n \geq 0)$, so that $R \subset \chi_E \cdot L_2$. Now note that if $f \in \chi_E \cdot L_2$ and $f \perp R$ then $f \perp Pe_n$ and also $f \perp e_n - Pe_n$, because $e_n - e_n \cdot \phi$ vanishes on E and f vanishes on E'. Hence $f = 0$ and $R = \chi_E \cdot L_2$.

COMPACT OPERATORS

The reader will have noticed that in passing from the spectral representation of normal operators on a finite-dimensional space to that on an infinite-dimensional space we went from finite sums to their natural analogues, Stieltjes integrals, without considering the apparently natural case of infinite sums. The finite-dimensional situation naturally leads to the conjecture that each normal operator should have a decomposition of the form $\sum_{i=1}^{\infty} \lambda_i E_i$, hopefully with this series converging in norm. We know, however, that this is not the case, at least for the operator M, or, more generally, for any operator that has no eigenvalues. If $A = \sum_i \lambda_i E_i$, in which the E_i are pairwise orthogonal projections with sum $I (E_i E_j = 0, i \neq j; \sum_i E_i = I)$, then for $f = E_i f$ we have $Af = \lambda_i f$. We are therefore led to investigate conditions that may be imposed on an operator which forces its spectrum to consist only of eigenvalues, and indeed only countably many eigenvalues (see Exercise 6). The relevant concept is that of a *compact* operator which we now investigate.

From Appendix 1 we recall that a set M of a metric space X is called *compact* if every sequence $\{x_k\}$ of elements of M contains a convergent subsequence $\{x_k'\}$ with limit in M. In finite-dimensional spaces every closed bounded set is compact. We know, however, that in infinite-dimensional spaces this is not the case; for example, the unit ball of l_2 is not compact.

Returning now to our study of operators, observe that if A is any bounded linear transformation then A must map bounded sets into bounded sets. Indeed, the inequality $\|x\| \leq M$ implies $\|Ax\| \leq M\|A\|$. Our definition of a compact operator requires much more. It is convenient to call a set *relatively compact* if its closure is compact.

DEFINITION A. *A (bounded linear) operator A on a Banach space is called* compact *if it maps bounded sets into relatively compact sets.*

Every linear operator of finite rank is compact because it takes every bounded set into a bounded subset of a finite-dimensional space. In infinite-dimensional spaces there is in general an abundance of bounded but *not* compact operators. The identity operator is one example. The identity on l_2 takes the unit ball S of l_2 into a set that is not relatively compact; hence the operator is not a compact operator.

It follows from the definition that if A is compact then for any operator B the products AB and BA are compact. Indeed if S is a bounded set so is $B(S)$; hence its image under A is relatively compact so that AB carries bounded sets into relatively compact sets. Similarly, $A(S)$ is relatively compact and since the continuous image of a compact set is compact (a simple exercise) $B(A(S)) = (BA)(S)$ is also relatively compact.

This observation shows that if dim $H = \infty$ then 0 belongs to the spectrum of every compact operator on H. Indeed if $0 \notin \sigma(A)$ and A is compact, then so is $A^{-1}A = I$; hence dim $H < \infty$.

We are now ready to state the spectral theorem for compact normal operators.

THEOREM A. *Let A be a compact normal operator on H. Then*
  (1) *$\sigma(A)$ consists of a finite or countably infinite set of eigenvalues, each of finite multiplicity.*[1]
  (2) *If $\sigma(A)$ is infinite, then 0 is its only limit point.*
  (3) *An orthonormal sequence of eigenvectors $\{\phi_i\}$ of A with ϕ_i corresponding to λ_i exists such that for each $x \in H$ we have the Fourier expansions*

$$Ax = \sum_{i=1}^{\infty} \langle Ax, \phi_i \rangle \phi_i = \sum_{i=1}^{\infty} \lambda_i \langle x, \phi_i \rangle \phi_i,$$

$$A^*x = \sum_{i=1}^{\infty} \langle A^*x, \phi_i \rangle \phi_i = \sum_{i=1}^{\infty} \bar{\lambda}_i \langle x, \phi_i \rangle \phi_i.$$

  (4) *The sequence $\{\phi_i\}$ is complete in H if and only if 0 is not an eigenvalue of A, that is, if and only if $Ax \neq 0$ for $x \neq 0$.*

We may cast the theorem into a form similar to our preceding results by the observation that the operator E_i, defined by

$$E_i x = \langle x, \phi_i \rangle \phi_i,$$

is a projection on H. Moreover, $E_i x \perp E_j x$ for $i \neq j$, and for each $x, y \in H$ we have

$$Ax = \sum_i \lambda_i \langle x, \phi_i \rangle \phi_i = \sum_i \lambda_i E_i x,$$

$$\langle Ax, y \rangle = \sum_i \lambda_i \langle E_i x, y \rangle.$$

[1]An eigenvalue λ of A is of finite multiplicity if $\{x : Ax = \lambda x\}$ is finite-dimensional.

The latter equation expresses $\langle Ax, y \rangle$ as a Stieltjes integral of $\phi(\lambda) = \lambda$ with respect to the function $\langle E(\lambda)x, y \rangle$ which has a jump of $\langle E_i x, y \rangle$ at each $\lambda = \lambda_i$ but is otherwise constant. If 0 is not an eigenvalue of A, so that the $\{\phi_i\}$ form a basis for H, we have $\sum E_i = I$, and the first equation expresses the fact that $A = \sum_{i=1}^{\infty} \lambda_i E_i$, where the series is convergent in the operator norm:

$$\left\| A - \sum_{i=1}^{N} \lambda_i E_i \right\| \to 0, \quad \text{as } N \to \infty.$$

Example 1. Here we consider the linear operator $A : l_2 \to l_2$, defined by the equations

$$y_i = \sum_{k=1}^{\infty} a_{ik} x_k, \qquad i = 1, 2, \dots, \tag{4}$$

where $y = (y_1, y_2, \dots)$, $x = (x_1, x_2, \dots) \in l_2$ and $y = Ax$. It is not difficult to show that every linear operator on l_2 can be given such a representation. By using the Cauchy-Schwarz inequality, we find that

$$\|A\| \leq \left(\sum_{i,j=1}^{\infty} |a_{ij}|^2 \right)^{1/2}. \tag{5}$$

If the right-hand side of this inequality is finite, we shall show that A is a compact operator.

First we note that the convergence of the double summation implies that for every $\varepsilon > 0$ an N exists such that

$$\left(\sum_{i,j=n}^{\infty} |a_{ij}|^2 \right)^{1/2} < \varepsilon.$$

Thus, if A_n is the transformation $y = A_n x$ defined by

$$y_i = \begin{cases} \sum_{j=1}^{n} a_{ij} x_j, & i = 1, \dots, n, \\ 0, & i = n + 1, \dots, \end{cases}$$

then $\|A - A_n\| < \varepsilon$. Hence the range of A_n is an ε-net for the range of A. However, since the range of A_n is finite-dimensional, it is compact and by the corollary to Theorem K, Appendix 1, the range of A is compact.

Example 2. For our second example we consider the linear operator K on $L_2(a,b)$ whose value at $t \in [a,b]$ is given by

$$(Kx)(t) = \int_a^b k(t,s)x(s)ds, \qquad x \in L_2(a,b).$$

The kernel $k(t,s)$ is assumed to be uniformly continuous on the square

$[a,b] \times [a,b]$; that is, for every $\varepsilon > 0$, $\delta > 0$ can be found such that

$$|k(t_1,s) - k(t_2,s)| < \varepsilon, \qquad s \in [a,b], \tag{6}$$

whenever $|t_1 - t_2| < \delta$. Using the Cauchy-Schwarz inequality we can easily prove that for any $x \in L_2(a,b)$

$$|(Kx)(t)| \le \|x\| \left[\int_a^b |k(t,s)|^2 ds \right]^{1/2}, \tag{7}$$

$$|(Kx)(t_1) - (Kx)(t_2)| \le \|x\| \left[\int_a^b |k(t_1,s) - k(t_2,s)|^2 ds \right]^{1/2}. \tag{8}$$

From Eq. 8 we see that Kx is a continuous function for each $x \in L_2(a,b)$ and that as x ranges over a bounded set the corresponding set of functions Kx is equicontinuous. From Eq. 7 this set is also bounded. Therefore by Arzela's theorem it follows that the image $K(S)$ of any bounded set $S \subset L_2(a,b)$ is relatively compact in $C(a,b)$. Since uniform convergence implies L_2 convergence, it follows that $K(S)$ is compact in $L_2(a,b)$, and consequently the operator K is compact.

R E M A R K. The conditions of continuity of the kernel k are by no means necessary for K to be a compact operator on L_2. The indefinite integral operator T defined by

$$(Tf)(t) = \int_0^t f(s)ds = \int_0^1 k(s,t)f(s)ds, \qquad f \in L_2(0, 1).$$

$$k(s,t) = \begin{cases} 1, & 0 \le s \le t, \\ 0, & t < s, \end{cases}$$

is compact, but clearly k is not continuous.

So far we have not shown that the spectrum of an operator is nonempty. Clearly this is imperative for most of our results to have content. To complete this section we must remedy that defect.

Let T be an operator and for $\lambda \notin \sigma(T)$ put $R_\lambda(T) = (T - \lambda I)^{-1}$. From Exercise 10(b) we have

$$\|R_\lambda(T)\| \le (|\lambda| - \|T\|)^{-1}, \qquad |\lambda| > \|T\|. \tag{9}$$

From Exercise 9(c) we have

$$R_\lambda(T) - R_{\lambda_0}(T) = R_{\lambda_0}(T) \sum_0^\infty (\lambda - \lambda_0) R_{\lambda_0}(T)^n - R_{\lambda_0}(T)$$

$$= R_{\lambda_0}(T) \sum_1^\infty (\lambda - \lambda_0)^n R_{\lambda_0}(T)^n.$$

Hence

$$\|R_\lambda(T) - R_{\lambda_0}(T)\| \le \|R_{\lambda_0}(T)\|\{(1 - |\lambda - \lambda_0| \cdot \|R_{\lambda_0}(T)\|)^{-1} - 1]$$
$$\le |\lambda - \lambda_0| \cdot \|R_{\lambda_0}(T)\|^2(1 - |\lambda - \lambda_0| \cdot \|R_{\lambda_0}(T)\|)^{-1}. \quad (10)$$

Fix μ and λ not in $\sigma(T)$. By multiplying the identity

$$T - \mu I = (T - \lambda I) - (\mu - \lambda)I,$$

first on the left by $R_\mu(T)$ and then on the right by $R_\lambda(T)$, we obtain

$$R_\mu(T) - R_\lambda(T) = (\mu - \lambda)R_\mu(T)R_\lambda(T). \quad (11)$$

THEOREM B. *If $H \ne \{0\}$ and $T \in \beta(H)$ then $\sigma(T)$ is not empty.*

P R O O F. If $\sigma(T)$ is empty, then $R_\lambda(T)$ is defined in the entire complex plane; it goes to 0 as $|\lambda| \to \infty$ by Eq. 9 and depends continuously on λ by Eq. 10. Fix $x, y \in H$ and consider the complex-valued function

$$\phi_{x,y}(\lambda) = \langle R_y(T)x, y \rangle.$$

The continuity of $R_\lambda(T)$, together with Eq. 11, shows that $\varphi_{x,y}$ is analytic in the entire plane. Since $\phi_{x,y} \to 0$ as $|\lambda| \to \infty$, $\phi_{x,y}$ is bounded. Hence by Liouville's theorem $\phi_{x,y}$ is constant and that constant is 0. Because this holds for all y, $R_\lambda(T)x$ must be the 0 vector, and since x is arbitrary $R_\lambda(T)$ is the 0 operator. But then $I = R_\lambda(T)(T - \lambda I) = 0$, which contradicts the assumption that $H \ne \{0\}$.

Exercises

In this set of Exercises, A is a compact operator on the Hilbert space H.

3. Prove that every nonzero point of the spectrum of A is an eigenvalue.
   HINT: Pick $0 = \lambda \in \sigma(A)$ and assume that a sequence $\|x_n\| = 1$ exists such that $Ax_n - \lambda x_n \to 0$. Choose a convergence subsequence from $\{Ax_k\}$. Use the relation $x_{n_k} = (1/\lambda)[Ax_{n_k} - (Ax_{n_k} - \lambda x_{n_k})] \to 1/\lambda y$ to complete the proof.

4. Prove that each compact self-adjoint operator has at least one eigenvalue. HINT: Use the fact that a self-adjoint operator has a norm equal to its spectral radius.

5. Prove that each eigenspace of a compact operator is finite-dimensional. HINT: Observe that if this is not so an infinite orthonormal set in the eigenspace may be constructed.

6. Prove that if $\alpha > 0$ the compact operator A can have at most a finite number of eigenvectors corresponding to $\lambda \in \sigma(A)$ for which $|\lambda| \ge \alpha$.

HINT: Assume that the opposite is true and construct a contradiction. To phrase this problem another way we find that 0 is the only limit point of $\sigma(A)$.

THE POLAR DECOMPOSITION OF AN OPERATOR

There are many useful analogies between operators on a Hilbert space and complex numbers. For example, we have already observed a reasonable notion of positivity for operators. We call a self-adjoint operator A positive if the quadratic form (Ax,x) is non-negative. From the spectral representation of such an operator it is trivial that it has a square root $A^{1/2}$, which is characterized by the conditions $A^{1/2} \geq 0$. $(A^{1/2})^2 = A$. This fact gives us another characterization of positivity: A is positive if and only if $A = B^*B$ for some operator B. This makes clear the analogy between the adjoint of an operator and the complex conjugate of a complex number.

The preceding suggests that we ought to be able to decompose an operator into its "real" and "imaginary" parts. We are led to suspect that $\text{Re}A = \frac{1}{2}(A + A^*)$, $\text{Im}A = \frac{1}{2}i(A - A^*)$. Clearly, we have

$$A = \frac{1}{2}(A + A^*) + i[\frac{1}{2}i(A - A^*)],$$

$$[\frac{1}{2}(A + A^*)]^* = \frac{1}{2}(A + A^*),$$

$$[\frac{1}{2}i(A - A^*)]^* = [\frac{1}{2}i(A - A^*)].$$

We see then that if A is an arbitrary operator then there exists self-adjoint operators B and C with $A = B + iC$. This relation implies that $A^* = B - iC$ so that $2B = A + A^*$ and similarly $2iC = A - A^*$. In other words, B and C are uniquely determined by A.

Each complex number z also has a polar decomposition $z = re^{i\theta}$. Since $r = (\bar{z}z)^{1/2}$, we expect that, for an operator A, r should correspond to a positive operator—in fact to the operator $(A^*A)^{1/2}$. What about the factor $e^{i\theta}$? Noting that $\bar{e}^{i\theta}e^{i\theta} = 1$, we could expect to find a unitary operator V such that

$$A = V(A^*A)^{1/2}.$$

This is almost the case, as we can show. First, however, we need a definition.

DEFINITION. *An operator T on H is an* isometry *if* $\langle Tx,Ty \rangle = \langle x,y \rangle$ *for all $x,y \in H$. T is said to be a* partial isometry *if it is an isometry on the orthogonal complement of its null space.*

It is easy to see that T is an isometry if and only if T preserves norms: $\|Tx\| = \|x\|$ for all $x \in H$ (Exercise 13). Note also that $\langle x,y \rangle = \langle Tx,Ty \rangle = \langle T^*Tx,y \rangle$ for all $x,y \in H$ is equivalent to $T^*T = I$. It follows that an isometry T is unitary if and only if it maps H *onto* itself, in which case each $x \in H$ may be written $x = Ty$ for some y so that

$$TT^*x = T(T^*Ty) = Ty = x, \qquad TT^* = I.$$

The standard example of an isometry that is not unitary is the unilateral shift on l_2. We are now ready to obtain the polar decomposition of a bounded operator.

THEOREM C. *Let A be an operator on H. Then there is a partial isometry V and a positive operator R such that $A = VR$.*

PROOF. We have already seen that R should be the operator $(A^*A)^{1/2}$. With this for R, it is not difficult to find V. We have

$$\|Rx\|^2 = (R^2x,x) = (A^*Ax,x) = \|Ax\|^2, \tag{12}$$

and this shows that we may define an isometric mapping V_0 on the range of R as follows: for $y = Rx$ put $V_0y = Ax$. We must check that this definition of V_0 is unambiguous in the sense that if y has two representations $y = Rx_1$, $y = Rx_2$, the vectors Ax_1 and Ax_2 are identical. This, however, follows from

$$\|Rx_1 - Rx_2\| = \|R(x_1 - x_2)\| = \|A(x_1 - x_2)\| = \|Ax_1 - Ax_2\|.$$

Using the same identity, we see that if $y = \lim_n Rx_n$ belongs to the closure of the range of R the vectors Ax_n will converge to some vector z. This allows us to extend V_0 onto $\overline{RH}$ by putting $V_0y = z$. Since

$$\|y\| = \lim\|Rx_n\| = \lim\|Ax_n\| = \|z\|,$$

it follows that V_0 remains isometric on this larger domain. Finally, we put $H_1 = (RH)^\perp$ and take V as the 0 operator on H_1, and V_0 on $\overline{RH}$. Clearly, V is a partial isometry on H, and for any $x \in H$

$$VRx = V_0(Rx) = Ax.$$

This completes the proof.

COROLLARY. *If A is invertible then $A = VR$, where R is positive and V is unitary.*

PROOF. This follows from the fact that if A is invertible then A is bounded below:

$$\|Ax\| \geq C\|x\|, \qquad \text{all } x \in H.$$

Hence by Eq. 9 so is R. Because R is self-adjoint, this means that R is invertible (see Exercise 11(a)). Then $V = AR^{-1}$ is the product of two invertible operators and is itself invertible.

In Section 3.4 we obtained a canonical dyadic decomposition of an operator of finite rank. We now proceed to generalize this decomposition to compact linear transformations.

THEOREM D. *Let T be a compact linear transformation from H_1 into H_2. Then there exist positive scalars $\{\lambda_n\}$ and orthonormal sequences $\{f_n\}$ in H_1, $\{e_n\}$ in H_2, such that*

$$T = \sum_1^\infty e_n > \lambda_n < f_n$$

in the sense that

$$\lim_{N \to \infty} \| T - \sum_1^N e_n > \lambda_n < f_n \| = 0.$$

PROOF. By a slight modification in the proof of Theorem C we can show that T may be written $T = VR$, where $R = (T^*T)^{1/2}$; T^* is the conjugate of T. Here R is a positive operator on H_1 and V is a bounded linear transformation from H_1 into H_2, characterized by

$$Vy = Tx \quad \text{if} \quad y = Rx,$$

$$Vy = 0 \quad \text{if} \quad y \perp \text{range } R.$$

Now R is compact, because T is compact. Hence by the spectral theorem for R we have

$$Rx = \sum_1^\infty \lambda_n \langle x, f_n \rangle f_n,$$

where the λ_n are the nonzero eigenvalues of R (counted according to multiplicity) and $\{f_n\}$ is a corresponding sequence of eigenvectors.

Since

$$Rf_n = \lambda_n f_n, \qquad \lambda_n > 0,$$

we have $f_n = R(\lambda^{-1} f_n)$. This implies that $e_n = V f_n$ is an orthonormal sequence in H_2:

$$\langle e_n, e_m \rangle = \langle V f_n, V f_m \rangle = \langle T(\lambda_n^{-1} f_n), T(\lambda_m^{-1} f_m) \rangle$$

$$= \lambda_n^{-1} \lambda_m^{-1} \langle f_n, T^*T f_m \rangle = \lambda_n^{-1} \lambda_m^{-1} \langle f_n, R^2 f_m \rangle$$

$$= \lambda_n^{-1} \lambda_m^{-1} \langle f_n, \lambda_m^2 f_m \rangle = \delta_{nm}.$$

Finally,

$$Tx = VRx = V \left(\sum_1^\infty \lambda_n \langle x, f_n \rangle f_n \right) = \sum_1^\infty \lambda_n \langle x, f_n \rangle e_n.$$

Exercises

7. Let S be the unilateral shift on l_2 (see Example 2, Section 3.3). Use the fact that the geometric series $\sum_0^\infty \lambda^n$ is convergent to $(1 - \lambda)^{-1}$ for all $|\lambda| < 1$ to show that each point of the open disk $|\lambda| < 1$ is an eigenvalue of S^*.

8. If A is an operator, then A is invertible if and only if A^* is invertible

(see the proof of Theorem C, Section 3.3). Use this statement to show that, for any A, $\sigma(A^*) = \overline{\sigma(A)}$.

9. (a) We have seen that the space $\beta(H)$ of bounded operators on the Hilbert space H is a Banach space. If $A \in \beta(H)$ has norm $\|A\| < 1$, then

$$\left\| \sum_{k=n}^{n+p} A^k \right\| \leq \sum_{k=n}^{n+p} \|A\|^k \leq \sum_{k=n}^{\infty} \|A\|^k = \|A\|^n (1 - \|A\|)^{-1}.$$

This shows that the partial sums $\{\sum_{k=0}^{n} A^k\}_{1}^{\infty}$ form a Cauchy sequence in $\beta(H)$; hence there is a $B \in \beta(H)$ such that

$$B = \lim_{n \to \infty} \sum_{k=0}^{n} A^k = \sum_{0}^{\infty} A^k.$$

Show that $B(I - A) = I = (I - A)B$, hence that $\sum_{0}^{\infty} A^k = (I - A)^{-1}$. Note also that $\|(I - A)^{-1}\| \leq \sum_{0}^{\infty} \|A\|^k = (1 - \|A\|)^{-1}$.

(b) If T is an operator, then $T - \lambda I$ is invertible for all $|\lambda| > \|T\|$. HINT: Write $T - \lambda I = -\lambda(I - \lambda^{-1}T)$ and use (a). This shows that $\sigma(T)$ is contained in the closed disk about the origin of radius $\|T\|$, hence in particular that $\sigma(T)$ is a *bounded* subset of the plane. Note also that $\|(T - \lambda I)^{-1}\| \leq (|\lambda| - \|T\|)^{-1}$ for all $|\lambda| \geq \|T\|$.

(c) If T is an operator, show that $\sigma(T)$ is *closed*. HINT: It is enough to prove that the complement for $\sigma(T)$ is open and, for this, that if $T - \lambda_0 I$ is invertible then there is an $\varepsilon > 0$ such that $T - \lambda I$ is invertible for all $|\lambda - \lambda_0| < \varepsilon$. Write

$$T - \lambda I = T - \lambda_0 I - (\lambda - \lambda_0)I$$

$$= (T - \lambda_0 I)\{I - (\lambda - \lambda_0)(T - \lambda_0 I)^{-1}\}$$

and use Exercise 10(a).

10. (a) Use Eqs. 11 and 12, and Exercise 9(b) to show that the unilateral shift on l_2 has the closed unit disk as its spectrum.

(b) Let H be a Hilbert space with an orthonormal basis $\{e_n\}_{-\infty}^{\infty}$ and define the *bilateral* shift U on H by

$$Ue_n = e_{n+1}, \qquad n = 0, \pm 1, \pm 2, \dots.$$

Show that U is unitary and that $\sigma(U)$ is the unit circle.

11. (a) Let A be an operator H and suppose that A is bounded below:

$$\|Ax\| \geq m\|x\|, \qquad \text{all } x \in H,$$

for some $m > 0$. Show that A is one-to-one and that the range of A is closed.

(b) For any operator A, $R(A)^\perp = N(A^*)$. Hence A has a dense range if and only if its adjoint is one-to-one.

(c) If A is normal, then $\|A^*x\| = \|Ax\|$ all $x \in H$; hence A is invertible if and only if A is bounded below.

(d) If $A = A^*$, then $\sigma(A)$ is a subset of the real axis. HINT: Use the identity

$$|\lambda - \bar{\lambda}| \cdot \|x\|^2$$

$$= |\langle (A - \lambda)x, x \rangle - \langle x, (A - \lambda)x \rangle| \leq 2\|(A - \lambda)x\| \cdot \|x\|.$$

(e) If $A = A^*$, show that A is positive if and only if $\langle Ax, x \rangle \geq 0$ all $x \in H$.

(f) If U is unitary, then $\sigma(U)$ is a subset of the unit circle. HINT: Use (c) and the triangle inequality:

$$\|(U - \lambda)x\| \geq |\,\|Ux\| - \|\lambda x\|\,| = |(1 - |\lambda|)| \cdot |\|x\|.$$

(g) If A is an operator, we say that λ is an *approximate eigenvalue* of A if a sequence $\{x_n\}$ of unit vectors is such that $\|(A - \lambda)x_n\| \to 0$. Use (c) to show that if A is normal then $\sigma(A)$ consists precisely of the approximate eigenvalues of A.

12. (a) Let A be an operator on H. A is normal if and only if

$$\|Ax\| = \|A^*x\|, \qquad \text{all } x \in H.$$

HINT: $\|Ax\|^2 - \|A^*x\|^2 = \langle Ax, Ax \rangle - \langle A^*x, A^*x \rangle$.

(b) Suppose that A is normal. So is $A - \lambda I$, and consequently $\|(A - \lambda I)x\| = \|(A^* - \bar{\lambda} I)x\|$, all $x \in H$. This shows that if x is an eigenvector of A corresponding to the eigenvalue λ then x is an eigenvector of A^* corresponding to the eigenvalue $\bar{\lambda}$.

(c) If A is normal and $Ax = \lambda x$, $Ay = \mu y$ with $\lambda \neq \mu$, then $x \perp y$. HINT: Look at the difference $\langle Ax, y \rangle - \langle x, A^*y \rangle$.

(d) If A is normal and $M_\lambda = \{x \in H : Ax = \lambda x\}$ are the eigenspaces of A, then the M_λ reduce A and are pairwise orthogonal.

13. (a) Show that the following are equivalent conditions on an operator T:

$$(1) \quad \|Tx\| = \|x\|, \qquad \text{all } x \in H,$$

$$(2) \quad \langle Tx, Ty \rangle = \langle x, y \rangle, \qquad \text{all } x, y \in H.$$

HINT: Verify the identity

$$4\langle Tx, Ty \rangle = \langle T(x + y), T(x + y) \rangle - \langle T(x - y), T(x - y) \rangle$$

$$+ i\langle T(x + iy), T(x + iy) \rangle - i\langle T(x - iy), T(x - iy) \rangle.$$

   (b) Show that if T is a partial isometry on H then T^*T is the projection of H onto the orthogonal complement of the null space of T. Conversely, any operator T for which T^*T is a projection is a partial isometry.

REFERENCES

See also [A1, chs. IV, V], [A21, ch. XI], [A56, chs. IV, V], [A57], [A72], and [A83, ch. VI].

6 A SUPPLEMENT ON UNIQUENESS

During the course of Section 4.2 several of the theorems were stated without proof to promote a degree of conciseness. The theorems in question are important tools in the applications, and since the proofs are not known to be available elsewhere they are given in this appendix. For simplicity Theorems E and F are subdivided into several smaller theorems with proofs that can be easily assimilated.

We begin with the proof of Theorem M, Section 4.2 (relabeled Theorem A).

THEOREM A. *The following are equivalent properties of* B:
  (1) *B is smooth.*
  (2) *At each point of ∂U there is at most one (hence exactly one) supporting hyperplane of U.*
  (3) *The functional $x \to \|x\|$ has a (Gateaux) derivative at each point of ∂U; that is,*

$$\lim_{\varepsilon \to 0} \frac{\|x + \varepsilon z\| - \|x\|}{\varepsilon} = G(x,z)$$

exists for $x \in \partial U$ and $z \in B$. Moreover $G(x,z)$ is a real linear function of z of norm 1 whenever it is defined.

PROOF. The equivalence of (1) and (2) have been established in Section 4.2.

Now fix $x \in \partial U$ and suppose that the limit defining $G(x,z)$ exists for each $z \in B$. We show that $G(x,z)$ is a real linear functional on B of norm 1. By the

421

Hahn-Banach theorem x has an extremal so that an $f \in B^*$ exists such that $f(x) = 1 = \|f\|$. Let $z \in B$ be given. Then, for $\varepsilon > 0$, we have

$$\|x + \varepsilon z\| \geq |f(x + \varepsilon z)| = |1 + \varepsilon f(z)|,$$

$$\|x - \varepsilon z\| \leq |f(x - \varepsilon z)| = |1 - \varepsilon f(z)|,$$

and consequently

$$\frac{\|x + \varepsilon z\| - 1}{\varepsilon} \geq \frac{|1 + \varepsilon f(z)| - 1}{\varepsilon},$$

$$\frac{\|x - \varepsilon z\| - 1}{-\varepsilon} \leq \frac{|1 - \varepsilon f(z)| - 1}{-\varepsilon}.$$

Now a simple application of L'Hôpital's rule shows that the limits on the right exist and are equal with the value

$$\lim_{\eta \to 0} \frac{|1 + \eta f(z)| - 1}{\eta} = \operatorname{Re} f(z).$$

Using this and the hypothesis that $G(x,z)$ exists, we obtain

$$G(x,z) \geq \operatorname{Re} f(z),$$

$$G(x,z) \leq \operatorname{Re} f(z).$$

Since z is arbitrary, it now follows that $G(x,z) = \operatorname{Re} f(z)$ is a real linear function of z, which has norm ≤ 1. It is obvious from the definition of G that $G(x,x) = 1$, and it follows that $z \to G(x,z)$ defines a real linear functional of norm 1. This proves the final assertion of the theorem. Moreover, we obtain the implication $(3) \Rightarrow (1)$ by noting that the preceding argument shows that any linear functional of norm 1 that assumes the value of 1 at x has real part $G(x,z)$. Consequently, the relations $f, g \in U^*$, $f(x) = g(x) = 1$ imply $\operatorname{Re} f = g$, and this in turn implies $f = g$ (see Theorem J, Section 4.1) so that B is smooth.

Suppose that B is smooth and let $x \in \partial U$ and $z \in B$ be given. We show that the limit defining $G(x,z)$ exists. Now $\|x + \varepsilon z\|$ is a convex function of the real variable ε, for, if $0 < \alpha < 1$, we have

$$\|x + [\alpha\varepsilon + (1 - \alpha)\eta]z\| = \|\alpha(x + \varepsilon z) + (1 - \alpha)(x + \eta z)\|$$

$$\leq \alpha\|x + \varepsilon z\| + (1 - \alpha)\|x + \eta z\|.$$

It therefore follows from the theory of convex functions (see Krasnosel'skii [A51], for example) that this function has right and left derivatives at $\varepsilon = 0$ and that

$$a = \lim_{\varepsilon \to 0^+} \frac{\|x - \varepsilon z\| - \|x\|}{-\varepsilon} \leq \lim_{\varepsilon \to 0^+} \frac{\|x - \varepsilon z\| - \|x\|}{\varepsilon} = b.$$

It is enough to show that $a = b$.

Now by hypothesis for each $\varepsilon \geq 0$ there is a unique f_ε in B^* of norm 1 such that $f_\varepsilon(x + \varepsilon z) = \|x + \varepsilon z\|$. Let $f = f_0$. We claim that $b = f(z)$. To prove this note that $\{f_\varepsilon\}$ as a subset of the (weak star) compact set of U^*, has a limit point $g \in U^*$ and accordingly we may choose a sequence of ε's which tend to zero such that $f_\varepsilon(y) \to g(y)$ for each $y \in B$. Since

$$f_\varepsilon(x) = \|x + \varepsilon z\| - \varepsilon f_\varepsilon(z)$$

it follows that $g(x) = \|x\| = 1$; hence by uniqueness of f we have $g = f$. Again, using the uniqueness of f, we find that the equality

$$\frac{f_\varepsilon(x)}{\|x + \varepsilon z\| - f_\varepsilon(z)} = 1$$

implies

$$1 > |\|x + \varepsilon z\| - \varepsilon f_\varepsilon(z)|.$$

Using this and the fact that f has norm 1, we obtain

$$0 \leq \mathrm{Re}\, \frac{\|x + \varepsilon z\| - f(x + \varepsilon z)}{\varepsilon} = \frac{\|x + \varepsilon z\| - 1}{\varepsilon} - \mathrm{Re}\, f(z)$$

$$= \mathrm{Re}\, \frac{\|x + \varepsilon z\| - \varepsilon f_\varepsilon(z) - 1}{\varepsilon} + \mathrm{Re}\,(f_\varepsilon(z) - f(z))$$

$$\leq \mathrm{Re}\,(f_\varepsilon(z) - f(z)).$$

It then follows that $b = \mathrm{Re}\, f(z)$. By an exactly similar argument we show that $a = \mathrm{Re}\, f(z)$. This completes the proof of the implication $(1) \Rightarrow (3)$.

THEOREM B.   *Let $B_1, B_2, \ldots, B_n$ be normed spaces each of which is rotund. For $x = (x_1, \ldots, x_n) \in \prod_{i=1}^n B_i$, define the norm $|\quad|$ of x by*

$$|x| = \left(\sum_{i=1}^n \|x_i\|^p \right)^{1/p}, \qquad 1 < p < \infty,$$

where $\|x_i\|$ is the norm of x_i in B_i. Then $|\quad|$ is a rotund norm on $B = \prod_{i=1}^n B_i$. Conversely, if this is a rotund norm on B, then each of the factors (with its given norm) is rotund.

   P R O O F .   We first show that $|\quad|$ is indeed a norm on B. This function is clearly positive-definite and absolutely homogeneous so that only the triangle inequality must be verified.

   Now, if $x = (x_1, \ldots, x_n)$ and $y = (y_1, \ldots, y_n)$ belong to B, we have

$$|x + y| = \left(\sum_{i=1}^n \|x_i + y_i\|^p \right)^{1/p} \leq \left(\sum_{i=1}^n (\|x_i\| + \|y_i\|)^p \right)^{1/p}$$

$$\leq \left(\sum \|x_i\|^p \right)^{1/p} + \left(\sum \|y_i\|^p \right)^{1/p} = |x| + |y|,$$

where the last inequality is Hölder's inequality (for $l_p(n)$) applied to the vectors

$$(\|x_1\|, \ldots, \|x_n\|), (\|y_1\|, \ldots, \|y_n\|).$$

To prove the rotundity of this product norm, suppose first that $B = B_1 \times B_2$ is a product of two factors. A number of equivalent definitions of rotundity were given, one of them being that every $x \in B$ of norm 1 is an extreme point of the unit ball U of B. Precisely, for each $|x| = 1$, the conditions $x = \frac{1}{2}(y + z)$, $|y| = 1$, $|z| = 1$ imply $x = y = z$. We now show that every $x = (x_1, x_2) \in B$ of norm 1 is an extreme point, or, equivalently, if $(x_1, x_2) = \frac{1}{2}(y_1, y_2) + \frac{1}{2}(z_1.z_2)$, with

$$|(y_1, y_2)| = (\|y_1\|^p + \|y_2\|^p)^{1/p} = 1,$$

$$|(z_1, z_2)| = (\|z_1\|^p + \|z_2\|^p)^{1/p} = 1,$$

and $(y_1, y_2) \neq (z_1, z_2)$, then $|(x_1, x_2)|$ is strictly less than 1. There are two cases.

C A S E 1. Suppose that $\|y_1\| = \|z_1\|$ and $\|y_2\| = \|z_2\|$. Then

$$|(x_1, x_2)|^p = \|\tfrac{1}{2}(y_1 + z_1)\|^p + \|\tfrac{1}{2}(y_2 + z_2)\|^p < [\tfrac{1}{2}(\|y_1\| + \|z_1\|)]^p$$
$$+ [\tfrac{1}{2}(\|y_2\| + \|z_2\|)]^p = \|y_1\|^p + \|y_2\|^p = 1,$$

since both $y_1 = z_1$ and $y_2 = z_2$ cannot hold. This, together with the rotundity of B_1 and B_2, implies that both $\|y_1 + z_1\| = \|y_1\| + \|z_1\|$, and $\|y_2 + z_2\| = \|y_2\| + \|z_2\|$ cannot hold.

C A S E 2. Here $(\|y_1\|, \|y_2\|)$ and $(\|z_1\|, \|z_2\|)$ are distinct vectors in R^2. The p-norm is a rotund norm on R^2; hence the p-norm of the sum of these two vectors is strictly less than the sum of their p-norms.

$$[(\|y_1\| + \|z_1\|)^p + (\|y_2\| + \|z_2\|)^p]^{1/p}$$
$$< (\|y_1\|^p + \|y_2\|^p)^{1/p} + (\|z_1\|^p + \|z_2\|^p)^{1/p} = 2.$$

Hence

$$|(x_1, x_2)| = (\|\tfrac{1}{2}(y_1 + z_1)\|^p + \|\tfrac{1}{2}(y_2 + z_2)\|^p)^{1/p}$$

$$\leq \{[\tfrac{1}{2}(\|y_1\| + \|z_1\|)]^p + [\tfrac{1}{2}(\|y_2\| + \|z_2\|)]^p\}^{1/p}$$

$$= \tfrac{1}{2}[(\|y_1\| + \|z_1\|)^p + (\|y_2\| + \|z_2\|)^p]^{1/p} < 1.$$

Now, for an induction hypothesis, suppose that the theorem is true for less than n factors and let $B = \prod_{i=1}^{n} B_i$. Then by hypothesis

$$B^1 = \prod_{i=1}^{n-1} B_i$$

is rotund with the norm

$$|(x_1, x_2, \ldots, x_{n-1})| = \left(\sum_{i=1}^{n-1} \|x_i\|^p \right)^{1/p}.$$

Now $B = B^1 \times B_n$ algebraically, and if $x \in B$ then

$$|x|^p = \sum_{i=1}^{n-1} \|x_i\|^p + \|x_n\|^p = |(x_1, x_2, \ldots, x_{n-1})|^p + \|x_n\|^p;$$

that is, the norm on B is a p-norm on a product of two factors, each of which is rotund. The induction step, hence the theorem, now follows from $n = 2$.

Note that the rotundity of the factors is also necessary for this product norm to be rotund. Thus, if x, $y \in B_1$, then

$$|x + y| = |(0, \ldots, 0, x, 0, \ldots, 0) + (0, \ldots, 0, y, 0, \ldots, 0)|$$

$$\leq |(0, \ldots, 0, x, 0, \ldots, 0)| + |(0, \ldots, 0, y, 0, \ldots, 0)|$$

$$= |x| + |y|,$$

and equality holds if and only if $x = \lambda y$ or $y = \lambda x$ for some $\lambda \geq 0$.

In particular, for $p = 2$, we see that the Euclidean norm

$$|(x_1, x_2, \ldots, x_n)| = \left(\sum_{i=1}^{n} \|x_i\|^2 \right)^{1/2}$$

is a rotund norm on B. The next result shows that this may be generalized slightly.

THEOREM C. *Let B, B_1 be as before and let $[a_{ij}]$ be a positive-definite symmetric $n \times n$ matrix, each of whose elements is non-negative. The function*

$$x \to \|\|x\|\| = \left(\sum_{i,j=1}^{n} a_{ij} \|x_i\| \cdot \|x_j\| \right)^{1/2}$$

is a rotund norm on B. Conversely, if for each such matrix $[a_{ij}]$ this function yields a rotund norm on B, each of the factors B_i is rotund (with the given norm on B_i).

P R O O F . If $x = (x_1, x_2, \ldots, x_n)$ belongs to B, let us write $\underline{x}$ for the n-tuple $(\|x_1\|, \|x_2\|, \ldots, \|x_n\|)$. Then with $[\ ,\ ]$, denoting the usual inner product in real n-dimensional Hilbert space, we are to prove that the function

$$x \to \|\|x\|\| = [A\underline{x}, \underline{x}]^{1/2}$$

is a norm on B. By the hypothesis that A is positive-definite, we have $[A\underline{x}, \underline{x}] \geq 0$ with equality if and only if $\underline{x} = 0$. Thus $\|\|x\|\| > 0$ unless $x = 0$.

It is clear that $\||\lambda x\|| = |\lambda| \cdot \||x\||$ for all complex scalars λ. Also, if $y = (y_1, y_2, \ldots, y_n) \in B$, then

$$\||x + y\||^2 = \sum a_{ij}\|x_i + y_i\| \cdot \|x_j + y_j\|$$

$$\leq \sum a_{ij}(\|x_i\| + \|y_i\|)(\|x_j\| + \|y_j\|)$$

$$= \sum a_{ij}\|x_i\| \cdot \|x_j\| + 2\sum a_{ij}\|x_i\| \cdot \|y_j\| + \sum a_{ij}\|x_i\| \cdot \|y_j\|$$

$$= \||x\||^2 + 2[Ax, y] + \||y\||^2.$$

Next, using the fact that any positive matrix has a unique self-adjoint square root and the Schwartz inequality in n-dimensions, we get

$$|[Ax,y]|^2 = |[A^{1/2}x, A^{1/2}y]|^2 \leq [A^{1/2}x, A^{1/2}x][A^{1/2}y, A^{1/2}y]$$

$$= [Ax,x][Ay,y] = \||x\||^2 \cdot \||y\||^2.$$

Thus

$$\||x + y\||^2 \leq \||x\||^2 + 2\||x\|| \cdot \||y\|| + \||y\||^2 = (\||x\|| + \||y\||)^2,$$

which proves that the asserted functional is a norm on B.

Finally, observe that the proof of the triangle inequality in B used the triangle inequality in each B_i and the Schwarz inequality in n-dimensions. Thus, if $x, y \in B$ and $\||x + y\|| = \||x\|| + \||y\||$, then $\|x_i + y_i\| = \|x_i\| + \|y_i\|$ for each i, and the vectors $A^{1/2}\hat{x}$, $A^{1/2}\hat{y}$ are linearly dependent. Since A, and therefore $A^{1/2}$, is invertible, this second condition implies the linear dependence of $\hat{x}$ and $\hat{y}$. It follows that x and y are linearly dependent vectors in B, hence that $\|| \; \||$ is a rotund norm on B.

The converse follows from Theorem B by taking $p = 2$ and the identity matrix for $[a_{ij}]$.

THEOREM D. *Let $B = \prod_{i=1}^{n} B_i$, with B_i rotund, and let the norm of $x = (x_1, \ldots, x_n)$ in B be given by*

$$|x| = \left(\sum_{i=1}^{n} \|x_i\|^p\right)^{1/p}, \qquad 1 < p < \infty.$$

If ϕ is a bounded linear functional on B, the functionals $\phi_i \in B_i^*$, $i = 1, \ldots, n$ are such that we have

$$\langle x, \phi \rangle = \sum_{i=1}^{n} \langle x_i, \phi_i \rangle.$$

Furthermore

$$|\phi| = \left(\sum_i \|\phi_i\|^q\right)^{1/q}, \qquad \left(\frac{1}{p} + \frac{1}{q} = 1\right).$$

P R O O F . The fact that each bounded linear functional ϕ on B can be written

$$\langle x, \phi \rangle = \sum_i \langle x_i, \phi_i \rangle$$

with $\phi_i \in B_i^*$ is well known. We prove only the second assertion.

Now, if $x \in B$, then

$$|\langle x, \phi \rangle| = \left| \sum_i \langle x_i, \phi_i \rangle \right| \leq \sum_i |\langle x_i, \phi_i \rangle|$$

$$\leq \sum_i \|x_i\| \cdot \|\phi_i\| \leq \left(\sum_i \|x_i\|^p \right)^{1/p} \left(\sum_i \|\phi_i\|^q \right)^{1/q},$$

so that

$$|\phi| \leq \left(\sum_i \|\phi_i\|^q \right)^{1/q}.$$

To prove the reverse inequality let $\bar{\phi}_i$ be the extremal[1] of ϕ_i in B_i and set $x = (\alpha_i \bar{\phi}_i, \ldots, \alpha_n \bar{\phi}_n)$, where

$$\alpha_i = (\alpha^{-1} \|\phi_i\|)^{q-1}, \qquad \alpha = \left(\sum_i \|\phi_i\|^q \right)^{1/q}.$$

Then

$$|x|^p = \sum_i \|\alpha_i \bar{\phi}_i\|^p = \sum_i \alpha_i^p$$

$$= \alpha^{p(1-q)} \sum_i \|\phi_i\|^{p(q-1)} = \alpha^{-q} \sum_i \|\phi_i\|^q = 1,$$

so that x has norm 1. Finally,

$$\langle x, \phi \rangle = \sum_i \langle \alpha_i \bar{\phi}_i, \phi_i \rangle = \sum_i \alpha_i \|\phi_i\|$$

$$= \alpha^{1-q} \cdot \sum_i \|\phi_i\|^q = \alpha^{1-q} \cdot \alpha^q = \alpha.$$

Hence $|\phi| \geq \alpha$ and this completes the proof.

COROLLARY 1. *Let B and ϕ be as above. If $\bar{\phi}_i$ is the extremal of ϕ_i in B_i, the extremal $\bar{\phi}$ of ϕ is given by*

$$\bar{\phi} = (\alpha_1 \bar{\phi}_1, \alpha_2 \bar{\phi}_2, \ldots, \alpha_n \bar{\phi}_n),$$

$$\alpha_i = (\alpha^{-1} \|\phi_i\|)^{q-1}, \qquad \alpha = \left(\sum_i \|\phi_i\|^q \right)^{1/q}.$$

---

[1] Recall that the extremal Φ of a function ϕ on a rotund Banach space B is the unique vector x in B of norm 1 satisfying $\langle x, \phi \rangle = \|\phi\|$.

COROLLARY 2. *If each B_i is also reflexive and smooth, the extremal $\bar{x}$ of $x = (x_1, x_2, \ldots, x_n)$ in B is given by*

$$\bar{x} = (\beta_1 \bar{x}_1, \beta_2 \bar{x}_2, \ldots, \beta_n \bar{x}_n),$$

where

$$\beta_i = (\beta^{-1} \|x_i\|)^{p-1}, \qquad \beta = \left(\sum_i \|x_i\|^p \right)^{1/p}$$

and $\bar{x}_i$ is the extremal of x_i in B_i^*.

PROOF. Since $B_i = (B_i^*)^*$ and B_i^* is rotund, we may apply Theorem D to conclude that the conjugate space of ΠB_i^*, normed by

$$|\phi| = \left(\sum_i \|\phi_i\|^q \right)^{1/q}, \qquad \frac{1}{p} + \frac{1}{q} = 1,$$

is isometrically isomorphic to the space B normed with the corresponding p-norm. Thus each x in B may be regarded as a functional on ΠB_i^* and the result follows from Corollary 1.

THEOREM E. *Let $B = \prod_{i=1}^n$, B_i rotund, be normed as in Theorem B. If $\phi = (\phi_1, \phi_2, \ldots, \phi_n)$ is a bounded linear functional on B, then*

$$\|\|\phi\|\| = \left(\sum_{i,j} b_{ij} \|\phi_i\| \cdot \|\phi_j\| \right)^{1/2},$$

where $[b_{ij}]$ is the inverse of the matrix $[a_{ij}]$.

PROOF. For $x = (x_1, x_2, \ldots, x_n)$ in B and $\phi = (\phi_1, \phi_2, \ldots, \phi_n)$ in B^* let us write $\hat{x}$ and $\hat{\phi}$ for the n-tuples $(\|x_1\|, \|x_2\|, \ldots, \|x_n\|)$ and $(\|\phi_1\|, \|\phi_2\|, \ldots, \|\phi_n\|)$, respectively. With this notation we have

$$\|\|x\|\|^2 = \sum_{i,j} a_{ij} \|x_i\| \cdot \|x_j\| = [A\hat{x}, \hat{x}],$$

where [,] is the usual inner product in the real Hilbert space of n-dimensions. Now

$$|\langle x, \phi \rangle| = |\sum_i \langle x_i, \phi_i \rangle| \leq \sum_i |\langle x_i, \phi_i \rangle| \leq \sum_i \|x_i\| \cdot \|\phi_i\|.$$

We recognize the last expression as $[\hat{x}, \hat{\phi}]$ and compute it as follows:

$$[\hat{x}, \hat{\phi}] = [A^{-1/2} A^{1/2} \hat{x}, \hat{\phi}] = [A^{1/2} \hat{x}, A^{-1/2} \hat{\phi}]$$

$$\leq \|A^{1/2} \hat{x}\| \, \|A^{-1/2} \hat{\phi}\| = [A\hat{x}, \hat{x}]^{1/2} [A^{-1} \hat{\phi}, \hat{\phi}]^{1/2}.$$

Thus it follows that $\|\|\phi\|\|^2 \leq [A^{-1} \hat{\phi}, \hat{\phi}] = \sum_{i,j} b_{ij} \|\phi_i\| \cdot \|\phi_j\|$, where (b_{ij}) is the inverse of the matrix $A = (a_{ij})$.

Now let $x_i \in B_i$ be the extremal of ϕ_i:

$$\|x_i\| = 1, \qquad \langle x_i, \phi_i \rangle = \|\phi_i\|$$

and set $x = (\gamma_1 x_1, \gamma_2 x_2, \ldots, \gamma_n x_n)$, where

$$\gamma_i = \gamma^{-1} \sum_j b_{ij} \|\phi_j\|, \qquad \gamma = \left(\sum_{i,j} b_{ij} \|x_i\| \cdot \|x_j\| \right)^{1/2}.$$

Then for this choice of x we have

$$\|x\|^2 = \sum_{i,j} a_{ij} \|x_i\| \cdot \|x_j\| = \sum_{i,j} a_{ij} \gamma_i \gamma_j$$

$$= \gamma^{-2} \sum_{i,j} a_{ij} \left(\sum_k b_{ik} \|\phi_k\| \right) \left(\sum_l b_{jl} \|\phi_l\| \right)$$

$$= \gamma^{-2} \sum_{i,k,l} b_{ik} \|\phi_l\| \cdot \|\phi_k\| \sum_j a_{ij} b_{jl}$$

$$= \gamma^{-2} \sum_{i,k} b_{ik} \|\phi_i\| \cdot \|\phi_k\| = \gamma^{-2} \cdot \gamma^2 = 1,$$

where we have used the fact that the ith row of A is orthogonal to the lth row of B unless $i = l$. Also,

$$\langle x, \phi \rangle = \gamma^{-1} \cdot \sum_i \langle \gamma_i x_i, \phi_i \rangle = \gamma^{-1} \cdot \sum_i \gamma_i \|\phi_i\|$$

$$= \gamma^{-1} \cdot \sum_i \|\phi_i\| \sum_j b_{ij} \|\phi_j\| = \gamma^{-1} \cdot \gamma^2 = \gamma.$$

We conclude that $\|\phi\| \geq \gamma$, hence, by the first part of the argument, that $\|\phi\| = \gamma$.

COROLLARY 1. *With B and ϕ as in Theorem E and $\bar{\phi}_i$ the extremal of ϕ_i in B_i, the extremal $\bar{\phi}$ of ϕ in B is given by*

$$\bar{\phi} = (\gamma_1 \bar{\phi}_1, \gamma_2 \bar{\phi}_2, \ldots, \gamma_n \bar{\phi}_n),$$

where

$$\gamma_i = \gamma^{-1} \cdot \sum_i b_{ij} \|\phi_j\|, \qquad \gamma = \sum_{i,j} b_{ij} \|\phi_i\| \cdot \|\phi_j\|.$$

COROLLARY 2. *If, in addition, each B_i is smooth and reflexive, the extremal of $x = (x_1, \ldots, x_n)$ in B is given by*

$$\bar{x} = (\delta_1 \bar{x}_1, \delta_2 \bar{x}_2, \ldots, \delta_n \bar{x}_n),$$

where

$$\delta_i = \delta^{-1} \cdot \sum_j a_{ij} \|x_j\|, \qquad \delta = \sum_{i,j} a_{ij} \|x_i\| \cdot \|x_j\|.$$

As another example in the technique of constructing extremals we prove Theorem F.

THEOREM F. *Let B_1, B_2 be rotund, smooth, and reflexive and let F be a bounded linear transformation from B_1 into B_2. Let B denote the space B_1 equipped with the norm*

$$|x| = (\|x\|^2 + \|Fx\|^2)^{1/2}.$$

Then B is rotund, smooth, and reflexive with $B^* = B_1^*$ and the extremal x' of an x in B is given by

$$x' = \frac{\|x\|\bar{x} + \|Fx\|F^*(\overline{Fx})}{(\|x\|^2 + \|Fx\|^2)^{1/2}},$$

where the bars denote extremals in B_1 and B_2, respectively.

P R O O F .　Since F is bounded, we have

$$\|x\|^2 \leq \|x\|^2 + \|Fx\|^2 = |x|^2 \leq (1 + \|F\|^2)\|x\|^2,$$

so that $|\ |$ is an equivalent norm on B_1. Hence B and B_1 have the same bounded linear functionals and, in particular, B is reflexive. If $B(F)$ denotes the graph of F in $B_1 \times B_2$, then $(x, Fx) \to x$ is a (linear) isometry on $B(F)$ onto B. Since $B_1 \times B_2$ (with the obvious norm) is rotund (Theorem B), its isometric copy B is also rotund. Because smoothness is also preserved under isometries and any subspace of a smooth space is smooth, it remains only to prove that $B_1 \times B_2$ is smooth.

Now by Theorem D of this appendix the dual of $B_1 \times B_2$ may be identified with the space of pairs $(f_1, f_2) \in B_1^* \times B_2^*$ with the norm

$$\|(f_1, f_2)\| = (\|f_1\|^2 + \|f_2\|^2)^{1/2}.$$

Since B_1^* and B_2^* are rotund by hypothesis, an application of Theorem D shows that $(B_1 \times B_2)^*$ is rotund, which is equivalent to the smoothness of $B_1 \times B_2$.

Finally, with $M(x) = \|x\|\bar{x} + \|Fx\|F^*(\overline{Fx})$, observe that

$$\langle x, M(x) \rangle = \|x\|\langle x, \bar{x} \rangle + \|Fx\|\langle Fx, \overline{Fx} \rangle$$

$$= \|x\|^2 + \|Fx\|^2 = |x|^2.$$

For any $y \in B$

$$|\langle y, M(x) \rangle| = |\|x\|\langle y, \bar{x} \rangle + \|Fx\|\langle Fy, \overline{Fx} \rangle|$$

$$\leq \|x\| \cdot \|y\| + \|Fx\| \cdot \|Fy\|$$

$$\leq (\|x\|^2 + \|Fx\|^2)^{1/2}(\|y\|^2 + \|Fy\|^2)^{1/2} = |x| \cdot |y|.$$

In other words, the functional $\phi(x) = M(x)/|x|$ has the value $|x|$ at x and is of norm 1 in B^* and therefore is the extremal of x in B.

R E M A R K .   It follows from the proof that $|M(x)| = |x|$ for each x in B and that M is onto B^*. The function M is also antihomogeneous:

$$M(\lambda x) = |\lambda x|(\lambda x)' = |\lambda|\,|x|\,\frac{|\lambda|}{\lambda}\,x' = \bar{\lambda}M(x).$$

Finally, M is also one-to-one, for

$$|x|x' = M(x) = M(y) = |y|y'$$

implies that

$$|x| = |y|$$

and that

$$x = |x|x'' = |x|(|x|x')' = |y|(|y|y')' = y.$$

7 INVERTING LINEAR TRANSFORMATIONS

If X and Y are finite-dimensional linear spaces and T is a transformation from X to Y, the question whether T is invertible is easy to answer; that is, there exists a transformation S from Y to X with the properties that ST and TS are the identity transformations on X and Y, respectively, precisely when T is one-to-one and maps X onto Y. If we introduce the concept of linearity, the question of invertibility becomes ambiguous, at least until we have proved the theorem that *any* transformation inverse to T is necessarily linear. In other words, T has a linear inverse if and only if T has an inverse.

If, in addition, we suppose that X and Y are *normed* spaces and T is a bounded linear transformation from X to Y, we encounter still another ambiguity in the question of invertibility of T. This, however, is resolved, by the theorem that any linear transformation on a finite-dimensional normed linear space is automatically bounded. In short, for finite-dimensional Banach spaces, the question "has the bounded linear transformation T a bounded linear inverse transformation?" turns out to be equivalent to asking the much simpler question "is T one-to-one and onto?"

Consider the case in which X and Y are assumed to be arbitrary Banach spaces and T is linear and bounded from X to Y. Clearly, T must be one-to-one and onto if it is to have an inverse, and these conditions are sufficient to guarantee that the inverse is linear. It is a surprising fact that these conditions also imply that the inverse is *bounded*; that is, if T is a bounded linear transformation from X onto Y and T is one-to-one, then T has a bounded linear inverse. This theorem is due to Banach and ranks with the Hahn-Banach theorem as one of the most useful tools of functional analysis. Instead of proving this result, we state a slightly more general theorem from which it follows.

THEOREM A (The Open Mapping Theorem). *Let X and Y be Banach spaces and let T be a bounded linear transformation from X onto Y. T is an open map; that is, if G is an open set in X, then T(G) is an open set in Y.*

By way of a remark we emphasize that it is specifically required that both X and Y be *complete* and that T be *onto*. The theorem is not true in the absence of either of these assumptions (see Exercise 1). We may paraphrase the result by stating that any bounded transformation with closed range maps sets that are open in the domain into sets that are open in its range. An equivalent way of stating the result is the following: if T maps onto Y and U_X, U_Y denote the unit balls in X and Y, then for some positive constant α we have $\alpha U_Y \subset T(U_X)$. In other words, an $\alpha > 0$ exists such that if $y \in Y$ and $\|y\| \le \alpha$ then the equation $Tx = y$ has at least one solution x with $\|x\| \le 1$. In less precise language, if T is onto, then T cannot map a "fat" set onto a "skinny" one. For example, the operator T on E^3, defined by

$$T(x_1, x_2, x_3) = (x_1, x_2, 0),$$

clearly does *not* map onto E^3, and this is reflected in the fact that it sends the sphere

$$\{(x_1, x_2, x_3) : |x_1|^2 + |x_2|^2 + |x_3|^2 \le 1\}$$

—a "fat" set—onto the disk

$$\{(x_1, x_2, 0) : |x_1|^2 + |x_2|^2 \le 1\}$$

—a "skinny" set in E^3. Note, however, that regarded as a map into E^2, that is, $T(x_1, x_2, x_3) = (x_1, x_2)$, T is *onto*, and this is reflected in the fact that $\{(x_1, x_2, x_3) : |x_1|^2 + |x_2|^2 + |x_3|^2 < 1\}$, which is an open set in E^3, is mapped onto an open set in E^2.

We may appreciate the depth of the theorem from the following list of its corollaries.

COROLLARY 1. *If T is a one-to-one bounded linear transformation from the Banach space X onto the Banach space Y, then T has a bounded linear inverse.*

P R O O F. Since T is one-to-one and onto, a linear mapping S from Y to X exists such that ST and TS are the identity maps on X and Y, respectively. Moreover, since by the theorem T carries open sets into open sets, the inverse image under S of each open set in X is open in Y. This means that S is continuous and finally, since continuity is the same as boundedness for linear transformations, that S is bounded.

R E M A R K 1. A consequence of Corollary 1 is that any one-to-one bounded linear transformation with closed range is automatically bounded below, that is, $\|Tx\| \geq k\|x\|$ for some $k > 0$. Conversely, it is easy to see that if T is bounded below it is one-to-one and has closed range.

Note also that the theorem asserts that every nonzero bounded linear functional on X is an open mapping. For example, if $\phi \in B^*$ and $U = \{x \in B : \|x\| < 1\}$, then $\phi(U)$ is an open set in the field of scalars.

In order to state the next corollary we introduce the following terminology: if X is a linear space and $\| \ \|_1$ and $\| \ \|_2$ are both norms on X, we say that these norms are *comparable* if one dominates the other; that is, if for some positive constant k we have either

$$\|x\|_1 \leq k\|x\|_2, \qquad \text{all } x \in X$$

or

$$\|x\|_2 \leq k\|x_1\|, \qquad \text{all } x \in X.$$

For example,

$$\|x\|_1 = \sup\{|x(t)| : t \in [0,1]\}$$

and

$$\|x\|_2 = \left[\int_0^1 |x(t)|^2 dt \right]^{1/2}$$

define comparable norms on the linear space X of functions continuous on the unit interval.

We call $\| \ \|_1$ and $\| \ \|_2$ *equivalent* norms on X if positive constants k_1, k_2 exist such that

$$k_1\|x\|_1 \leq \|x\|_2 \leq k_2\|x\|_1, \qquad \text{all } x \in X.$$

Thus two norms on X are equivalent if and only if there is only one notion of Cauchy sequence in X (i.e., $\|x_n - x_m\|_1$ is small if and only if $\|x_n - x_m\|_2$ is small). If two norms are equivalent on X, the normed space $\{X, \| \ \|_1\}$ is complete if and only if the normed space $\{X, \| \ \|_2\}$ is complete. Since, in the preceding example $\{X, \| \ \|_1\}$ is complete, whereas $\{X, \| \ \|_2\}$ is not, it follows that these two norms cannot be equivalent norms on X. Corollary 2 shows that this is essentially the only way we can construct comparable, but not equivalent, norms.

COROLLARY 2. *Let X be a linear space and let $\| \ \|_1, \| \ \|_2$ be comparable norms on X. If the normed spaces $\{X, \| \ \|_1\}$ and $\{X, \| \ \|_2\}$ are both complete, then $\| \ \|_1, \| \ \|_2$ are in fact equivalent norms on X.*

P R O O F. We may suppose that $\|x\|_1 \leq k\|x\|_2$ for all $x \in X$. Let X_1 and X_2 denote the space X equipped with the norms $\| \ \|_1$ and $\| \ \|_2$, respectively. By assumption the identity mapping $i : X_2 \to X_1$ is bounded. Since this mapping is clearly one-to-one, linear, and onto X_1 and since X_2 and X_1 are Banach spaces, it follows from the open mapping theorem that i has a bounded inverse which maps X_1 onto X_2. In other words, for all $x \in X_1$

$$\|x\|_2 = \|i^{-1}(x)\|_2 \leq l\|x\|_1$$

for some positive constant l, and this is what we set out to prove.

R E M A R K. Recall that each norm on a vector space X defines a collection of open sets of X (i.e., a topology on X). The preceding corollary states that if X is a Banach space with respect to two different norms and if the collection of open sets defined by one norm contains those defined by the other, then these two norms must actually define the *same* open sets.

If X is a finite-dimensional vector space, then *any* two norms on X are equivalent, so that the phenomenon of comparable, but not equivalent, norms can occur only in infinite dimensions. The proof of the first assertion is not easy, but it is based on the fact that if $\| \ \|$ is a norm on X then $\|x_n\| \to 0$ if and only if each coordinate of x_n converges to 0 in the scalar field. In fact, once this is shown, it follows that there is only one notion of convergence in X, and it is easy to see that this last fact implies that any two norms on X are equivalent.

COROLLARY 3 (The Closed Graph Theorem). *Let T be a linear transformation defined on the Banach space X with values in the Banach space Y. Then T is bounded if and only if the conditions*

$$\text{(a)} \quad x_n \to x, \qquad x_n \in X,$$

$$\text{(b)} \quad Tx_n \to y, \qquad y \in Y,$$

imply $y = Tx$.

P R O O F. If T is bounded, then $x_n \to x$ implies $Tx_n \to Tx$, and therefore if (b) also holds we have $y = \lim Tx_n = Tx$, so that the condition of the corollary is trivially necessary for T to be bounded.

Conversely, suppose the condition of the corollary is satisfied for T. Putting

$$\|(x,y)\| = \max\{\|x\|, \|y\|\}, \qquad x \in X, y \in Y,$$

we obtain the Banach space $X \times Y$. The set

$$G(T) = \{(x, Tx) : x \in X\}$$

is clearly a linear manifold in $X \times Y$, and under the present hypothesis $G(T)$ is in fact closed. Indeed, if $(x, y) \in X \times Y$ is a limit point of $G(T)$, then for some sequence $\{x_n\}$ in X we have

$$\|(x_n, Tx_n) - (x, y)\| \to 0,$$

and this is equivalent to

$$x_n \to x \text{ in } X,$$

$$Tx_n \to y \text{ in } Y.$$

Consequently, using (b), we get $y = Tx$, so that $(x,y) = (x,Tx) \in G(T)$.

We now define a linear transformation Φ from the Banach space $G(T)$ onto X by

$$\Phi(x,Tx) = x.$$

Since Φ is evidently one-to-one, we conclude from Corollary 1 that Φ^{-1} is also bounded. Noting that

$$\|Tx\| \leq \|(x,Tx)\|$$

expresses the fact that $\psi : (x,Tx) \to Tx$ is a bounded mapping from $G(T)$ into Y, we conclude that the composition $\psi\Phi^{-1} = T$ is also bounded and this completes the proof.

REMARK 3. The set $G(T)$ introduced in the preceding proof is called the *graph* of the transformation T. The corollary then asserts that a linear transformation from one Banach space into another is bounded whenever its graph is a closed subset of the product space, and this clearly justifies its name.

The closed graph theorem gives an often useful criterion for proving that a linear transformation T defined on a Banach space X is bounded. Indeed, T is bounded if the conditions $x_n \to 0$, $Tx_n \to y$ imply that $y = 0$. Note, however, that for this application it is essential that the domain of T be all of X. For example, the differential operator

$$Tx = \frac{dx}{dt}$$

is well-defined on a linear manifold of $C(0,1)$; it has closed graph but is not bounded (Exercise 2).

As an application of the ideas in the preceding discussion, let us prove Theorem B.

THEOREM B. *Let T be a bounded linear transformation from the Banach space X into the Banach space Y. If T is one-to-one and has closed range, then T^* maps Y^* onto X^*.*

PROOF. It follows from the hypothesis and the open mapping theorem that T is bounded below

$$\|Tx\| \geq \alpha\|x\|, \qquad \text{all } x \in X$$

for some positive constant α. We want to show that if $f \in X^*$ is given, then f belongs to the range of T^*.

Now it follows from the inequality in Theorem B that the mapping $Tx \to f(x)$ is well-defined, bounded, and linear. Indeed, if $Tx = Ty$, then $x = y$ (since T is one-to-one); hence $f(x) = f(y)$, and the inequality

$$|f(x)| \le \|f\| \cdot \|x\| \le (\alpha^{-1}\|f\|)\|Tx\|$$

proves the boundedness. By the Hahn-Banach theorem we may now extend this mapping onto all of Y (preserving linearity and boundedness) to obtain a vector $\phi \in Y^*$. Then for all $x \in X$ we have

$$\langle Tx, \phi \rangle = \phi(Tx) = f(x) = \langle x, f \rangle$$

and this means that f belongs to the range of T^*; in fact, $f = T^*\phi$.

REMARK 4. The converse of the preceding result is also true; that is, if T^* maps Y^* *onto* X^*, then T is one-to-one and has closed range. This proof is based on the following facts:

(a) If the range of T^* is dense, then T is one-to-one.
(b) If the range of T^* is closed, then so is the range of T.

To prove (a) note that if $Tx = 0$ then for all $\phi \in Y^*$ we have

$$0 = \langle Tx, \phi \rangle = \langle x, T^*\phi \rangle.$$

This means that x, regarded as a linear functional on X^*, vanishes on a dense subset of X^*, and therefore $x = 0$ (by a corollary of the Hahn-Banach theorem).

The proof of (b) can be found in [A22, p. 488]; see also [A77, ch. IX].

Exercises

1. Let M be the operator "multiplication by x" in $L_2(0,1)$:

$$(Mf)(x) = xf(x), \qquad f \in L_2(0,1).$$

Then M is defined on a Banach space and maps onto a normed space. Show that M is not an open map. HINT: Assume that $M(U) \supset \alpha U$ for some $\alpha > 0$ when U is the unit ball in $L_2(0,1)$ and then show that this implies that $\alpha x/\|Mx\| \in U$ whenever $0 \ne x \in U$. Now show that this is absurd, for it implies that the range of M is all of $L_2(0,1)$.

2. Let X be the subset of $C(0,1)$ consisting of those functions x that have a continuous derivative x'. Then X is a linear manifold in $C(0,1)$, and we may define a transformation T on X by putting $Tx = x'$ for $x \in X$. Show that the graph of T is closed and that T is not bounded.

HINT: For the first part note that if $x_n \to 0$ and $x_n' \to y$, then

$$\int_0^t x_n'(s)ds \to \int_0^t y(s)ds.$$

For the second part consider the functions $x_n(t) = t^n$.

3. We derived the closed graph theorem from Corollary 1. Show that conversely, by assuming the closed graph theorem, we can prove that each one-to-one and onto bounded transformation is invertible.

8 VARIABLE END POINT PROBLEMS

In this appendix we consider extensions of the optimization problems studied in Chapter 4, in which it was assumed that the target $\xi \in D$ and the transformation $T: B \to D$ were fixed known quantities. In many physical problems these assumptions are unrealistic, and it is the objective of Appendix 8 to weaken these conditions in a number of useful ways which do not disturb the central role played by the solution to the classical problem.

Using the notation of Chapter 4, we formulate the central problem of this section.

Problem 3.   Let $\{T_t : t \in v\}$ denote a parameterized family of bounded linear transformations defined on B with values in D. Determine the elements, $u \in B$, $\xi_t \in D$, and $t \in v$, that minimize a functional $J(u,t,\xi_t)$ over the class of tuplets (u,t,ξ_t) which satisfies these side constraints:

(a) $\xi_t - T_t u = 0, \qquad t \in v,$
(b) $\|u\| \leq k,$
(c) $\psi_i(\xi_t, t) = 0, \qquad i = 1, 2, \ldots, m, \qquad t \in v.$

By judicious choice of the functional $J(u,t,\xi_t)$ and constraint functions $\{\psi_i\}$ it is clearly possible to generate a broad class of subproblems within the framework of Problem 3. In this section three cases analogous to the problem of Bolza (see [B13, Sec. 76]) are discussed. In these examples emphasis is placed on the use of the pseudoinverse concept as a tool in solving the more general problems.

Before proceeding with the analysis, let us recall a theorem that deals with ordinary constrained minimization.

THEOREM A. *Let $f(x_1, \ldots, x_n)$ denote an objective function to be extrem-ized[1] which in addition to the r independent side constraints*

$$g_j(x_1, \ldots, x_n) = 0, \qquad j = 1, \ldots, r < n,$$

is at least twice differentiable at a point $(\bar{x}_1, \ldots, \bar{x}_n)$. If $\bar{x} = (\bar{x}_1, \ldots, \bar{x}_n)$ is a local constrained extremum for $f(x)$, it is necessary that scalars $(\lambda_1, \ldots, \lambda_r)$ exist for which

$$J^* = f(x_1, \ldots, x_n) + \sum_{j=1}^{r} \lambda_j g_j(x_1, \ldots, x_n)$$

has an unconstrained extremum at $\bar{x}$. If, in addition, the relationship

$$\sum_{i,j=1}^{n} \frac{\partial^2 f}{\partial x_i \partial x_j}\bigg|_{\bar{x}} z_i z_j > 0 \qquad (\text{or} < 0)$$

holds for all $z = (z_1, \ldots, z_n)$ satisfying

$$\sum_{j=1}^{n} \frac{\partial g_j}{\partial x_i}\bigg|_{\bar{x}} z_j = 0,$$

this is sufficient to guarantee that $\bar{x}$ is a constrained extremal of f.

REMARK 1. If $\bar{x}$ is an unconstrained extremum of $J^*(x)$, then the $n + r$ equations

$$\frac{\partial J^*(\bar{x})}{\partial x_i} = 0, \qquad i = 1, \ldots, n,$$

$$g_j(\bar{x}) = 0, \qquad j = 1, \ldots, r,$$

in the $n + r$ unknowns $(x_1, \ldots, x_n, \lambda_1, \ldots, \lambda_r)$ must be satisfied.

REMARK 2. If H is the matrix with (i,j) elements,

$$h_{ij} = \frac{\partial^2 f}{\partial x_i \partial x_j}\bigg|_{\bar{x}}, \qquad i, j = 1, \ldots, n,$$

and $\nabla_x g$ denotes the tuplet $\nabla_x g = (\partial g/\partial x_1, \ldots, \partial g/\partial x_n)$, the sufficient condi-tions may be phrased as being

$$[z, Hz] \geq 0$$

for all $z = (z_1, \ldots, z_n)$ satisfying

$$[\nabla_x g_j, z] = 0.$$

---

[1]The point $\bar{x}$ of the metric space X is called a local extremum of the functional f if $f(\bar{x}) \geq f(x)$ or $f(\bar{x}) \leq f(x)$ for all x in some neighborhood of $\bar{x} \in X$. For a local constrained extremum one of these inequalities must hold for all points in the intersection of some neighborhood of $\bar{x}$ and the set of all points satisfying the constraints.

A proof of Theorem A, along with geometric interpretations of the Lagrange multipliers, is given in [B13] (see also Kao [B56]).

Problem 3a. Let B and D be fixed Banach spaces, let v be a subset of the real line, and let $\{T_t : t \in v\}$ be a parameterized family of bounded linear transformations sending B onto D. Determine the elements $u \in B$, $t \in v$, that minimize $J(u,\xi_t,t) = g(\xi_t,t) + \|u\|^2$ over the class of tuples (u,ξ_t,t) which satisfies these side constraints:

(a) $\xi_t - T_t u = 0$,

(b) $\psi_i(g_t,t) = 0$, $\qquad i = 1, 2, \ldots, m^1$

R E M A R K 3. Observe that if the set v consists of a single point $t = t_0$ and the functions g, $\psi_1, \ldots, \psi_m$ vanish identically this problem reduces to Problem 1 of Chapter 4.

Let us assume that optimal values $(\bar{\xi}_t,\bar{t}_0)$ exist, which, with the function $\bar{u}$, constitute a solution of Problem 3a. Fixing (ξ_t,t) at $(\bar{\xi}_t,\bar{t})$, let us observe now that $J(\bar{\xi}_t,\bar{t},u)$ is proportional to $\|u\|^2$. In view of (a), it follows that $\bar{u}$ is the minimum norm solution to the equation

$$\bar{\xi}_t = T_t u, \qquad t = \bar{t}.$$

Since, for each $t \in v$, the function T_t can be defined in the usual manner, the best choice of u is precisely

$$\bar{u} = T_t^\dagger \bar{\xi}_t, \qquad t = \bar{t}.$$

Substitution of this expression into Problem 3a reduces that problem to one of minimizing the functional

$$J(\xi_t,t) = g(\xi_t,t) + \|T_t^\dagger \xi_t\|^2, \qquad (t,\xi_t) \in v \times D$$

with respect to the constraints

$$\psi_i(\xi_t,t) = 0, \qquad i = 1, \ldots, m < \dim(D).$$

If $D = R^n$ this formulation has the form of an ordinary constrained minimization problem, and Theorem A may be employed.

Example. The composite system of Figure 2.16, Section 2.5, provides a useful setting for illustrating Problem 3a. Let $r_0 = (s_0,t_0)$ and $r_f = (s_f,t_f)$ denote fixed tuplets in $v = \sigma \times \tau$ and let $z(r_f) = (y(s_f),x(t_f))$ be an element of R^n. In the notation of Problem 3a consider the two constraints

$$\psi_1(z(r_0)) = z(r_0) = 0,$$

$$\psi_2(z(r_f)) = [z(r_f),z(r_f)] - 1 = 0,$$

---

[1]If dim $D < \infty$, we assume also that $m < \dim D$.

which are to be satisfied in conjunction with the constraint

$$z(r_f) = [T(u,v)](r_f) = T_f(u,v)$$

while minimizing the functional,

$$J[(u,v)] = \|z_f - \hat{z}\|^2 + \sum_{k=0}^{f} h_k[u(s_k), u(s_k)] + \int_{t_0}^{t_f} [v(s),v(s)]ds$$

$$= \|z_f - \hat{z}\|^2 + \|(u,v)\|^2. \tag{1}$$

To solve this problem we write the transformation T_f in its polar canonical form (assume for convenience all $\mu_i \neq 0$),

$$T_f = \sum_{i=1}^{n} e_i > \mu_i < f_i. \tag{2}$$

Hence the pseudoinverse of T_f is given by

$$T_f^\dagger = \sum_{i=1}^{n} f_i > \mu_i^{-1} < e_i,$$

and it is then immediate that

$$\|(\bar{u},\bar{v})\|^2 = \|T_f^\dagger z(r_f)\|^2 = [z_f, E^*\Lambda^{-2}Ez_f],$$

where Λ is the matrix $\Lambda = \text{diag}[\mu_1, \ldots, \mu_n]$ and E is the matrix whose ith row is the tuplet e_i, $i = 1, \ldots, n$. The example problem is thus reduced to the minimization of

$$J = \|z_f - z\|^2 + [z_f, E^*\Lambda^{-2}Ez_f],$$

while satisfying the single constraint

$$[z_f, z_f] = 1 = 0. \tag{3}$$

Proceeding in the manner prescribed by Theorem A, we construct the functional

$$J^* = \|z_f - \hat{z}\|^2 + [z_f, E^*\Lambda^{-2}Ez_f] + \lambda\{[z_f, z_f] - 1\}, \tag{4}$$

and by equating the gradient of J^* with respect to z_f to zero we obtain

$$\nabla_{z_f}J^* = 2z_f - 2\hat{z} + 2E^*\Lambda^{-2}Ez_f + 2\lambda z_f = 0 \tag{5}$$

or

$$[(1 + \lambda)I + E^*\Lambda^{-2}E]z_f = \hat{z}, \tag{6}$$

where λ is chosen to satisfy Eq. 3. We set $Ez_f = \beta$ and $E\hat{z} = \gamma$ and Eq. 6 reduces to

$$[(1 + \lambda)I + \Lambda^{-2}]\beta = \gamma. \tag{7}$$

Because $(I + \lambda)I + \Lambda^{-2}$ is the matrix diag $[(1 + \lambda + \mu_1^{-2}), \ldots, (1 + \lambda + \mu_n^{-2})]$, the singularity of this operator is easily determined. Furthermore, the fact that $E^* = E^{-1}$ (recall that the set $\{e_i\}_1^n$ is orthonormal) leads to the equalities

$$1 = [z_f, z_f] = [E^{-1}\beta, E^{-1}\beta] = [\beta, \beta] \tag{8}$$

and thus the example problem has been reduced to the investigation of the relatively simple relationships of Eqs. 7 and 8.

REMARK 4. If the term $\|z_f - \hat{z}\|^2$ is omitted from the functional $J[(u,v)]$ of Eq. 1, the form of Eq. 7 is

$$\Lambda^{-2}\beta = -\lambda\beta. \tag{9}$$

Similarly, $J[(u,v)]$ reduces to

$$J[(u,v)] = [\beta, \Lambda^{-2}\beta],$$

which combine to imply the result that β is a unit eigenvector corresponding to a minimum eigenvalue of Λ^{-2}. Thus the solution is given by $u = (1/\mu_j)f_j$, in which f_j is any one of the functionals in the decomposition of T_f corresponding to the largest value of the set $\{\mu_i\}_1^n$.

REMARK 5. The example problem is typical of a problem class which may be approached in several ways. To see that it may be considered as a variation on Problem 2(a), Section 4.4, identify H_1 as E^n. To simplify notation let $k = (u,v)$. Also let F be the transformation T_f itself and $H(T_f)$ the graph of T_f. Using the fact that $z_f = T_f k$, we find that $J[(u,v)] = J(k)$ (Eq. 1) may be written

$$J(k) = \|T_f k - \hat{z}\|^2 + \|k\|^2$$

$$= \|(k, T_f k) - (\bar{k}, T_f \bar{k})\|^2 + \|(\bar{k}, \hat{k}, \bar{z}, \hat{z})\|^2,$$

where $(\bar{k}, T_f \bar{k})$ is the orthogonal projection of the element $(0,z)$ on the linear subspace $H(T_f)$.

The transformation $G : H(T_f) \to E^n$, defined by

$$G(k, T_f k) = T_f k, \qquad k \in H_1,$$

allows the example to be restated as the problem of finding the element $\omega = (k, T_f k) \in H(T_f)$ in which

$$\|\omega - \bar{\omega}\|^2$$

is minimized while satisfying

$$\|G\omega\|^2 = 1.$$

In physical situations for which the control energy is at a premium it may well happen that the solution to any of the various minimum-energy problems will require a control function whose energy exceeds that available in the physical prime movers. In anticipation of the occurrence of these cases, it is important to consider how to best employ the energy available to accomplish the control objective. Several possibilities are evident: allowing a variable arrival time, allowing a variable end point, or both, while minimizing a "soft" performance index of the form

$$J(u) = \|\xi - \hat{\xi}\|^2 + \|u\|^2.$$

The next problem deals with the case in which arrival time and end point are fixed, and the question is one of doing as well as possible with the alloted energy.

   Problem 3b.   Let y denote a given element of D and $T:B \to D$, the usual bounded linear transformation. Find an element $u \in B$ which minimizes

$$J(u) = \|\xi - Tu\| \tag{10}$$

while satisfying

$$\|u\| \le k.$$

It is not difficult to show that $K = \{y - Tu: \|u\| \le k\}$ is a closed convex set; hence (assuming that D is rotund and reflexive) it has a unique element of minimum norm. In other words, there is a $u \in B$ of norm at most k which minimizes $J(u)$, and Problem 3b always has a solution. It follows easily from the definition of $T^\dagger$ that $0 \in K$ if and only if $\|T^\dagger\xi\| \le k$. Consequently, the vector $T^\dagger\xi$ solves 3b if and only if $\|T^\dagger\xi\| \le k$.

If $\|T^\dagger\xi\| = k$, any $u \in B$ of norm $\le k$ which satisfies $0 = \xi - Tu$ must agree with $T^\dagger\xi$, and in this case 3b has a unique solution. If $\|T^\dagger\xi\| < k$, for any v in the null space of T of norm at most $k - \|T^\dagger\xi\|$ the vector $v + T^\dagger\xi$ is a solution of 3b.

We consider next the case $\|T^\dagger\xi\| > k$ in more detail. For convenience we assume that $B = H$ is a Hilbert space and that D is E^n. Let kC denote the set of vectors kx with x in C; evidently

$$kC = \{x : x = Tu, \|u\| \le k\}.$$

The canonical form for T,

$$T = \sum_{i=1}^{n} e_i > \mu_i < f_i,$$

will be useful. From the example in Section 3.4 it follows that the set kC can also be expressed as

$$kC = \{x : x = \sum_{i=1}^{n} e_i > \mu_i\alpha_i, \ \sum_{i=1}^{n} \alpha_i^2 \le k^2\}. \tag{11}$$

Similarly, scalars $\beta_1, \ldots, \beta_n$ are such that

$$\xi = \sum_{i=1}^{n} e_i > \beta_i.$$

The orthonormality of the set $\{e_i\}_1^n$ justifies the equalities

$$\|\xi - Tu\|^2 = \left\| \sum_{i=1}^{n} e_i > (\beta_i - \mu_i \alpha_i) \right\|^2$$

$$= \sum_{i=1}^{n} (\beta_i - \mu_i \alpha_i)^2,$$

and thus the Hilbert space problem reduces to an ordinary constrained minimization problem.

Problem.   From the tuplets $\alpha = \mathrm{col}(\alpha_1, \ldots, \alpha_n)$ satisfying

$$[\alpha,\alpha] \le k^2$$

determine the element that minimizes the functional

$$[\beta - \Lambda\alpha, \beta - \Lambda\alpha],$$

where $\Lambda = \mathrm{diag}\,[\mu_1, \ldots, \mu_n]$ and $\beta = \mathrm{col}(\beta_1, \ldots, \beta_n)$.

Since $\xi \in kC$, it is necessary to consider only the tuplets that satisfy $[\alpha,\alpha] = k^2$. By use of the single Lagrange multiplier λ the solution to the reduced problem must ensure, as a necessary condition, that

$$J(\alpha) = [\beta - \Lambda\alpha, \beta - \Lambda\alpha] + \lambda^{-1}([\alpha,\alpha] - 1)$$

will take on a minimum at α. Since all quantities are real and Λ is self-adjoint, the gradient of $J^*(\alpha)$ is given by

$$\nabla_\alpha J^*(\alpha) = 2\{-\Lambda\beta + (\lambda I + \Lambda^2)\alpha\};$$

thus the problem reduces to the question of finding scalars $\alpha_1, \ldots, \alpha_n, \lambda$ such that

$$\alpha = [\lambda I + \Lambda^2]^{-1}\beta, \tag{12}$$

$$[\alpha,\alpha] = k \tag{13}$$

hold simultaneously.

The matrix $[\lambda I + \Lambda^2]$ is diagonal and thus easily inverted. Indeed, it is immediate that

$$[\lambda I + \Lambda^2]^{-1} = \mathrm{diag}\,[\ldots, \mu_i/(\lambda + \mu_i^2), \ldots].$$

Thus for fixed β

$$[\alpha,\alpha](\lambda) = \sum_{i=1}^{n} \left(\frac{\mu_i \beta_i}{\lambda + \mu_i^2} \right)^2. \tag{14}$$

If $[\alpha,\alpha](0) < k$, then $\|T^\dagger \xi\| < k$. If $[\alpha,\alpha](0) = k$, then $\|T^\dagger \xi\| = k$. Hence only the case $[\alpha,\alpha](0) > k$ is of interest here. Since $[\alpha,\alpha](\lambda)$ is monotonically decreasing with λ and $[\alpha,\alpha](\lambda) \to 0$ as $\lambda \to \infty$, it is clear that a λ always exists and that this problem has a solution.

As a final variation on Problem 3 let us mention a class of minimum-time problems.

Problem 3c. Let $\{T_t : t \in v\}$ denote the usual family of bounded linear transformations defined on B with values in D. Determine the $u \in H$ which minimizes

$$J(t) = t$$

over the class of elements which satisfies these constraints.

(a) $\xi(t) - T_t u = 0,$
(b) $\|u\| \leq k.$

Let us first assume that the target is fixed with respect to t (i.e., $\xi(t) = \xi$) and that the dependence of T_t on t has the following form: in the space B, which consists of functions defined on v, we define the closed linear subspaces B_t by the equality

$$B_t = \{x \in B : x(s) = 0, s > t\}.$$

Letting P_t denote the projection of B onto B_t (here P_t may be computed by multiplication with the characteristic function of the interval $[t_0, t]$ where t_0 is the smallest element of v) the transformation $\{T_t\}$ is then assumed to satisfy

$$T_t u = T P_t u, \qquad u \in B. \tag{15}$$

Under these conditions the set C_t, defined by

$$C_t = T_t U,$$

expands with increasing t (see Exercise 1); that is $C_{t_1} \subseteq C_{t_2}$ whenever $t_1 < t_2$.

Assume now that T_t is onto for every $t \geq t_0' > t_0$. The functional $\|T_t^\dagger \xi\|$ decreases monotonically with increasing t. Problem 3c evidently is equivalent to finding the smallest $t \in v$ such that $\|T_t^\dagger \xi\| = k$. Let t_1 be this smallest number. A natural duality exists between the two problems. Find the element $u \in T_t^{-1}(\xi)$ which

(a) minimizes $\|u\|$ with respect to the constraint $t = t_1$,
(b) minimizes t with respect to the constraint $\|u\| = R$,

namely, that $u_\xi = T_{t_1}^\dagger \xi$ is the solution (set of solutions) to both.

As we attempt to loosen these restrictions on Problem 3c, the analysis tends toward the study of many special cases. First note that it is *not* necessarily true that a $t \in v$ exists such that $\xi \in C_t$. Exercise 2, for instance, illustrates that C_t may be contained within a fixed bounded set for all $t \in v$. In fact, Exercise 8 shows that when T_t does *not* take the form of Eq. 15 the set C_t may actually shrink with increasing t. Finally, if the target ξ varies with t, the function $\|T_t^\dagger \xi(t)\|$ can be made to exhibit very peculiar properties (see Exercise 5).

Exercises

1. Let B denote a Banach function space on the interval $[0, t_f]$. Show that $B_t = \{x \in B : x(s) = 0, s \in (t, t_f]\}$ is a closed linear subspace of B. Show that U_t, the unit ball of B_t, expands with increasing t. If $T : B \to D$ show also that $C_t = T(U_t)$ expands with increasing t. Give an example in which $C_{t_1} = C_{t_2}$, even though $t_1 < t_2$.

2. Consider the scalar-valued linear dynamic system

$$x(t) = e^{-t}x(0) + \int_0^t e^{-t+s}u(s)ds.$$

Let the forced response define a mapping from $L_\infty(0, t)$ onto R. Show that the set C_t expands monotonically with increasing t but never exceeds the interval $[-1, 1]$.

3. Consider the scalar-valued system defined by

$$x(t_1) = T_{t_1}u = \int_0^{t_1} \exp[\lambda(t_1 - s)]\, u(s)ds, \qquad \lambda < 0.$$

Let $H = L_2(m; 0, t_1)$, in which m is the weighting function: $m(t) = \exp[2\beta t]$, $t \in [0, t_1]$. As a linear operator from H in R, show that $\|T_{t_1}\|$, as a function of t_1, is monotone decreasing for every $\beta > 0$ and monotone increasing for $\beta \le 0$. Show also that the norm of the transformation

$$x(t_1) = T'_{t_1} = \int_0^{t_1} e^{-\lambda s}u(s)ds$$

is nondecreasing for all β.

4. Assume that T is fixed, that the spaces B, T_t of Problem 3c are Hilbert spaces, and that the sets $C_t = TU_t$, $t \in v$ are ellipses. A measure of the growth of C_t as t increases from t_1 to t_2 is given by the change in the eigenvalues of $T_t T_t^*$. Show that if $\lambda_i(t)$ denotes the ith eigenvalue of this matrix,

$$\lambda_i(t_2) \simeq \lambda_i(t_1) + [e_i, T(P_{t_2} - P_{t_1})T^*e_i], \qquad i = 1, \dots, n$$

is a first-order approximation for the change in λ_i with t. Here P_t denotes the orthogonal projection of H on the subspace H_t. HINT: see Exercise 3, Section 3.4.

5. In the system of Exercise 2 set $x(0) = 0$ and take $B = L_\infty(0,t)$. Determine a function $\xi(t_1) = x(t_1)$ such that $\|T_{t_1}^\dagger \xi(t_1)\|$ is monotone decreasing, monotone increasing, and oscillatory about a fixed curve.

9 DISTRIBUTIVE PARAMETER SYSTEMS

The majority of our system examples have dealt with lumped parameter systems which were represented by families of ordinary differential and/or difference equations. All physical systems, however, are intrinsically distributive in nature, and we should anticipate that a closer inspection of the physical laws governing system behavior would result in a mathematical model involving families of partial differential and/or difference equations. Moreover, in such diverse physical plants as distillation columns, chemical and nuclear reactors, large-scale air-conditioning systems, continuous furnaces, and compressible or elastic control actuators the spatial energy distributions preclude approximation by lumped parameter models. Thus it is not surprising that distributive problems have occupied an increasing share of the literature.

It is impossible, of course, to cover all aspects of these systems in the space of these few short pages. Because our treatment must be selective, no further mention of partial difference or nonlinear equations is made. We shall see that distributive parameter systems fit nicely into the same axiomatic framework used in the text to analyze lumped parameter systems. Some differences do occur, such as the distinctions between the underlying concrete function spaces involved, but it will become apparent as the treatment unfolds that many distributive systems are nothing more than glorified infinite dimensional examples of the various sections in the book.

THE MATHEMATICAL MODEL

Large-scale distributive systems can require mathematical models of considerable diversity. However, certain ingredients are present in most applications, and before proceeding with detailed technical matters it will be helpful to introduce some of these factors along with the basic notation to be used.

The independent variables of a distributive system usually consist of a temporal variable t and a finite tuplet of spatial variables $(\alpha_1, \ldots, \alpha_n)$. The range of values for the temporal variable is denoted by τ and Ω denotes the subset of R^n (or C^n) for which the spatial variables have significance. Sometimes Ω is dependent on t, in which case we write Ω_t, $t \in \tau$. The set

$$\Delta = \{(t,\alpha) : \alpha = (\alpha_1, \ldots, \alpha_n) \in \Omega_t, t \in \tau\}$$

is the region of interest for the independent variables.

The dependent variables consist of a finite collection $\{x_i : i = 1, \ldots, m\}$ of scalar-valued functions defined on the set Δ. These variables must satisfy certain families of partial differential equations in the interior of Δ and certain boundary conditions on $\partial\Delta$, both of which are specified by the dynamics of the system under consideration. The system forcing functions may act over the interior of Ω and/or on its boundary. A distributive system problem is called well defined if knowledge of the forcing functions, the boundary conditions, appropriate initial conditions, and the partial differential equations themselves is sufficient to define the system behavior uniquely.

To illustrate these factors, consider the second-order linear equation with a single independent spatial variable α and one dependent variable x:

$$a_{11}x_{tt} + 2a_{12}x_{t\alpha} + a_{22}x_{\alpha\alpha} + a_{10}x_t + a_{01}x_\alpha + a_{00}x = f, \tag{1}$$

in which the dependence of the functions $\{a_{ij}, f, x\}$ on the tuplet (t,α) has been suppressed and the subscript notation denotes partial derivatives; for instance,

$$x_{\alpha t} = \frac{\partial^2 x(t,\alpha)}{\partial\alpha\partial t}, \qquad (t,\alpha) \in \Delta.$$

In addition to the forcing function f in Eq. 1, boundary forces may be present. For example, if $\Omega = [a,b]$, a typical effect of boundary forces on the system takes the form

$$x(t,a) = h_1(t), \qquad x(t,b) = h_2(t), \qquad t \in \tau. \tag{2}$$

Finally, if $\tau = [t_0, t_f]$, the system's initial conditions may typically take the form

$$x(t_0,\alpha) = x^0(\alpha), \qquad x_t(t_0,\alpha) = x^1(\alpha), \qquad \alpha \in \Omega. \tag{3}$$

To avoid confusion, a few words concerning the boundary and initial conditions are in order. Equations 2 should always be interpreted as an abbreviation for the more precise conditions:

$$\lim_{\alpha \to a^+} x(t,\alpha) = h_1(t), \qquad \lim_{\alpha \to b^-} x(t,\alpha) = h_2(t), \qquad t \in \tau.$$

Similarly, Eq. 3 is an abbreviation of the conditions

$$\lim_{t \to t_0^+} x(t,\alpha) = x^0(\alpha), \qquad \lim_{t \to t_0^+} x_t(t,\alpha) = x^1(\alpha), \qquad \alpha \in \Omega;$$

that is, the boundary and initial value conditions are to be interpreted as limits of x from the interior of Δ.

Some ground rules for the smoothness of the various functions involved must also be established. In view of Eq. 1, it is clear that for the solution x, if it exists, we must be able to interpret a first partial derivative in t and first and second partial derivatives in α. Furthermore, these derivatives when combined with the coefficients $\{a_{ij}\}$ must be compatible with the function space chosen for f. Similar remarks hold for the functions x^0, h_1, h_2. In particular, these functions must be continuous and consistent; that is,

$$x^0(a) = h_1(0), \qquad x^0(b) = h_2(0),$$

if the solution x is to be a continuous function.

Although Eq. 1 is fairly simple, a surprising number of important applications fall within its framework. The reader may already have recognized such classical engineering problems as the vibrating string equation ($x_{tt} = a^2 x_{\alpha\alpha} + f$), the heat diffusion equation ($x_t = a^2 x_{\alpha\alpha} + f$), the telegraph equation ($x_{\alpha\alpha} - a^2 x_{tt} = 0$), and Laplace's equation in its several forms. These and other classical examples of physical systems which satisfy Eq. 1 have been discussed in depth in a number of fine references (see [A27], [A29], [A60], or [A90]). In a slightly different vein several authors (see, for instance, [B24], [B110], [B117], [B118]) have considered problems of control using the following two examples as motivation.

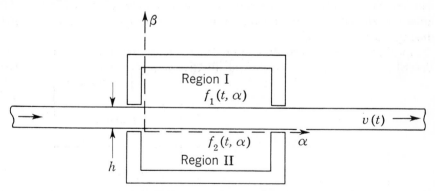

Figure A9.1 A continuous furnace.

Example 1. Consider the continuous furnace of Figure A9.1.[1] A continuous strip of homogeneous material is fed with flow rate v into the furnace by a variable-speed transport mechanism. The temperatures of regions I and II of

[1]Figures A9.1 and A9.2 are taken from P. K. C. Wang, "Control of Distributed Parameter Systems," in *Advances in Control Systems*, Vol .I, Academic Press, New York, 1964. Used with permission.

the furnace are denoted by $f_1(t,\alpha)$ and $f_2(t,\alpha)$, respectively. The spatial domain for the variables (α,β) is given by

$$\Omega \doteq \{(\alpha,\beta) : \alpha \in [0,1],\ \beta \in [0,h]\}.$$

The temperatures f_1, f_2, and the flow rate v are the manipulable controls of the system.

Consider first the case in which the material is thin and the temperature distributions are spatially uniform in the two regions of the furnace (i.e., $f_1 = f_2 = f$). The temperature $x(t,\alpha)$ of the material can be approximately described by the equation

$$x_t(t,\alpha) = \mu x_{\alpha\alpha}(t,a) + v(t)x_\alpha(t,\alpha) + \sigma[x(t,\alpha) - f(t,\alpha)], \qquad (4)$$

in which μ is the coefficient of diffusivity and σ is a constant proportional to the surface conductivity. On the other hand, if the material is thick and stationary and f_1 and f_2 are independent of α, the equation governing the temperature distribution interior to the strip and in the β-direction is

$$x_t(t,\beta) = \mu x_{\beta\beta}(t,\beta)$$

with the boundary conditions $x(t,0) = f_1(t)$, $x(t,h) = f_2(t)$. In both cases initial conditions must be specified to complete the formulation of the problem.

Example 2.   In many aerodynamic re-entry vehicles ablative shields are necessary to protect the vehicle from damage caused by aerodynamic heating. The velocity and attitude of the vehicle must be closely controlled so that the ablation rate will not exceed a certain maximum allowable value at any time during the re-entry flight.

In Figure A9.2 a one-dimensional version of the ablation problem is described. One surface ($\alpha = b$) of the ablative slab is insulated and the other

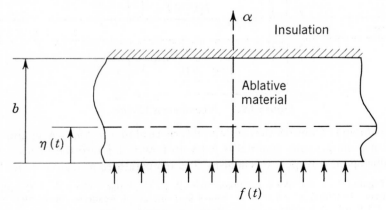

Figure A9.2   An ablative surface.

($\alpha = 0$) is subjected to the normalized heat input f. Let $x(t,\alpha)$ denote the slab temperature at the time of initial re-entry and t_1 the time at which $x(t,0)$ reaches the melting point x_m. The diffusion equation

$$x_t(t,\alpha) = \mu x_{\alpha\alpha}(t,\alpha), \qquad x(t_0,\alpha) = x^0(\alpha)$$

and the boundary conditions

$$x_\alpha(t,0) = \frac{1}{\kappa} f(t), \qquad x_\alpha(t,b) = 0, \qquad t \in [t_0,t_1]$$

describe the slab temperature during the premelt time interval.

At time t_1 the slab surface begins to melt, and we assume that melted material is immediately removed by aerodynamic forces. If $\eta(t)$ denotes the depth of erosion of this process at time $t \geq t_1$, the slab temperature is still governed by the diffusion equation with the modified initial conditions

$$\eta(t_1) = 0, \qquad x(t_1^-,\alpha) = x(t_1^+,\alpha).$$

and boundary conditions

$$x(t,\eta(t)) = x_m,$$

$$\rho L \eta_t(t) - \kappa x_\alpha(t,\eta(t)) = f(t),$$

$$x_\alpha(t,l) = 0,$$

where κ, ρ, and L represent the thermal conductivity, the density, and the latent heat of melting of the slab, respectively.

THE SEPARATION OF VARIABLES METHOD

It is often possible to reduce a partial differential equation by a separation of variables technique to a family of equivalent ordinary differential equations. It is helpful to survey the general aspects of this technique before proceeding to the examples.

To illustrate the method, consider Eq. 1 with $f = 0$. A solution x to this equation (and auxiliary conditions) of the form

$$x(t,\alpha) = A(\alpha)T(t), \qquad (t,\alpha) \in \Delta$$

is assumed to exist when A, T are scalar valued functions of a single variable. By substituting this expression into Eq. 1 and dividing through by $x(t,\alpha)$ we obtain

$$a_{11}\left(\frac{T''}{T}\right) + 2a_{12}\left(\frac{T'}{T}\right)\left(\frac{\dot{A}}{A}\right) + a_{22}\left(\frac{\ddot{A}}{A}\right) + a_{10}\left(\frac{T'}{T}\right) + a_{01}\left(\frac{\dot{A}}{A}\right) + a_{00} = 0, \quad (5)$$

where, for example, the notation

$$\frac{T'}{T} = T^{-1}\frac{dT}{dt}, \qquad \frac{\dot{A}}{A} = A^{-1}\frac{dA}{d\alpha}$$

is used and the expressions hold for $(t,\alpha) \in \Delta$. Now if a_{11} and a_{10} are independent of α, a_{22} and a_{01} are independent of t, $a_{12} = 0$, and $a_{00}(t,\alpha) = a_{00}^1(t) + a_{00}^2(\alpha)$, Eq. 3 may be written in the form

$$a_{11}\frac{T''}{T} + a_{10}\frac{T'}{T} + a_{00}^1 = -\left(a_{22}\frac{\ddot{A}}{A} + a_{01}\frac{\dot{A}}{A} + a_{00}^2\right).$$

Because the left-hand side is independent of t and the right-hand side is independent of α, we conclude that both sides are constant. Hence for some scalar λ Eq. 5 is replaced by the two ordinary differential equations

$$a_{11}T'' + a_{10}T' + a_{00}^1 T = \lambda T, \qquad t \in \tau, \tag{6}$$

$$a_{22}\ddot{A} + a_{01}\dot{A} + a_{00}^2 A = -\lambda A \qquad \alpha \in \Omega. \tag{7}$$

If the function x is to satisfy auxiliary conditions, then T and A must inherit equivalent constraints. Without loss of generality (see Exercise 1) consider the case $f_1 = f_2 = 0$ in Eq. 2. The equivalent boundary conditions on A are

$$A(a) = A(b) = 0. \tag{8}$$

To solve the original problem we must locate those values $\{\lambda_n\}$ for which Eqs. 7 and 8 have solutions $\{A_n\}$ and associated solutions $\{T_n\}$ for Eq. 6. A linear combination $\Sigma C_n A_n T_n$ must be constructed to satisfy Eq. 1 and the system initial conditions.

This problem is considered in a moment. First, let us note that the conditions imposed on the coefficients $\{a_{ij}\}$ may be weakened in the following (not very surprising) way. If the conditions
(1)   there exists a change of variables, $\beta = \beta(t,\alpha)$, $\gamma = \gamma(t,\alpha)$ with nonvanishing Jacobian[1] on Δ such that
(2)   the resultant partial differential equation has the form

$$b_{11}x_{\beta\beta} + b_{22}x_{\gamma\gamma} + b_{10}x_\beta + b_{01}x_\gamma + b_{00}x = 0,$$

(3)   where the functions b_{11}, b_{10} are independent of γ, the functions b_{22}, b_{01} are independent of β, and $b_{00}(\beta,\gamma) = b_{00}^1(\beta) + b_{00}^2(\gamma)$ hold on Δ,

then there exist two second-order ordinary differential equations, both containing a parameter, which are equivalent to Eq. 1.

[1]This condition ensures that this change of variables is reversible.

With regard to conditions (1) and (2) it can be shown (see [B96], p. 45) that if the coefficients $\{a_{ij}\}$ are twice continuously differentiable, Eq. 1 can always be brought to one of the following canonical forms:

(1) If $a_{12}^2 - a_{11}a_{22} > 0$, the *hyperbolic* form:

$$x_{\beta\beta} - x_{\gamma\gamma} + b_{10}x_\beta + b_{01}x_\gamma + b_{00}x = 0.$$

(2) If $a_{12}^2 - a_{11}a_{22} = 0$, the *parabolic* form:

$$x_{\beta\beta} + b_{10}x_\beta + b_{01}x_\gamma + b_{00}x = 0.$$

(3) If $a_{12} - a_{11}a_{22} < 0$, the *elliptic* form:

$$x_{\beta\beta} + x_{\gamma\gamma} + b_{10}x_\beta + b_{01}x_\gamma + b_{00}x = 0.$$

When $\{a_{ij}\}$ are functions of (t,α), Eq. 1 may belong to a different class in different regions of Δ according to the value of $a_{12}^2 - a_{11}a_{22}$. On the other hand, for more than two independent variables examples of second-order partial differential equations can be constructed for which it is impossible to bring the equation to analogous canonical forms in even an arbitrarily small region. However, the general second-order equation with constant coefficients in any finite number of variables can be reduced to a canonical form (see [A90], p. 7).

These statements do not guarantee that condition (3) will be fulfilled nor are they necessarily helpful in locating the necessary change of variables. Hence the separation of variables methods is limited for practical purposes to equations that occur naturally (and with surprising regularity) in the proper form.

THE STURM-LIOUVILLE PROBLEM

A major distinction that exists between partial and ordinary differential systems is the boundary value problem posed in Eqs. 7 and 8. Because this problem arises from the separation of variables and inherits its boundary conditions from the original partial differential equation, it may take a variety of forms. To display its important aspects, it is enough (see Exercise 2) to consider the second-order differential operator

$$(Lz)(s) = \frac{d}{ds}\left[p(s)\frac{dz(s)}{ds}\right] - q(s)z(s), \qquad a \le s \le b,$$

where p, q are real-valued continuous functions on $[a,b]$ and $p(s) > 0$. A boundary value problem of the Sturm-Liouville type consists in finding nontrivial solutions to the equation

$$(Lz)(s) = \lambda\rho(s)z(s), \qquad s \in [a,b], \tag{9}$$

which satisfy the boundary conditions

$$U_1(z) = \alpha_1 z(a) + \alpha_2 \dot{z}(a) + \alpha_3 z(b) + \alpha_4 \dot{z}(b) = 0,$$
$$U_2(z) = \beta_1 z(a) + \beta_2 \dot{z}(a) + \beta_3 z(b) + \beta_4 \dot{z}(b) = 0,$$
$$\tag{10}$$

which obviously include the simpler conditions $z(a) = 0$, $z(b) = 0$. Viewing this problem as an eigenvalue problem, we find that solutions do not necessarily exist for every λ.

It can be shown (see [B28], [A44, Section 6.3], [A84, Section 9.1], and [B122]), that if the boundary conditions satisfy consistency relations, solutions to the Sturm-Liouville problem do exist and furthermore this problem may be reduced to one involving an integral operator; that is, a *Green's function* $G(t,s)$ exists such that whenever

$$z(t) = \lambda \int_a^b G(t,s)\rho(s)z(s)ds, \qquad t \in [a,b], \tag{11}$$

z also satisfies Eqs. 9 and 10. The references cited (see also Exercises 4 and 5) detail the properties of the Green's function and techniques for its construction. Important to our discussion are the facts that $G(t,s) = G(s,t)$, s, $t \in [a,b]$ and that G is uniformly continuous in both variables. Hence the linear operator $y \to z$ of Eq. 11 is self-adjoint and compact on the space $L_2(a,b)$ (see Example 2, Appendix 5).

The consequences of this last observation are quite gratifying. From Appendix 5 we have the following:

(1)   There is a denumerably infinite set of eigenvalues $\{\lambda_i\}$ whose only limit point is zero. The set $\{|\lambda_i|\}$ has a maximum.

(2)   The eigenfunctions of the operator $y \to z$ can be normalized to form a complete orthonormal basis $\{e_i\}$ for the space $L_2(a,b)$. (In the present setting $x \perp y \Rightarrow 0 = \int_a^b x(s)y(s)\rho(s)ds$.)

It is also not difficult to show that:

(3)   If $q(s) \geq 0$, $s \in [a,b]$, then $\lambda_n \geq 0$.

(4)   If f is twice continuously differentiable and satisfies $f(a) = f(b) = 0$, the series

$$f(s) = \sum_{n=1}^{\infty} f_n e_n(s), \qquad f_n = \langle f, e_n \rangle$$

converges uniformly and absolutely.

Appendix 2 discusses complete orthonormal sets in a Hilbert space. Attention is called in particular to Example 2 of that appendix. By comparison with Eq. 9 it is clear that the Hermite polynomials, the Laguerre functions, and the Legendre polynomials all arise from particular forms of the Sturm-Liouville problem. For example, if

$$q(s) = 0, \qquad p(s) = \exp\{-s^2\}, \qquad \rho(s) = \exp\{s^2\}.$$

and $a = -\infty$, $b = \infty$,

$$\lambda_n = 2n, \qquad n = 1, 2, \ldots$$

and $\{e_n\}$ are the normalized Hermite polynomials.

CONSTRUCTING THE SOLUTION

Assume now that the eigenvalues $\{\lambda_n\}$ and the orthonormal eigenfunctions $\{A_n\}$ arising from Eqs. 7 and 8 have been identified. Use of the values $\{\lambda_n\}$ in Eq. 6 produces a set of solutions $\{T_n\}$, each of which (note that the equation is second order) contains two arbitrary parameters. Each function $x_n(t,\alpha)$ $= T_n(t)A_n(\alpha)$, $n = 1, 2, \ldots$, satisfies Eq. 1 and the boundary conditions. The same statement is true of the function

$$x(t,\alpha) = \sum_{n=1}^{\infty} T_n(t)A_n(\alpha) \tag{12}$$

if it converges and can be differentiated twice term-by-term with respect to t and α.

To determine the homogeneous solution the parameters in Eq. 12 must be chosen to satisfy the initial conditions

$$x(t_0,\alpha) = \sum_{n=1}^{\infty} T_n(t_0)A_n(\alpha), = x^0(\alpha), \qquad \alpha \in [a,b], \tag{13}$$

$$x_t(t_0,\alpha) = \sum_{n=1}^{\infty} T'_n(t_0)A_n(\alpha) = x^1(\alpha), \qquad \alpha \in [a,b]. \tag{14}$$

If x^0, $x^1 \in L_2(a,b)$, the completeness of the orthonormal basis $\{A_n\}$ ensures that these functions may be expanded.

$$x^0(\alpha) = \sum_{n=1}^{\infty} C_n A_n(\alpha), \qquad C_n = \langle x^0, A_n \rangle, \tag{15}$$

$$x^1(\alpha) = \sum_{n=1}^{\infty} c_n A_n(\alpha), \qquad c_n = \langle x^1, A_n \rangle; \tag{16}$$

hence by equating series the arbitrary parameters in Eq. 12 can be determined.

One important factor has been passed over and that is the convergence and the term-by-term differentiability of the series in Eq. 12. Here problems can arise, for example, because the series in Eqs. 13 and 14 converge in L_2, whereas the function in Eq. 12 should be twice differentiable in both variables. It can be shown, however (see [A84], Section 9.7), that if a solution x exists which is continuous on Δ and satisfies the boundary and initial conditions, x *can* be expanded as in Eq. 12. In other words, whenever physical reasoning can establish the existence of a solution, formal series manipulations can be used to arrive at the correct result, although the steps may be mathematically unsound.

Once the solution to the homogeneous problem has been determined, the formal method of solving the nonhomogeneous equation is quite straightforward. If the forcing function f is defined (measurable) on Δ and

$$\int_a^b \int_{t_0}^{t_f} |f(t,\alpha)|^2 \, dt \, d\alpha < \infty,$$

the series expansion

$$f(t,\alpha) = \sum_{n=1}^{\infty} u_n(t) A_n(\alpha), \qquad u_n(t) = \langle f(t,\cdot), A_n \rangle, \qquad n = 0, 1, \ldots \quad (17)$$

holds on Δ (see Example 3, Appendix 2). Retracing our steps in the separation of variables process we come to the conclusion that the scalars $\{\lambda_n\}$ and the orthonormal basis $\{A_n\}$ are defined as before. The functions $\{T_n\}$, however, must now satisfy

$$a_{11}(t)T_n''(t) + a_{10}(t)T_n'(t) + (a_{00}^1(t) - \lambda_n)T_n(t) = u_n(t),$$

$$t \in [t_0, t_f], \qquad n = 1, 2, \ldots, \quad (18)$$

together with initial conditions $(T_n(t_0), T_n'(t_0))$ determined as before from a comparison of Eqs. 13 and 14 with Eqs. 15 and 16. Again it can be shown that whenever the original problem has a well-defined solution these formal methods will produce the right result.

It is instructive to organize these results in the following manner. Let A denote the infinite matrix with nonzero entries only in diagonal 2×2 blocks in the form[1]

$$[A]_{nn} = \begin{bmatrix} 0 & 1 \\ -(a_{00}^1(t) - \lambda_n) & -a_{10}(t) \end{bmatrix}, \qquad n = 1, 2, \ldots, \quad t \in [t_0, t_f]$$

and let u be the infinite tuplet $u = (0, u_1, 0, u_2, \ldots, 0, u_n, 0, \ldots)$. Then the entire family of Eq. 18 may be identified with the infinite tuplet z which satisfies

$$\dot{z}(t) = A(t)z(t) + u(t), \qquad z(t_0) = z^0, \qquad t \in [t_0, t_f], \quad (19)$$

where

$$z_{2n-1}(t_0) = T_n(t_0), \qquad z_{2n}(t_0) = T_n'(t_0), \qquad n = 1, 2, \ldots.$$

---

[1]Since the case in which a_{11} of Eq. 18 vanishes must be treated separately, we have, without loss of generality, set $a_{11} = 1$ in forming this matrix.

If Φ denotes the infinite matrix satisfying

$$\dot{\Phi}(t,t_0) = A(t)\Phi(t,t_0), \qquad \Phi(t_0,t_0) = I,$$

the solution of Eq. 19 may be formally written as

$$z(t) = \Phi(t,t_0)z(t_0) + \int_{t_0}^{t} \Phi(t,s)u(s)ds, \qquad t \in [t_0,t_f]. \tag{20}$$

Finally, if ω is the infinite tuplet defined by

$$\omega(\alpha) = (A_1(\alpha), 0, A_2(\alpha), 0, \ldots, 0, A_n(\alpha), 0, \ldots), \qquad \alpha \in [a,b], \tag{21}$$

the solution x to the nonhomogeneous equation can be written as

$$x(t,\alpha) = [\omega(\alpha),z(t)] = \sum_{n=1}^{\infty} \omega_n(\alpha),z_n(t), \qquad (t,\alpha) \in \Delta.$$

Example 3. To illustrate these remarks in a concrete setting, let us consider in some detail the nonhomogeneous diffusion equation and the constraint conditions

(a) $\quad x_t(t,\alpha) = k^2 x_{\alpha\alpha}(t,\alpha) + f(t,\alpha), \qquad t > t_0, \qquad \alpha \in (0,b),$
(b) $\quad x(t,0) = x(t,b) = 0, \qquad\qquad\quad t > t_0,$
(c) $\quad x(0,\alpha) = x^0(\alpha), \qquad\qquad\qquad\quad \alpha \in (0,b).$ $\qquad\qquad$ (22)

In this case Eqs. 6 and 7 take the form

$$A''(\alpha) + \lambda A(\alpha) = 0, \qquad \alpha \in (0,b), \tag{23}$$

$$\dot{T}(t) + k^2\lambda T(t) = 0, \qquad t > t_0, \tag{24}$$

whereas the boundary conditions are simply $A(0) = A(b) = 0$.

For the determination of A we must solve the eigenvalue problem

$$A''(\alpha) + \lambda A(\alpha) = 0, \qquad A(0) = A(b) = 0. \tag{25}$$

It is easily shown that only for the values

$$\lambda_n = \left(\frac{n\pi}{b}\right)^2, \qquad n = 1, 2, \ldots, \tag{26}$$

do nontrivial solutions to Eq. 25 exist, these solutions being proportional to the functions

$$A_n(\alpha) = \sqrt{\frac{2}{b}} \sin(\lambda_n^{1/2}\alpha), \qquad n = 1, 2, \ldots, \qquad \alpha \in [0, b], \tag{27}$$

which constitute an orthonormal basis for $L_2(0,b)$. Similarly, the functions

T_n which satisfy Eq. 24 for these scalars are evidently proportional to the functions

$$T_n(t) = \exp\{-k^2\lambda_n t\}, \qquad n = 1, 2, \ldots.$$

Thus any scalar multiple of the functions

$$x_n(t,\alpha) = T_n(t)A_n(\alpha), \qquad n = 1, 2, \ldots, \qquad (t, \alpha) \in \Delta, \tag{28}$$

satisfies the homogeneous form of Eq. 22 and the boundary conditions.

To complete the solution of the homogeneous form of Eq. 22 we formally construct the function

$$x(t,\alpha) = \sum_{n=1}^{\infty} C_n x_n(t,a), \qquad (t,\alpha) \in \Delta, \tag{29}$$

which automatically satisfies the boundary conditions for all scalars $\{C_n\}$. If the initial conditions are to be satisfied, we must have

$$x^0(\alpha) = \sum_{n=1}^{\infty} C_n A_n(\alpha);$$

that is, the C_n are the Fourier coefficients of the function x^0 expanded along the orthonormal basis $\{A_n\}$ for $L_2(0,b)$:

$$C_n = \langle x^0, A_n \rangle = \sqrt{\frac{2}{b}} \int_0^b x^0(\alpha) \sin(\lambda_n^{1/2}\alpha)d\alpha, \qquad n = 1, 2, \ldots. \tag{30}$$

The formal solution which we have constructed in Eqs. 29 and 30 thus satisfies the boundary and initial conditions on the homogeneous equation. It remains to show that this infinite summation converges to a function that is smooth enough to have one partial derivative in t and two partial derivatives in α on the interior of Δ and is a continuous function at the boundary. In the present example it is well known (see [A90], p. 173) that if $x^0(0) = x^0(b) = 0$ and x^0 is sectionally continuous our series fulfills all these requirements and is the bona fide free response of Eq. 22.

To determine the system-forced response the scalar functions $\{u_n\}$ are first computed by the formula

$$u_n(t) = \langle f(t, \cdot), A_n \rangle = \sqrt{\left(\frac{2}{b}\right)} \int_0^b f(t,\alpha) \sin(\lambda_n^{1/2}\alpha)d\alpha, \qquad t \geq t_0 \tag{31}$$

and then used to define the infinite system

$$\dot{T}_n(t) = -(\lambda_n k)^2 T_n(t) + u_n(t), \qquad n = 1, 2, \ldots, \qquad t \geq t_0$$

$$T_n(t_0) = C_n = \langle x^0, A_n \rangle, \qquad n = 1, 2, \ldots.$$

The infinite diagonal matrix A is evidently

$$A = \text{diag}\,[-k^2\lambda_1, \ldots, -k^2\lambda_n, -\ldots],$$

hence the infinite system transition matrix Φ has the form

$$\Phi(t,s) = \text{diag}\,\{\exp\,[-k^2\lambda_1(t-s)], \ldots, \exp\,[-k^2\lambda_n(t-s)], \ldots\},$$

$$t, s \geq t_0. \quad (32)$$

Letting z, z^0, ω, and u be the infinite tuplets, we obtain

$$z(t) = (T_1(t), T_2(t), \ldots, T_n(t), \ldots), \qquad t \geq t_0,$$

$$z^0 = (C_1, C_2, \ldots, C_n, \ldots),$$

$$\omega(\alpha) = (A_1(\alpha), A_2(\alpha), \ldots, A_n(\alpha), \ldots), \qquad \alpha \in [0,b], \quad (33)$$

$$u(t) = (u_1(t), u_2(t), \ldots, u_n(t), \ldots), \qquad t \geq t_0,$$

respectively. The total system response is governed by the equations

$$z(t) = \Phi(t,t_0)z^0 + \int_{t_0}^{t} \Phi(t,s)u(s)ds, \qquad t \geq t_0,$$

$$x(t,\alpha) = [\omega(\alpha),z(t)] = \sum_{n=1}^{\infty} \omega_n(\alpha)z_n(t), \qquad (t,\alpha) \in \Delta. \quad (34)$$

Recall the vector-valued function space $\mathbf{L}_p(X;\tau)$ of Section 4.2. Here X is taken as an l_p, $1 \leq p \leq \infty$, space. Then Φ may be interpreted as the linear transformation which sends $l_p \to \mathbf{L}_p(l_p;\tau)$ according to the rule

$$(\Phi z^0)(t) = \Phi(t,t_0)z^0, \qquad z^0 \in l_p, \qquad t \in \tau.$$

Similarly, Φ_k denotes the linear transformation $l_p \to l_{p'}$ defined by

$$\tilde{\Phi}_k z^0 = \tilde{\Phi}(t_k,t_0)z^0, \qquad z^0 \in l_{p'}. \quad (35)$$

By using Eq. 32 we have no difficulty in showing that each of these transformations is bounded.

The forced response may be identified with the linear transformation $\tilde{F}$ defined between $\mathbf{L}_p(l_p,\tau)$ spaces by the equation

$$(\tilde{F}u)(t) = \int_{t_0}^{t} \Phi(t,s)u(s)ds, \qquad t_0,t \in \tau$$

or when t is fixed as the linear map $\tilde{F}_k$ with the same domain but range l_p

and defined by

$$\tilde{F}_k u = \int_{t_0}^{t_k} \Phi(t_k,s)u(s)ds. \tag{36}$$

The transformations $\tilde{F}$, $\tilde{F}_k$ are bounded.

With the aid of Figure A9.3 we may rapidly summarize our results. The

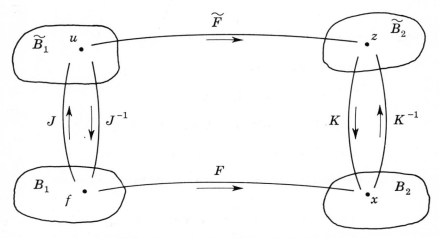

Figure A9.3   A conceptual model for distributive systems.

forced response of the physical distributive system is shown as a linear mapping $x = Fu$ between the multivariable function spaces B_1 and B_2. By means of Eq. 17 the linear transformation $Jf = u$, defined on B_1 and with values in $\tilde{B}_1$ (an infinite-dimensional vector-valued function space), is established. Equation 19 defines the linear transformation $z = \tilde{F}u$ which sends $\tilde{B}_1$ into a second infinite-dimensional vector-valued function space $\tilde{B}_2$. Equation 21 defines the transformation $Kz = x$ from $\tilde{B}_2$ into B_2.

It is clear from the development that $F = K\tilde{F}J$, and when K, J are invertible $\tilde{F} = K^{-1}FJ^{-1}$ holds as well. Thus a natural flexibility exists in the choice of mathematical models for the system. We have not introduced norms into the discussion, but it should be apparent, for instance, that the minimum norm problems of Chapter 4 can be posed without difficulty in the present setting.

OPTIMAL CONTROL PROBLEMS FOR DISTRIBUTIVE SYSTEMS

Returning our attention now to Chapter 4, we note that the results of this chapter hold for transformations with infinite-dimensional ranges. From the concluding remarks of the preceding section it is clearly possible that the techniques of Chapter 4 can be applied to problems of optimal control for distributive systems. Indeed, the generality of these techniques leaves only the task of working out the mechanics of solution for specific examples.

To take advantage of the concrete results derived in Example 3 we shall consider problems of optimal control for the diffusion system. Several of the references cited have considered related problems. The reader will also find the thesis of Fahmy [B32] a useful source of other results.

Consider the system of Eq. 22 with the following modifications. Forcing functions $\{h_1, h_2\}$ may occur on the boundary on the system; that is, the boundary conditions become

$$x(t,0) = h_1(t), \qquad x(t,b) = h_2(t), \qquad t \in (t_0, t_k).$$

Furthermore, the forces on the interior of Δ may now consist of two kinds; the usual distributive force defined on all of Δ and a finite number of forces $\{g_1, \ldots, g_m\}$ concentrated at the fixed spatial positions $\{\alpha_i : 0 < \alpha_1 < \cdots < \alpha_m < b\}$, respectively. In mathematical terms, the force f of Eq. 22 should be replaced by a function of the form

$$f(t,\alpha) + \sum_{i=1}^{m} \delta(\alpha - \alpha_i) g_i(t), \qquad (t,\alpha) \in \Delta.$$

The functions $\{f, h_1, h_2, g_1, \ldots, g_m\}$, taken in various combinations as manipulable controls and/or external disturbances, generate a wealth of concrete control problems. If suitable Banach spaces B_f, B_g, B_h, and B_x are defined for the functions f, $g = (g_1, \ldots, g_m)$, $h = (h_1 h_2)$, and x, we find from the linearity Eq. 22 that each of the minimum norm problems of Chapter 4 can be meaningfully formulated. Because the mechanics of solution are analogous to the finite-dimensional cases treated earlier, it should suffice to concentrate attention on the simplest case, namely minimum-energy problems.

The linearity of the diffusion equation sometimes allows complex optimization problems to be solved in simple stages. The simplest fundamental problem is that in which only the distributive force f is present (i.e., $g = 0$, $h = 0$). To take advantage of the notation used in Figure A9.3, let us introduce the Hilbert space H_1 of all functions, measurable on Δ, and finite with respect to the norm induced by the inner product

$$\langle x, y \rangle = \int_{t_0}^{t_k} \int_0^b x(t,\alpha) y(t,\alpha) \, dt \, d\alpha, \qquad x, y \in H_1.$$

Since the functions $\{A_n\}$ constitute a complete orthonormal basis in $L_2(0,b)$, Parseval's identity shows that for (almost every) $t \in [t_0, t_k]$ the set $\{u_n\}$ of Eq. 31 satisfies

$$\sum_{n=1}^{\infty} |u_n(t)|^2 = \left(\frac{2}{b}\right) \int_0^b |f(t,\alpha)|^2 \, d\alpha, \qquad t \in [t_0, t_k].$$

Hence by taking $\hat{H}_1$ as $\mathbf{L}_2(l_2;[t_0,t_k])$ this equality implies, for the $u \in \hat{H}_1$ of Eq. 33, that

$$\|u\|_{\hat{H}_1} = \|f\|_{H_1}.$$

In other words, the mapping of J of Figure A.93 preserves norms (i.e., it is a linear isometry).

This observation implies that we may reformulate our problem in terms of the transformation $\tilde{F}$. To do this the tuplet x^k is defined by the expression

$$z^k = (z_1^k, \ldots, z_n^k, \ldots), \qquad z_n^k = \langle z^k, A_n \rangle, \qquad n = 1, 2, \ldots.$$

The tuplet $\xi = l_2$ is then defined (see Eq. 35) by the equation

$$\xi = z^k - \Phi(t_k, t_0) z^0.$$

(Observe that ξ_i, the ith component of ξ, is given by $\xi_1 = z_i^k - \exp[-k\lambda_i (t_k - t_0)] z_i^0$, $i = 1, 2, \ldots$.) In terms of these definitions the problem posed is entirely equivalent to the problem of finding the minimum norm preimage u_ξ of $\xi \in \hat{H}_2 = l_2$ under $\tilde{F}_k$ of Eq. 36. The optimal control f can then be computed by the rule $f = J^{-1} u_\xi$.

The problem posed has evidently been reduced to determining the pseudo-inverse for $\tilde{F}_k$. This we can readily do. First we note that $\tilde{F}_k^*: l_2 \to \mathbf{L}_2(l_2;\tau)$ is the transformation defined by

$$(\tilde{F}_k^* x)(t) = \Phi^*(t_0, t) x, \qquad x \in l_2, \, t \in [t_0, t_k];$$

hence operator $\tilde{F}_k \tilde{F}_k^*$ on l_2 is the infinite matrix

$$\tilde{F}_k \tilde{F}_k^* = \int_{t_0}^{t_k} \Phi(t_k, s) \Phi^*(t_k, s) ds, \tag{37}$$

which in the present case is diagonal: $\tilde{F}_k \tilde{F}_k^* = \text{diag}[\gamma_1, \gamma_2, \ldots, \gamma_n, \ldots]$ with nonzero elements

$$\gamma_j = \int_{t_0}^{t_k} \exp[-2k^2 \lambda_j (t_k - s)] ds = \{1 - \exp[-2k^2 \lambda_j (t_k - t_0)]\} / 2k^2 \lambda_j,$$

$$j = 1, 2, \ldots. \tag{38}$$

$\tilde{F}_k^\dagger$ can (in the Hilbert space case) be determined from the polar form of $\tilde{F}_k$ which we now compute. Let $\{e_i\}$ denote the usual coordinate basis for l_2, $\mu_i = [\gamma_i]^{1/2}$, $i = 1, 2, \ldots$, scalars and $\{g_i\}$, the orthonormal vectors of $\mathbf{L}_2(l_2;\tau)$, defined

$$g_i(t) = \mu_i^{-1} \exp[-k^2 \lambda_i (t_k - t)] e_i, \qquad t \in [t_0, t_k], \qquad i = 1, 2, \ldots.$$

The polar form of $\tilde{F}_k$ is given by

$$\tilde{F}_k = \sum_{i=1} e_i > \mu_i < g_i.$$

REMARK 1. Observe that $\tilde{F}_k$ is compact. By combining Eqs. 26 and 38 we see that for large n,

$$\mu_n \simeq b/\sqrt{2\pi kn}.$$

Hence not only is the spectrum of $(\tilde{F}_k\tilde{F}_k^*)^{1/2}$ discrete but it has zero as a limit point. As a consequence, the system is *not* controllable in the sense that every bounded range element has a bounded preimage under $\tilde{F}$. In other words, $\tilde{F}_k^{\dagger}$ *cannot* be written as a *bounded* transformation. We can, of course, write $\tilde{F}_k^{\dagger}$ as an unbounded transformation and determine those elements $\xi \in l_2$ for which $\|\tilde{F}_k^{\dagger}\xi\|$ is finite.[1]

It is evident that the expression

$$\tilde{F}_k^{\dagger} = \sum_{i=1}^{\infty} g_i > \mu_i^{-1} < e_i$$

is the desired transformation. Our earlier observation on the scalars $\{\mu_j\}$ now shows that $\mu_j^{-1} \to \infty$ as $j \to \infty$, which exhibits the unboundedness of $\tilde{F}_k^{\dagger}$. It is clear that $\xi = (\xi_1, \xi_2, \ldots) \in l_2$ will have a finite preimage in $\mathbf{L}_2(l_2;\tau)$ under $\tilde{F}_k$ if and only if

$$\sum_{i=1}^{\infty} |\mu_i^{-1}\xi_i|^2 < \infty.$$

REMARK 2. Consider now the diffusion system with h_1, $h_2 = 0$ and the system control function of the form

$$f(t,\alpha) = \sum_{i=1}^{m} \delta(\alpha - \alpha_i)g_i(t), \qquad (t,\alpha) \in \Delta.$$

From the physical standpoint the input f has been spatially constrained to act only at the points $\{\alpha_i\}$. This physical constraint (see Fahmy [B32]) affects the system mathematical model only by the addition of the (loosely speaking $\infty \times m$) input constraint matrix

$$B = \begin{bmatrix} b_{11} & \cdots & b_{im} \\ \vdots & & \vdots \\ b_{n1} & \cdots & b_{nm} \\ \vdots & & \vdots \end{bmatrix},$$

---

[1]For a more careful discussion of Hilbert space pseudoinverses of transformation, which are not *onto*, the reader is referred to F. J. Beutler, "The Operator Theory of the Pseudo Inverse," *Journal of Mathematical Analysis and Applications* **10**, 450–470 (1965), and G. F. Votruba, "On Generalized Inverses and Sinular Equations in Functional Analysis," Doctoral Dissertation, University of Michigan, Ann Arbor, 1964.

where

$$b_{nj} = \sqrt{\frac{2}{b}} \sin\left(\frac{n\pi\alpha_j}{b}\right), \qquad j = 1, \ldots, m, \qquad n = 1, 2, \ldots.$$

Equation 34 becomes

$$z(t) = \Phi(t,t_0)z^0 + \int_{t_0}^{t} \Phi(t,s)Bg(s)ds, \qquad t \geq t_0, \tag{39}$$

where $g = (g_1, \ldots, g_m)$ and Φ is defined in Eq. 32.

It is clear that the forced response of Eq. 39 with $t = t_k$ defines a linear mapping $T: [L_2(t_0,t_k)]^m \to l_2$. The adjoint mapping T^* has the form

$$(T^*\lambda)(t) = B^*\Phi^*(t_k,t)\lambda, \qquad t \in [t_0,t_k], \qquad \lambda \in l_2,$$

and it can be shown that TT^* is an infinite nondiagonal matrix with typical element

$$(TT^*)_{ij} = \left(\frac{2}{k\pi}\right)^2 \frac{1 - \exp[-(i^2 + j^2)(k\pi/b)^2(t_k - t_0)]}{i^2 + j^2} \sum_{l=1}^{m} \sin\left(\frac{i\pi\alpha_l}{b}\right) \sin\left(\frac{j\pi\alpha_l}{b}\right).$$

Again TT^* is compact, and inversion is complicated not only by the presence of nondiagonal terms but by the considerations pointed out in Remark 1. On its range, however, $T^\dagger$ may as usual be written

$$T^\dagger = T^*(TT^*)^{-1}.$$

R E M A R K 3 . To complete our survey of the methods for control of the diffusion system we now consider control from the boundary. Here the functions $f, g_1, \ldots, g_m$ are all identically zero and the system of Example 3 must be controlled by choice of the boundary functions

$$x(t,0) = h_1(t), \qquad x(t,b) = h_2(t), \qquad t \in (t_0,t_k).$$

As before, we seek a solution x of the form

$$x(t,\alpha) = \sum_{n=1}^{\infty} T_n(t)A_n(\alpha),$$

where the set $\{A_n\}$ is defined in Eq. 27. By integrating the expression

$$T_n(t) = \sqrt{\frac{2}{b}} \int_{0}^{b} x(t,\alpha)A_n(\alpha)d\alpha$$

twice by parts we can obtain the formal results

$$\dot{T}_n(t) = -\left(\frac{n\pi k}{b}\right)^2 T_n(t) + \frac{2n\pi k^2}{b^2} [h_1(t) - (-1)^n h_2(t)],$$

$$n = 1, 2, \ldots, \qquad t \in [t_0,t_k].$$

Let the tuplet z and the matrix Φ be defined as before. In terms of the matrices N,M defined, respectively, by

$$\underset{(\infty \times 2)}{N} = \begin{bmatrix} 1 & 1 \\ 1 & -1 \\ 1 & 1 \\ 1 & -1 \\ \cdot & \cdot \\ \cdot & \cdot \\ \cdot & \cdot \end{bmatrix}$$

and

$$M = \text{diag}\left[\frac{2\pi k^2}{b^2}, \dots, \frac{2n\pi k^2}{b^2}, \dots\right],$$

the forced response, at time t_f, may be identified with the linear transformation $G: [L_2(t_0,t_k)]^2 \rightarrow l_2$ defined by the expression

$$Gu = \int_{t_0}^{t_k} \Phi(t_k,s)MNu(s)ds, \qquad u \in [L_2(t_0,t_k)]^2.$$

The transformation G^* takes the obvious form and operator GG^* on l_2 is well defined, having as a typical element

$$(GG^*)_{mn} = \begin{cases} 0, & m+n \text{ odd}, \\ \dfrac{4mnk^2}{(m^2+n^2)b^2}\{1 - \exp[-(m^2+n^2)\left(\dfrac{\pi k}{b}\right)^2(t_k - t_0)]\}, & m+n \text{ even}. \end{cases}$$

Hence it is clear that the minimum energy transfer problem $x^0(\alpha) \rightarrow x^f(\alpha)$ may be formulated and studied within the usual framework.

With these remarks and the following exercises we conclude our discussion of distributive systems. In addition to the references already cited the reader may be interested in the following articles: [B12], [B21], [B22], [B23], [B30], [B31], [B42], [B71], [B76], [B78], [B79], [B115], [B117], [B118], [B119], and [B120].

Exercises

1. Assume that the boundary conditions for Eq. 5 take the form

$$x(t,0) = \mu_1(t), \qquad x(t,l) = \mu_2(t), \qquad t \in \tau,$$

where μ_1, μ_2 have the first derivative μ_1', μ_2', respectively. Define the function γ by the expression $\gamma(t,\alpha) = \mu_1(t) + (\alpha/l)[\mu_2(t) - \mu_1(t)]$, $(t,\alpha) \in \Delta$. Show that the substitution $x(t,\alpha) = y(t,\alpha) + \gamma(t,\alpha)$ reduces the present problem of nonhomogeneous boundary conditions to the preceding case with a change in the forcing function.

2. Let a_{11} be a nonvanishing function on $[a,b]$. Show that the differential equation

$$a_{11}y'' + a_{10}y' + a_{00}y = -\lambda y$$

can be written in the form

$$[py']' + qy = -\lambda ry.$$

HINT:

$$p(t) = \exp\left[\int_a^t a_{10}(s)/a_{11}(s)ds\right], \quad r(t) = p(t)/a_{11}(t), \quad q(t) = r(t)a_{00}(t).$$

3. Show that the differential operator L of Eq. 9 is formally self-adjoint (see Eq. 36, Appendix 4) and strictly self-adjoint on the interval $[a,b]$ if every x,y in the domain of L satisfy the boundary conditions $\{p(t)[x'(t)y(t) - x(t)y'(t)]\}_a^b = 0$.

In the next three exercises we refer directly to the Sturm-Liouville problem posed in Eqs. 9 and 10 of this appendix.

4. Let x,y be nontrivial functions in the null space of L satisfying $U_1[x(a)] = 0$, $U_2[y(b)] = 0$, respectively. Verify that the function $A = p[xy' - x'y]$ is constant on $[a,b]$. HINT: Observe that $x(py')' - y(ps')' = [p(xy' - yx')]' = 0$.

5. Assume the A of Exercise 4 is nonzero and define the function G by the expression

$$G(t,x) = \begin{cases} \dfrac{-x(t)y(s)}{A}, & t < s, \\[2ex] \dfrac{-x(s)y(t)}{A}, & s < t. \end{cases}$$

Show the following:
(a) G satisfies the boundary conditions at $t = a$, $t = b$.
(b) G is continuous at $t = s$.
(c) G_t has a discontinuity of magnitude $-1/p(s)$ at $t = s$; that is, $G_t(s^+,s) - G_t(s^-,s) = -1/p(s)$.
(d) $LG = 0$ on both intervals $[a,s]$ and $(s,b]$.
(e) If $y(t) = \int_a^b G(t,s)h(s)ds$, then $Ly = h$ and y satisfies the boundary conditions at $t = a$, $t = b$.

6. Consider the homogeneous heat diffusion equation

$$x_t(t,\alpha,\beta) = x_{\alpha\alpha}(t,\alpha,\beta) + x_{\beta\beta}(t,\alpha,\beta), \qquad (t,\alpha,\beta) \in \Delta$$

defined on the square $\Delta = \{(t,\alpha,\beta): t \geq t_0, 0 < \alpha < a, 0 < \beta < b\}$ and accompanied by the boundary conditions $x(t,0,\beta) = x(t,a,\beta) = x(t,\alpha,0) = x(t,\alpha,b) = 0$. Show that for scalars $[\lambda_{m,n} = (n\pi/a)^2 + (m\pi/b)^2: m, n = 1, 2, ...]$. The system can be separated. Using Example 3 of Appendix 2 and this appendix as models, develop the free and forced response equations for this system.

7. Show that the forced response of the system of Remark 3 can be written

$$x(t,\alpha) = \int_{t_0}^{t} G_1(t - s,\alpha)h_1(s)ds + \int_{t_0}^{t} G_2(t - s,\alpha)h_2(s)ds,$$

where $G_1(t - s,\alpha) = G_2(t - s, b - \alpha)$ and

$$G_2(t - s,\alpha) = \sum_{n=1}^{\infty} 2\pi n(-1)^{n+1} \sin\left(\frac{n\pi\alpha}{b}\right) \exp\left[-\left(\frac{n\pi k}{b}\right)^2 (t - s)\right].$$

8. Show that the forced response of the system described in Remark 2 can be written in the form

$$x(t,\alpha) = \sum_{p=1}^{m} \int_{t_0}^{t} W(\alpha,\alpha_p,t,s)f_p(s)ds,$$

where

$$W(\alpha,\alpha_p,t,s) = \sum_{n=1}^{\infty} \exp\left[-\left(\frac{n\pi k}{b}\right)^2 (t - s)\right] \sin\left(\frac{n\pi\alpha}{b}\right) \sin\left(\frac{n\pi\alpha_p}{b}\right).$$

9. Consider the diffusion system with all controls $f, g = (g_1, ..., g_m)$ and $h = (h_1,h_2)$ present simultaneously. Show that if the controls (f,g,h) carry out a transfer $x^0(\alpha) \to x^k(\alpha)$ with minimum norm then

$$f = \tilde{F}_k^* E^{-1}\xi, \qquad g = T^* E^{-1}\xi, \qquad h = G^* E^{-1}\xi,$$

where $\xi = z(t_k) - \Phi(t_k,t_0)z(t_0)$ and $E = \tilde{F}_k\tilde{F}_k^* + TT^* + GG^*$.

10. (See Fahmy [B32].) Consider the system defined by

$$\frac{\partial x(t,\alpha)}{\partial t} = k^2 \frac{\partial^2 x(t,\alpha)}{\partial \alpha^2}, \qquad (t,\alpha) \in \Delta$$

with the auxiliary condition

$$x(t_0,\alpha) = 0, \qquad\qquad\qquad \alpha \in \overline{\Omega} = [0,b],$$

$$\frac{\partial x(t,0)}{\partial \alpha} = \gamma^2[x(t,0) - v(t)], \qquad t \in [t_0,t_1],$$

$$\frac{\partial x(t,b)}{\partial \alpha} = 0, \qquad\qquad\qquad t \in [t_0,t_1].$$

Here γ^2 is a constant and the time dependent function $v(t)$ is related to the control input $u(t)$ by the first-order ordinary differential equation

$$\frac{dv(t)}{dt} - \sigma^2 v(t) = u(t), \qquad t \in [t_0,t_1],$$

where σ^2 is a constant. Physically, this mathematical model represents the process of one-sided heating of metal. Show that the eigenfunctions associated with this problem are given by

$$S_n(\alpha) = \cos\left\{\beta_n\left(1 - \frac{\alpha}{b}\right)\right\}, \qquad \alpha \in [0,b], \qquad n = 1, 2, \ldots,$$

and that the state of the system, x, is given by

$$x(t,\alpha) = \int_{t_0}^{t} K(t - s,\alpha)u(s)ds,$$

where the kernel $K(\tau,\alpha)$ has the form

$$K(\tau,\alpha) = \sum_{n=1}^{\infty} [C_n \exp\{-\sigma\tau\} + D_n \exp\{-(k\beta_n/b)^2\tau\}]S_n(\alpha)$$

with C_n and D_n being well-defined scalars. From this show that the state of the system can be put in the form

$$x(t,\alpha) = \sum_{n=1}^{\infty} R_n(t)S_n(\alpha),$$

and apply the above technique to solve the minimum energy problem.

11. (See Fahmy [B32].) Consider the performance index given by

$$J(f) = \frac{1}{2}\int_{t_0}^{t_1}\int_{0}^{b} \overline{P}(t,\alpha)|f(t,\alpha)|^2 d\alpha dt,$$

where $\overline{P}(t,\alpha)$ is a bounded strictly positive measurable function. Show that the Fourier expansion of $\overline{P}(t,\alpha)f(t,\alpha)$ with respect to the orthonormal complete system $\{\phi_n = \sqrt{2/b} \sin(n\pi/b)\alpha\}$ on $[0,b]$ is given by

$$\bar{P}(t,\alpha)f(t,\alpha) = \sum_{n=1}^{\infty} d_n(t)\phi_n(\alpha), \qquad (t,\alpha) \in [t_0,t_1] \times [0,b],$$

where

$$d_n(t) = (1/\sqrt{2b}) \sum_{m=1}^{\infty} \{u_m(t)(C_{m-n}(t) - C_{m+n}(t))\}, \qquad n = 1, 2, \ldots,$$

$$u_n(t) = \sqrt{2/b} \int_0^b f(t,\alpha) \sin(n\pi/b)\alpha d\alpha, \qquad n = 1, 2, \ldots,$$

$$C_n(t) = \sqrt{2/b} \int_0^b \bar{P}(t,\alpha) \cos(n\pi/b)\alpha d\alpha, \qquad n = 0, 1, 2, \ldots,$$

and

$$C_{-n}(t) = C_n(t), \qquad n = 1, 2, \ldots,$$

for all $t \in [t_0,t_1]$. Using Parseval's theorem show that the above performance index has the equivalent form

$$J(f) = J(u) = \frac{1}{2} \int_{t_0}^{t_1} [u(s),P(s)u(s)]ds,$$

where P is the infinite symmetric matrix whose (m,n)th entry is given by

$$[P]_{mn}(t) = (1/\sqrt{2b})(C_{m-n}(t) - C_{m+n}(t)), \qquad t \in [t_0,t_1].$$

12. (See Fahmy [B32].) Consider the diffusion system of Eq. (22) with zero initial conditions (i.e., $x^0(\alpha) = 0$). Let the performance index be given by

$$J(f) = \frac{1}{2} \int_{t_0}^{t_1} \int_0^b \bar{P}(t,\alpha)|f(t,\alpha)|^2 d\alpha dt + \frac{1}{2} \int_{t_0}^{t_1} \int_0^b \bar{Q}(t,\alpha)|x_f(t,\alpha)|^2 d\alpha dt,$$

where $\bar{P}$ and $\bar{Q}$ are bounded strictly positive measurable functions and x_f is the system response under the control input f. Let $y(t)$ be defined as

$$y(t) = P(t)u^*(t),$$

where $P(t)$ is as in Exercise 11 and $u^*(t)$ is the optimal control element $u^*(t) = (u_1^*(t), \ldots, u_n^*(t), \ldots)$; then $y(t)$ satisfies the matrix second-order ordinary differential equation

$$\ddot{y}(t) = [-A^* + \dot{Q}(t)Q^{-1}(t) + Q(t)AQ^{-1}(t)]\dot{y}(t)$$
$$+ [\dot{Q}(t)Q^{-1}(t)A^* + Q(t)AQ^{-1}A^* + Q(t)P^{-1}(t)]y(t),$$

where the infinite matrix $Q(t)$ is related to $\bar{Q}(t,\alpha)$ in the same way as $P(t)$ is related to $\bar{P}(t,\alpha)$ and the matrix A is that of Eq. 19. Show that if $P = Q = $ Identity, the nth component of the optimal control vector is given by

$$u_n^*(t) = [[t_1 - t_0]^{-1} \exp \{(nk\pi/b)^2(t_1 - t_0)\}$$
$$+ [2(nk\pi/b)^2]^{-1} \exp \{-(nk\pi/b)^2(t_1 - t)\}]\xi_n,$$

for all $t \in [t_0,t_1]$ and sufficiently large n. Here, ξ_n is the nth Fourier coefficient of the terminal state $x^1(\alpha)$ with respect to the system $\{\phi_n(\alpha) = \sqrt{2/b} \sin (n\pi/b)\alpha\}$.

13. (See Fahmy [B32].) Let $P = Q = $ Identity in the above problem. Show that the optimal control input function $f^*(t,\alpha)$ satisfies the backward diffusion equation

$$\frac{\partial f(t,\alpha)}{\partial t} = -k^2 \frac{\partial^2 f(t,\alpha)}{\partial \alpha^2} + x(t,\alpha), \qquad (t,\alpha) \in \Delta.$$

By differentiating this equation twice and substituting Eq. 22(a) in the resulting equation, show that $f^*(t,\alpha)$ satisfies the fourth-order partial differential equation

$$k^4 \frac{\partial^4 f(t,\alpha)}{\partial \alpha^4} - \frac{\partial^2 f(t,\alpha)}{\partial t^2} + f(t,\alpha) = 0, \qquad (t,\alpha) \in \Delta.$$

REFERENCES

LIST A: TEXTS

1. A. C. Aitken, *Determinants and Matrices*, Oliver and Boyd, Edinburgh, and Interscience, New York, 1956.
2. N. I. Akhiezer and I. M. Glazman, *Theory of Linear Operators in Hilbert Space*, Vols. I and II, Frederick Ungar, New York, 1961.
3. N. I. Akhiezer and M. Krein, *Some Questions in the Theory of Moments*, American Mathematical Society, Providence, R.I., 1962.
4. K. W. Anderson and D. W. Hall, *Sets, Sequences, and Mappings: The Basic Concepts of Analysis*, Wiley, New York, 1963.
5. *Nonlinear Integral Equations*, P. M. Anselone, Ed., University of Wisconsin Press, Madison, 1964.
6. B. H. Arnold, *Intuitive Concepts in Elementary Topology*, Prentice-Hall, Englewood Cliffs, N.J., 1962.
7. F. Ayres, Jr., *Schaum's Outline Series Theory and Problems of Matrices*, Schaum, New York, 1962.
8. S. Banach, *Theorie des operations lineaires*, Chelsea, New York, 1955.
9. R. G. Bartle, *The Elements of Real Analysis*, Wiley, New York, 1964.
10. R. Bellman, *Introduction to Matrix Analysis*, McGraw-Hill, New York, 1960.
11. R. P. Boas, Jr., *A Primer of Real Functions*, The Mathematical Association of America, 1960.

12. N. Bourbaki, *Elements de mathematique*, Livre VI, *Espaces vectoriels topologiques*, Hermann et Cie, Act. Sci, et Ind., 1189, 1229, Paris, 1953, 1955.

13. W. M. Brown, *Analysis of Linear Time-Invariant Systems*, McGraw-Hill, New York, 1963.

14. S. S. L. Chang, *Synthesis of Optimum Control Systems*, McGraw-Hill, New York, 1961.

15. E. A. Coddington, *An Introduction to Ordinary Differential Equations*, Prentice-Hall, Englewood Cliffs, N.J., 1961.

16. E. A. Coddington and N. Levinson, *Theory of Ordinary Differential Equations*, McGraw-Hill, New York, 1955.

17. R. G. Cooke, *Infinite Matrices and Sequence Spaces*, Macmillan, London, 1950.

18. J. Cronin, *Fixed Points and Topological Degree in Nonlinear Analysis*, Mathematical Survey No. 11, American Mathematical Society, Providence, R.I., 1964.

19. H. F. Davis, *Fourier Series and Orthogonal Functions*, Allyn and Bacon, Boston, 1963.

20. M. M. Day, *Normed Linear Spaces*, Springer-Verlag, Berlin, 1962.

21. J. A. Dieudonné, *Foundations of Modern Analysis*, Academic Press, New York, 1960.

22. N. Dunford and J. T. Schwartz, *Linear Operators. Part I. General Theory*, Interscience, New York, 1958.

23. N. Dunford and J. T. Schwartz, *Linear Operators. Part II. Spectral Theory: Self-Adjoint Operators in Hilbert Space*, Interscience, New York, 1963.

24. H. G. Eggleston, *Problems in Euclidean Space: Application of Convexity*, Pergamon, New York, 1957.

25. L. E. El'sgol'ts, *Calculus of Variations*, Pergamon; Addison-Wesley, Reading, Mass., 1962.

26. L. E. El'sgol'ts, *Qualitative Methods in Mathematical Analysis*, American Mathematical Society, Providence, R.I., 1964.

27. B. Epstein, *Partial Differential Equations—An Introduction*, McGraw-Hill, New York, 1962.

28. L. Fox, *Numerical Solution of Ordinary and Partial Differential Equations*, Pergamon; Addison-Wesley, Reading, Mass., 1962.

29. A. Friedman, *Generalized Functions and Partial Differential Equations*, Prentice-Hall, Englewood Cliffs, N.J., 1963.

30. B. Friedman, *Principles and Techniques of Applied Mathematics*, Wiley, New York, 1956.

31. I. M. Gelfand and S. V. Fomin, *Calculus of Variations*, Prentice-Hall, Englewood Cliffs, N.J., 1963.

32. G. Goertzel and N. Tralli, *Some Mathematical Methods of Physics*, McGraw-Hill, New York, 1960.

33. J. F. Gray, *Sets, Relations, and Functions*, Holt, Rinehart and Winston, New York, 1962.

34. S. Goldberg, *Introduction to Difference Equations*, Wiley, New York, 1961.

35. P. R. Halmos, *Finite-Dimensional Vector Spaces*, Van Nostrand, Princeton, N.J., 1958.

36. P. R. Halmos, *Introduction to Hilbert Space and the Theory of Spectral Multiplicity*, Chelsea, New York, 1957.

37. P. R. Halmos, *Measure Theory*, Van Nostrand, Princeton, N.J., 1950.

38. G. H. Hardy, J. E. Littlewood, and G. Polya, *Inequalities*, Cambridge University Press, New York, 1952.

39. S. Hartman and J. Mikusinski, *The Theory of Lebesgue Measure and Integration*, Pergamon, New York, 1961.

40. F. B. Hildebrand, *Methods of Applied Mathematics*, Prentice-Hall, Englewood Cliffs, N.J., 1952.

41. E. Hille and R. S. Phillips, *Functional Analysis and Semi-Groups*, American Mathematical Society, Providence, R.I., 1957.

42. K. Hoffman and R. Kunze, *Linear Algebra*, Prentice-Hall, Englewood Cliffs, N.J., 1961.

43. I. M. Horowitz, *Synthesis of Feedback Systems*, Academic Press, New York, 1963.

44. J. Indritz, *Methods in Analysis*, Macmillan, New York, 1963.

45. E. I. Jury, *Sampled-Data Control Systems*, Wiley, New York, 1958.

46. W. Kaplan, *Ordinary Differential Equations*, Addison-Wesley, Reading, Mass., 1958.

47. W. Kaplan, *Operational Methods for Linear Systems*, Addison-Wesley, Reading, Mass., 1962.

48. J. L. Kelley, I. Namioka, and Co-authors, *Linear Topological Spaces*, Van Nostrand Co., Princeton, N.J., 1963.

49. A. N. Kolmogorov and S. V. Fomin, *Elements of the Theory of Functions and Functional Analysis*, Vol. 1, *Metric and Normed Spaces*, Graylock, Albany, N. Y., 1957.

50. A. N. Kolmogorov and S. V. Fomin, *Elements of the Theory of Functions and Functional Analysis*, Vol. 2, *Measure. The Lebesgue Integral. Hilbert Space*, Graylock, Albany, N.Y., 1961.

51. M. A. Krasnosel'skii and Y. B. Rutickii, *Convex Functions and Orlicz Spaces*, Gordon and Breach, New York, 1961.

52. M. A. Krasnosel'skii, *Topological Methods in the Theory of Nonlinear Integral Equations*, Macmillan, New York, 1964.

53. B. C. Kuo, *Analysis and Synthesis of Sampled-Data Control Systems*, Prentice-Hall, Englewood Cliffs, N.J., 1963.

54. K. Kuratowski, *Introduction to Set Theory and Topology*, Pergamon, Oxford; Addison-Wesley, Reading, Mass., 1962.

55. S. Lefschetz, *Differential Equations: Geometric Theory*, Interscience, New York, 1963.

56. L. A. Liusternik and V. J. Sobolev, *Elements of Functional Analysis*, Frederick Ungar, Rinehart and Winston, New York, 1961.

57. E. R. Lorch, *Spectral Theory*, Oxford University Press, New York, 1962.

58. B. Mendelson, *Introduction to Topology*, Allyn and Bacon, Boston, 1962.

59. K. S. Miller, *An Introduction to the Calculus of Finite Differences and Difference Equations*, Holt, Rinehart and Winston, New York, 1960.

60. K. S. Miller, *Partial Differential Equations in Engineering Problems*, Prentice-Hall, Englewood Cliffs, N.J., 1953.

61. K. S. Miller, *Linear Differential Equations in the Real Domain*, Norton, New York, 1963.

62. L. Mirsky, *An Introduction to Linear Algebra*, Oxford at the Clarendon Press, 1955.

63. I. P. Natanson, *Theory of Functions of a Real Variable*, Vols. I and II, Frederick Ungar, New York, 1955.

64. E. D. Nering, *Linear Algebra and Matrix Theory*, Wiley, New York, 1963.

65. L. Nirenberg, *Functional Analysis*, Lectures given in 1960–1961, New York University.

66. S. Perlis, *Theory of Matrices*, Addison-Wesley, Reading, Mass., 1952.

67. *Disciplines and Techniques of Systems Control*, John Peschon, Ed., Blaisdell, New York, 1965.

68. L. S. Pontryagin, *Ordinary Differential Equations*, Addison-Wesley, Reading, Mass., 1962.

69. L. S. Pontryagin, V. G. Boltyanskii, R. V. Gamkrelidze and E. F. Mishchenko, *The Mathematical Theory of Optimal Processes*, Interscience, New York, 1962.

70. C. H. Richardson, *An Introduction to the Calculus of Finite Differences*, Van Nostrand, Princeton, N.J., 1954.

71. R. D. Richtmyer, *Difference Methods for Initial-Value Problems*, Interscience, New York, 1958.

72. F. Riesz and B. Sz-Nagy, *Functional Analysis*, Frederick Ungar, New York, 1955.

73. W. Rudin, *Principles of Mathematical Analysis*, McGraw-Hill, New York, 1953.

74. T. L. Saaty and J. Bram, *Nonlinear Mathematics*, McGraw-Hill, New York, 1964.

75. L. Schwartz, *Theorie des distributions*, Tome II, Publication de L'Institut de Mathematique de L'Université de Strasbourg, Hermann, Paris, 1959.

76. G. E. Shilov, *An Introduction to the Theory of Linear Spaces*, Prentice-Hall, Englewood Cliffs, N.J., 1961.

77. G. F. Simmons, *Introduction to Topology and Modern Analysis*, McGraw-Hill, New York, 1963.

78. I. N. Sneddon, *Elements of Partial Differential Equations*, McGraw-Hill, New York, 1957.

79. S. L. Sobolev, *Applications of Functional Analysis in Mathematical Physics*, American Mathematical Society, Providence, R.I., 1963.

80. M. R. Spiegel, *Applied Differential Equations*, Prentice-Hall, Englewood Cliffs, N.J., 1958.

81. R. R. Stoll, *Linear Algebra and Matrix Theory*, McGraw-Hill, New York, 1952.

82. A. E. Taylor, *Advanced Calculus*, Ginn, Boston, 1955.

83. A. E. Taylor, *Introduction to Functional Analysis*, Wiley, New York, 1958.

84. G. P. Tolstov, *Fourier Series*, Prentice-Hall, Englewood Cliffs, N.J., 1962.

85. J. T. Tou, *Digital and Sampled-Data Control Systems*, McGraw-Hill, New York, 1959.

86. J. T. Tou, *Modern Control Theory*, McGraw-Hill, New York, 1964.

87. F. G. Tricomi, *Integral Equations*, Interscience, New York, 1957.

88. H. S. Tsien, *Engineering Cybernetics*, McGraw-Hill, New York, 1954.

89. Y. Z. Tsypkin, *Sampling Systems Theory and Its Applications*, Vols. 1 and 2, Macmillan, New York, 1964.

90. A. N. Tychonov and A. A. Samarski, *Partial Differential Equations of Mathematical Physics*, Vol. I, Holden-Day, San Francisco, 1964.

91. M. M. Vainberg, *Variational Methods for the Study of Nonlinear Operators*, Holden-Day, San Francisco, 1964.

92. V. Volterra, *Theory of Functionals and of Integral and Integro-differential Equations*, Dover, New York, 1959.

93. B. Z. Vulikh, *Introduction to Functional Analysis for Scientists and Technologists*, Addison-Wesley, Reading, Mass., 1963.

94. J. H. Williamson, *Lebesgue Integration*, Holt, Rinehart and Winston, New York, 1962.

95. L. A. Zadeh and C. A. Desoer, *Linear System Theory*, McGraw-Hill, New York, 1963.

96. R. Bellman, *Dynamic Programming*, Princeton University Press, Princeton, N.J., 1957.

97. G. Hadley, *Nonlinear and Dynamic Programming*, Addison-Wesley, Reading, Mass., 1964.

98. C. W. Merriam, *Optimization Theory and the Design of Feedback Control Systems*, McGraw-Hill, New York, 1964.

LIST B: ARTICLES, MONOGRAPHS, REPORTS AND SYMPOSIA

1. N. I. Akhiezer and M. Krein, "Some Questions in the Theory of Moments," *Nauch.-Teckh. Izd. Ukr.*, Kharkov, 1938. English translation published by American Mathematical Society, Providence, R.I., 1962.

2. M. Altman, "Approximation Methods in Functional Analysis," California Institute of Technology, Ma107c Notes, 1958–1959.

3. H. A. Antosiewicz, "Linear Control Systems," *Arch. Rational Mech. Anal.*, **12**, 313–324, 1963.

4. M. Athans, "Minimum-Fuel Control of Second-Order Systems with Real Poles," Fourth Joint Automatic Control Conference, Minneapolis, Minnesota, preprints by *A.I.Ch.E.*, 232–240, 1963.

5. M. Athans, "Time-, Fuel-, and Energy-Optimal Control of Nonlinear Norm-invariant Systems," *IEEE Trans. Autom. Control*, **AC-8**, No. 3, 196–202, July 1963.

6. M. Athans, P. Falb and R. Lacoss, "On Optimal Control of a Self-Adjoint System," Lincoln Laboratories, Massachusetts Institute of Technology, Report No. MS-709, 1962.

7. M. Athans, P. Falb and R. T. Lacoss, "Time-Optimal Velocity Control of a Spinning Space Body," *AIEE Trans. Appl. Ind.*, **82**, 1963.

8. T. G. Babunashvili, "The Synthesis of Linear Optimal Systems," *Dokl. Akad. Nauk SSSR*, **155**, 295–298, 1964 (English translation *J. SIAM Ser. A: Control*, **2**, No. 2, 1964).

9. A. V. Balakrishnan, "An Operator Theoretic Formulation of a Class of Control Problems and a Steepest Descent Method of Solution," *J. SIAM Ser. A: Control*, **1**, No. 2, 1963.

10. R. O. Barr and E. G. Gilbert, "Some Iterative Procedures for Computing Optimal Controls," Proceedings I.F.A.C. Conference, London, England, June 1966.

11. R. W. Bass and R. F. Webber, "On the Synthesis of Optimal Bang-Bang Feedback Control Systems with Quadratic Performance," to appear *Trans. IEEE, GAC.*

12. R. E. Bellman, I. Glicksberg and O. A. Gross, "On the 'Bang-Bang' Control Problem," *Quart. Appl. Math.* **14**, 11–18, 1956.

13. G. A. Bliss, *Lectures on the Calculus of Variations*, University of Chicago Press, Chicago, 1946.

14. H. D. Block, "Periodic Solutions of Forced Systems Having Hysteresis," *IRE, PGCT*, 423–431, 1960.

15. F. E. Browder, "The Solvability of Nonlinear Functional Equations," *Duke Math. J.*, **30**, 557–566, 1963.

16. F. E. Browder, "Remarks on Nonlinear Functional Equations," *Proc. Nat. Acad. Sci. U.S.*, **51**, 985–989, 1965.

17. F. E. Browder, "Continuity Properties of Monotone Nonlinear Operators in Banach Spaces," *Bull. Amer. Math. Soc.*, **70**, 551–553, 1965.

18. A. E. Bryson and W. F. Denham, "A Steepest Ascent Method for Solving Optimum Programming Problems," *J. Appl. Mech.*, **29**, Ser. E, No. 2, 247–257, 1962.

19. A. E. Bryson and W. F. Denham, "The Solution of Optimal Programming Problems with Inequality Constraints," IAS Paper No. 63–78, IAS Annual Meeting, New York, January 1963.

20. D. W. Bushaw, "Optimal Discontinuous Forcing Terms," *Contributions to the Theory of Nonlinear Oscillations*, Vol. IV, Princeton University Press, Princeton, N.J., 1958, pp. 29–52.

21. A. G. Butkovskii, "Optimum Processes in Systems with Distributed Parameters," *Avtomatika i Telemekhanika*, **22**, 17–26, January 1961.

22. A. G. Butkovskii, "The Maximum Principle for Optimum System with Distributed Parameters," *Avtomatika i Telemekhanika*, **22**, 1288–1301, October 1961.

23. A. G. Butkovskii, "Optimal Control of Systems with Distributed Parameters," Proc. Second IFAC Congress, 1963.

24. A. G. Butkovskii and A. Ya. Lerner, "Optimal Control of Systems with Distributed Parameters," *Avtomatika i Telemekhanika*, **21**, 682–691, June 1960.

25. S. Cater, "Note on a Theorem of Day," *Amer. Math. Monthly*, **69**, No. 7, 638–640, August-September 1962.

26. J. A. Cadzow, "A Study of Minimum Norm Control for Sampled-Data Systems." Proceedings of the Joint Automatic Control Conference, Troy, N.Y., June 1965.

27. J. A. Clarkson, " Uniformly Convex Spaces," *Trans. Amer. Math. Soc.*, **4**, 396–414, 1936.

28. C. L. Dolph, "The Structure of Linear Operator Theory in Hilbert Space for Engineers and Physicists," Department of Mathematics, University of Michigan, Ann Arbor, Michigan, Vols. I and II, 1964.

29. J. H. Eaton, "An Iterative Solution to Time-Optimal Control," *J. Math. Anal. and Appl.*, **5**, 329–344, 1962; "Errata and Addenda," *J. Math. Anal. and Appl.*, **9**, 147–152, 1964.

30. A. I. Egorov, " On Optimal Control of Processes in Distributed Objects," *Prikl. Mat. Mekhan.*, **27**, 688, 1963.

31. A. I. Egorov, "Optimal Control by Processes in Certain Systems with Distributed Parameters," *Avtomatika i Telemekhanika*, **25**, No. 5, 613–623, May 1964.

32. M. Fahmy, "A Solution Technique for a Class of Optimal Control Problems in Distributive Systems," Doctoral Dissertation, University of Michigan, Ann Arbor, 1965.

33. E. J. Fadden, "Computational Aspects of a Class of Optimal Control Problems," Doctoral Dissertation, University of Michigan, 1965.

34. P. L. Falb, "Infinite Dimensional Control Problem: On the Closure of the Set of Attainable States for Linear Systems," *J. Math. Anal. and Appl.*, **9**, No. 1, 12–22, August 1964.

35. I. Flugge-Lotz and H. Marbach, "The Optimal Control of Some Attitude Control Systems for Different Performance Criteria," *Trans. ASME*, Ser. D; *J. Appl. Mech*, **85**, 165–176, 1963.

36. J. S. Frame, "Matrix Functions and Applications," Part I–Part V, *IEEE Spectrum*, March–July 1964 issues.

37. B. Friedland, "The Design of Optimal Controllers for Linear Processes with Energy Constraints," Melpar Technical Note 62/2, March 1962.

38. R. V. Gamkrelidze, "The Theory of Time Optimal Processes in Linear Systems," *Izv. Akad. Nauk. SSSR*, **12**, 449–474, 1958.

39. E. G. Gilbert, "An Iterative Procedure for Computing the Minimum of a Quadratic Form on a Convex Set," Presented at First International Conference on Programming and Control, USAF Academy, Colorado, 1965.

40. I. M. Gelfand and S. V. Fomin, *Calculus of Variations* (English translation by R. A. Silverman), Prentice-Hall, Englewood Cliffs, N.J., 1963.

41. R. E. Goodson, "Optimal Control of Systems with Distributed Parameters," 1965 JACC Conference Proceedings.

42. R. G. Graham, "A Steepest-Ascent Solution of Multiple-Arc Vehicle Optimization Problems," Report No. TDR-269(4550-20-3), Contract No. AF 04(695)-269, Aerospace Corporation, El Segundo, California, December 1963.

43. W. G. Grimmell, "The Existence and Representation of Solutions to a Class of Linear Optimal Control Problems," Ph.D. Thesis, University of Michigan, Ann Arbor, 1965.

44. H. Halkin, "A Generalization of LaSalle's 'Bang-Bang' Principle," *J. SIAM Ser. A: Control*, **2**, No. 2, 1964.

45. C. A. Harvey, "Synthesis of Time-Optimal Control for Linear Processes," Honeywell Report No. U-RO 6325 (1964), Honeywell Corporation, Minneapolis, Minn.

46. M. R. Hestenes et al., *Computing Methods in Optimization Problems*, A. V. Balakrishnan and L. W. Neustadt, Eds., Academic Press, New York, 1964.

47. Y. C. Ho, "A Successive Approximation Techniques for Optimal Control Systems Subject to Input Saturation," *J. Basic Eng.*, **84**, Ser. D., No. 1, 33–40, 1962.

48. H. Hochstadt, "Laplace Transforms and Canonical Matrices," *Amer. Math. Monthly*, **71**, No. 7, 728–735.

49. R. C. James, "Characterizations of Reflexivity," *Studia Math.* **23**, 205–216, 1963/64.

50. R. E. Kalman, "On the General Theory of Control Systems," *Proc. First Intern. Congr. Autom. Control*, Moscow, USSR, 1960.

51. R. E. Kalman, Y. C. Yo, and K. S. Narendra, *Controllability of Linear Dynamical Systems*, Wiley, New York, 1963.

52. R. E. Kalman, "Mathematical Description of Dynamical Systems," *J. SIAM, Ser. A: Control*, **1**, No. 2, 1963.

53. R. E. Kalman, *The Theory of Optimal Control and the Calculus of Variations*, Mathematical Optimization Techniques, University of California Press, Berkeley, pp. 309–331, 1963.

54. L. V. Kantorovich, "Functional Analysis and Applied Mathematics," National Bureau of Standards, Report No. 1509, March 7, 1952.

55. L. V. Kantorovich and V. I. Krylov, *Approximate Methods of Higher Analysis*, Translated by C. D. Benster, Wiley, New York, 1959.

56. R. C. Kao, "Geometric Interpretation of LaGrange Multipliers," Rand Report No. T-2713, AD No. 298 197, The Rand Corporation, February 1963.

57. R. M. Kirillova, "A Limiting Process in the Solution of an Optimal Control Problem," *J. Appl. Math. and Mech.*, **24**, 398–405, 1960.

58. V. Klee et al., "Convexity," Proceedings of Symposia in Pure Mathematics, Volume VII, Seventh Symposium of American Mathematical Society, Providence, Rhode Island, 1963.

59. H. K. Knudsen, "An Iterative Procedure for Computing Time-Optimal Controls," *IEEE Trans. Autom. Control*, **AC-9**, No. 1, 23–30, January 1964.

60. G. M. Kranc and P. E. Sarachik, "An Application of Functional Analysis to the Optimum Control Problem," *Trans. Amer. Soc. Mech. Engrs., Basic Engineering*, **85**, 1963.

61. N. N. Krasovskii, "On the Theory of Optimal Regulation," *Avtomat. i Telemek.*, **18**, 960–970, 1957. English translation in *Automation and Remote Control*, **18**, 1005–1016.

62. N. N. Krasovskii, "On the Theory of Optimal Control," *Prikl. Mat. Mech.*, **23**, 625–639, 1959. English translation in *J. Appl. Math. Mech.*, **23**, 899–919.

63. E. Kreindler, "Contributions to the Theory of Time-Optimal Control," *J. Franklin Inst.*, **275**, No. 4, April 1962.

64. E. Kreindler and P. E. Sarachik, "On the Concepts of Controllability and Observability of Linear Systems," *PT GAC*, **AC-9**, No. 2, April 1964, 129–136. Errata: *IEEE, GAC*, **AC-10**, No. 1, January 1965.

65. R. Kulikowski, "On Optimal Control with Constraints," *Bull. Polish Acad. Sci.* (Ser. Tech. Sci.), **7**, 285–294, April 1959.

66. R. Kulikowski, "Concerning the Synthesis of the Optimum Nonlinear Control," *Bull. Polish Acad. Sci.* (Ser. Tech. Sci.), **7**, 391–399, June 1959.

67. R. Kulikowski, "Synthesis of a Class of Optimum Control Systems," *Bull. Polish Acad. Sci.* (Ser. Tech. Sci.), **7**, 663–671, November 1959.

68. R. Kulikowski, "Optimum Processes and Synthesis of Optimum Automatic Control Systems with Non-linear Invariable Elements," in Proceedings of the International Federation of Automatic Control Congress, Moscow, 1960, p. 473.

69. M. C. Kuo, "The Application of Functional Analysis to Solve a Class of Linear Control Problems," Doctoral Dissertation, University of Michigan, Ann Arbor, 1964.

70. H. O. Ladd, Jr., and B. Friedland, "Minimum Fuel Control of a Second-Order Linear Process with a Constraint on Time-to-Run," *Trans. ASME*, Ser. D., *J. Appl. Mech*, **86**, 160–168, 1964.

71. J. P. LaSalle, "The Time Optimum Control Problem," in *Contributions to the Theory of Nonlinear Oscillations*, Princeton University Press, Princeton, New Jersey, 1960, Vol. 5, pp. 1–24.

72. E. B. Lee, "Mathematical Aspects of the Synthesis of Linear Minimum Response Time Controllers," *IRE PGAC*, 283–289, 1960.

73. E. B. Lee, "On the Domain of Controllability for Linear Systems Subject to Control Amplitude Constraints," *IEEE Trans. Autom. Control*, **AC-8**, 172–173, April 1963.

74. E. B. Lee and L. Markus, "Optimal Control for Nonlinear Processes," *Archive for Rational Mechanics and Analysis*, **8**, No. 1, 36–58, 1961.

75. K. A. Lur'e, "On the Hamilton-Jacobi Method in Variational Problems

of Partial Differential Equations," *Prikl. Math. Mekhan*, **27**, 255, 1963.

76. K. A. Lur'e, "The Mayer-Bolza Problem for Multiple Integrals and the Optimization of the Performance of Systems with Distributed Parameters," *Prikl. Math. Mekhan*, **27**, 842, 1963.

77. L. Markus and E. B. Lee, "On the Existence of Optimal Controls," Paper No. 61-JAC-2, JACC, 1961.

78. I. McCausland, "On Optimum Control of Temperature Distribution in a Solid," *J. Electron. Control*, **14**, 655, 1963.

79. I. McCausland, "On-Off Control of Linear Systems with Distributed Parameters," PhD Dissertation, Department of Engineering, Cambridge University, Cambridge, England, 1963.

80. J. S. Meditch, "Synthesis of a Class of Linear Feedback Minimum Energy Controls," *IRE PGAC*, 376–378, 1963.

81. J. S. Meditch, "On Minimal Fuel Satellite Attitude Controls," Fourth Joint Automatic Control Conference, Minneapolis, Minnesota, preprints by *A.I.Ch.E.*, 558–564, 1963.

82. J. S. Meditch, "On the Problem of Optimal Thrust Programming for a Lunar Soft Landing," Presentation 1964 Joint Automatic Control Conference, Stanford, California.

83. S. G. Mikhlin, *The Problem of the Minimum of a Quadratic Functional*, Holden-Day, San Francisco, 1965.

84. G. J. Minty, "Monotone (Non-Linear) Operators in Hilbert Space," *Duke Math. J.*, **29**, 341–346, 1962.

85. G. J. Minty, "On a 'Monotonicity' Method for the Solution of Nonlinear Equations in Banach Spaces," *Proc. Nat. Acad. Sci.* U.S., **50**, 1038–1041, 1963.

86. G. J. Minty, "On the Solvability of Nonlinear Functional Equations of Monotonic Type," *Pacific J. Math.*, 249–255, 1964.

87. F. J. Murray, "On Complementary Manifolds and Projections in Spaces L_p and l_p," *Trans. Amer. Math. Soc.*, **41**, 138–152, 1937.

88. N. E. Nahi, "Two Classes of Optimum Linear Systems," Presentation 1964 Joint Automatic Control Conference, Stanford, California.

89. L. W. Neustadt, "Synthesizing Time-Optimal Control Systems," *J. Math. Anal. and Appl.*, **1**, 484–492, 1960.

90. L. W. Neustadt, "Minimum Effort Control Systems," *J. SIAM, Ser. A: Control*, **1**, No. 1, 16–31, 1963.

91. L. W. Neustadt, "The Existence of Optimal Controls in the Absence of Convexity Conditions," *J. Math. Anal. and Appl.*, **7**, 110–117, 1963.

92. L. W. Neustadt, "Discrete Time Optimal Control Systems," in J. P. LaSalle and S. Lefschetz, Eds., *International Symposium on Nonlinear*

Differential Equations and Nonlinear Mechanics, Academic Press, New York, 1963.

93. L. W. Neustadt, "Optimization, a Moment Problem and Nonlinear Programming," *J. SIAM, Ser. A: Control*, **2**, No. 1, 33–53, 1964.

94. B. Paiewonsky, "Synthesis of Time-Optimal Control for Linear Systems," A.R.A.P. (Princeton, N.J.) Tech. Memo 62-4, 1962.

95. B. Paiewonsky, "Time-Optimal Control of Linear Systems with Bounded Controls," in J. P. LaSalle and S. Lefschetz, Eds., *International Symposium on Nonlinear Differential Equations and Nonlinear Mechanics*, Academic Press, New York, 1963, pp. 333–365.

96. I. G. Petrovsky, *Lectures on Partial Differential Equations*, English translation by A. Schenitzer, Interscience, New York, 1955, Chapter 1.

97. R. R. Phelps, "Uniqueness of Hahn-Banach Extensions and Unique Best Approximation," *Trans. Amer. Math. Soc.*, **95**, 238–255, 1960.

98. L. S. Pontryagin, V. G. Boltyanskii, R. V. Gamkrelidze and E. F. Mishchenko, *The Mathematical Theory of Optimal Processes*, Wiley, New York, 1962.

99. W. A. Porter, "A New Approach to a General Minimum Energy Problem," presented at 1964 JACC Conference, Stanford, California, June 24–26, 1964.

100. W. A. Porter and J. P. Williams, "Minimum Effort Control of Linear Dynamic Systems," August 1964, Tech. Report 5892-20-F, Contract AF 33(657)-11501.

101. W. A. Porter and J. P. Williams, "A Note in the Minimum Effort Control Problem," *J. Math. Anal. and Appl.*, 1965.

102. W. A. Porter and J. P. Williams, "Extensions of the Minimum Effort Control Problem," *J. Math. Anal. and Appl.*, 1965.

103. W. T. Reid, "Ordinary Linear Differential Operators of Minimum Norm," *Duke Math. J.*, **29**, 591–606, 1962.

104. A. P. Robertson and W. Robertson, *Topological Vector Spaces*, Cambridge University Press, Cambridge, 1964.

105. I. W. Sandberg, "On the L_2 Boundedness of Solutions of Nonlinear Functional Equations," *Bell System Tech. J.*, **43**, No. 4, 1581–1818, July 1964.

106. I. W. Sandberg, "Conditions for the Causality of Nonlinear Operators Defined on a Function Space," to appear in *Quart. Appl. Math.*

107. I. W. Sandberg, "A Note on the Application of the Contraction-Mapping Fixed-Point Theorem to a Class of Nonlinear Functional Equations," *SIAM Review*, **7**, No. 2, 199–204, April 1965.

108. I. W. Sandberg, "On the Properties of Some Systems that Distort

Signals," *Bell System Tech. J.*, Part 1, **42**, 2033–2047, 1963; Part 2, **43**, 91–112, January 1964.

109. I. W. Sandberg and V. E. Benes, "On the Properties of Nonlinear Integral Equations That Arise in the Theory of Dynamical Systems," *Bell System Tech. J.*, **43**, November 1964.

110. Y. Sakawa, "Solution of an Optimal Control Problem in a Distributed-Parameter System," *IEEE Trans. Autom. Control*, **AC-9**, No. 4, 420–426, October, 1964.

111. T. K. Sirazetdinov "Concerning the Theory of Optimum Processes with Distributed Parameters," *Avtomatika i Telemekhanika*, **25**, 463, 1964.

112. L. M. Sonneborn and F. S. Van Vleck, "The Bang-Bang Principle for Linear Control Systems," *J. SIAM, Ser. A: Control*, **2**, No. 2, 1965, 151–159.

113. A. R. Stubberud, "Minimum Energy Control of a Linear Plant with Magnitude Constraint on the Control Input Signal," 1965 JACC Conference Proceedings.

114. J. Todd, Ed., *Survey of Numerical Analysis*, McGraw-Hill, New York, 1962.

115. F. Tung and P. K. C. Wang, "Analysis of Linear Distributed Systems with Random Parameters and Inputs," *J. Franklin Inst.*, **275**, No. 5, 381–391, May 1963.

116. F. M. Waltz, "Minimum Peak Amplitude Control," Doctoral Dissertation, University of Michigan, 1965.

117. P. K. C. Wang, "Control of Distributed Parameter Systems," chapter in *Advances in Control Systems*, Vol. I, Academic Press, New York, 1964.

118. P. K. C. Wang, "Optimum Control of Distributed Parameter Systems with Time Delays," *IEEE Trans. Autom. Control*, **AC-9**, No. 1, January 1964.

119. P. K. C. Wang and M. L. Bandy, "On the Stability of Equilibrium of a Diffusion System with Feedback Control," *IEEE Trans. Autom. Control*, 1964.

120. P. K. C. Wang and F. Tung, "Optimum Control of Distributed-Parameter Systems," *Trans. ASME, J. Basic. Eng.*, 67–79, March 1964.

121. W. M. Wonham and C. Johnson, "Optimal Bang-Bang Control with Quadratic Performance Index," *Trans. ASME*, Ser. D., *J. Appl. Mech.*, **86**, 107–115, 1964.

122. K. Yosida, *Lectures on Differential and Integral Equations*, Interscience, New York, 1960.

123. G. Zames, "Functional Analysis Applied to Nonlinear Feedback Systems," *IRE PGCT*, 392–404, 1963.

124. G. Zames, "Realizability for Nonlinear Feedback," *IEEE Trans. Circuit Theory*, **2**, No. 2, 186–194, June 1964.

125. E. H. Zarantonello, "Solving Functional Equations by Contractive Averaging," U.S. Army Math. Res. Center, T.S. R160, 1960.

126. E. H. Zarantonello, *The Closure of the Numerical Range Contains the Spectrum*, University of Kansas, Department of Mathematics, Technical Report No. 7, July 1964.

INDEX

DATE DUE

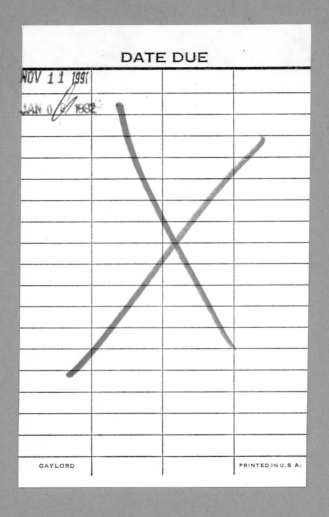

NOV 1 1 1991		
JAN 0 6 1992		
GAYLORD		PRINTED IN U.S A.